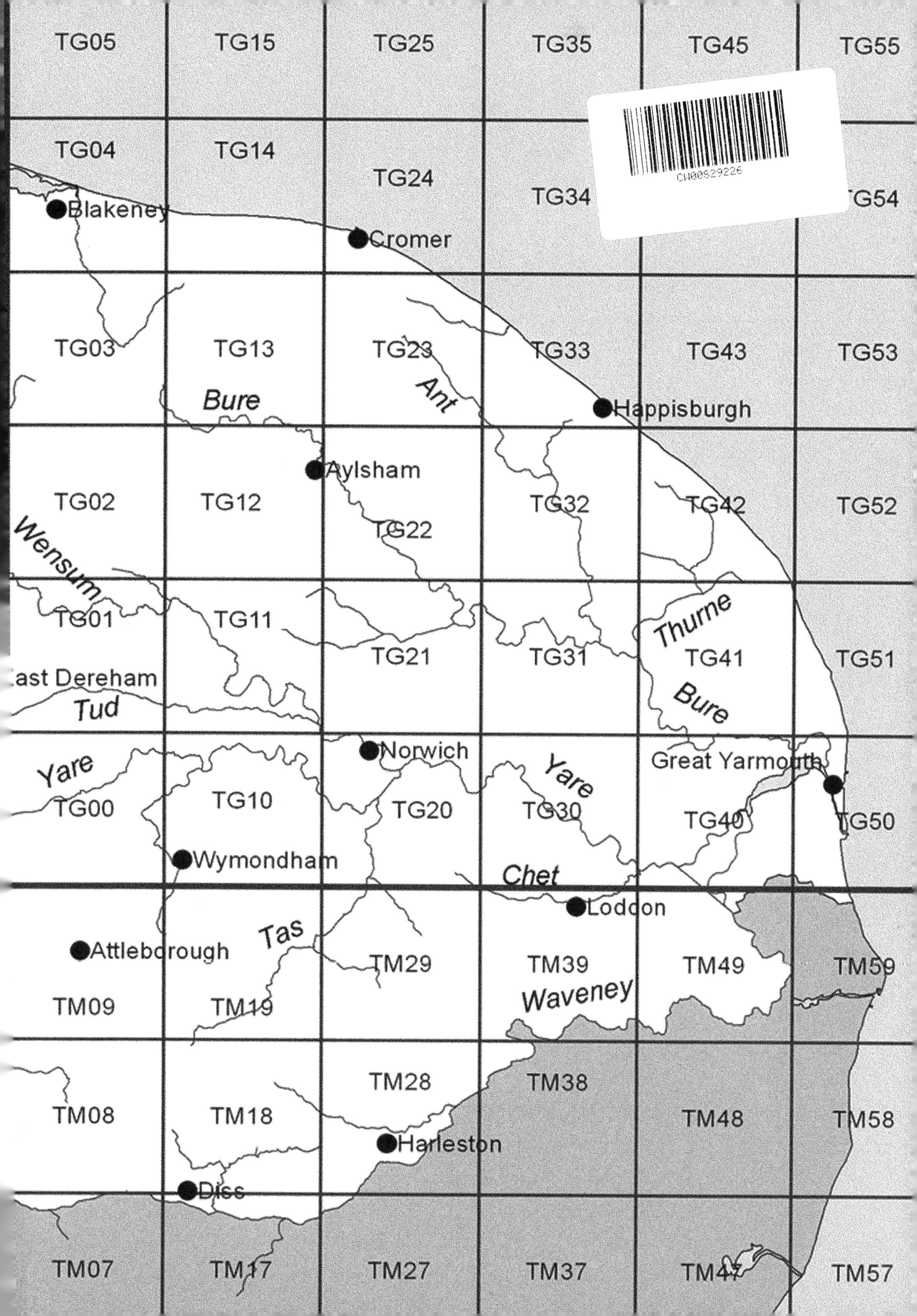

TG05 TG15 TG25 TG35 TG45 TG55

TG04 TG14 TG24 TG34 TG54

Blakeney
Cromer

TG03 TG13 TG23 TG33 TG43 TG53

Bure
Ant
Happisburgh

Aylsham

TG02 TG12 TG22 TG32 TG42 TG52

Wensum

TG01 TG11 TG21 TG31 TG41 TG51

Thurne
Bure
East Dereham
Tud

Norwich
Yare
Great Yarmouth

TG00 TG10 TG20 TG30 TG40 TG50

Wymondham
Chet
Loddon

Attleborough
Tas

TM29 TM39 TM49 TM59

TM09 TM19

Waveney

TM28 TM38

TM08 TM18 TM48 TM58

Harleston
Diss

TM07 TM17 TM27 TM37 TM47 TM57

The Norfolk Bird Atlas:

Summer and Winter Distributions 1999–2007

Moss Taylor and John H Marchant

Published by the British Trust for Ornithology

British Trust for Ornithology
The Nunnery
Thetford
Norfolk
IP24 2PU

01842 750050
info@bto.org
www.bto.org
Charity Number 216652 (England & Wales), SC039193 (Scotland)

First published in 2011
British Trust for Ornithology, Thetford

ISBN 978-1-906204-82-2

Design: O'Connor Design Consultants
www.o-connordesign.co.uk
info@o-connordesign.co.uk

Printed by: Printer Trento

Front cover: Holkham Beach by Lyndon Povey

Environment: The paper used for this book has been certified as coming from well-managed forests and other controlled sources according to the rules of the Forest Stewardship Council.

This book was printed and bound in Italy by Printer Trento, an FSC certified company for printing books on FSC mixed paper in compliance with the chain of custody and on-product labelling standards. Printer Trento has an ISO14001 certified environmental management system.

The Norfolk Bird Atlas 1999–2007

Moss Taylor and John H Marchant

This book is dedicated to everyone who contributes to bird surveys and bird recording in Norfolk

Foreword

By Andy Clements, Director of BTO

I FIRST CAME TO NORFOLK in search of birds in 1971 as a keen schoolboy who had recently set up my north London school's birdwatching club. Clear in my mind now from those early visits were the breeding Red-backed Shrikes at Santon Downham, a Baird's Sandpiper and long-staying Glaucous Gull at Cley, and a total lack of Marsh Harriers to compete with the only breeding birds at the time at Minsmere in Suffolk. How things have changed! Norfolk's geographical position, its Europe-facing coast and wealth of habitats has ensured it remains at the pinnacle of birding counties. The importance for birds is well documented in the overview section of this book, recognising new breeding colonists such as Mediterranean Gull, Little Egret and Goosander, and nationally important waterbirds in winter, including geese and swans, Bittern, Water Pipit and Black-tailed Godwit. The county provides shelter and food for a huge array of passage migrants and vagrants in both spring and autumn, and therefore Norfolk is of course important for birders too, with some of our keenest and most acute and active observers living and working in the county. Hosting the offices of the British Trust for Ornithology ensures Norfolk's core interest in our broader UK bird populations.

National and county bird atlases were pioneered in the UK and are important for a number of reasons. They provide a stocktaking of a region's complete avifauna, enhanced this time around with NBA's combination of breeding season and winter survey in one publication. This total picture is of immense significance in documenting an area's importance for birds and measuring its relative value alongside similar, or geographically broader areas. Our knowledge and information allows conservation priorities to be understood, targets to be set, and specific conservation management to be implemented. Atlas data are a key element for reporting on the broader health of our wildlife, and on how well we are doing in protecting it.

Although an atlas can only ever be a snapshot of the status of birds, this particular picture comes at a time of astonishing change to our environment and the birds that live in it. Documenting that change as seen through the populations of birds is a powerful use of bird atlas data, and NBA makes a solid contribution here through inclusion of population estimates alongside the distribution information. For me though, one of the main benefits of undertaking the task of recording the accurate distribution of birds in an atlas project is the participation from birders that this encourages. Everyone seems to enjoy taking part, finding and documenting good birds in their local area, building up complete lists, and seeing their contribution in the final publication. Atlases make patchwork purposeful.

NBA comes along at a time when the BTO's own *Bird Atlas 2007–11* is in its final year of fieldwork with a publication date for the Britain and Ireland Atlas of early 2013. Norfolk will therefore be readily comparable with the national picture, and I am sure much will be learnt and recognised of the crucial contribution made by Norfolk and its habitats to bird conservation early in the 21st century. It is a privilege that NBA will be the first publication of BTO Books and we will have to work hard to maintain the standard for future publications set by NBA.

All who contributed to NBA should be proud to have done so, and the wealth of information, depth and authority of writing, and quality of photographs and artwork are testament to the hard work of many. I hope you enjoy reading this book, and visiting it regularly for information over many years to come.

CHAPTER 1

The Norfolk Bird Atlas project

1.1 A new atlas of the birds of Norfolk

NORFOLK IS ARGUABLY THE FINEST county in Britain for birds and birdwatchers. It holds a large resident community of birdwatchers, many of whom have migrated to Norfolk with birds as a major draw, and for visiting birdwatchers there are multiple attractions of all kinds, year-round. A strong culture has developed for the recording and reporting of Norfolk's coastal birds, whether through estuaries counts, seawatching or intensive watching at the coastal reserves and observatories.

Migrant hunting has many fans in the county. Wherever rarities and scarce migrants are the main attraction, however, the regular and commonplace birds can become overlooked and under-reported – and this is especially true away from the county's birding hotspots. Over the years, comparatively little information has been gathered on the distribution and abundance of the commoner breeding birds and winter visitors, making it difficult to draw conclusions about their status in the county as a whole, and about how their populations might be changing. Surveys such as bird atlases and *BirdTrack*[1] (organised by BTO[2] on behalf of BTO, RSPB, BWI and SOC) are needed to supplement the ordinary submission of records to the county bird recorder. These surveys gather complete lists for birds in defined areas, ensuring that even the most mundane species and habitats are fully included in the bird recording system.

Atlases, which aim to ensure that every part of the county is searched for birds using a grid-square system, are a special case. The most compelling reason for compiling atlases of bird distributions is that even casual observations show that these distributions are changing. Effective bird conservation is fundamentally

[1] Full references for project and publication titles shown in italics are given in the References section on pages 505–506.

[2] For a key to abbreviations, please see page 518.

dependent on knowing which species are changing in numbers or range, and precisely where these species are gaining or losing ground. Armed with this information, and provided it is up to date, conservation bodies can be effective in concentrating their limited resources on the species and locations that are most in need of conservation action.

There have already been three published atlases that have mapped birds across all of Britain and Ireland at the 10-km scale – two in the breeding season (*1968–72 Atlas* and *1988–91 Atlas*) and one in winter (*1981–84 Winter Atlas*) – while a fourth atlas project covering both summer and winter is currently under way (*Atlas 2007–11*). For Norfolk there has also been a breeding bird atlas at the much finer, tetrad level (2x2-km squares) – Geoffrey Kelly's *The Norfolk Bird Atlas* (which, to avoid confusion, is referred to here as the *1980–85 NBBS*) was based on fieldwork carried out over the six summers from 1980 to 1985.

By 1999, with an interval of 14 years since the close of the *1980–85 NBBS* in 1985, there was a clear need for a new tetrad bird atlas for Norfolk. Even over this quite short interval, we expected that many range changes would be apparent among breeding birds. There was also scope for a new tetrad atlas to be more thorough and comprehensive than previous surveys. Methodology for local atlases had advanced since the 1980s and now included ways to quantify bird densities through timed counts. Most atlases had concentrated on either the breeding season or the winter, and there was the opportunity to join the vanguard of projects tackling these two periods of the year over the same period, with the consequent efficiencies of scale. A winter tetrad survey would be the first ever conducted in the county.

The aim of the new project would be to document bird distributions in Norfolk as thoroughly as possible at the start of the new millennium, and to set a baseline with which future atlas surveys of the county could be compared. We also aimed to compile a comprehensive database of bird records that would be available for future long-term comparisons of distribution and population size in the county, at 10-km and at tetrad level.

1.2 Planning and organisation

To gauge enthusiasm and assess the feasibility of organising fieldwork for a new county bird atlas, Moss Taylor arranged a meeting in May 1998 to which Norfolk's bird clubs, conservation organisations and major landowners were invited. The response was most encouraging and an NBA working group was set up to begin planning and organising the fieldwork. Pilot work was begun in December 1998 to establish appropriate recording methods and to help finalise recording forms and instructions.

Setting the survey boundaries

Norfolk is the fifth largest county in England, spanning 105 km from west to east and 65 km from north to south. The coastline stretches for over 130 km from Terrington Marsh on the south shore of the Wash in the west to the southern edge of Great Yarmouth in the east. The inland border follows the Rivers Waveney and Little Ouse in the south and cuts across to the River Nene in the west. Within this area lies a wide variety of bird-rich habitats, as described in Peter Lambley's chapter.

The area set for coverage by the new Norfolk Bird Atlas project (NBA) was the administrative county of Norfolk. This is precisely the area covered by the Norfolk Bird Report (*NBR*) and by the *1980–85 NBBS*, with boundaries with neighbouring counties that are entirely familiar to Norfolk birdwatchers. Though apparently plain and straightforward, however, there are elements of this definition that need some explanation.

First, as in all previous bird atlas projects, the limit of NBA coverage for summer and winter surveys was defined as the high water mark as shown on Ordnance Survey (OS) maps. With its shallow shores, Norfolk is a substantially larger county when the tide has dropped! This does not affect the mapping of breeding birds, which of course require dry land for nesting. Birds occupying the vast intertidal areas of Norfolk, however, such as the waders of the Wash for which the county is justly famous, are mapped only when they occur within the tetrads that contain at least some land above high water. Where sand and shingle are accreting, as between Blakeney Point and Scolt Head through longshore drift, and at Scroby

Sands off Great Yarmouth, some land that is permanently above the high water mark might not yet be mapped as such by the Ordnance Survey. Although such places are unlikely to hold any breeding birds, they have not been included in the NBA survey. Conversely, coastal erosion in many places is shifting the high water mark in a landward direction.

The birds of Norfolk's offshore waters have been outside the scope of this project, and seabirds are recorded only where they are visible from land. No county or national bird atlas has tackled the mapping of birds at sea, which so far remains the province of JNCC's Seabirds at Sea Team and of private consultancies.

An artificial island, the Outer Trial Bank (OTB), was built on the Wash mudflats in the mid 1970s as part of a feasibility study for a barrage scheme. Although more than a mile distant across open mud from the outermost edge of the saltmarsh, this remarkable structure is connected to the mainland at low tide. It is about 250 metres in diameter, and stands about twice as tall as any part of the Wash shoreline, with the exception of the cliffs at Hunstanton. The nearest parts of the mainland to the OTB are over a mile west of Norfolk and into Lincolnshire, but for some reason the county boundary has historically made a dogleg halfway across the open mudflat, putting the OTB and its surroundings firmly within administrative Norfolk. Almost as soon as it was completed, the OTB became an important breeding site for terns, as noted by the *1980–85 NBBS*, and is now Norfolk's main breeding site for large gulls. High-tide wader roosts and loafing Eiders[3] are other notable features of this remarkable site.

Although NBA has included the OTB in its coverage, as did the *1980–85 NBBS*, some other artificial and possibly transient parts of Norfolk have not been included in the NBA recording area. These include the new inshore sea defences off Sea Palling, one of which is partly in a tetrad containing no other land, and various offshore gas rigs and other structures, several of which are well out of sight from shore. None of these is known to hold any breeding birds, however, nor to hold any special significance for birds in winter.

DAVID TIPLING

'...the OTB became an important breeding site for terns, as noted by the *1980–85 NBBS*, and is now Norfolk's main breeding site for large gulls.'

NBA's inland recording boundary is even more troublesome, because, whereas Norfolk birdwatchers use the administrative county as their recording area, Suffolk bird recording uses the Watsonian vice county boundaries. The vice county system was designed for biological recording in 1852 but has been little used for birds and is more familiar now to recorders of other taxa, such as plants and insects. The original aim of the vice county system was to divide Britain and Ireland into recording areas, of county size or smaller, which would remain constant through time. Since then, a very large number of small differences have accumulated, and quite a few more-substantial ones, between the vice counties and the English administrative counties, with which people are naturally more familiar day to day. Until recently, it was very difficult for an observer to discover where the vice county boundaries lay, since there were no maps that combined the Watsonian boundaries with the modern OS. Nowadays, however, it is possible to use the internet to check a grid reference against a vice county map (*http://herbariaunited.org/gridrefVC*), and to download digitised vice county boundaries for computer

[3]Scientific names for bird species included in the main systematic sections of this book are given there and omitted elsewhere.

mapping programs. Vice county boundaries cut both Norfolk and Suffolk into two vice counties at the 1°E line of longitude, though bird recording in neither county takes any account of this division.

This difference in approach between Norfolk and Suffolk bird recording has practical effects in two areas along the county boundary. First, an area south of Breydon Water, formerly in Suffolk, remains part of the East Suffolk vice county, although it was transferred to administrative Norfolk partly in 1889 and more completely in 1974. This area, including the southern shore of Breydon Water, has recorded many rare birds over the years that have found places on both county lists! Second, an area lying south of the River Little Ouse, including Thetford Warren and the southern half of Thetford town, belongs to the West Suffolk vice county but has been administered by Norfolk since 1894. This area, which includes the BTO's headquarters in Thetford, is also intensively recorded for birds. These two areas, covered not only by Norfolk but also by the Suffolk Bird Report and by a recent Suffolk tetrad atlas project (Piotrowski 2003), are among a small number of ADRs, or 'areas of double recording', that have been catalogued for British birds by Ballance & Smith (2008).

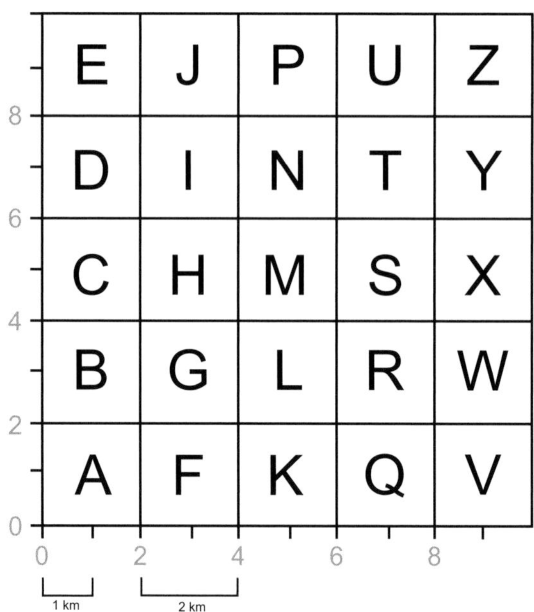

Figure 1.1 The 'DINTY' system of lettering tetrads within an Ordnance Survey 10-km square.

Recording units

As is common in fine-scale surveys of wildlife, the tetrad was chosen as the recording unit. Tetrads are 2x2-km squares made up of four 1-km squares and defined by the even-numbered grid lines on OS maps. There are thus 25 tetrads within each OS 10-km square. Tetrad referencing is not a standard part of the OS national grid, and several different protocols have been devised. The 'DINTY' system now prevails throughout biological recording.

In presenting a tetrad reference such as TF72A, the Ordnance Survey 10-km reference (TF72) is followed by the tetrad letter according to the key in Figure 1.1. The *1980–85 NBBS* used a different method, in which 'A' was the northwest tetrad in a 10-km square, but the data have since been converted to match other surveys.

A total of 1,459 tetrads contain at least some land within Norfolk, on the definitions employed for this atlas. Coastal tetrads number 107 while 123 lie across a boundary with one or more of the neighbouring counties – Lincolnshire, Cambridgeshire or Suffolk. In this survey, only the Norfolk parts of shared tetrads were surveyed. Thus, for example, Golden Orioles nested in at least one of the tetrads on the NBA list during the survey period but, because the birds were across the border in Suffolk, they are not included in our survey.

CHRIS KNIGHTS

'...but because the birds were across the border in Suffolk, they are not included in our survey.'

The county tetrad atlases currently being undertaken around Britain and Ireland in parallel with the national *Atlas 2007–11* do not distinguish between parts of tetrads that lie in different counties. The new Suffolk atlas now in progress will therefore be based on an approximation of tetrad boundaries to the vice county boundary, and might include parts of Norfolk along its entire northern border.

The choice of seasons

Bird distribution throughout the year is of considerable interest to birdwatchers and conservationists. It is of special interest to know where birds are breeding, because birds sometimes require special protection while they are nesting; also, large-scale maps of breeding distribution help to define the limits of discrete populations. Winter has also been chosen as a season for previous atlas work, because in midwinter birds have arrived from their breeding grounds and can be resident long enough for their winter destinations to be mapped. Maps of bird distribution covering all seasons, and therefore showing the arrival and departure periods as well as winter and summer residency, would be much more informative, however: monthly maps were pioneered in the Netherlands in the late 1970s (SOVON 1987), but there have been no year-round atlases yet for the UK.

The NBA has been conservative in choosing just two periods of the year for study, which we have labelled 'summer' and 'winter'. 'Summer' for NBA has been the months of April, May and June, although a few records for March and for early autumn have been included where they provided some evidence of breeding. The main focus of the summer survey has been on breeding birds, but the survey also recorded late winter visitors and migrant birds on spring passage during this three-month period.

'Winter' for NBA has been defined strictly as the three months of December, January and February. These are the months when autumn passage has effectively ceased and spring passage has yet to begin. There should therefore be little chance of recording birds that do not normally winter in the county, although birds are still mobile during this period. This survey period began later in the year than that of the *1981–84 Winter Atlas* for Britain and Ireland, which included records as early as 12th November. The current fieldwork for *Atlas 2007–11* in Britain and Ireland includes the whole of November. *Atlas 2007–11* also includes the whole of July within the period for formal breeding-season tetrad visits.

DAVID TIPLING

''Winter' for NBA has been defined strictly as the three months of December, January and February.'

1.3 Collecting and collating the field data

The county was divided loosely into six areas for the purposes of the survey: the Fens, the Brecks, the Broads, the northwest, the northeast and the southeast. The Nar Valley Ornithological Society (NarVOS) recording area, stretching from King's Lynn to Swaffham and East Dereham, was combined with the Fens. Each region was the responsibility of a working group member, who acted as a local organiser. The organiser's job was to match tetrads to volunteer fieldworkers and to ensure a regular flow of completed forms to Moss Taylor as county organiser.

NBA fieldwork started on 1st December 1999. The most important task was for volunteers to make two winter and two summer 'set visits' to every tetrad in the county. The set visits ensured that a certain minimum coverage to every tetrad was achieved, supported by visit dates and a record of the times of start and finish for each visit. There had been no equivalent to set visits for the *1980–85 NBBS*, for which the maps were plotted from simple undated lists of species and breeding evidence: no records now

DAVID TIPLING

'Birds of prey and other flying birds clearly searching for food were included...'

exist of the numbers of individual birds observed in each tetrad, nor of the effort expended, severely limiting the possibilities for comparing the results quantitatively with NBA.

Methods for winter set visits

Observers were asked to make one visit to each tetrad in each half of the three-month winter period ('early', 1st December to 15th January; 'late', 16th January to end February), ideally with at least two weeks between visits, and count individuals of all bird species encountered within the tetrad boundary. All birds seen or heard within the tetrad were to be counted, with the exception of birds flying over and not using the tetrad (such as geese or gulls flying to or from a roost, or seabirds flying offshore and not landing). Birds of prey and other flying birds clearly searching for food were included, on the grounds that they were using the tetrad, even if only speculatively. Non-native birds were all to be recorded, including species not on the British Ornithologists' Union's official *British List.*

The instructions suggested that the route taken should include a representation of all habitats present and should cover as much of the tetrad as possible. Observers were asked to record the approximate percentage of the tetrad that they had covered on each visit and the length of time spent in the field. No limits were placed on time spent in the field, but it was suggested that for the majority of tetrads the set visits would take three to four hours, depending on the types of habitats present and the number of birds encountered, and should start as soon as possible after dawn. Ideally, the same observer would make both the early and the late visits, and both within the same winter, although in a small number of cases (less than 5%) these ideals were not met.

Methods for summer set visits

Instructions for summer set visits were slightly different. Units for counting were not individual birds, as they had been in the winter, but 'pairs'. 'Pairs' were defined as:

- an adult male and female observed together or in the same vicinity
- an adult bird of either sex, not observed as one of a pair
- a young bird or a family of young, perhaps accompanied by one or both parents.

Non-breeding adults and unpaired birds were included in the assessment. For flocking species, such as Woodpigeons, half the number of birds in each flock, rounded up to a whole number, was recorded as the number of 'pairs'. Where birds could be sexed, the sex of the bird was taken into account: males were typically easier to observe than females. For songbirds, most 'pairs' were detected by hearing a singing male.

The two periods for breeding-season set visits were 1st April to 15th May and 16th May to 30th June. One or two observers did not follow these guidelines, however, and a few set visits were accepted as early as 29th March and as late as 12th August. Recording sheets had further columns for noting how many active nests or fledged broods were seen on each visit. The number of apparently occupied nests, rather than 'pairs', was recorded as the count for colonial species, such as gulls, terns, Grey Herons, Sand Martins and Rooks.

Breeding status was noted for each species and tetrad on the simple scale of 'likely', 'not likely' or 'unknown'. An assessment of 'likely' was allowed wherever breeding was either 'probable' or 'confirmed' according to previous bird atlas criteria (*eg 1980–85 NBBS*) except for code S (singing male) which, on its own, was not regarded as indicating likely breeding. Confirmed breeding was not noted specifically, except where a count of nests or broods had been submitted. Breeding was specifically recorded as 'not likely' for passage migrants, late winter visitors and other birds out of breeding habitat.

Supplementary records

Once a tetrad had received its four set visits, it was generally not necessary for it to be visited again. Observers and local organisers were aware, however, of the need to build as complete as possible a checklist for every tetrad, and conducted extra fieldwork to this purpose. Supplementary records were especially valuable for nocturnal or crepuscular species such as owls, Nightjar and Woodcock that were often missed during the set visits, and for scarcer species such as Spotted Flycatcher. NBA observers submitted supplementary records for squares they had already covered for set visits and for other squares they happened to visit.

Relevant records were also extracted from the *NBR* and from Norfolk sightings that appeared on the *BirdGuides* website. Further supplementary records were added to the database from a range of additional sources, such as BTO surveys.

Progress with set visits

To maintain the enthusiasm for a long-term project such as the NBA, feedback to the participants was essential. This was achieved partly through newsletters that were sent out to every contributor or interested observer each autumn. These kept observers up to date with progress and contact details for local organisers, and included preliminary species maps and short articles from fieldworkers. A short account of each year's achievements and results also appeared in the annual *NBR*.

Progress in making set visits was considerably faster in the winter period than in the summer, despite the far shorter days and less reliable weather of the winter months (Figure 1.2). We assume this was because many of the more-active fieldworkers had fewer prior commitments for surveys during the winter period. The outbreak of foot-and-mouth disease among farm livestock in early 2001 further delayed the summer fieldwork because, for several months in spring 2001, access on foot to the countryside was severely restricted. Only 91 tetrads were surveyed for NBA in that year.

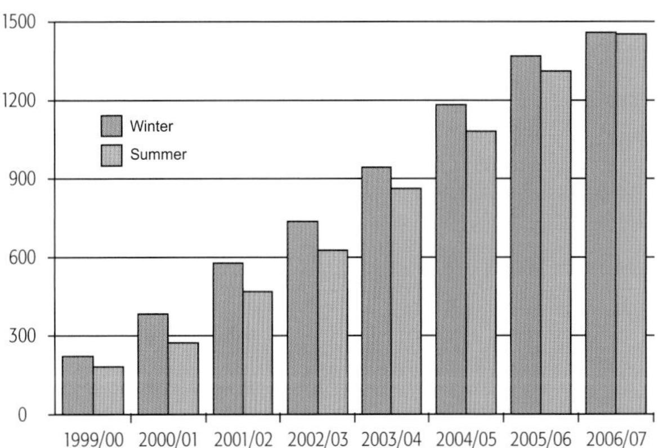

Figure 1.2 Cumulative number of tetrads in which set visits were completed in each of the NBA seasons. The total number of Norfolk tetrads is 1,459.

Plans for the conclusion of the project were not fixed until its rate of progress had become clear. It soon emerged that, because of the setback in 2001, eight years would be required to complete the set visits. Fieldwork finished on schedule at the end of the 2007 breeding season.

Observers for the NBA provided by far the best coverage ever achieved for any bird atlas of the county. Of the 1,459 tetrads, all but seven received both the summer set visits (99.5% coverage) and all but two tetrads the two winter set visits (99.9%). One tetrad was not recognised as having any land within Norfolk until it was too late to cover it and the other missing winter tetrad received only one of its set visits. The missing summer set visits arose largely because a promised set of counts arrived incomplete and had to be classed as supplementary data.

Building the NBA database

As completed set-visit recording sheets and supplementary record forms were received from NBA fieldworkers, Moss Taylor input the data into a relational database specifically customised in Microsoft Access. Supplementary records were added individually and by uploading data that had been submitted in spreadsheet format. By the end of the project the database had amassed more than 0.21 million NBA records (Table 1.1). The inputting of the data had taken Moss the equivalent of about twelve forty-hour weeks.

SEASON	SET-VISIT OBSERVATIONS	SUPPLEMENTARY OBSERVATIONS	TOTAL
SUMMER	74,491	11,377	85,868
WINTER	108,980	17,826	126,806
TOTAL	183,471	29,203	212,674

Table 1.1 Totals of NBA records in the database by the close of the project.

Although this had not been envisaged at the start of the project, the completed database also contains summary data from previous atlas surveys. A further 60,377 records from the *1980–85 NBBS* were commercially input for NBA from the master record cards from that survey – consent and finance for this having been generously provided by the Norfolk & Norwich Naturalists' Society.

Summary data for Norfolk 10-km squares from previous atlases of Britain and Ireland were supplied by BTO. Because it was not possible to subdivide the 10-km data by county, we decided to limit comparisons at this scale to the 62 10-km squares that are mainly in Norfolk and omit a further 11 squares partly in Norfolk but of which the larger part lay in another county.

The NBA database is a permanent record of bird atlas data for Norfolk that can be used, and perhaps added to, by future tetrad-based projects. It is currently being stored and maintained by courtesy of BTO at their headquarters in Thetford. The authors would welcome enquiries about its further use.

1.4 The nature of the NBA data

Once a database has been filled with numbers, there is inevitably a temptation for analysts to perform ever more complex calculations that treat these numbers as if they were precise measurements, rather than as estimates that each have a very wide range of uncertainty. Where analyses are performed without regard to the true nature of the data, they might sometimes lead to conclusions being drawn that are unsafe.

There are factors that are bound to influence the collection of data on birds that might not be immediately obvious to non-birdwatchers and that might limit the assumptions that may legitimately be made during data analysis. Some are to do with bird behaviour, which varies individually, with species, with time of day and season and with the weather, others with observers and others still that concern the nature of the site or interactions between these various elements.

The set visits are records of counts of birds detected by a particular observer, on a particular date, between a given start and end time, and in a given year. For a given species, each of these properties of the count contributes variation to the count. No observer covered everywhere in a tetrad where a bird might have been hiding, and some birds seen will have been passing through and present only briefly. Parts of tetrads to which access had been denied by landowners or which were difficult or dangerous to visit would be poorly represented in the counts, yet might be of particular value to some bird species. Many tetrads were surveyed only from roads or public paths, where bird density might not have been representative of the whole square.

Though many birds will have been overlooked altogether by NBA, some individuals will have been recorded in several different tetrads. A single patrolling Hen Harrier, or a flock of a thousand Golden Plovers, might well have visited several tetrads during a single morning. Long-lived birds even of relatively sedentary species might have been seen in several tetrads during the course of the project. Since NBA lasted for eight years, there will be many cases where species recorded in tetrads were not present in all of the years, because of short-term changes in distribution within the atlas period. In extreme cases, the cumulative distribution across the whole period will not represent the picture in any one year – for example the irruptive Waxwing, whose numbers and distribution are always very different between winters.

There will of course have been some errors in inputting, in data processing and in observation, for example in late summer counts treating birds that were actually fledged young as if they were adults. County and national rarities have been validated by the relevant bodies but we have not attempted any formal validation of records of common birds. Errors in bird identification, however, we believe will have been very few.

NBA has been an extremely successful project. While its data are most certainly fit for purpose, we ask readers and other users to bear their limitations in mind.

1.5 Using the database to map Norfolk's birds

The maps in this book were produced by linking the NBA database to a Geographical Information System (a GIS mapping program). Because the database is complex and can be queried in many ways, many different outputs to the mapping program can be calculated, both within and across species. The GIS itself offers many further options, so that a very wide range of maps can be drawn from the data. Already, far more maps have been prepared and evaluated than can be published.

The maps we have chosen for this book are simple presentations that encapsulate what we feel is the essence of the project. They show bird density in summer and in winter, measured as the maximum count recorded in each tetrad, from the early or the late set visit, or from a supplementary record. The inclusion of supplementaries ensures that the distribution maps show all NBA data, but allows there to be some bias towards tetrads from which such records were submitted. Also, since some observers covered many tetrads within a local area, it is possible that observer differences in recording ability or in time spent recording might appear as regional differences in apparent bird density. We experimented with correcting set-visit data for time spent in the field, or for the estimated percentage cover, but were unable to find correction factors that could sensibly apply to all species. We therefore use the simple unadjusted counts, which indeed show similar patterns to those produced after corrections for coverage and effort.

To allow readers to assess for themselves the effects of regional differences in coverage, we present four maps (Figures 1.3–1.6) that show where in the county the survey effort was concentrated. Less time spent on set visits is to be expected in tetrads with less than 400 ha of land within the county. It is possible, but by no means certain, that differences in effort between tetrads might have biased the likelihood of detection of certain species, or the size of the maximum count.

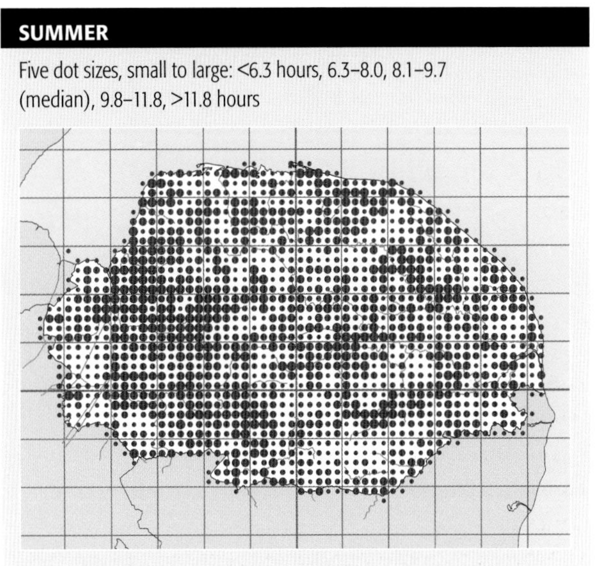

Figure 1.3 Time spent on summer set visits.

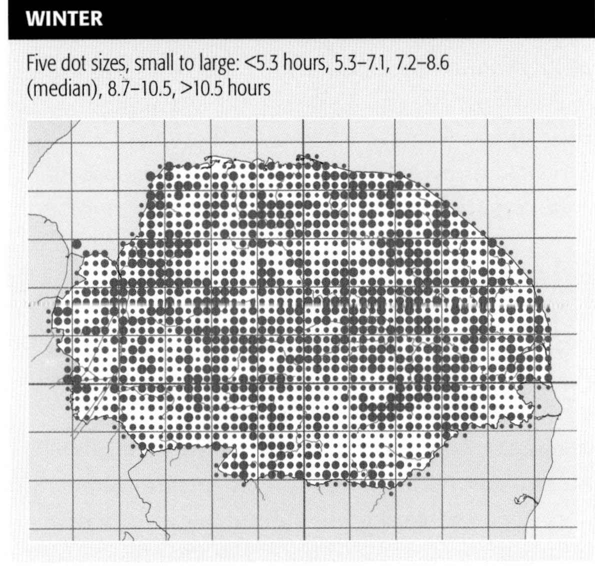

Figure 1.4 Time spent on winter set visits.

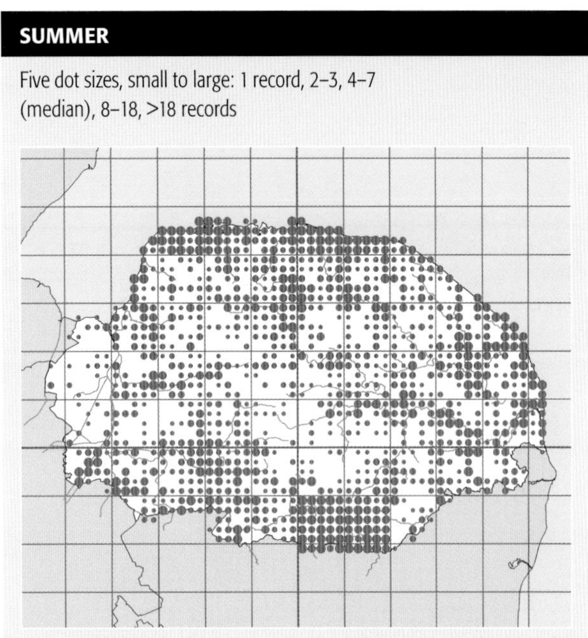

Figure 1.5 Number of supplementary summer records.

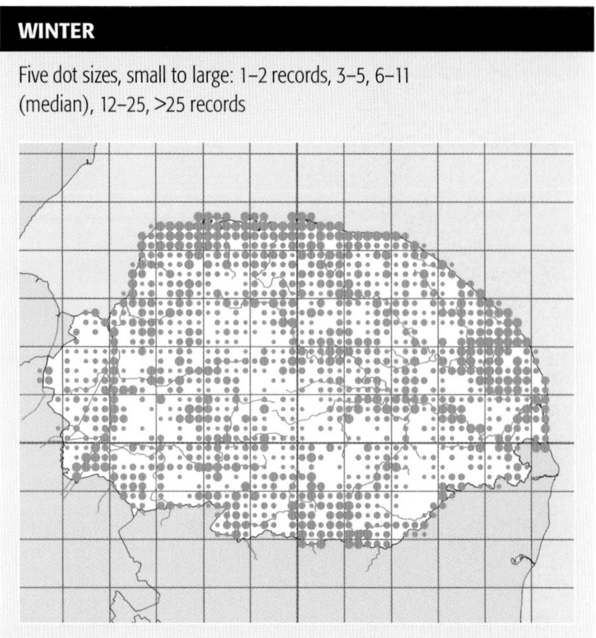

Figure 1.6 Number of supplementary winter records.

Observers in the King's Lynn area and around the Nar valley spent most time per tetrad on the two summer set visits; no large-scale patterns were evident elsewhere in the county (Figure 1.3). In winter, some of the same small patches of more-intensive coverage stand out, but with effort rather more even across the county (Figure 1.4). Supplementary records came mostly from prime birdwatching sites – around the coast, in the Broads, in Breckland and along the river valleys (Figures 1.5 & 1.6). The Diss area also provided more supplementaries than most other areas, especially for the summer period.

For the breeding season maps in the species texts, our approach of relating dot size to bird density is radically different from all previous atlases of the county, which have used the size of the dot to represent the likelihood of breeding (or, more correctly, the quality of breeding evidence obtained). Given that counts of birds are available, we feel that these are far more important to show in the maps, and we are keen to present quantitative information for the first time. The quality of breeding evidence is therefore relegated to a secondary level, showing as background shading in squares where breeding was at least likely. It is especially important to include this information for birds such as gulls and herons, where birds occur widely during the breeding season but where nesting is highly localised.

Also for the breeding season, many species show a 'change map' that displays the pattern of change in distribution, in terms of tetrads 'gained' or 'lost' since the *1980–85 NBBS*. We also tabulate the same information. These data get to the heart of the population monitoring aspects of our project. There are some problems, though, in comparing the two data sets – especially as we have no information on the distribution of survey effort in the 1980s.

In both surveys, the likelihood of recording a breeding species in a tetrad would have depended on whether or not the species was actually there, how many pairs there were, how easy the species is to detect, and how much effort and skill were applied to the search. An apparent gain of a tetrad might sometimes indicate increase in survey effort since the 1980s, or a population increase, rather than a real change in range, but we cannot now know to what extent these factors were important.

The fieldworkers for *1980–85 NBBS* recorded observations for six years, two fewer than for the present atlas, and were asked to record birds only when they were in potentially suitable breeding habitat. Breeding evidence was recorded in three categories (possible, probable and confirmed),

DAVID TIPLING

whereas in the present volume breeding status, where known, is categorised as likely or unlikely. These factors might also have affected whether a gain or a loss is reported. Given that we know that considerable effort was put into surveying almost every tetrad for NBA, we can be more confident that the losses since 1980–85 are real.

1.6 Recommendations for future surveys

Another atlas of Norfolk's birds at the 10-km scale is already nearing completion, as part of *Atlas 2007–11*, which is covering the whole of Britain and Ireland in summer and in winter. Tetrad data are being collected for this project but will not cover the whole county, and only the 10-km level will be reported. For comparison with previous county atlases at the tetrad scale, it would be ideal to begin a full repeat tetrad atlas for the county by about 2020. The methodology for future surveys, in Norfolk and elsewhere, must of course be determined as they arise and with reference to local circumstances, but we offer the following

'Supplementary records came mostly from prime birdwatching sites – around the coast, in the Broads, in Breckland and along the river valleys...'

assessment of our own methods, in case it is helpful to others planning county or local bird atlases.

Seasons for study

As birdwatchers we are well aware that, because of general differences between species and differences between individuals, bird movements across all species are hard to match to any simple divisions of the calendar. More radical approaches, which would map bird distributions year round and allow each species to reveal its individual seasonality, rather than have us impose fixed periods on them, are for the future: through *BirdTrack*, they have already begun.

If future surveys again find it necessary to define a winter and a summer period, we feel these should be kept as short as possible, consistent with the need to complete the fieldwork within a short period of years. Other atlas surveys have included all or part of November in the winter period. The case against is that many passage migrants are still arriving and departing in November but would have left the county by December, and this is especially true for a south-eastern coastal county like Norfolk. It should not be necessary for future surveys to class any of November as 'winter', since experience has shown that volunteer observers are generally more available for atlas work in the winter months than in the summer.

Set visits

Unlike the Timed Tetrad Visits (TTVs) designed for *Atlas 2007–11*, where observers could spend either one hour or two hours counting birds (although with options to 'stop the clock' for unrecorded lengths of time during the survey), tetrad visits for NBA were not given a limited duration. Instead, observers were allowed to spend as much time as they wanted on their visits, and then record what percentage of the tetrad they had included in their counts. Starting and finishing times were recorded.

Allowing unlimited time encouraged observers to be thorough. Most set visits at each season lasted around four hours. Tetrads with only a hectare or two in Norfolk could be covered in as little as 15 minutes. Some fieldworkers in rich tetrads apparently spent 12 hours or more on each set visit and one observer recorded 17 hours in the field on each of the summer visits to a tetrad. In such extreme cases, however, it seems most unlikely that active recording occupied the whole of the interval between the starting and finishing times, from which the duration of the visit was calculated.

In retrospect, however, it was a mistake not to fix a time for NBA set visits – at least for tetrads with a full 400 ha to be covered. Because of the variation in time spent between observers, and the tendency for observers to work within a limited area of the county, it was possible for additional time spent to feed through into the distribution maps as areas of higher-than-average bird density. In theory, it should be possible for differences in time spent in each tetrad to be corrected mathematically but, because species differ in the nature of their relationship between count and time spent, this proved to be impractical. In any case, there can be no correction for differences in observer ability, which have a very similar effect and might be at least as important as differences in time spent.

We would recommend fixing a period for set visits in future surveys. Setting a longer period than for *Atlas 2007–11* TTVs, say three or four hours, would fit better with how Norfolk observers chose to contribute to NBA. As further minor differences from *Atlas 2007–11* TTVs, we would recommend recording the starting time of the count, as well as the duration, and not allowing any 'stop the clock' options (except for a genuine break in observation), because these might be interpreted by observers in a variety of ways.

'Pair' as the unit for breeding-season counts

Since the launch of BBS in 1994, the individual bird has become the most familiar counting unit for breeding birds. It has been adopted as such by *Atlas 2007–11*. Birds that are clearly not adults are, at least in theory, omitted from the counts. The resulting totals of adult birds recorded for BBS are used directly to estimate population change and sometimes the size or density of the breeding population.

The main difficulty with this method, for estimating the size of a breeding population, is that males and females differ in their detectability – differences being most evident when males are defending territories and females are incubating, and less so at other times. Thus, ten birds counted on a breeding survey might indicate a minimum of ten breeding pairs in the area, if all were singing males for example, or as few as five pairs, if all the breeding adults (and no fledged juveniles) were counted. Whether a count consisted mostly of one sex of birds or of a more-even mixture of males and females would depend heavily on the stage of breeding in that locality and year, and also on the time of day, the weather and the nature of the terrain.

NBA took 'breeding pair' as its unit for the breeding-season set visits. For this method, any indication of a breeding pair will count as one unit – including for example a singing male, a female, a pair, two birds together of unknown sex, or a family party. This method overrides some of the problems of estimating a number of pairs from a count of individuals, making the estimation of population size much more straightforward. Importantly, there is less scope for the inclusion of juvenile birds to influence the counts. The only practical difficulty we encountered was for birds that were not breeding, where flocks or single individuals had to be converted to a number of 'pairs'. It is possible also that some observers counted individuals rather than pairs at both seasons, through force of habit, or because they were confused by the difference in methods between the two seasons. Nevertheless, we strongly recommend this method for consideration for future breeding-season bird surveys.

Recording breeding evidence

We strongly favour the system developed subsequently to NBA for *Atlas 2007–11*, in which observers are encouraged to record breeding evidence for every breeding-season record. Codes include the standard, long-established ones for breeding evidence, as devised for the *1968–72 Atlas*, with the addition of extra codes such as F (flying over), M (migrant) and U (summering non-breeder).

For a tetrad atlas, it is very important to emphasise to observers the need for the breeding evidence to relate directly to breeding within the particular tetrad to which it is applied. For example, Swifts mating aerially over open farmland or forest are clearly providing evidence of breeding but nesting might not necessarily be occurring within the tetrad over which they were observed. If no suitable nesting habitat exists, it would be absurd to record 'likely breeding' for that tetrad, yet there were indications that some NBA observers did provide such records. Similarly, the mobility of juveniles of many species within a few days or weeks of fledging might take them very quickly into tetrads in which the species had not bred: Black-headed Gull and Starling provide very obvious evidence of this behaviour but the problem might apply to any species. Codes for proven breeding based on recently fledged young should be applied only where it is highly unlikely that the birds had moved from another tetrad, for example because they were too close to fledging to have done so.

Breeding evidence was not requested for NBA. Instead, observers were asked simply to record whether breeding was likely, without saying whether any evidence was obtained. The returns were doubtless rather subjective and in some cases might have taken into account the past as well as the present ranges of the species.

It is clearly a massive task to gather proof of breeding for every species in every Norfolk tetrad. Nevertheless, we would recommend that future county surveys set out to do this and to record all the evidence that is obtained. The results would no doubt be incomplete at tetrad level but would allow breeding ranges to be defined quite adequately and would be of value into the future as a more objective record of what was observed.

While collecting breeding evidence is clearly important, quantification of the data is even more so. We recommend to future atlas surveys that the level of breeding evidence obtained should not be the primary focus of the resulting maps and that displaying estimates of breeding numbers in each square is much more revealing and should be given precedence.

Change maps

The change maps produced for this book, to compare the 1980–85 summer distributions with those from NBA, have been designed according to some radical new principles, which we would strongly recommend for consideration in future comparisons between atlas maps.

First, whereas change maps typically show only the squares where gains and losses have occurred, we have also indicated the squares that were occupied in both atlases. This has the enormous advantage that the eye can readily compare the distribution of both gains and losses with that of tetrads where the species also occurs, but where no gain or loss has been noted. The change map is therefore self-contained and can be interpreted fully without reference to either of the original distribution maps.

Second, we have employed symbols for gains and for losses that are readily distinguishable from each other by colour and by shape. This ensures that gains and losses can be easily read from the maps by the colour blind and would be clear even if reproduced in monochrome.

Third, the gain and loss symbols are of approximately equal weight but are more prominent than the indication of 'no change'. Thus the eye is led to the main point of the map, the gains and losses, but to both of these equally. We have used shading of a neutral colour to indicate no change, and bold, intuitively shaped symbols to indicate gains and losses.

CHAPTER 2

The summer and winter distribution of Norfolk's birds, 1999–2007

2.1 Taxonomic listing

IN THE MAIN SPECIES TEXTS that follow this introduction, the ordering and naming of species accords with the current online version of the BOU's *British List*, incorporating the revised sequence for grebes and passerines presented in the BOU Records Committee's 38th report (BOURC 2010). This radically new ordering of families and species might be unfamiliar now to many readers but it has already been adopted by *NBR* and will no doubt quickly become more widely known.

2.2 Interpreting the tables

Each main species text contains two standard tables. Rows and columns in these tables are explained below, followed by a fuller explanation of how the population estimates were arrived at. In both tables, rows that convey no information have been omitted.

Summary of NBA 1999–2007

The first table summarises the content of the database purely as it relates to the NBA period. Contents of the rows are described below. Two figures are often given for the summer, separated by a spaced forward slash (solidus). As indicated by the column header, the first figure refers to all summer records and the second only to those tetrads where breeding was either proven or considered 'likely'.

- **Tetrads occupied**. These are the numbers of tetrads in which the species was recorded during 1999–2007 in summer and winter, with the percentage that this represents of the total 1,459 tetrads in the county. Percentages are given to the nearest whole number, or as '<1%' (less than 1%) where the closest whole number would be zero. These numbers are comparable between seasons and across species.

- **Summer only/winter only.** Species present in Norfolk in summer and in winter sometimes occupy different tetrads at each season. The values in this row show the numbers of tetrads occupied in summer but not in winter, and in winter but not in summer. They are presented because the degree of difference between the summer and winter distributions is not always evident by comparing the summer and winter maps. Low figures relative to the previous row reveal that there is little difference between the tetrads occupied in the two seasons, whereas high figures show considerable turnover between the seasons. All tetrads occupied in summer are included, whether breeding was likely or not. These figures are of special value because NBA has surveyed summer and winter birds during the same period of years.

- **Mean maximum count per occupied tetrad.** Maximum count is the highest value for the tetrad and may come from a set visit or a supplementary count. The frequency distribution of maximum counts among tetrads is unlikely to be simple and might convey a lot of biological information about the species, although this is outside the scope of this book. We have chosen to present a mean value (a simple average) as a way to compare the numbers of birds that were counted per tetrad between the two seasons, and between species. Readers should be aware, however, that the mean might not be a frequent value in the data set and that the counts of birds recorded are always likely to be incomplete. Means are for occupied tetrads only and exclude all zero values. They are presented to the nearest whole number. Counts for the breeding season are of 'pairs', even in tetrads where breeding was not considered likely. Winter counts are of individual birds.

- **Summed maximum counts.** The sum of the maximum counts is the total of the maximum counts recorded in each of the county's tetrads, whether from a set visit or a supplementary record. It is also the number of occupied tetrads multiplied by the mean maximum count although, because the mean maximum counts are rounded to a whole number, this might not always be obvious. This total is a step on the way to producing a population estimate. If it is much lower than our population estimate, we think that there were many additional birds that were present but not included in the counts. Where the summed maximum count is higher than the population estimate, we consider that there was considerable movement of birds between tetrads and that this outweighed the number of birds that were missed.

- **Population estimates.** These are our attempts to quantify for the first time the population sizes of every summering and wintering bird species in Norfolk. The figures apply particularly to the NBA period – 2000–07 for summer estimates and 1999/2000–2006/07 for winter. The process of producing bird population estimates for the county is described more fully later in this section. For species that breed in Norfolk, the summer estimates are for breeding numbers. The units for this are normally 'bp' (breeding pairs), but (following *APEP06*) other units such as 'singing males' or 'nesting females' have been used where these are more appropriate to the species' biology. For non-breeding birds in summer, the units are 'individuals' and 'none' indicates either that no birds were recorded or that the few birds that occurred have been regarded as transient rather than summering. Winter estimates are presented as the number of individual birds; 'none' has been entered where the species was absent, or where we think the few birds observed were migrants rather than winterers. Typically, estimates are given as a broad range: a lower limit of zero is given for species that are likely to have been completely absent in some years.

Comparisons with previous atlases

The function of the second table is to summarise information on range changes in comparison with each of the previous bird atlases for the county. There are three previous atlases for which data are available only at 10-km scale. For the *1980–85 NBBS*, data were collected at tetrad level but have been summarised here also at 10-km level, and both comparisons are presented. The four previous atlases have produced up to five rows in this table, therefore.

For comparisons at 10-km scale, the numbers and percentages are based on the 62 10-km squares that can be unequivocally assigned to Norfolk and omit a further 11 squares partly in Norfolk but of which the larger part lies in another county. For the tetrad comparison, the units are the 1,459 tetrads that contain some land in Norfolk. Comparisons are all for the breeding season except for that with the *1981–84 Winter Atlas*. They are presented in order of starting year but note that the *1980–85 NBBS* and *1981–84 Winter Atlas* were concurrent.

The columns in these tables provide the following information.

- **Squares occupied**. These are the numbers and percentages of Norfolk squares that were occupied by the species in the previous atlases of the county, as named in the left-hand column. Some data for rare species from the previous atlases were not available in the original publications from those surveys, but we are able to tabulate them here. A few minor differences remain, having proved difficult to trace, between the totals published by Kelly (1986) and the data for the *1980–85 NBBS* that are now in the NBA database.

- **1999–2007**. These are the best comparable figures from the NBA project (see below). The figure for tetrads also appears in the first table.

- **Losses and gains**. Losses are the numbers of squares occupied in the previous atlas but not in NBA, and gains are the gains of individual squares shown by NBA since the previous atlas. Note that in some cases there might be little or no overall change in the numbers of occupied squares but substantial individual gains and losses.

In interpreting the numbers of occupied grid squares, and the changes in numbers of squares that have occurred since previous atlases, it is important for readers to recognise that the numbers of squares occupied by a species, and the numbers of gains and losses, are strongly dependent on the size set for the squares. Range changes calculated at the tetrad level are likely to be much more marked than those at the 10-km scale. Colonisations and extinctions experienced by observers at finer scales still, such as small woodlands or wetlands, or villages or neighbourhoods, might of course be of great local significance but might not be evident at all on the maps, even at tetrad level.

In all the atlas comparisons, the figures are heavily dependent on the quality of coverage in the earlier surveys, for which we have no information. Had effort been too low in the previous survey, a species with no real change of range could now be expected to show an apparent increase in the number of squares occupied, given the thorough coverage of every tetrad that was completed for NBA. A further factor is the eight-year period of NBA, compared to the three winters and maximum of six summers spanned by the previous projects. Given the increased effort for NBA, our maps and tables can be expected to some degree to under-represent the real range losses that have occurred and to overstate some of the gains.

Mismatches between atlases in the way that breeding likelihood was recorded complicate the comparisons of breeding range. The square totals include 'possible', 'probable' and 'confirmed' breeding in the case of the *1968–72 Atlas* and *1980–85 NBBS*, and both 'breeding' and 'seen' categories of the *1988–91* Atlas. In all these atlases, all categories refer to birds seen in potential breeding habitat, since birds seen out of habitat were not included. There is a minor exception for colonial seabirds, which were presented differently from other species in the *1988–91 Atlas*: for Fulmar, Cormorant, Shag, gulls and terns, the squares treated as occupied in that atlas are only those where breeding is known to have occurred. For NBA, only squares in which breeding was at least likely have been included, since these figures provide the most reliable comparisons with the earlier data. Thus NBA's records of summering non-breeders, spring and early-autumn migrants and birds nesting in nearby tetrads, all recorded as 'breeding not likely', are not included in the comparisons with earlier surveys.

Estimates of population size

The estimation of absolute population sizes is by no means a necessary part of an atlas project, for which relative abundances are far more relevant.

Nevertheless, we have attempted to estimate both midwinter and midsummer population sizes for all of Norfolk's birds, in many cases for the first time, and present them (tentatively, and with some trepidation) in the tables in the species texts. We hope the results will be of interest to readers and of some practical value to conservationists (see Chapter 5).

It is important that our estimates are not taken, in comparison with other Norfolk population estimates past or future, as evidence that actual bird numbers have changed: changes in the population estimates could very easily stem from methodological improvements, or from differences of opinion, rather than from real population change among the birds. Population change is, however, a major theme of this book. Where we wish to draw attention to trends in breeding population, we use national change estimates, drawn from the BTO's Common Birds Census (CBC) and the BTO/JNCC/RSPB Breeding Bird Survey (BBS), that cover the 25 years between 1982 and 2007. These are the years that tally most closely with the period between the two tetrad atlas projects in Norfolk: these figures, and more up-to-date ones, are available on the *Birdtrends* pages of the BTO web site (*www.bto.org/birdtrends*).

The population estimates we have prepared are intended to cover the whole NBA period (1999/2000–2006/07 for winter and 2000–07 for summer). We present the figures as a range which we hope encompasses both the changes during the eight-year period and the uncertainty that would accompany each annual estimate. Readers should be aware that the ranges might not be wide enough, or that in some cases both the upper and lower limits might be wrong, despite our best efforts.

The starting point of our assessment has been the maximum counts made for NBA in each of the county's tetrads, in each season. When summed, these would already be the population estimates we are looking for – except that there are usually likely to be far more birds in a tetrad than is indicated by the maximum count. This is especially true for tetrads where access was poor or hours in the field relatively low, and for inconspicuous species, where even with thorough coverage the count might easily be an order of magnitude too low. For other species, summing the counts across tetrads might give too high a figure, because the same individuals have been seen in more than one tetrad during the NBA survey. These might be species that roam widely within each winter, especially in large flocks such as those of Pink-footed Goose and Golden Plover. They might also be species, such as Snow Bunting and Shore Lark, that often appear in different tetrads in different winters. Movement between tetrads is likely to be less of a problem during summer, but overestimation might still occur for rarer or more nomadic breeders, which might occupy a different range of tetrads each year. For both seasons, we have also borne in mind that the lists of occupied tetrads have accumulated over an eight-year period and that numbers might have been considerably weaker in some years than in others.

We have no data that could help us to make the necessary adjustments to the summed NBA maximum counts, nor to set appropriate intervals between upper and lower limits, and we have simply used our best judgment. The extent to which we have adjusted the maximum counts, up or down, has generally been similar for related species or species with similar detectability or habits. Summer and winter estimates have been cross-checked, to ensure that they are consistent, allowing for the productivity of resident populations and any immigration or emigration that is likely to occur between the seasons.

In setting our estimates, we have also used external data, where available. Monthly maximum wildfowl counts, as set out in the county bird reports, have been a useful source, as have *The Birds of Norfolk* (*BoN*; 1999) and the published results of county and national surveys. We have checked that our estimates accord with the most recent set of national estimates produced by the Avian Population Estimates Panel (*APEP06*). Finally, we have reviewed the estimates across all species, summer and winter, and made sure that, in our opinion, the species are ranked appropriately.

2.3 Interpreting the maps

Summer and winter distributions

The summer maps show, in red, the maximum summer count recorded, per species and tetrad, as a large, medium-sized or small dot within each tetrad. The winter maps show the equivalent values for the winter period, in blue. Large dots indicate relatively high densities. Small dots are to be expected on the coast, and along the county boundary, in tetrads with little land in Norfolk.

The key to dot sizes and counts differs for each species and season, depending on the frequency distribution of the count data, and is indicated next to each map. Units for the summer maps are always 'pairs', even in squares where breeding was not likely.

Light red shading of tetrads on the summer maps indicates tetrads where breeding either was proven or was considered likely. Tetrads with red dots but no shading are those where the species occurred in the summer period but was thought not to have nested. All tetrads that recorded the species in winter are shaded in light blue on the winter map, because this helps to illustrate continuous areas of distribution and to draw attention to isolated squares.

The OS 10-km and 100-km grid lines are shown as background to each map, along with county boundaries in black and the major rivers and streams in green.

Change maps

For many of the breeding species a map is also included that shows the pattern of change in breeding distribution since 1980–85. These use the comparison between the *1980–85 NBBS* and the NBA that is available within the NBA database. The change maps have been designed on original principles, as discussed in the previous chapter.

Neutral shading (salmon pink) indicates squares where the species was present in both atlases, while green plus signs and black crosses indicate gains and losses respectively. Maps with little change, therefore, are predominantly pink (*eg* Woodpigeon), those with mostly gains are green (*eg* Sparrowhawk), and those with many losses are mostly black (*eg* Lesser Redpoll).

Each of the three symbol types has two sizes, being large where either the breeding status in 1980–85 was 'probable' or 'confirmed', or breeding in the NBA period was considered at least 'likely', or both these conditions were met.

- **Large symbols** therefore indicate loss, gain or no change for a bird probably breeding or likely to be breeding within the tetrad.

- **Small symbols** mean that a gain or a loss was indicated, but not necessarily as a breeding species within the tetrad. A small green symbol indicates that the species was unrecorded in 1980–85 and present during the NBA period, but its breeding status then was 'unknown'. A small black symbol means that breeding status in 1980–85 was 'possible' and that during the NBA period the species was either unrecorded or definitely not breeding.

Confidentiality

Rare breeding birds in Britain are still subject to illegal persecution by gamekeepers and egg collectors and, in some cases, might be vulnerable to too close or too persistent observation by over-ardent birdwatchers who fail to follow *The Birdwatcher's Code*. For these reasons, it is wise to keep the detailed breeding localities of some rare species confidential. The Rare Breeding Birds Panel (*www.rbbp.org.uk*) is the body responsible for gathering and archiving records of rare breeding birds in the UK. With advice from them, we have considered it unwise, for a few rare species that breed in the county, to publish maps at tetrad scale. In all these cases, we have substituted maps at a coarser scale, either for breeding status or for all tetrad records, and in some cases have collated the tetrad dots and placed them centrally within their 10-km square. Change maps are not shown where these might compromise confidentiality by identifying vulnerable tetrads.

There are no breeding species known to NBA that we have not been able to report.

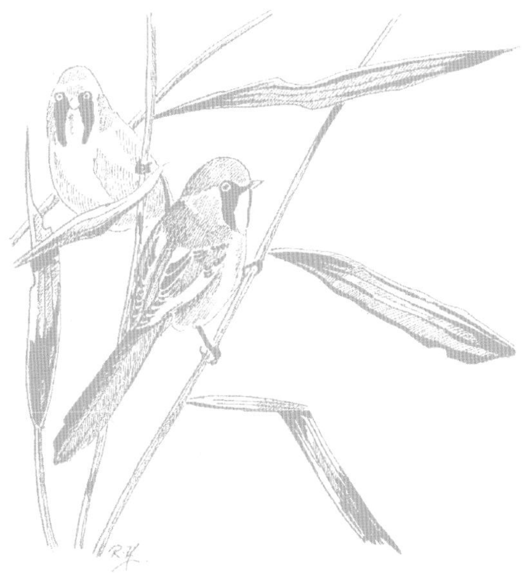

Mute Swan
Cygnus olor

NBA 1999–2007	SUMMER: ALL/BREEDING	WINTER
TETRADS OCCUPIED	453 (31%) / 328 (22%)	529 (36%)
SUMMER/WINTER ONLY	72	148
MEAN PER OCCUPIED TETRAD	4 / 5	12
SUMMED MAX COUNTS	1,833 / 1,482	6,268
POPULATION ESTIMATE	300–400 bp	1,500–2,500

PREVIOUS ATLASES	SQUARES OCCUPIED	1999–2007	LOSSES	GAINS
1968–72 (10 KM)	54 (87%)	53 (85%)	5	4
1980–85 (TETRAD)	306 (21%)	328 (22%)	105	127
1980–85 (10 KM)	52 (84%)	53 (85%)	4	5
1981–84 WINTER (10 KM)	57 (92%)	58 (94%)	1	2
1988–91 (10 KM)	55 (89%)	53 (85%)	3	1

MUTE SWANS ARE associated with larger waters throughout the county and are a familiar sight all year on Norfolk's Broads and rivers.

Mute Swans feed on aquatic vegetation and increasingly in recent years on growing cereals, which has brought them into conflict with farmers. During the summer, breeding pairs are found on lakes, meres, gravel pits, dykes, slow-flowing rivers and coastal lagoons. Once a pair bond has been established, it typically persists for the rest of the birds' lives. Their bulky nests, often reused over several years, are constructed amongst reeds or on waterside banks. Incubating females are easily seen, and even the presence of those hidden in reedbeds is apparent by the male patrolling the nearby water, so NBA observers should have located nearly every occupied tetrad.

The NBA summer map shows the very distinct association with the main river systems within the county. In the east, the pattern of distribution radiates out from Breydon Water and the Halvergate Marshes, through Broadland and along the Rivers Bure, Yare and Waveney. In the west, the occupied tetrads follow the Great Ouse and the Ouse Washes, and upstream along the Rivers Nar, Wissey and Little Ouse and their associated Fenland dykes. In addition, smaller numbers were present along the coastal marshes in north Norfolk. A very similar pattern was found by the *1980–85 NBBS.*

NBA counts include immature and other non-breeding Mute Swans, sometimes in substantial herds, as well as birds that were nesting. For example, nearly

SUMMER

Small dots 1, medium 2–3, large 4–56 ('pairs')
Shading – breeding proved or considered likely

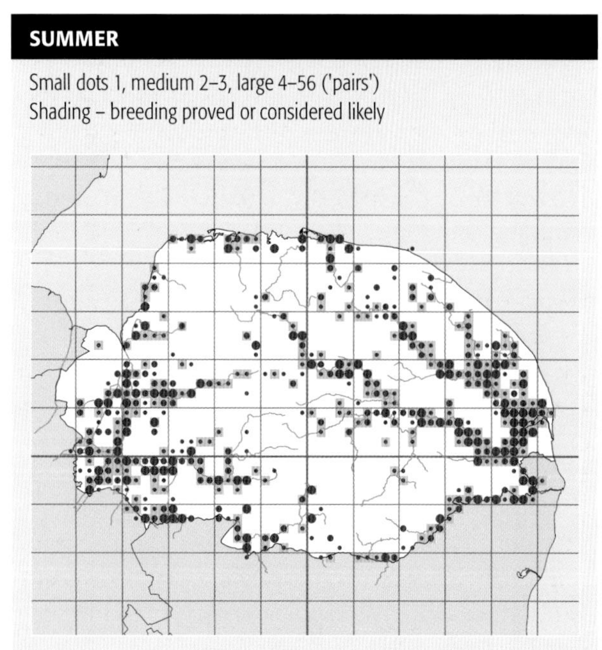

WINTER

Small dots 1–2, medium 3–8, large 9–246 (birds)

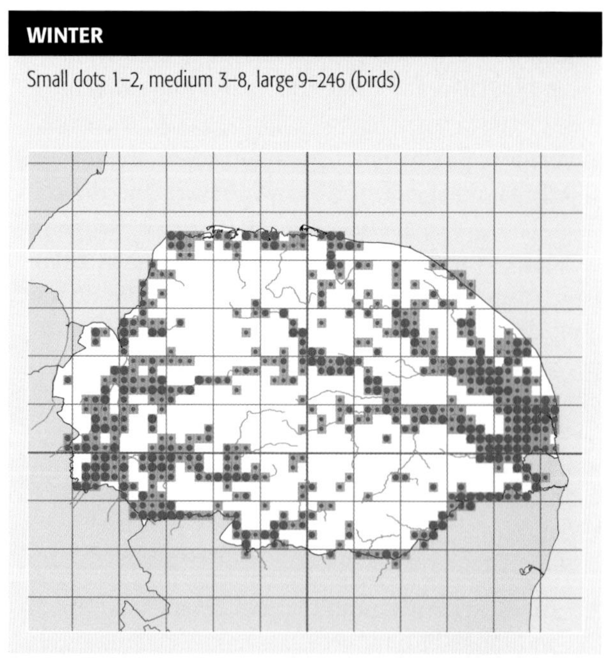

DAVID TIPLING

300 Mute Swans were present during the summer in the Welney area and 140 at Breydon Water.

Since Mute Swans are largely sedentary, with breeding pairs remaining in their territories throughout the year, it is not surprising that the summer and winter distribution maps are almost identical. The main difference is that, outside the breeding season, swans may move away from the river systems to graze in the surrounding arable fields, on harvested oil-seed rape or winter cereal, or in meadows. Many immatures and non-breeders gather at traditional feeding sites during the winter months, where Bewick's and Whooper Swans may join them. During NBA winters, four tetrads were found to hold three-figure counts of Mute Swans. The maximum counts were 246 at Hardley Flood, 200 at Welney, 149 at Nar Valley Fisheries and 118 at Langley Marshes.

'Once a pair bond has been established it typically persists for the rest of the birds' lives.'

CHANGE SINCE 1980–85

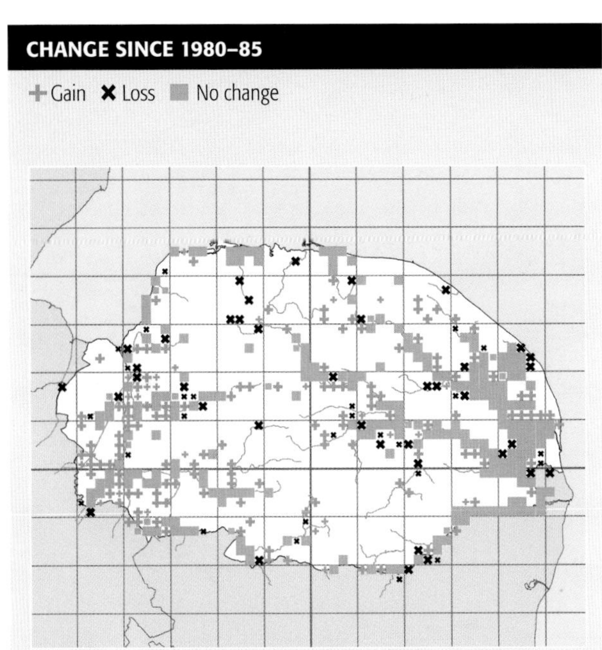

Numbers of Mute Swans in Europe increased during the first half of the 20th century, but during the 1960s and early 1970s, the British population fell as a result of a series of hard winters, increasing power-line casualties and mortality due to poisoning from lead fishing weights. The use of lead for fishing weights was banned in 1987, since when numbers have once again risen nationally (*Birdtrends*). The change map indicates that there has been substantial infilling of range throughout Norfolk since the 1980s, in line with the national population increase.

Bewick's Swan
Cygnus columbianus

NBA 1999–2007	SUMMER: ALL/BREEDING	WINTER
TETRADS OCCUPIED	4 (<1%) / none	112 (8%)
SUMMER/WINTER ONLY	3	111
MEAN PER OCCUPIED TETRAD	2 / none	147
SUMMED MAX COUNTS	10 / none	16,445
POPULATION ESTIMATE	3–10 individuals	3,000–5,000

PREVIOUS ATLASES	SQUARES OCCUPIED	1999–2007	LOSSES	GAINS
1981–84 WINTER (10 KM)	28 (45%)	25 (40%)	11	8

NORFOLK IS A MAJOR winter destination for the Bewick's Swans that nest on the European Russian tundra. Most break their journey in Estonia and in the Netherlands, and arrive in Norfolk from the east from late October onwards. Numbers peak in January. Most leave Norfolk by early March, but occasional stragglers or flightless birds, perhaps injured by collisions with power lines at Welney, remain through the summer.

In the 1940s, small numbers wintered in Norfolk, but since then the population on the Ouse Washes has increased steadily, where conservation bodies have

DAVID TIPLING

purchased extensive areas of wetland. During the late 1960s, artificial feeding was introduced at Welney but nowadays comparatively few Bewick's Swans take advantage, as this source of food has been appropriated by the larger and more dominant Whooper Swans.

Bewick's Swans overwinter in large herds at traditional, inland wetland sites, where open freshwater, on which they roost at night, is close to suitable areas of grazing, such as flooded grasslands. In recent years they have also begun to feed on stubbles and winter cereals. The NBA winter map shows that the species is virtually restricted to the Fens and Broadland, although east–west movements are observed widely across the county at passage times. In the Welney area, numbers have increased almost annually, and a record count of 5,122 roosting Bewick's Swans was made in early January 2004. Although Bewick's Swans are highly gregarious outside the breeding season, long-term monogamous pair bonds are maintained and family parties remain together within the large herds. During NBA winters, the proportion of first-winter birds among the Welney visitors averaged about 10%.

Over the years some traditional feeding sites have become established in Broadland, such as Catfield/Wood Street, Ludham/St Benet's and Waxham/Horsey/West Somerton, with the Catfield birds tending to roost at Hickling Broad and those from Ludham on Ranworth Broad. Far smaller numbers are recorded in Broadland than in the Fens, but nevertheless important numbers are present, especially in late winter, as some Fenland birds pause in the Broads on their return migration.

WINTER

Small dots 1–12, medium 13–76, large 77–4,000 (birds)

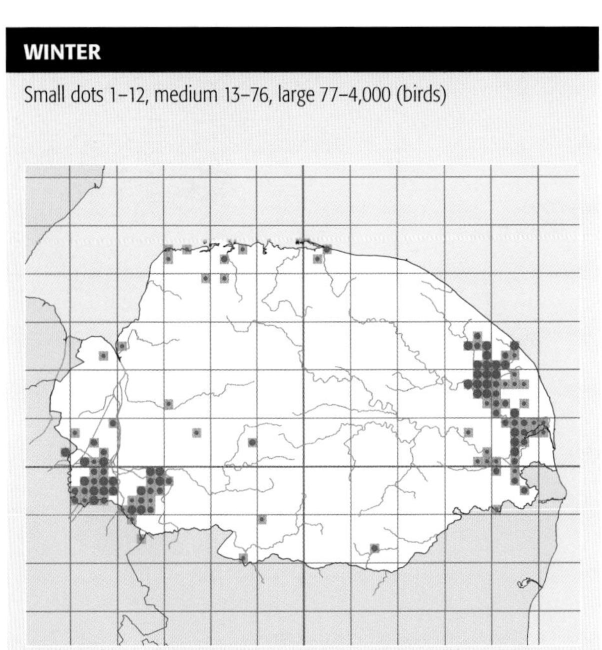

'In the 1940s, only small numbers wintered in Norfolk, but since then the population on the Ouse Washes has increased steadily, where conservation bodies have purchased extensive areas of wetland.'

Peak counts made for NBA included 420 at Hickling Broad, 381 at Ludham, 350 at Potter Heigham and 320 at Ranworth Broad, while in January/February 2003 the herd at St Benet's Level gradually built up as Fenland birds moved east and peaked at 734 on 20th February. In the Breydon Water area, up to 250 have been recorded on the Halvergate Marshes.

Whooper Swan

Cygnus cygnus

NBA 1999–2007	SUMMER: ALL/BREEDING	WINTER
TETRADS OCCUPIED	16 (1%) / none	98 (7%)
SUMMER/WINTER ONLY	8	90
MEAN PER OCCUPIED TETRAD	8 / none	73
SUMMED MAX COUNTS	127 / none	7,148
POPULATION ESTIMATE	3–10 individuals	1,500–2,500

PREVIOUS ATLASES	SQUARES OCCUPIED	1999–2007	LOSSES	GAINS
1981–84 WINTER (10 KM)	19 (31%)	33 (53%)	5	19

THE WHOOPER SWAN'S Icelandic population of around 16,000 birds winters mainly in Britain and in Ireland. In addition, at least 200 Finnish birds are believed to winter in Britain. Traditionally, the winter distribution of Whooper Swans has been mainly in northern England, Scotland and Ireland. However, in recent years the Ouse Washes have become the most important site in Britain & Ireland, as increasing numbers have overwintered there. Since the winter of 1989/90, when a record total of 686 was present, numbers increased progressively, reaching 3,051 by January 2004. During the NBA winters, an average 18% of Whooper Swans at Welney have been first-winter birds, substantially higher than the 10% recorded for Bewick's Swans. It is likely that this partly explains the increasing winter population at this site, along with a low mortality rate and some recruitment from other wintering areas (Kemp 2004).

The Ouse Washes provide the ideal wintering site for Whooper Swans, which flight out to arable fields at dawn, along with Bewick's Swans, to feed largely on the post-harvest waste of sugar-beet tops, potatoes and winter stubbles, returning at dusk to roost on the flooded washes. They have also taken advantage of the additional artificial feeding that takes place every afternoon at the Welney WWT reserve.

The NBA winter map clearly shows that the Fens are one of only two areas in Norfolk that hold good numbers of Whooper Swans, the other being the northern Broads. In Broadland, two main arable areas are used regularly by wintering Whooper Swans: Ludham/Wood Street/Catfield and Hickling/Horsey/Waxham, the latter group roosting at night on Hickling or Horsey Broads. In contrast to Bewick's Swans, however, Whooper Swans are scarce in the Breydon Water area. Since the 1990s, the number of Whooper Swans in Broadland has steadily fallen and during NBA winters the maximum site counts included 116 at Catfield/Potter Heigham, 70 at Ludham and 64 roosting on Horsey Mere. Elsewhere in the county, ones

WINTER

Small dots 1–4, medium 5–24, large 25–2,000 (birds)

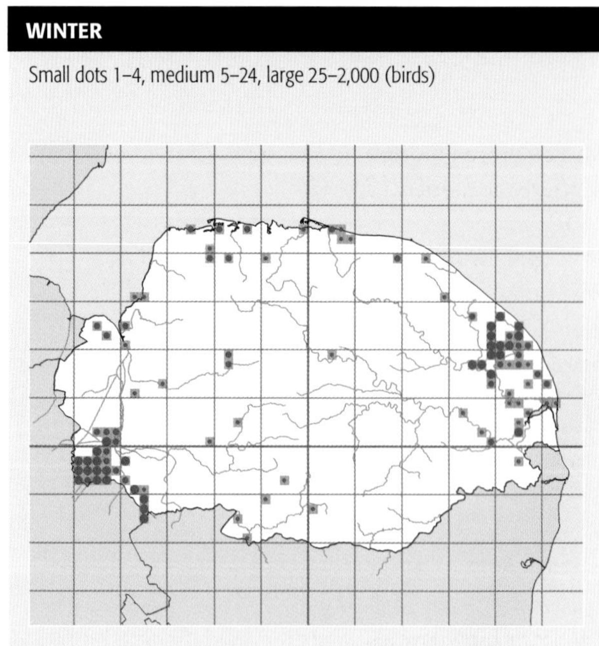

DAVID TIPLING

and twos are reported in most winters at a few well-scattered localities.

Whooper Swans are present in Norfolk for a longer period than are Bewick's Swans, the first arriving in mid October, mainly from a northerly direction, and the last normally leaving in mid April. In some years, considerable numbers of Whooper Swans are still present in April. In 2001, for example, 224 were at Welney on 7th April, falling to 120 by 12th, with the final 27 not departing until 27th. Unfortunately, some birds are killed through collisions with overhead power lines: others become flightless, through accident or illness, and as a result up to ten have been present throughout the summer at Welney. On occasion, immature birds have also oversummered in north Norfolk.

'The NBA winter map clearly shows that the Fens are one of only two areas in Norfolk that hold good numbers of Whooper Swans, the other being the northern Broads.'

Bean Goose
Anser fabalis

NBA 1999–2007	SUMMER: ALL/BREEDING	WINTER
TETRADS OCCUPIED	3 (<1%) / 1 (<1%)	85 (6%)
SUMMER/WINTER ONLY	3	85
MEAN PER OCCUPIED TETRAD	1 / 1	12
SUMMED MAX COUNTS	3 / 1	962
POPULATION ESTIMATE	0–1 bp (*fabalis*)	140–240 *fabalis*, 20–40 *rossicus*

PREVIOUS ATLASES	SQUARES OCCUPIED	1999–2007	LOSSES	GAINS
1968–72 (10 KM)	none	1 (2%)	0	1
1980–85 (TETRAD)	none	1 (<1%)	0	1
1980–85 (10 KM)	none	1 (2%)	0	1
1981–84 WINTER (10 KM)	17 (27%)	19 (31%)	6	8
1988–91 (10 KM)	none	1 (2%)	0	1

TWO RACES OF BEAN GEESE winter in Norfolk, the larger Taiga Bean Goose, nominate *fabalis*, which breeds in the forest zone from Fenno-Scandia eastwards to the Ural Mountains, and the smaller Tundra Bean Goose *rossicus*, which nests in the Russian high Arctic. Nowadays it is the least numerous of the four species of grey goose that occur regularly in Britain. Norfolk holds a significant proportion of its British population.

Taiga Bean Geese have been wintering in the Yare valley since at least the early 1920s and in recent decades this has been the only site in England that is used annually. The first birds arrive from mid-November onwards, and numbers generally peak in January, with the first birds leaving on their return migration later that month. Thus they spend only eight to ten weeks in Norfolk each year. The NBA winter map shows that the flock, which usually numbers between 150 and 200, remains within a fairly restricted area centred on Cantley Marshes. The highest count during the NBA period was of 270 in early January 2002. Ten years earlier, Yare valley counts were typically around 500 birds. In earlier years, Buckenham Marshes were favoured but as sheep were introduced to that area, a shorter sward resulted, which was not favoured by the Bean Geese. Only a few isolated records of birds of this race were reported from elsewhere in the county.

Tundra Bean Geese were first recognised in Norfolk in the winter of 1987/88 but it is likely that most of the earlier Bean Geese located away from the Yare valley had actually been of this race. Three main areas hosted *rossicus* during the NBA period: the coast and adjacent arable land of north Norfolk, the northern part of Broadland and the Fens. In north and east Norfolk, the Bean Geese often associate with the very large flocks of Pink-footed Geese that graze the stubbles and sugar beet fields, although they usually remain slightly apart from the Pink-feet. In the Fens, Welney has been used as a regular wintering site by a small flock of *rossicus* for several years, the number varying from four to nine. At all sites, single-figure counts of this race of the Bean Geese are the norm, although an exceptional influx

WINTER — Taiga Bean Goose

Small dots 1, medium 2–12, large 13–270 (birds)

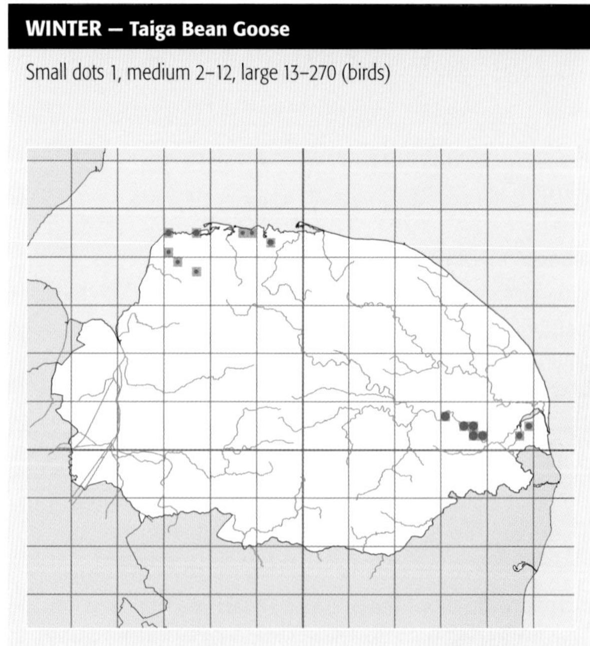

MIKE GOULD

occurred in early December 2004, involving over 200 birds. The largest flocks reported at that time included 112 at Breydon Water on 12th December 2004, 96 at Methwold Fens on 3rd January 2005, and up to 49 at Hickling and 39 at Welney.

During NBA fieldwork, progressively more Tundra Bean Geese were found each winter in Norfolk, with the exception of 2000/01. Although some of the records may well relate to the same wandering individuals, and the increase may in part be due to more careful scrutiny of the flocks of Pink-footed Geese, it is likely that there has been a genuine rise in the number of Tundra Bean Geese wintering in Norfolk. The total, however, remains small, with fewer than 50 birds being involved most years.

WINTER – Tundra Bean Goose

Small dots 1–2, medium 3–8, large 9–96 (birds)

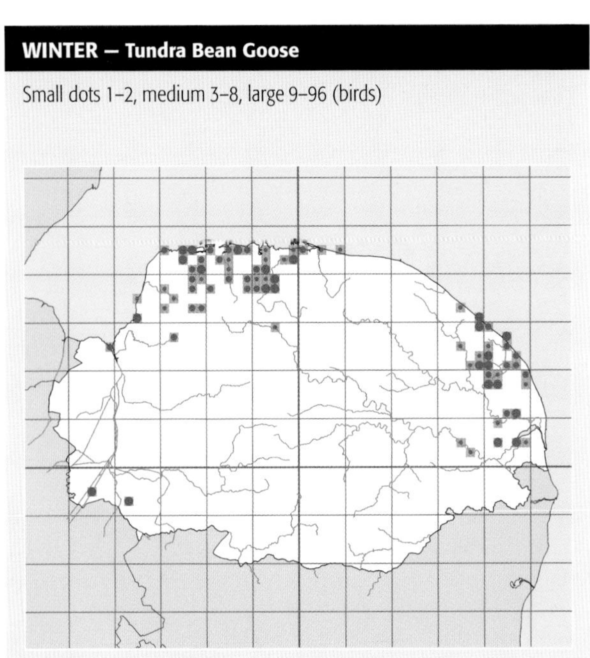

'Bean Goose is the least numerous of the four species of grey goose that occur regularly in Britain. Norfolk holds a significant proportion of its population.'

The only summer records of Bean Geese for NBA were from southeast Norfolk, near Earsham, where a small group of feral birds has been resident, mainly on the Suffolk side of the Waveney, for some years. In April 2005 a pair was observed flying out of an oil-seed rape field in this area and landing in an area of thick, coppiced woodland. The observer was amazed, a month later, to come across presumably the same pair with a brood of five or six goslings! Taiga Bean Geese are unique amongst the indigenous western Palaearctic geese in nesting within dense coniferous forest or birch scrub (*BWP1*), so a nest site within woodland would not be unexpected. So far, however, this remains the only known instance of nesting by feral Bean Geese in Britain.

Pink-footed Goose

Anser brachyrhynchus

NBA 1999–2007	SUMMER: ALL/BREEDING	WINTER
TETRADS OCCUPIED	10 (<1%) / none	168 (12%)
SUMMER/WINTER ONLY	5	163
MEAN PER OCCUPIED TETRAD	51 / none	4,665
SUMMED MAX COUNTS	514 / none	783,645
POPULATION ESTIMATE	10–20 individuals	100,000–150,000

PREVIOUS ATLASES	SQUARES OCCUPIED	1999–2007	LOSSES	GAINS
1981–84 WINTER (10 KM)	19 (31%)	38 (61%)	0	19

ENORMOUS FLOCKS OF Icelandic Pink-footed Geese have become an increasingly familiar sight in northwest Norfolk over recent decades. Skeins of geese, leaving their coastal roost sites, are often seen and heard flying inland, where they feed on harvested sugar beet fields.

Pink-footed Geese are highly gregarious throughout the year, and especially so during the winter months. They roost at night on coastal mudflats and sandbanks, as well as on inland waters, flighting inland at dawn to graze on grassland, cereals, stubbles and beet fields. The NBA map clearly demonstrates the main areas in northwest and east Norfolk, in which the geese were feeding. In general, large open fields with few hedges are favoured, many also being on sloping ground. Here the flocks are able to detect the approach of any potential danger, and therefore presumably feel more secure.

In northwest Norfolk three main nocturnal roost sites have become established, at Snettisham, Scolt Head and Wells/Warham, but there is considerable interchange among these over the period of the winter, and the birds' night-time behaviour changes with the weather. It is as birds fly to and from the roosts that the most accurate coordinated counts of the number of Pink-footed Geese wintering in Norfolk are obtained. In east Norfolk, flocks are centred on the Horsey/Heigham Holmes area, roosting at night on flooded marshes adjacent to Horsey Mere, and in the Breydon Water/Halvergate/Lower Bure area from where roosting birds move to the Berney Marshes RSPB reserve.

In the early 1980s, when fieldwork was being undertaken for the *1981–84 Winter Atlas*, three-quarters of the Pink-footed Geese wintering in Britain

were found in Scotland, while on occasion the Ribble Estuary in Lancashire held up to 34,000. The Wash and northwest Norfolk were also beginning to attract flocks of 5,000 birds or more, but it was only once controlled flooding had been introduced on the grazing marshes at Holkham that really large numbers began to overwinter in the county.

During the winter of 1999/2000, the first of NBA fieldwork, almost 65,000 Pink-footed Geese wintered in northwest Norfolk, with additional flocks of up to 8,000 at Heigham Holmes and 6,600 at Breydon Water. These three areas have remained the main traditional wintering sites for the geese, although it has been only in the northwest of the county that the wintering population has expanded so spectacularly. For example, in the winter of 2004/05 northwest Norfolk held 137,500 out of a county total of 152,500. This represented over 50% of the world population of Pink-footed Geese.

WINTER

Small dots 1–100, medium 101–3,000, large 3,001–50,000 (birds)

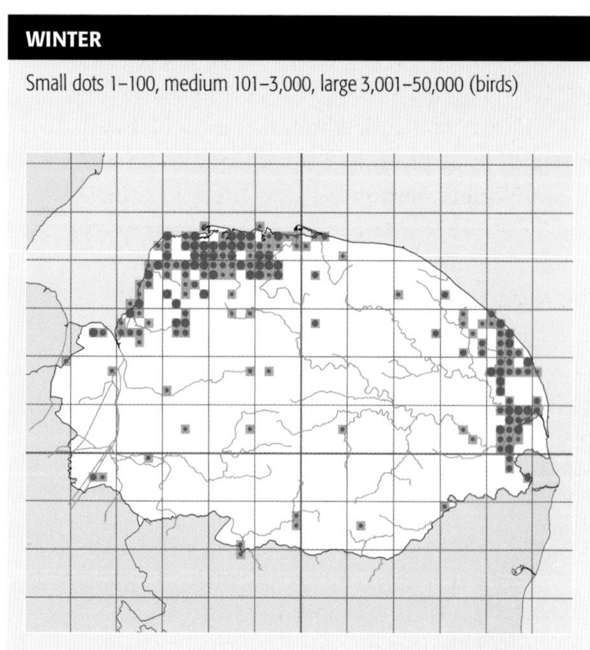

DAVID TIPLING

During the course of the winter, the vast flocks of geese are highly mobile, moving around from field to field as the sugar beet is harvested. Counts of 30,000–40,000 were made in several tetrads in the Brancaster/Docking area and at Wighton, while 50,000 were estimated to be present on Holkham GM on occasion. In east Norfolk, maximum roost-site counts included 10,165 at Horsey Mere and 15,880 at Berney Marshes.

'During the course of the winter, the vast flocks of geese are highly mobile, moving around from field to field as the sugar beet is harvested.'

The remarkable increase in overwintering Pink-footed Geese in Norfolk in recent years is related, at least in part, to the abundance of sugar beet that is currently grown in the county. After lifting the beet, modern farm machinery removes the tops and leaves, which are then left on the fields to be ploughed in later. Whereas previously this material would have been used as fodder, it is now available as a rich source of nutrition for the geese. However, the local sugar beet industry is under threat from imports from eastern Europe and cheaper imports of sugar cane from third-world countries. In addition, the breeding grounds of Pink-footed Geese in Iceland, where 87% of the world population nests, is also under threat from two new hydroelectric power schemes. Thus the species may be facing an uncertain future at home and abroad (Bloomfield 2003a).

Most Pink-footed Geese leave the county on their return migration in February or March, but three-figure counts are not unusual in April and early May: for example, 750 were still present at Holkham GM during the first week of May in 2005. Occasional sick or injured birds oversummer.

White-fronted Goose

Anser albifrons

NBA 1999–2007	SUMMER: ALL/BREEDING	WINTER
TETRADS OCCUPIED	8 (<1%) / 1 (<1%)	62 (4%)
SUMMER/WINTER ONLY	none	54
MEAN PER OCCUPIED TETRAD	1 / 1	70
SUMMED MAX COUNTS	8 / 1	4, 359
POPULATION ESTIMATE	0–1 bp (*albifrons*)	900–1,400 *albifrons* 5–10 *flavirostris*

PREVIOUS ATLASES	SQUARES OCCUPIED	1999-2007	LOSSES	GAINS
1968–72 (10 KM)	none	1 (2%)	0	1
1980–85 (TETRAD)	none	1 (<1%)	0	1
1980–85 (10 KM)	none	1 (2%)	0	1
1981–84 WINTER (10 KM)	26 (42%)	20 (32%)	11	5
1988–91 (10 KM)	none	1 (2%)	0	1

TWO RACES OF White-fronted Geese winter in Britain, but rarely overlap in wintering ranges or migration routes. The European form, nominate *albifrons*, breeds in northern Russia and has wintering sites in southern England and South Wales, while *flavirostris* from west Greenland winters almost exclusively in Scotland and in Ireland.

Since the early 1970s, increasing numbers of European White-fronted Geese have wintered in northwestern Europe as a whole, although progressively fewer have crossed the North Sea to Britain.

In winter White-fronted Geese feed almost exclusively on grassland, favouring low-lying wet pastures bordering coastal marshes or along inland river valleys (*1981–84 Winter Atlas*). This is borne out by the NBA winter map. Traditionally, just five areas in the county have hosted wintering White-fronted Geese regularly. In northwest Norfolk, the wet grazing marshes at Holkham hold several hundred during the winter. Three areas in east Norfolk are favoured: the marshes of the upper Thurne valley around Heigham Holmes and Hickling, Breydon Water and the Halvergate Marshes, and the mid-Yare valley, particularly at Cantley. The maximum counts during the NBA period at each of these sites were 975 at Holkham, 800 at Heigham Holmes/Hickling, 500 at Halvergate Marshes and 200 at Cantley. However, most of these peaks were noted in the first three NBA winters and counts less than half these sizes have become the norm since 2003. The only other site that holds a regular wintering flock of White-fronted Geese is on the Ouse Washes, at Welney, but normally numbers there have been below 40.

The main arrival of White-fronted Geese takes place in December, and so the NBA data include birds still on autumn passage. Similarly, in mild winters, the departure of White-fronted Geese from England also takes place during the winter recording period, in February, and most of the peak site counts were made in that month.

Greenland White-fronted Geese, identified by their darker overall appearance and orange bills, occur as rare winter visitors to Norfolk, often

WINTER – European or unspecified

Small dots 1–3, medium 4–35, large 36–648 (birds)

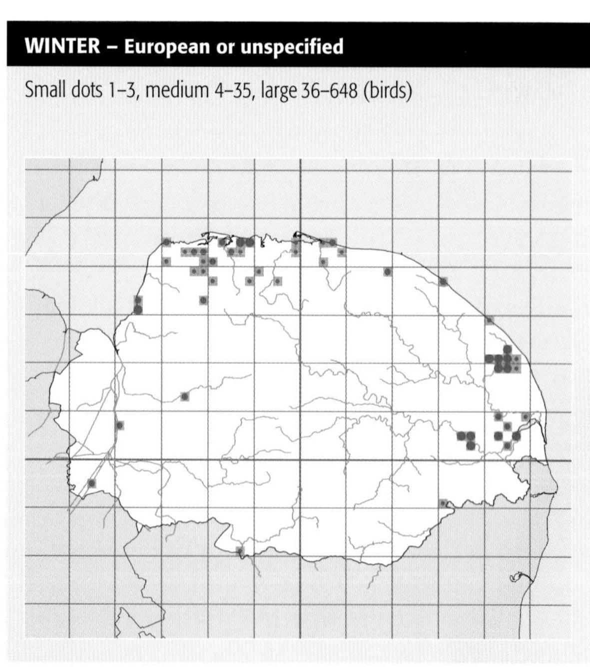

DAVID TIPLING

amongst Pink-footed Geese. Following the first identification of *flavirostris* in Norfolk in 1960, only 11 more were found up to 1998. However, with

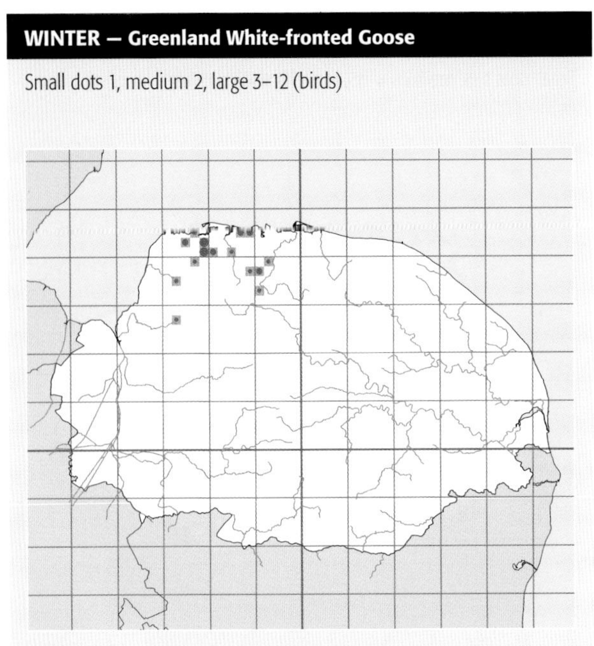
WINTER – Greenland White-fronted Goose

Small dots 1, medium 2, large 3–12 (birds)

'In winter, White-fronted Geese feed almost exclusively on grassland, favouring low-lying wet pastures bordering coastal marshes or along inland river valleys.'

increasingly careful scrutiny of the large flocks of Pink-footed Geese, about six are now seen every winter. The highest number recorded during NBA fieldwork was 12 in the winter of 2000/01, including a group of two adults and six first-winter birds at Welney from 17th January to 11th April 2001.

Most White-fronted Geese have left Norfolk well before the end of March and the few that were recorded in summer related to either introduced or injured birds, such as the pair that bred at Stiffkey Fen in 2000 and one that remained resident in the Breydon Water area for four years up to summer 2002.

Canada Goose

Branta canadensis

NBA 1999–2007	SUMMER: ALL / BREEDING	WINTER
TETRADS OCCUPIED	360 (25%) / 228 (16%)	299 (20%)
SUMMER/WINTER ONLY	159	98
MEAN PER OCCUPIED TETRAD	6 / 8	41
SUMMED MAX COUNTS	2,145 / 1,751	12,268
POPULATION ESTIMATE	700–1,000 bp	2,000–4,000

PREVIOUS ATLASES	SQUARES OCCUPIED	1999–2007	LOSSES	GAINS
1968–72 (10 KM)	48 (77%)	50 (81%)	5	7
1980–85 (TETRAD)	198 (14%)	228 (16%)	113	143
1980–85 (10 KM)	46 (74%)	50 (81%)	4	8
1981–84 WINTER (10 KM)	53 (85%)	53 (85%)	4	4
1988–91 (10 KM)	52 (84%)	50 (81%)	5	3

CANADA GEESE were introduced from North America into England in the 17th century, as ornamental wildfowl on the lakes of the large estates. Nowadays they are familiar and widespread almost everywhere in Britain.

In Norfolk, the species inhabits areas of open water, such as parkland lakes, flooded gravel pits, Breckland meres and the Broads, often nesting on inaccessible islands. The NBA summer map shows that much of the distribution follows the courses of the rivers, with few pairs close to the watersheds, especially in the northwest of the county. Canada Geese often nest in loose colonies, each subpopulation being based on a group of waters; some clustering is apparent on the map, which also shows non-breeding flocks. The highest numbers of breeding pairs or broods in a single locality reported during the NBA period were 12 at Holkham NNR, ten at Burnham Norton and eight at Snetterton GP.

Whereas Canada Geese remain within a relatively small area during the summer months, until they gather at their moulting sites in July and August, they are far more mobile and gregarious in winter. Flocks regularly flight from lakes and broads to feed on grassland and fields of winter cereal, where they may come into conflict with farmers.

The NBA winter map demonstrates the greater degree of clustering that occurs at this season, with the larger flocks being concentrated in fewer tetrads. The flooded gravel pits in west Norfolk, the parkland lakes in the eastern half of the county and the Broads are particularly favoured. The highest winter counts during the NBA period were 460 at Blickling Park Lake and in the Brecks 400 each at Nunnery Lakes, East Harling

SUMMER

Small dots 1, medium 2–4, large 5–120 ('pairs')
Shading – breeding proved or considered likely

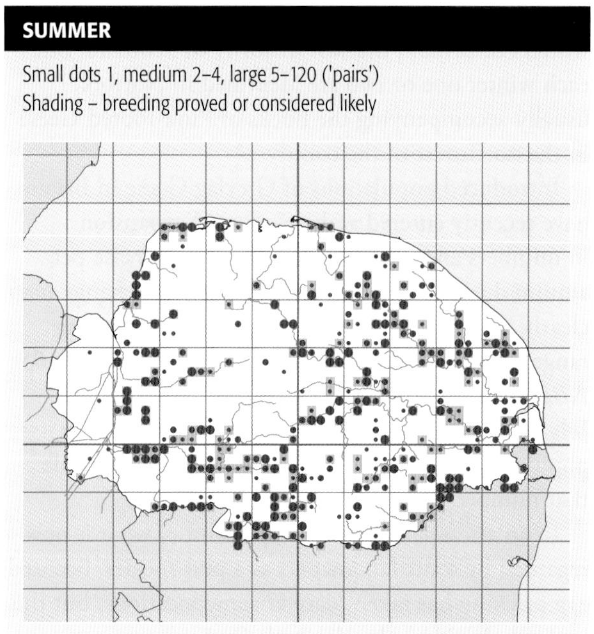

WINTER

Small dots 1–4, medium 5–25, large 26–460 (birds)

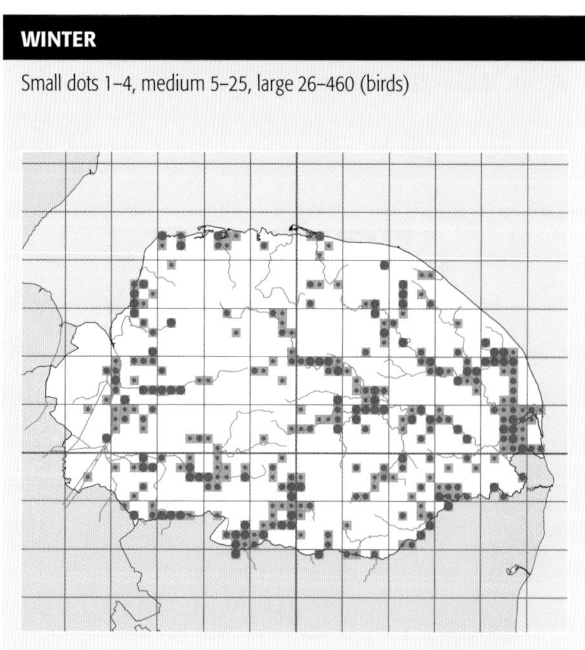

DAVID TIPLING

and Cranwich GP.

Over the last 40 years, the Norfolk population of Canada Geese has fluctuated, and the number of occupied atlas squares in both summer and winter, has varied surprisingly little. In 1965, almost 2,000 Canada Geese were present at Holkham, but a national census in 1967–69 located only 700–800 birds in the whole of north Norfolk and identified Norfolk as the only county in which the species had declined. The *1980–85 NBBS* states that the Canada Goose was then the most numerous and widespread of the three species of geese breeding ferally in the county, a description now applicable to the Greylag.

CHANGE SINCE 1980–85

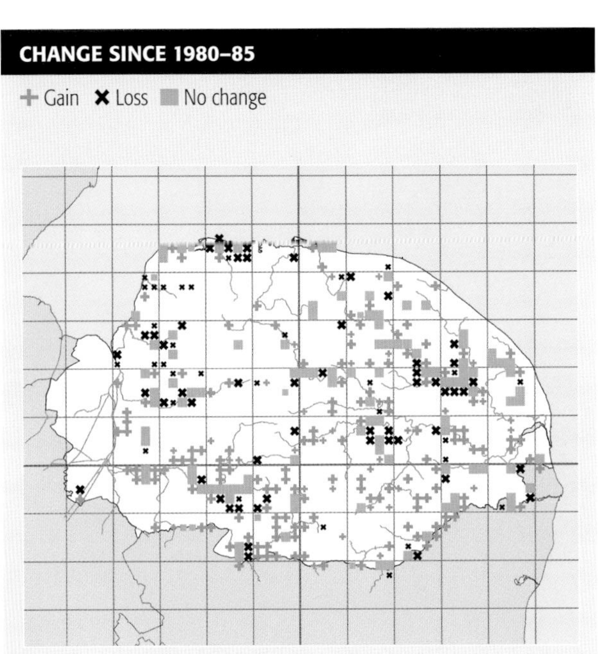

Nationally, the Canada Goose population has been increasing exponentially, at a rate measured at 9% per annum throughout the 1990s (*Birdtrends*). The change map indicates that substantial expansion of breeding range has occurred in Norfolk, particularly in the south of the county, with some range loss in north Norfolk. Unusually, though, in national terms, the Greylag is both more numerous and more widespread in Norfolk than the Canada Goose. It may be that the population expansion of Greylags has to some extent limited that of Canadas in the county.

Most winters one or two Canada Geese of one or other of the smaller races are found in Norfolk, mostly among flocks of Pink-footed Geese. Cackling Geese, now separated from Canada Goose as *Branta hutchinsii*, were also recorded during the NBA period (see Table 3.2). The origin of these birds is unclear but some may be genuine vagrants from the Canadian tundra.

Barnacle Goose

Branta leucopsis

NBA 1999–2007	SUMMER: ALL / BREEDING	WINTER
TETRADS OCCUPIED	55 (4%) / 11 (<1%)	108 (7%)
SUMMER/WINTER ONLY	22	75
MEAN PER OCCUPIED TETRAD	3 / 6	21
SUMMED MAX COUNTS	189 / 65	2,270
POPULATION ESTIMATE	5–20 bp	300–400

PREVIOUS ATLASES	SQUARES OCCUPIED	1999–2007	LOSSES	GAINS
1968–72 (10 KM)	none	6 (10%)	0	6
1980–85 (TETRAD)	none	11 (<1%)	0	11
1980–85 (10 KM)	none	6 (10%)	0	6
1981–84 WINTER (10 KM)	17 (27%)	35 (56%)	5	23
1988–91 (10 KM)	1 (2%)	6 (10%)	1	6

WITH ITS STRIKING black and white plumage, the Barnacle Goose is perhaps the most attractive goose that winters regularly in Norfolk. In the wild state, it breeds alongside such charismatic species as Gyr Falcon *Falco rusticolus* and Arctic fox *Alopex lagopus*, but an expanding feral population in the Baltic, the Netherlands and Britain has irrevocably blurred the distinction between high-Arctic visitors and more local birds descended from introduced stock.

Before introductions began in Britain, there were three distinct native populations of Barnacle Geese – breeding in Greenland, Svalbard and northern Russia – each wintering in a different area of Europe. Ring recoveries have demonstrated that birds from each of these populations

DAVID TIPLING

have occurred in Norfolk over the years. Barnacle Geese were first proved to breed in Norfolk at Hethersett Park in 1995 (Dorling 2001), with four pairs by 2001. Breeding also occurred at Holkham Park, Pensthorpe, Barton Broad and the Nar Valley Fisheries during the NBA period. The NBA summer map indicates that rather few Barnacle Geese were recorded in north and east Norfolk at this season, supporting the view that many of the winter sightings there refer to immigrants. Influxes from the Continent, which would doubtless often include introduced birds, are suspected to occur during periods of hard weather.

The NBA winter map shows two fairly distinct parts of the county in which Barnacle Geese occurred. In northwest Norfolk, a few were reported in most winters, usually consorting with the vast flocks of Pink-footed Geese, and presumably, like some of them, Greenland breeders. Most of these reports concerned single-figure counts and larger parties, such as 180 at Brancaster, probably included wandering introduced birds. The clusters of occupied tetrads in east and central Norfolk, especially those involving higher numbers, related to the known introduced populations in these areas and especially in east Suffolk, which do range more widely during the winter months. Maximum counts during the NBA years included 365 at Lound, 250 at Earsham, 100 in the Yare valley and 75 at both Hethersett Park and Postwick Marshes.

'Barnacle Geese were first proved to breed in Norfolk at Hethersett Park in 1995, with four pairs by 2001.'

SUMMER

Small dots 1, medium 2–5, large 6–26 ('pairs')
Shading – breeding proved or considered likely

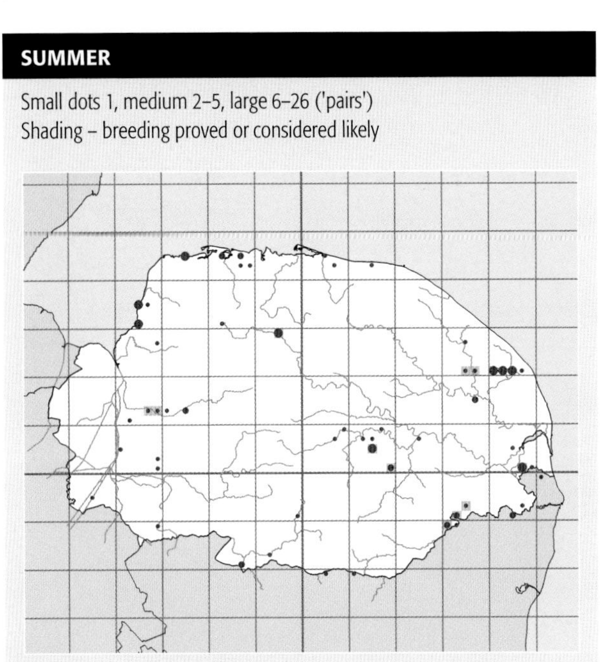

WINTER

Small dots 1–2, medium 3–7, large 8–365 (birds)

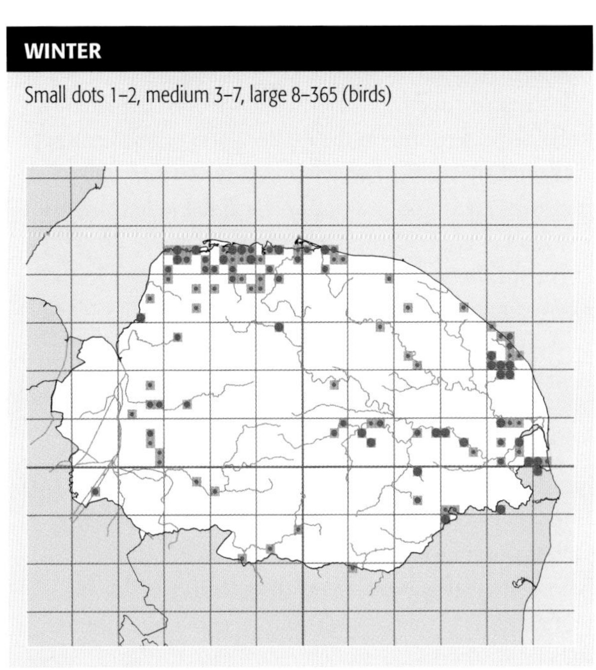

Brent Goose
Branta bernicla

NBA 1999–2007	SUMMER: ALL / BREEDING	WINTER
TETRADS OCCUPIED	25 (2%) / none	101 (7%)
SUMMER/WINTER ONLY	none	76
MEAN PER OCCUPIED TETRAD	112 / none	437
SUMMED MAX COUNTS	2,790 / none	44,135
POPULATION ESTIMATE	200–300 individuals (*bernicla*)	8,000–10,000 *bernicla*, 20–50 *hrota*, 1–3 *nigricans*

PREVIOUS ATLASES	SQUARES OCCUPIED	1999-2007	LOSSES	GAINS
1981–84 WINTER (10 KM)	18 (29%)	22 (35%)	4	8

DAVID TIPLING

THE BRENT GOOSE IS the smallest wild goose wintering in Britain, and is a very common winter visitor to Norfolk. In recent years, large flocks of this small, dark goose with its guttural chattering have become a familiar sight in coastal areas, especially in north Norfolk.

During the 19th century, the largest flocks in the county numbered only a few hundred birds, but even then Blakeney Harbour was one of the favoured sites. Numbers fell sharply in the 1930s, but by the early 1960s north Norfolk held a regular wintering population of 5,000 Brent Geese, reaching 15,000 by the mid 1990s.

From the first returning Brent Geese reach Norfolk in September until early December, the flocks spend most of their time in the intertidal shallows on the saltmarshes, upending to feed on the underwater eelgrass *Zostera* and other marine plants. Once these have been depleted the geese begin to graze on the higher parts of the saltings and since the 1970s have ventured away from the intertidal feeding zones onto grass and arable land, even visiting fields a few miles inland.

The greatest concentration of Brent Geese is found along the coast between the Wash and Blakeney, with birds spreading further east and further inland as the winter progresses. The adult geese show strong winter site fidelity, as has been demonstrated by ringing and by the reappearance of some distinctively plumaged individuals in subsequent winters (McCallum 2001). Birds tend to remain in the same general area once winter quarters have become established, but there are strong diurnal movements and, especially on darker nights, birds gather at night into a smaller number of intertidal roosting areas.

During the NBA winters the largest counts of Brent Geese, involving 2,000–4,000 birds, were generally on the Wash at Terrington Marsh and Ousemouth/Lynn Point, and in north Norfolk at Brancaster, Scolt Head, Wells, Stiffkey and Blakeney/Cley. A coordinated roost count for WeBS in January 2007 provided a north coast total of 6,913, whereas 10,000–13,000 wintered there as recently as 1999/2000. During the NBA, the arable fields around the Great Walsingham and Langham areas hosted feeding flocks of up to 1,000. Four at Welney in 2002 had clearly lost touch temporarily with the coast. Brent Geese have always been very scarce in east Norfolk during the winter

WINTER – Dark-bellied Brent Goose

Small dots 1–36, medium 37–527, large 528–4,000 (birds)

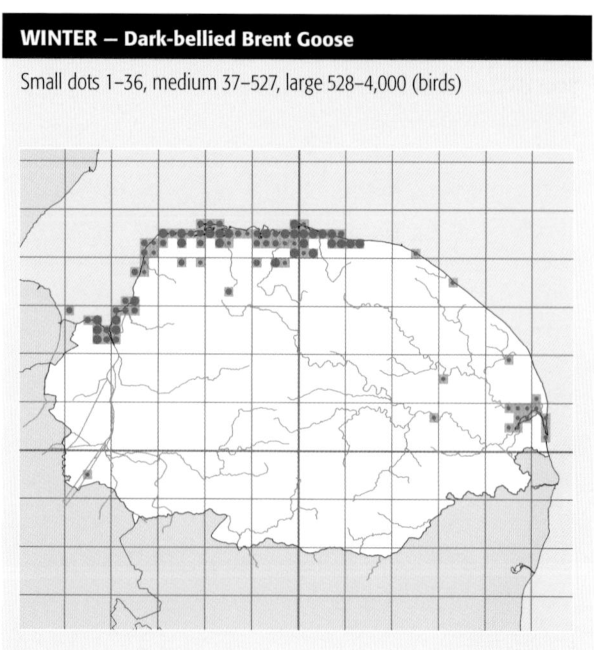

and the NBA maximum was only 12, at Breydon Water. The current total Norfolk winter population is probably in the region of 8,000–10,000 birds. Most are of the nominate race *bernicla* (Dark-bellied Brent Goose), which breeds in the western Russian Arctic and winters around southeast England from the Wash to the Solent.

As with other large waterfowl, Brent Geese remain in their family parties throughout the winter. Since first-winter birds are readily recognised by the pale barring on their upperparts it is possible to assess the breeding success year by year. In December 1999, 15–20% of the Brent Geese were young birds, which indicated the most successful breeding season in the Russian Arctic since 1991. The summer of 2005 was even better with 32% juveniles at Cley and 39% at Scolt Head in December.

A notable feature of recent years has been the large numbers still present in April and May, for example 1,500 at Stiffkey on 5th May 2002. Some birds now summer along the north Norfolk coast, including eight at Blakeney Harbour in 2001 and 12–14 at Scolt Head in 2005.

Two other Brent Goose races visit Norfolk in small numbers – the Light-bellied Brent Goose *hrota* of which separate populations breed in Svalbard and in eastern Canada, and which winters mainly in Denmark and in Ireland, and the Black Brant *nigricans*, which in the wild state breeds in eastern Siberia, Alaska and northwest Canada, and winters around North Pacific coasts. Individuals of these two races are normally found with Dark-bellied birds but often slightly apart from the main group.

Riviere, in describing the status of Brent Geese up to the 1930s, stated that both the Dark-bellied and Light-bellied races occurred in Norfolk in equal numbers. Nowadays, Light-bellied Brent Geese are very scarce winter visitors, normally being found singly or in groups of two or three. However, 22 were found at Stiffkey Fen on 22nd January 2002 and 18 in the Cockthorpe/ Stiffkey Fen area from 18th January to 17th March 2003. The map shows a much more limited distribution than that of nominate *bernicla*.

The first Black Brant in Norfolk was found at Cley in November 1982 and remained all winter. What was almost certainly the same bird returned to the Cley/ Salthouse area for the next six winters. Since then the Black Brant has become an annual visitor to Norfolk, with five or six adults being present most winters. In January 2001, a male Black Brant and a female Dark-bellied Brent Goose were present at Burnham Deepdale with their four hybrid offspring until early May. There were several similar pairings in subsequent winters with accompanying hybrids. In addition, a pure-bred juvenile Black Brant moulting into first-winter plumage was identified at Cockthorpe on 20th January 2002, only the second British record of one in this plumage. Another first-winter Black Brant was subsequently found at Snettisham in the following month, along with its two parents. Up to three adult Black Brants have occurred together at Terrington Marsh and at Titchwell.

WINTER – Light-bellied Brent Goose

Small dots 1, medium 2–3, large 4–22 (birds)

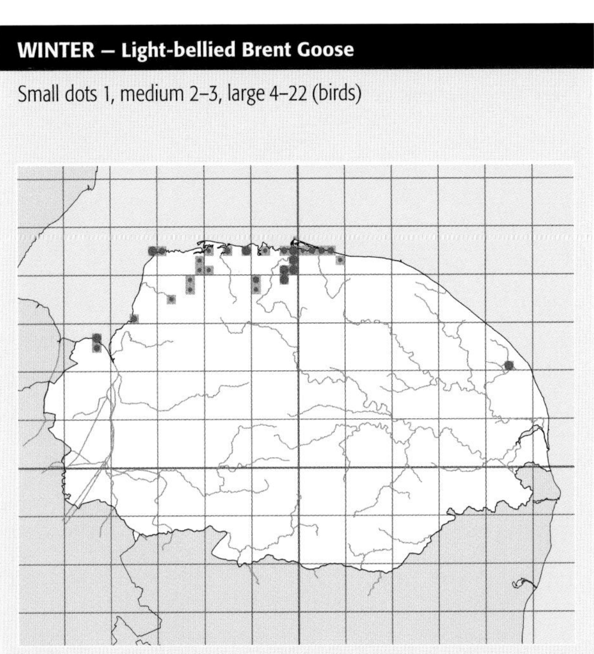

WINTER – Black Brant

Small dots 1, medium 2, large 3 (birds)

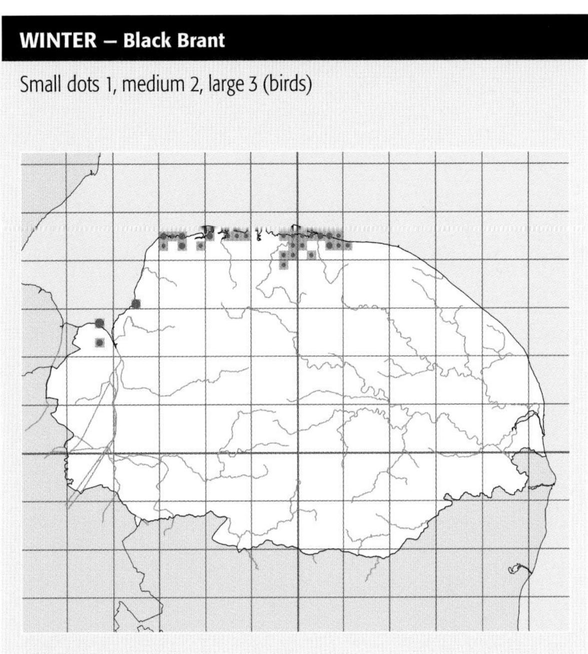

Egyptian Goose

Alopochen aegyptiaca

NBA 1999–2007	SUMMER: ALL / BREEDING	WINTER
TETRADS OCCUPIED	409 (28%) / 276 (19%)	491 (34%)
SUMMER/WINTER ONLY	101	183
MEAN PER OCCUPIED TETRAD	3 / 3	7
SUMMED MAX COUNTS	1,152 / 927	3,258
POPULATION ESTIMATE	750–900 bp	1,500–2,000

PREVIOUS ATLASES	SQUARES OCCUPIED	1999–2007	LOSSES	GAINS
1968–72 (10 KM)	13 (21%)	53 (85%)	0	40
1980–85 (TETRAD)	88 (6%)	276 (19%)	36	224
1980–85 (10 KM)	29 (47%)	53 (85%)	1	25
1981–84 WINTER (10 KM)	33 (53%)	57 (92%)	0	24
1988–91 (10 KM)	44 (71%)	53 (85%)	2	11

THE EGYPTIAN GOOSE, which is more closely related to the shelducks than to other geese, is a native of Africa that was introduced to ornamental parkland lakes in England in the 18th century and was first recorded in Norfolk in 1808. Since then the county has become the British stronghold for the species, with a well-established and thriving introduced population.

Egyptian Geese require areas of open water, adjacent pastures for grazing and old trees with holes in which to nest.

Such conditions are ideally met on many of the county's large estates where artificial lakes surrounded by parkland have been created and at many of the county's other wetlands. During the breeding season, pairs are well dispersed, being highly territorial and aggressive towards other members of their species. In Norfolk, as in other parts of England, Egyptian Geese nest primarily in cavities in mature trees, but occasionally in thick vegetation on the ground or among bales of straw.

The NBA summer map shows that the species is widespread throughout the county with localised concentrations in north Norfolk, especially at Holkham Park, where up to 15 pairs breed, in central Norfolk along the River Wensum and in Broadland. The map also demonstrates the almost total absence of Egyptian Geese from the Fens, where suitable nest sites may be lacking, and from parts of south and east Norfolk.

Egyptian Geese have a lengthy breeding season, eggs

SUMMER

Small dots 1, medium 2–3, large 4–30 ('pairs')
Shading – breeding proved or considered likely

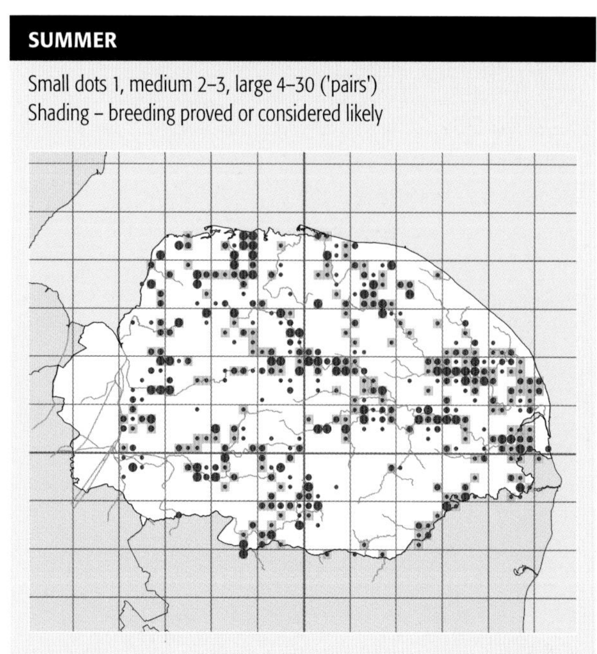

WINTER

Small dots 1, medium 2–4, large 5–106 (birds)

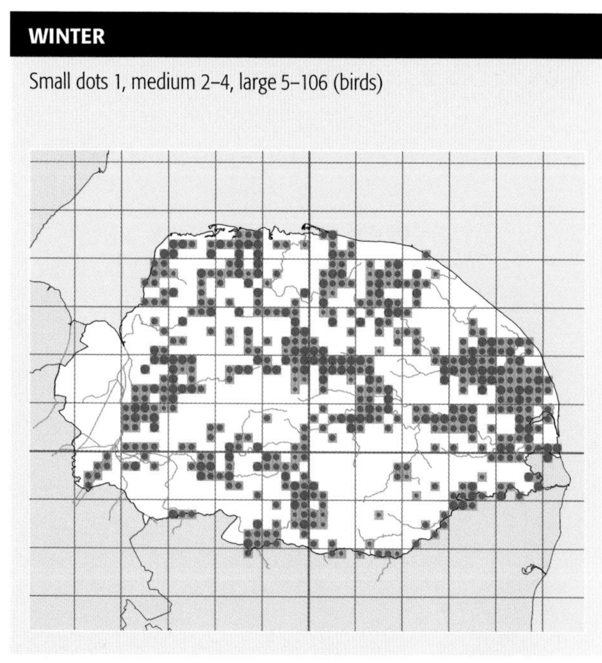

DAVID TIPLING

being laid anytime from January to June. Many pairs were already on territory and some already nesting during the NBA's winter period. Adverse late-winter weather takes its toll on susceptible early goslings and, as they remain in the downy stage of development for longer than most other water birds, many are taken by Carrion Crows or pike. In fact, the mortality of goslings is so high that often only one or two reach the fledging stage.

In late summer many adults and young gather at moulting sites, where they become flightless for a few weeks. Holkham Park has always held the largest moulting flock and a record count of 296 was made in June 2002. Other large regular moulting flocks are at Sennowe Park and Blickling Park.

After moulting, Egyptian Geese disperse again throughout the county. As well as early breeders, the winter map shows birds in non-breeding situations, such as feeding in fields of winter cereals or root crops, on wet pasture, or taking advantage of food pellets in open pig units. Pairs remain together throughout the year and winter flocks are small compared with the gatherings of moulting birds. However, 51 were feeding together at Barford in December 2006 and the highest winter counts during the years of the NBA were 106 at Horning, 104 at Pentney GP and 92 at Holkham Park Lake.

CHANGE SINCE 1980–85

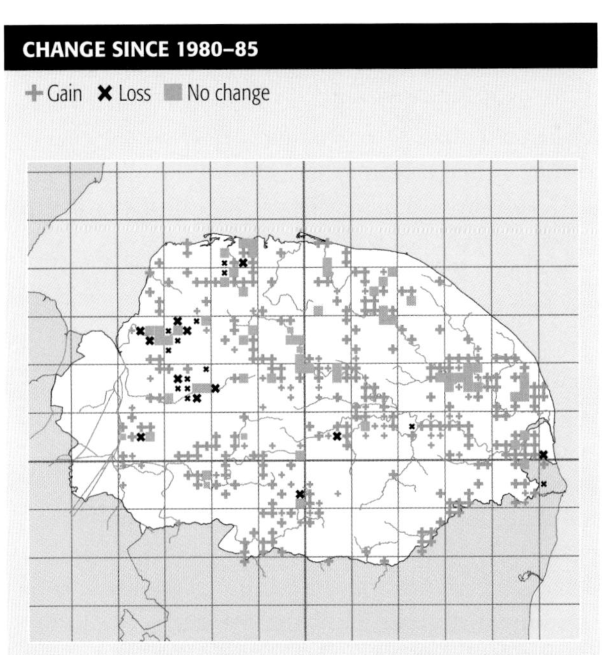

There has been a very substantial range increase in Norfolk since the *1968–72 Atlas*. At that time Egyptian Geese were recorded in only 13 of the 10-km squares in Norfolk, increasing to 29 during the *1980–85 NBBS*, 44 in the second British & Irish breeding atlas in 1988–91 and 53 during the NBA period. The change map shows the marked expansion in inland Norfolk since 1980–85. Sites colonised by breeding pairs include many small wetlands, including the farm reservoirs that have proliferated across otherwise waterless areas in recent decades.

Numbers have been poorly monitored, but Sage (2002) estimated that the breeding population in Holkham Park was increasing at the rate of 6% per year. It is likely that well over 750 pairs now breed annually in Norfolk.

Shelduck
Tadorna tadorna

NBA 1999–2007	SUMMER: ALL / BREEDING	WINTER
TETRADS OCCUPIED	471 (32%) / 223 (15%)	239 (16%)
SUMMER/WINTER ONLY	279	47
MEAN PER OCCUPIED TETRAD	6 / 8	43
SUMMED MAX COUNTS	2,715 / 1,816	10,200
POPULATION ESTIMATE	100–200 bp	2,500–3,000

PREVIOUS ATLASES	SQUARES OCCUPIED	1999–2007	LOSSES	GAINS
1968–72 (10 KM)	36 (58%)	49 (79%)	5	18
1980–85 (TETRAD)	283 (19%)	223 (15%)	182	122
1980–85 (10 KM)	50 (81%)	49 (79%)	7	6
1981–84 WINTER (10 KM)	45 (73%)	54 (87%)	3	12
1988–91 (10 KM)	45 (73%)	49 (79%)	5	9

DAVID TIPLING

'Like geese, to which they are closely related, Shelducks are monogamous and pair bonds persist from one year to the next.'

ALTHOUGH SHELDUCK reach their greatest numbers in muddy estuaries, the species now breeds very widely inland and might be encountered almost anywhere in the county.

Following a decline in the 19th century, the species recovered steadily throughout the 20th century and, although formerly breeding almost exclusively within a short distance of the coast, spread inland to nest. The vast majority still winter in intertidal habitats. Winter flocks disperse during January to March, when pairs begin to occupy their summer territories. They defend their chosen feeding territories with great vigour in the spring, driving off others of their own species. Pairs also start to prospect for suitable nesting burrows, which may be several miles away from their main feeding areas at this season. Like geese, to which they are closely related, Shelducks are monogamous and pair bonds persist from one year to the next.

The NBA summer map shows three main areas where occupied tetrads were concentrated: around the Wash, along the north Norfolk coast and around Breydon Water. Around the coast, breeding pairs were located amongst sand dunes and on grazing marshes, while favoured inland habitats included farmland, pastures and heathland. Shelducks do not breed until they are two years old and the summer population therefore contains a substantial proportion of non-breeders. The maximum counts of breeding pairs during the years of the NBA period included 35–40 at Scolt Head, 26 at Blakeney Point, 21 at Holkham NNR and 19 at Holme, while inland concentrations included 15–20 at Gooderstone/Hilborough and 19 in the mid-Yare RSPB reserves.

After fledging, young Shelducks gather into crèches, looked after by just a few adult birds. The remaining adults leave for communal moulting areas, which traditionally were in the Heligoland Bight in northwest Germany. However, in recent years, increasing numbers of Norfolk's breeding population have moulted in the Wash, and this trend no doubt accounted for the 3,600 that were present off North Wootton in June 2005. Inland breeding areas are typically empty of Shelduck from late July until reoccupation of territories begins in January or February.

In winter, most Shelducks were recorded, as in the summer, around the Wash, along the north Norfolk coast and around Breydon Water. The species is mainly coastal in winter, feeding on snails, crustaceans and worms that it sieves from soft estuarine mud. The largest winter concentrations occurred in the Wash, where a peak count of 3,530 was recorded at Snettisham in February 2002. Elsewhere in north Norfolk, Scolt Head held a maximum of 421 and Blakeney Point 373. Only a few inland areas held birds throughout the winter – most inland dots resulted from early return to breeding areas. The highest inland count was of 245 at Hardley Flood in December 2002.

The change map shows a remarkable breeding colonisation of inland Norfolk since the 1980s, especially in Breckland. Density remained low, however, and some pairs may have been recorded in more than one tetrad. The number of occupied 10-km squares increased from just 36 in 1968–72 to 50 in the *1980–85 NBBS* and 49 during the NBA summers. During the last 20 years, however, winter numbers at the Wash have declined: there were as many as 14,560 there in December 1985. Similarly, up to 1,300 were present at Breydon Water until 1987 compared with fewer than 150 in recent winters. Nowadays, the average winter population for the whole of the county is probably in the region of 2,500–3,000 birds.

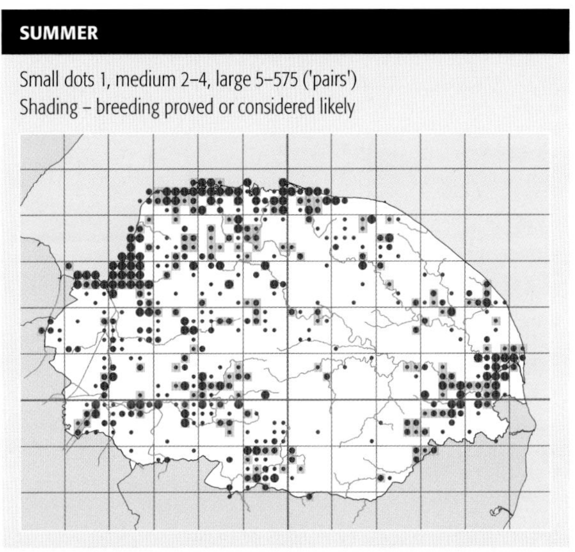

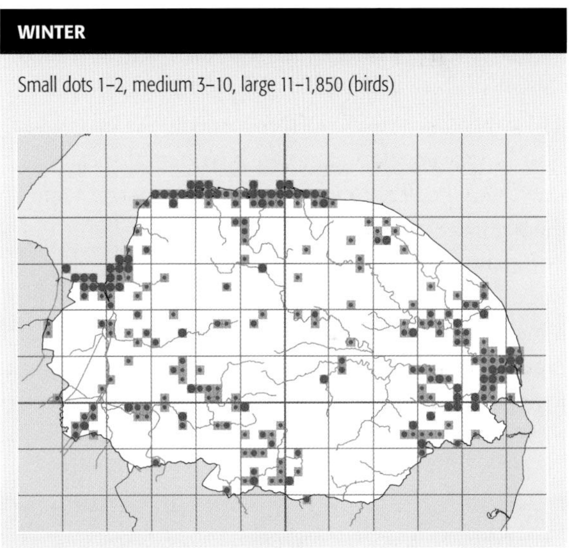

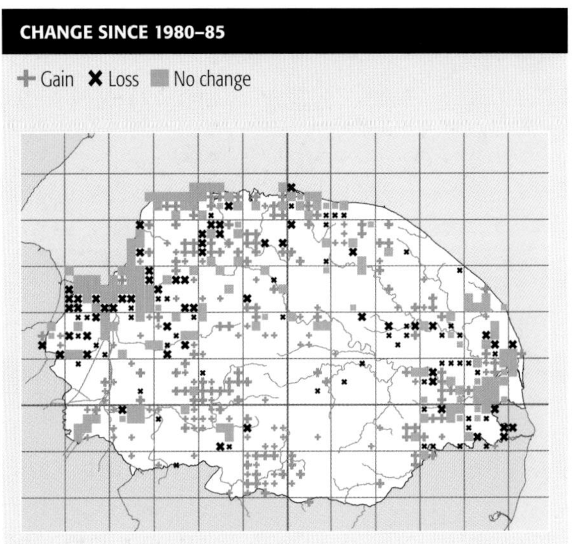

Mandarin

Aix galericulata

NBA 1999–2007	SUMMER: ALL/BREEDING	WINTER
TETRADS OCCUPIED	38 (3%) / 2 (<1%)	28 (2%)
SUMMER/WINTER ONLY	27	17
MEAN PER OCCUPIED TETRAD	1 / 1	2
SUMMED MAX COUNTS	51 / 2	51
POPULATION ESTIMATE	10–15 bp	30–50

PREVIOUS ATLASES	SQUARES OCCUPIED	1999–2007	LOSSES	GAINS
1968–72 (10 KM)	2 (3%)	2 (3%)	2	2
1980–85 (TETRAD)	3 (<1%)	2 (<1%)	3	2
1980–85 (10 KM)	2 (3%)	2 (3%)	1	1
1981–84 WINTER (10 KM)	1 (2%)	21 (34%)	0	20
1988–91 (10 KM)	7 (11%)	2 (3%)	5	0

THIS DUCK IS NATIVE to a small area of the Far East but is very popular as an ornamental species in wildfowl collections. Despite earlier escapes and deliberate releases from collections, a free-flying population was not established in Britain until the early 20th century. Between 1968–72 and 1988–91, a marked expansion of the British range took place, especially in southern and central England. It remains a very scarce and localised breeding bird in Norfolk, however, and a drake Mandarin with its multi-coloured plumage and distinctive orange 'sails' is a rare and generally unpredictable sight here.

Mandarins inhabit fresh water, both still and flowing, which is bordered by overhanging trees and shrubs. During the breeding season they are rather secretive woodland birds, adept at weaving through trees in flight, nesting in holes particularly in oak trees. Their spring and summer diet consists of aquatic invertebrates while in the autumn and winter they feed on acorns, chestnuts and beechmast.

The NBA summer map shows clusters of records in a few scattered areas, mainly in the northern half of the county. The vast majority of summer records related to single birds or pairs, many of which were on park lakes, but also on some stretches of flowing water. Few were noted in Broadland, nor at coastal localities, although a pair flew in off the sea at Cley and landed on the reserve in April 2004.

Four sites were responsible for the majority of records. In northwest Norfolk, eight Mandarin ducklings from Windsor Great Park were introduced to the royal estate at Sandringham in 1973, and 20

SUMMER

Small dots 1, medium 2, large 3–4 ('pairs')
Shading – breeding proved or considered likely

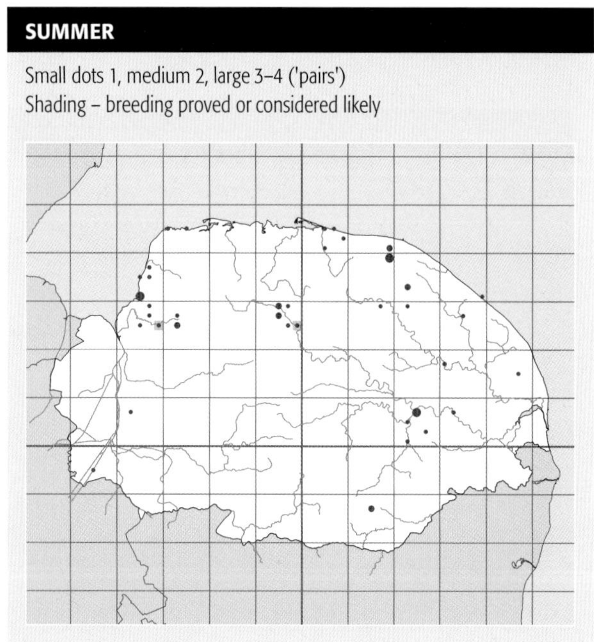

WINTER

Small dots 1, medium 2, large 3–13 (birds)

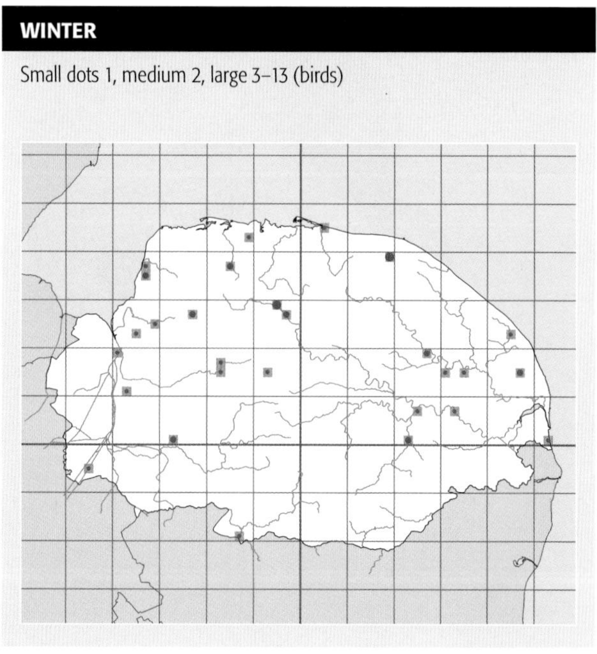

years later the population of free-flying birds there had increased to 100. No doubt their progeny were responsible for the few continuing sightings in that part of the county. In central Norfolk, a female and brood of ducklings were recorded at Guist Common in 2000, the adults perhaps having started life in the collection at Pensthorpe, which may have been the source of most of the records made along the upper reaches of the River Wensum.

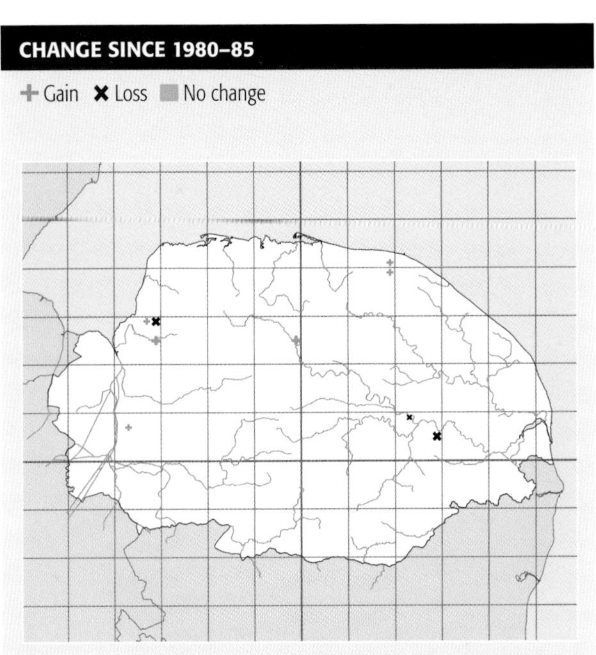

Felbrigg Lake in north Norfolk has been the most reliable site at which to see Mandarins in Norfolk for at least the last 20 years. Breeding was proved here in 1986, but although up to four drakes and some accompanying females occurred intermittently during the NBA years, no further proof of nesting was obtained. Indeed, most records at this site relate to Mandarins sitting or asleep on fallen and low branches at one corner of the lake, and they are very rarely seen within the woodland itself. The fourth site was in southeast Norfolk in the Caistor St Edmunds/Stoke Holy Cross area, where a pair was present for a number of years during the NBA period.

The winter map shows a more diffuse pattern, with fewer clusters, and with surprisingly little direct overlap with the summer distribution. Ringing shows Mandarins to be quite mobile, and some individuals may well be moving into or out of the county with the change of season. As in the summer, most records referred to ones and twos, and Felbrigg Lake, with 13 in December 1999, was the only site to hold more than four.

The change map and the comparisons of winter distribution with 1981–84 are evidence of a gradual increase in Mandarin sightings in Norfolk over recent decades. Time will tell whether this is the beginning of a more fully established population in the county.

Wigeon
Anas penelope

NBA 1999–2007	SUMMER: ALL / BREEDING	WINTER
TETRADS OCCUPIED	41 (3%) / 3 (<1%)	208 (14%)
SUMMER/WINTER ONLY	5	172
MEAN PER OCCUPIED TETRAD	4 / 4	403
SUMMED MAX COUNTS	169 / 11	83,883
POPULATION ESTIMATE	0–2 bp	30,000–50,000

PREVIOUS ATLASES	SQUARES OCCUPIED	1999–2007	LOSSES	GAINS
1968–72 (10 KM)	5 (8%)	1 (2%)	4	0
1980–85 (TETRAD)	17 (1%)	3 (<1%)	16	2
1980–85 (10 KM)	10 (16%)	1 (2%)	9	0
1981–84 WINTER (10 KM)	43 (69%)	48 (77%)	4	9
1988–91 (10 KM)	12 (19%)	1 (2%)	11	0

THE HANDSOME ADULT drake Wigeon, with its distinctive creamy crown stripe, is a common winter visitor to flooded meadows at both coastal and inland localities. It is the only duck that grazes in compact flocks and often associates with grazing geese. Those wintering in western Europe breed mainly in Fenno-Scandia and Siberia.

The NBA winter map shows three main areas in which Wigeon were concentrated: along the north Norfolk coast, on the Ouse Washes and around Breydon Water and the Yare valley. At coastal sites, Wigeon congregate on saltings and tidal marshes, as well as on flooded freshwater marshes a short distance inland. On the Ouse Washes and in Broadland, the flooded pastures along the river valleys prove particularly attractive, especially where water levels are controlled and shooting is restricted. Peak numbers occur in January and the maximum counts during the NBA at the main wintering sites were: 14,630 at Holkham NNR, 15,067 at Welney, 21,700 at Breydon Water/Berney and 8,000 at Cantley/Buckenham. On the Wash, Snettisham and Ken Hill Marsh peaked at 3,800 and elsewhere in Broadland Ranworth Broad held up to 4,000.

Breeding in Norfolk, first recorded at Hickling in 1944, has always been very sporadic, with most attempts being along the north coast, particularly at Holkham. This is borne out by the NBA summer map, which shows that most occupied tetrads were in the north of the county. The vast majority of Wigeon have left Norfolk by the end of March and only a few stragglers usually remain into April, although 112 were still present at Holkham in May 2000. There was

SUMMER

Small dots 1, medium 2–4, large 5–53 ('pairs')
Shading – breeding proved or considered likely

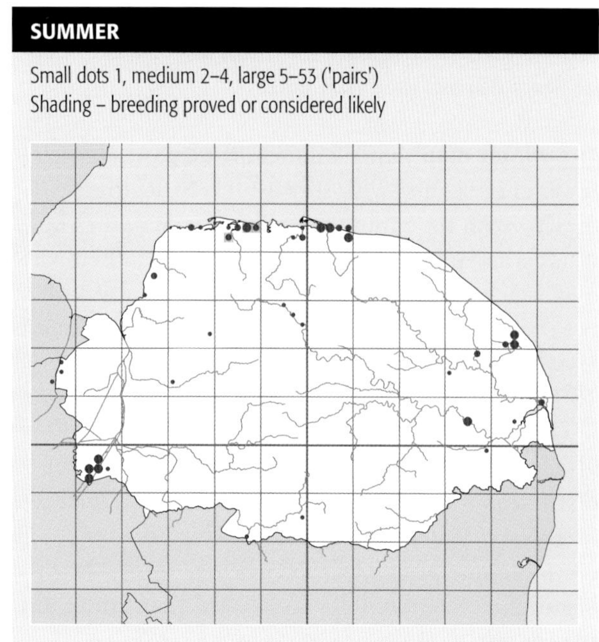

WINTER

Small dots 1–11, medium 12–122, large 123–17,900 (birds)

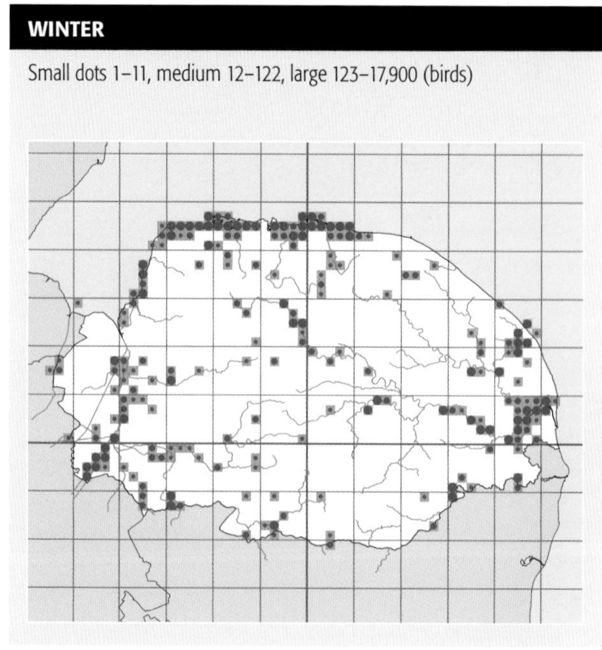

DAVID TIPLING

'The vast majority of Wigeon have left Norfolk by the end of March and only a few stragglers usually remain into April.'

only a single confirmed breeding record for the species during the NBA period, with ducklings being seen at Holkham NNR in 2002. However, breeding was suspected there in several other summers with up to six pairs being present. Elsewhere in north Norfolk, pairs also summered in one or more years at Holme and Titchwell, and in the Yare valley at Buckenham.

Whereas many of these oversummering pairs were probably healthy wild birds, others may have been escapes from collections or injured birds from the winter's wildfowling.

Gadwall

Anas strepera

NBA 1999–2007	SUMMER: ALL / BREEDING	WINTER
TETRADS OCCUPIED	254 (17%) / 153 (10%)	228
SUMMER/WINTER ONLY	105	79
MEAN PER OCCUPIED TETRAD	4 / 5	33
SUMMED MAX COUNTS	986 / 779	7,585
POPULATION ESTIMATE	150–200 bp	1,500–2,000

PREVIOUS ATLASES	SQUARES OCCUPIED	1999–2007	LOSSES	GAINS
1968–72 (10 KM)	37 (60%)	41 (66%)	6	10
1980–85 (TETRAD)	112 (8%)	153 (10%)	62	103
1980–85 (10 KM)	40 (65%)	41 (66%)	6	7
1981–84 WINTER (10 KM)	42 (68%)	52 (84%)	3	13
1988–91 (10 KM)	38 (61%)	41 (66%)	9	12

ALTHOUGH LONG RECOGNISED as a winter visitor to Britain, the species was not known to have bred in England until 1850, when a pair of migrants caught in the Dersingham decoy were released at Narford after having their wings clipped. Within 25 years a substantial breeding population, apparently from this single pair's progeny, had become established in the Brecks. However, it was not until the 1950s that Gadwalls bred regularly in Broadland. Its range has since continued to expand.

Gadwalls are almost exclusively vegetarian, feeding on the leaves and stems of aquatic plants. Even the ducklings feed on plant matter from a very early age. Therefore they favour fairly shallow areas of fresh water, usually surrounded by luxuriant vegetation, such as flooded gravel pits, parkland lakes, lagoons, scrapes, Breckland meres and the Broads.

The NBA summer map shows localised concentrations along the reserves of the north Norfolk coast and in Broadland and Breckland. Most of the Gadwalls in inland tetrads in central Norfolk were located on park lakes or gravel pits. During the breeding season the species is noticeably territorial and so pairs are generally well dispersed. The two areas consistently holding the highest concentrations of breeding pairs (45–50 each) during the NBA were Holkham NNR and the mid-Yare RSPB reserves. Two other sites, Holme

SUMMER

Small dots 1, medium 2–3, large 4–50 ('pairs')
Shading – breeding proved or considered likely

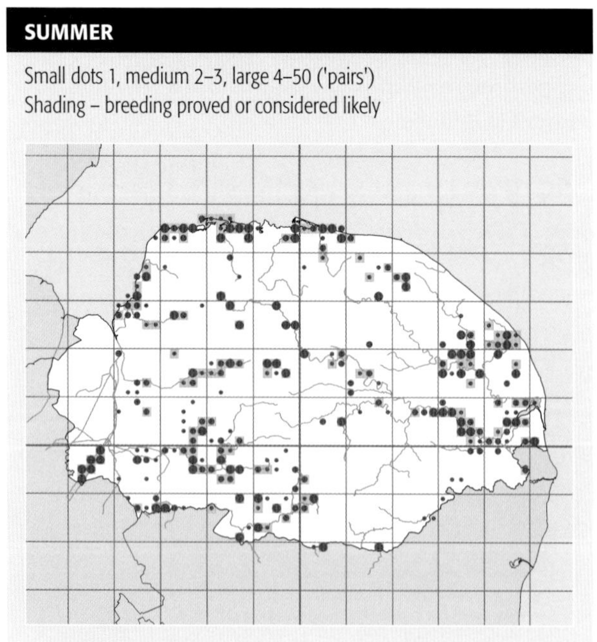

WINTER

Small dots 1–4, medium 5–20, large 21–368 (birds)

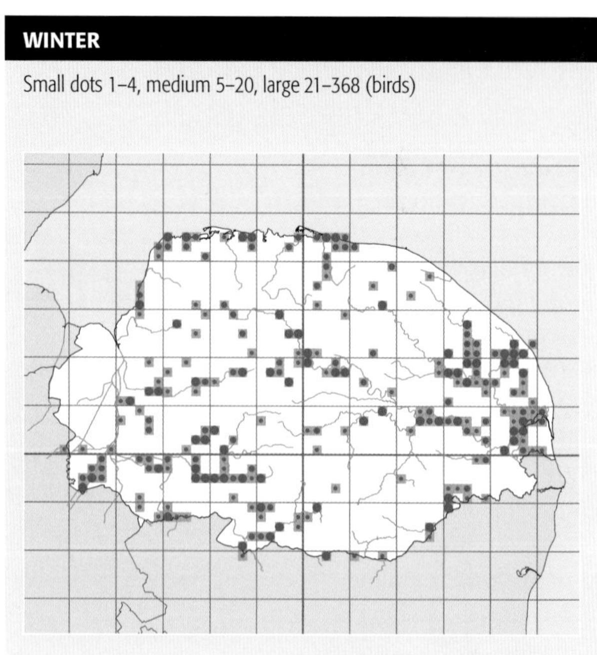

DAVID TIPLING

and Welney, each hosted 15 or more breeding pairs most summers. At all of these locations, about half the number of pairs present was subsequently seen with broods of ducklings. It is likely that about 150–200 breeding pairs are present in Norfolk each summer.

During the winter, Gadwalls generally remain in small flocks of up to about 30 birds, although far larger numbers are recorded at certain favoured localities scattered throughout the county. During the 1990s, Welney, Stanford Water and Gunton Park were the three sites where the highest winter counts were normally made. However, during the NBA winters some additional localities have hosted the biggest flocks – for example 368 at Whitlingham Lane CP, 307 at Martham Broad and 300 at Horsey Mere. It may well be that with the passage of time these waters have developed lusher underwater vegetation. At some of these sites even higher numbers have been recorded during the autumn months.

As Gadwalls disperse more widely during the winter, and are joined by migrants from the Continent, it is not surprising that the NBA winter map shows a basically similar distribution to that in the summer, but with rather more inland tetrads occupied. Severe weather affects the short-term distribution, as was demonstrated at Quidenham, where a small pool that normally holds just a handful of Gadwall remained as open water during a freeze and briefly attracted 150.

The change map indicates that the colonisation of Norfolk by breeding Gadwalls has continued since 1980–85, with considerable expansion in all areas of the county. Comparison with the *1981–84 Winter Atlas* shows evidence of range increase also in the winter period, with records from 84% of 10-km squares during the NBA winters.

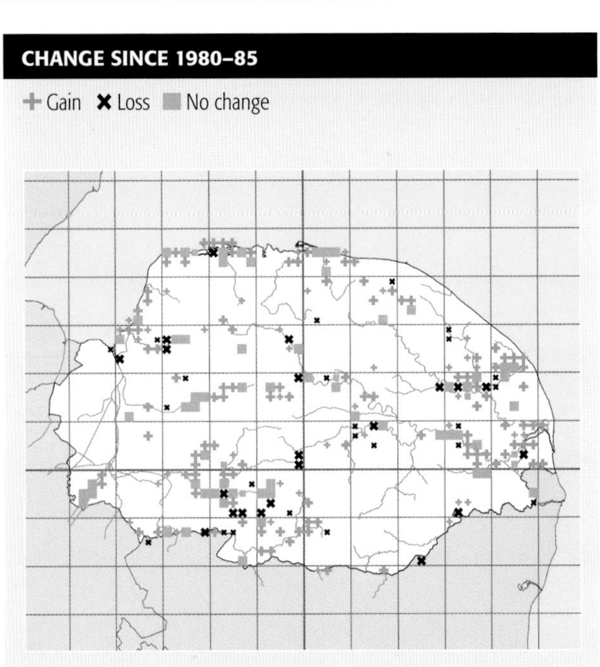

Teal

Anas crecca

NBA 1999–2007	SUMMER: ALL / BREEDING	WINTER
TETRADS OCCUPIED	115 (8%) / 25 (2%)	440 (30%)
SUMMER/WINTER ONLY	19	344
MEAN PER OCCUPIED TETRAD	4 / 4	116
SUMMED MAX COUNTS	466 / 91	50,856
POPULATION ESTIMATE	4–16 bp	15,000–20,000

PREVIOUS ATLASES	SQUARES OCCUPIED	1999–2007	LOSSES	GAINS
1968–72 (10 KM)	46 (74%)	13 (21%)	35	2
1980–85 (TETRAD)	101 (7%)	25 (2%)	95	19
1980–85 (10 KM)	39 (63%)	13 (21%)	27	1
1981–84 WINTER (10 KM)	54 (87%)	60 (97%)	1	7
1988–91 (10 KM)	34 (55%)	13 (21%)	23	2

THE TEAL, THE SMALLEST indigenous duck in the western Palaearctic, has been undergoing a marked contraction in its breeding range in Britain during the last 30 years for reasons that are not clearly understood.

Stevenson, writing in the second half of the 19th century, described the species as a scarce breeder in Norfolk, although by 1930 *Riviere* stated that it had become more abundant as a breeding bird in the county. Since then it has reverted to its former status.

Although small numbers of Teal summer annually at wetlands scattered throughout the county, as shown on the NBA summer map, confirmed breeding is only obtained for a very few pairs each year. They nest in dense vegetation around the periphery of small, isolated pools, often forming part of a larger wetland area. Nests are not easy to locate and even after hatching the female and her brood will tend to remain hidden in reedbeds or other waterside vegetation, seldom swimming out into open water. Despite breeding tending to be sporadic, even at favoured locations, five sites in Norfolk hosted breeding Teal in more than one NBA summer: Holme, Holkham NNR, Berney, the mid-Yare reserves and Welney. The last site was the most productive with a record of 12 pairs producing eight broods in 2000. It is almost certainly significant that all five sites include protected wetland reserves. Elsewhere, confirmed or likely breeding also occurred at Titchwell, Roydon Common, King's Lynn BF, Pensthorpe and Ranworth Broad.

The Teal is best known as a very common winter visitor to the county from northern and eastern Europe. The NBA winter map shows that it was widely distributed, with concentrations on the coastal marshes, saltings and freshwater pools along the north Norfolk coast, on the flooded grazing marshes and Broads in east

SUMMER

Small dots 1, medium 2–3, large 4–50 ('pairs')
Shading – breeding proved or considered likely

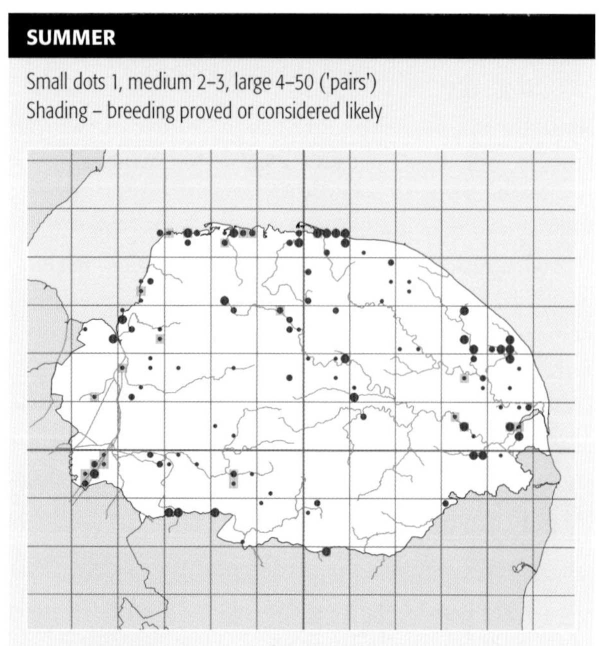

WINTER

Small dots 1–5, medium 6–36, large 37–5,000 (birds)

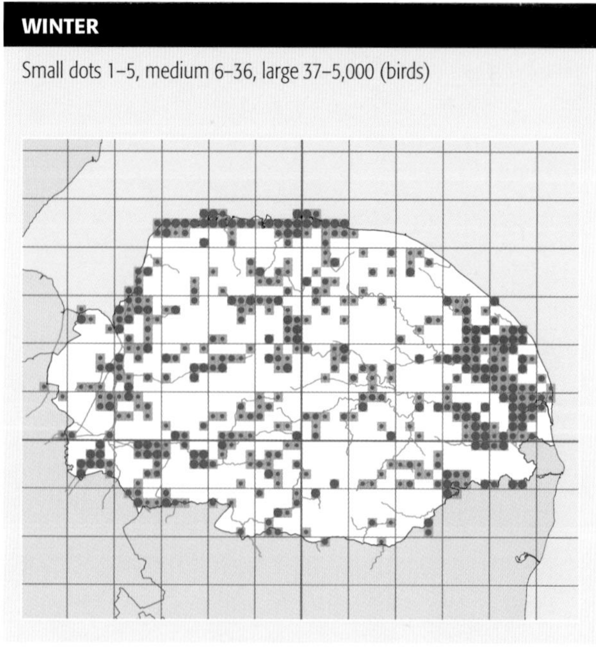

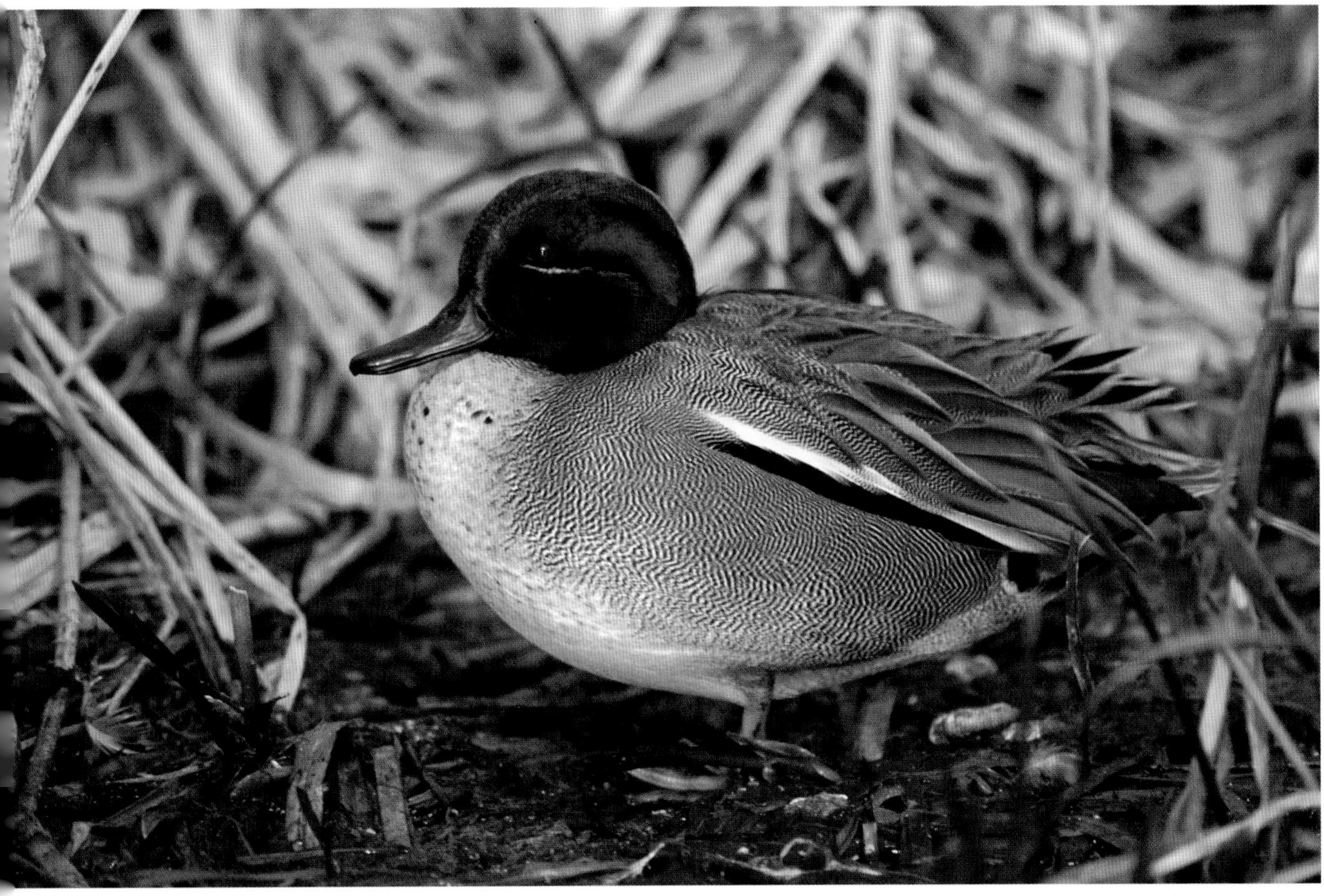

DAVID TIPLING

Norfolk and in the Fens, especially on the Ouse Washes. Many of the inland records were from parkland lakes, river valleys, flooded gravel pits and Breckland meres, while even small ponds and pools, often enclosed by trees, held flocks of up to 100. Their presence in these isolated and enclosed sites was often given away by the distinctive double-whistle calls of the drakes.

CHANGE SINCE 1980–85

+ Gain ✖ Loss ■ No change

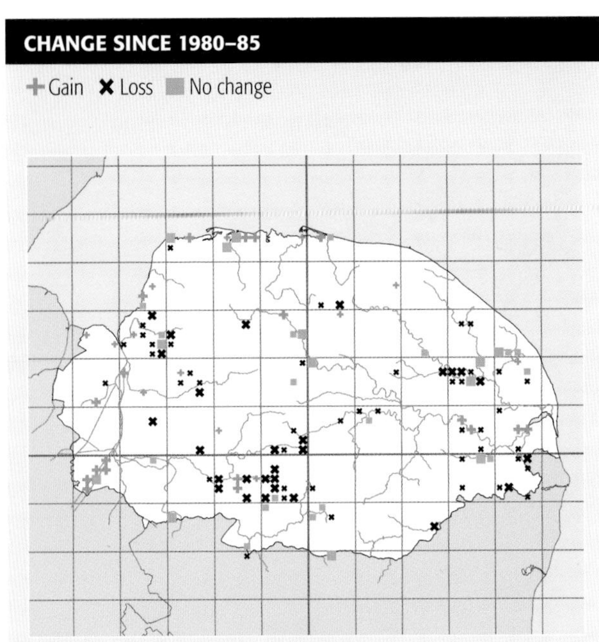

Over the course of the NBA fieldwork, the counts at four sites peaked at over 3,000 with a county record of 6,487 in the Breydon Water/Berney area in December 2001, 5,000 at Horsey Mere, where artificial feeding attracted wildfowl, and 3,500 at both Cantley BF and Welney. Teal are highly susceptible to cold winter weather and move south or west to avoid such conditions. Severe flooding, as occurs from time to time at Welney, also has an impact on the number present, as they leave to find more suitable feeding areas. By contrast, areas of temporary shallow flooding often prove very attractive to the species.

In 1980–85, two centres of regular breeding were noted: the Ranworth district of Broadland, and the meres, marshes and pingos of Breckland. Although approximately the same number of occupied tetrads were recorded during the *1980–85 NBBS* and NBA surveys, breeding was considered likely in only one quarter as many tetrads during the latter survey. In both surveys, many April and May records will have referred to birds still in winter quarters or on spring passage.

Mallard

Anas platyrhynchos

NBA 1999–2007	SUMMER: ALL/BREEDING	WINTER
TETRADS OCCUPIED	1,282 (88%) / 1,103 (76%)	1,174 (80%)
SUMMER/WINTER ONLY	178	70
MEAN PER OCCUPIED TETRAD	9 / 10	36
SUMMED MAX COUNTS	11,467 / 10,883	42,317
POPULATION ESTIMATE	4,000–6,000 bp	10,000–20,000

PREVIOUS ATLASES	SQUARES OCCUPIED	1999–2007	LOSSES	GAINS
1968–72 (10 KM)	62 (all)	62 (all)		
1980–85 (TETRAD)	1,020 (70%)	1,103 (76%)	166	249
1980–85 (10 KM)	62 (all)	62 (all)		
1981–84 WINTER (10 KM)	62 (all)	62 (all)		
1988–91 (10 KM)	61 (98%)	62 (all)	0	1

THE MALLARD IS THE most numerous and widespread species of resident waterfowl in Britain. Because of its adaptability and its history of domestication, many Mallards live in a feral or semi-tame state on village ponds and in urban parks.

Mallards may be found on any area of water, no matter how small, as well as on rivers and streams, coastal saltings, brackish pools and even shallow saline water. This adaptability is well demonstrated by the very widespread distribution shown on the NBA summer map, with particular concentrations in the Fens, Broadland and southeast Norfolk. Although the majority nest close to water, some breed a considerable distance away and the female has to escort the newly hatched brood on a potentially hazardous journey to the nearest water. The species breeds from early spring through to late summer, and in the milder winters young ducklings may be reported even in December. The parents of

DAVID TIPLING

these broods may well have been hatched themselves earlier the same year, as Mallards are known to be capable of breeding when only six months old.

NBA returns doubtless included many non-breeding birds but it is likely that the species bred in nearly all tetrads in which it was recorded. The largest recorded concentration of breeding Mallards was recorded each year at Holkham NNR, where the number of summering pairs varied from 142 to 170 during the NBA summers, of which an average of 60% had broods.

The NBA winter map indicates just how widespread the species is at this season, with concentrations in north Norfolk, Broadland and the Fens. As in summer, any area of open water may host Mallards, as do grazing marshes and even fields of stubble, potatoes or sugar beet. Estimating the wintering population of Mallards in Norfolk is difficult. Firstly, varying numbers of hand-reared birds are released by wildfowlers each year, for example a count of 840 Mallards at Shadwell Park in 2002 involved many such birds. Secondly, very many small bodies of water are not yet covered by the Wetland Bird Survey's monthly counts.

Although the species is so common, winter flocks tend to be considerably smaller than those of Teal and Wigeon, and there are few large concentrations of wild-type birds, despite the local breeders being augmented by winter visitors from Fenno-Scandia. Nevertheless some noteworthy counts were made during the winters of the NBA survey, including 1,572 at Welney and 1,000 at Snettisham. A concentration of 1,300 at Hardley Flood in December 2002 may well have included hand-reared releases, as may 900 at Bittering GP in December 2003. The largest count on the Broads was of 535 at Hickling/Heigham Sound in December 2005.

National trends in Mallard have been complex, with breeding birds increasing strongly but fewer continental birds arriving to winter (*Birdtrends*). The change map suggests considerable infilling of range, especially in central and southern Norfolk. Direct comparisons with previous atlases are difficult, however, because observers in earlier surveys were more likely to have ignored feral birds of domestic origin, which most observers now recognise as belonging fully to this species. Such birds are often abundant in town and village situations, as at Diss Mere where 150–200 are regularly recorded.

SUMMER

Small dots 1–3, medium 4–8, large 9–250 ('pairs')
Shading – breeding proved or considered likely

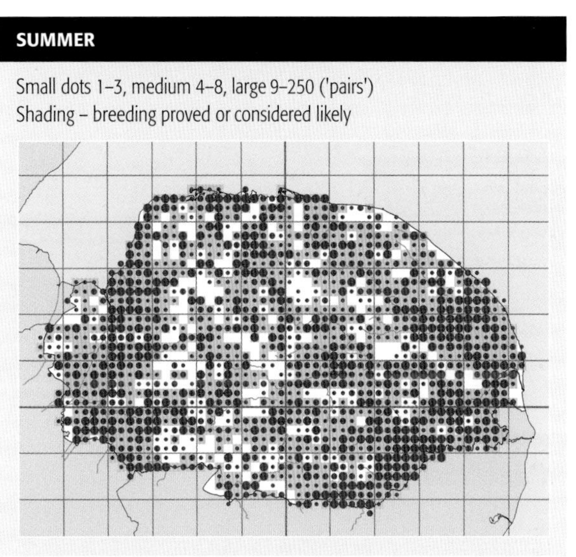

WINTER

Small dots 1–7, medium 8–25, large 26–1,300 (birds)

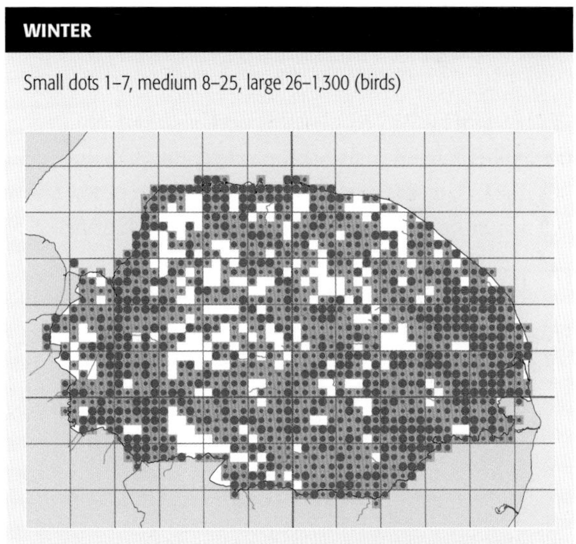

CHANGE SINCE 1980–85

+ Gain, ✖ Loss, ■ No change.

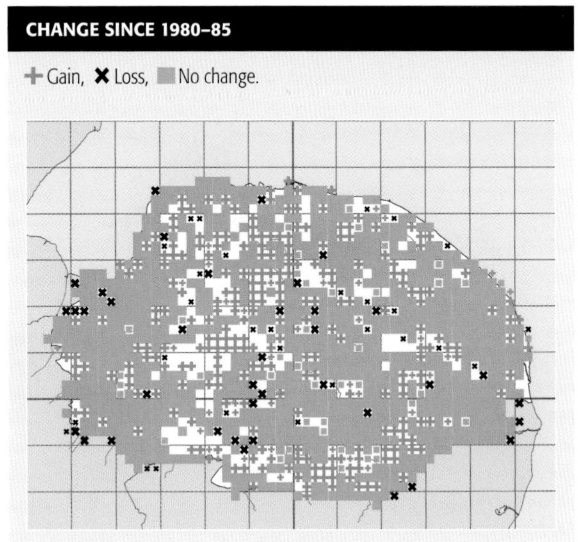

Pintail

Anas acuta

NBA 1999–2007	SUMMER: ALL/BREEDING	WINTER
TETRADS OCCUPIED	23 (2%) / 1 (<1%)	72 (5%)
SUMMER/WINTER ONLY	11	60
MEAN PER OCCUPIED TETRAD	1 / 1	97
SUMMED MAX COUNTS	29 / 1	6,987
POPULATION ESTIMATE	0–1 bp	2,000–3,000

PREVIOUS ATLASES	SQUARES OCCUPIED	1999–2007	LOSSES	GAINS
1968–72 (10 KM)	2 (3%)	1 (2%)	2	1
1980–85 (TETRAD)	4 (<1%)	1 (<1%)	3	0
1980–85 (10 KM)	4 (6%)	1 (2%)	3	0
1981–84 WINTER (10 KM)	20 (32%)	27 (44%)	5	12
1988–91 (10 KM)	3 (5%)	1 (2%)	3	1

WITH ITS LONG SLENDER neck and long pointed tail, the drake Pintail is one of the most elegant of all the ducks. It is one of Britain's rarest breeding ducks and is best known as a winter visitor from northern and eastern Europe.

Pintails favour shallow waters surrounded by open marshland as breeding habitat and they have always been rather erratic breeders in Britain with usually fewer than 50 pairs breeding in any one year. In the spring of 1988, up to 46 pairs were displaying on the Ouse Washes alone (mainly in the Cambridgeshire section) but the water levels there are rarely managed in a suitable manner to encourage the species to nest (*1988–91 Atlas*). There have been very few records of confirmed breeding in Norfolk but a female with three ducklings was seen at Cley in August 2001 (the same site at which the species last bred in the county in 1993). The NBA summer map, however, does show that several other scattered localities hosted Pintails during the NBA summers, including a pair at Holkham NNR in 2005 that may have made an unsuccessful breeding attempt. The vast majority of summer records concerned single pairs or single birds and no more than six sites were involved in any one year. A pair with two fully grown young on the duck pond at Salthouse in July 2004 were almost certainly of avicultural origin.

Pintails are common winter visitors to Norfolk, although their distribution is extremely localised. The NBA winter map demonstrates the five main areas where the species tends to concentrate: the Ouse Washes, the inner shores of the Wash, Scolt Head/Brancaster Harbour, Cley/Blakeney

DAVID TIPLING

SUMMER

Small dots 1, medium 2, large 3 ('pairs')
Shading – breeding proved or considered likely

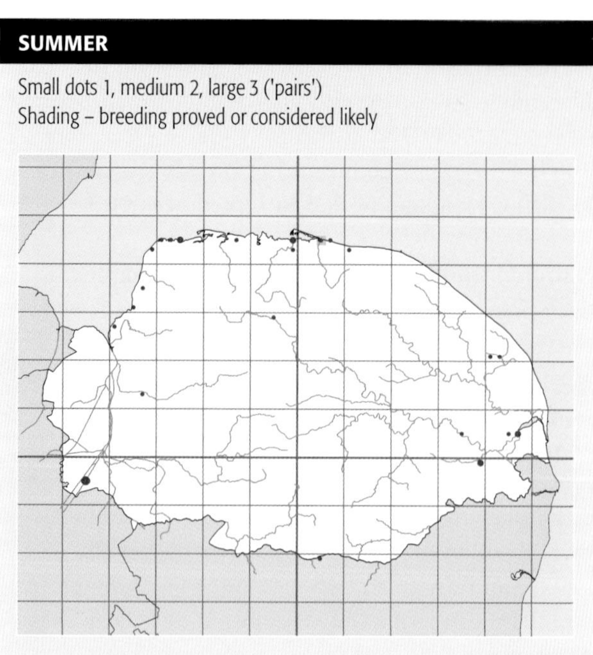

DAVID TIPLING

WINTER

Small dots 1–3, medium 4–46, large 47–1,290 (birds)

Harbour and Breydon Water/Berney. To these should be added Tottenhill GP, a tiny wetland by comparison, which has been a traditional site for the species for many years, but which is mainly used for loafing or roosting, rather than as a feeding area.

Pintails are highly mobile and quick to take advantage of an area of temporary flooding. Some sites, depending on the degree of flooding, are more favoured in one particular winter; in recent years, however, increasing numbers have been attracted to the Breydon Water/Berney area. Selected maximum site counts during NBA winters were 1,290 at Welney, 250 at Tottenhill GP, 328 at Snettisham, 420 at Scolt Head/Brancaster Harbour, 593 at Blakeney Harbour, 800 at Cley and 571 at Breydon Water/Berney. It is likely that the typical winter population of Pintails in Norfolk is in the region of 2,500.

Garganey
Anas querquedula

NBA 1999–2007	SUMMER: ALL / BREEDING	WINTER
TETRADS OCCUPIED	60 (4%) / 10 (<1%)	1 (<1%)
SUMMER/WINTER ONLY	59	none
MEAN PER OCCUPIED TETRAD	2 / 3	1
SUMMED MAX COUNTS	98 / 32	1
POPULATION ESTIMATE	3–8 bp	0–1

PREVIOUS ATLASES	SQUARES OCCUPIED	1999–2007	LOSSES	GAINS
1968–72 (10 KM)	16 (26%)	6 (10%)	10	0
1980–85 (TETRAD)	21 (1%)	10 (<1%)	15	4
1980–85 (10 KM)	11 (18%)	6 (10%)	6	1
1981–84 WINTER (10 KM)	none	1 (2%)	0	1
1988–91 (10 KM)	10 (16%)	6 (10%)	5	1

ARGUABLY A DRAKE GARGANEY is one of the most handsome ducks in Norfolk's wetlands. The species is unique among British waterfowl in being a trans-Saharan summer visitor.

As a species on the edge of its breeding range in Britain, it is subject to considerable annual fluctuations. The largest arrivals occur in warm springs, with more pairs breeding after periods of wet weather, which results in plenty of shallow pools on water meadows and coastal freshwater marshes (*1988–91 Atlas*). At least one pair bred or attempted to breed in Norfolk in each of the NBA summers, with a maximum of five pairs in 2001; Garganey are unobtrusive, secretive birds, however, and some breeding attempts in Norfolk must be missed each year. Probably as a result of wetland drainage, fewer pairs now breed in Norfolk than during the 19th century, when it was described as being widely, though sparingly, distributed (*Stevenson*).

Garganey favour small, sheltered, shallow fresh water or brackish pools with floating vegetation and surrounded by flooded grassland or other low growth. Such conditions are found at many of the county's wetland reserves. In north Norfolk, the string of coastal wetlands from Holme to Kelling WM, the Broadland reserves and those along the Yare valley all hosted Garganey at some point during the NBA period. In the west, Garganey were recorded annually at Snettisham, Welney and

SUMMER

Small dots 1, medium 2–3, large 4–7 ('pairs')
Shading – breeding proved or considered likely

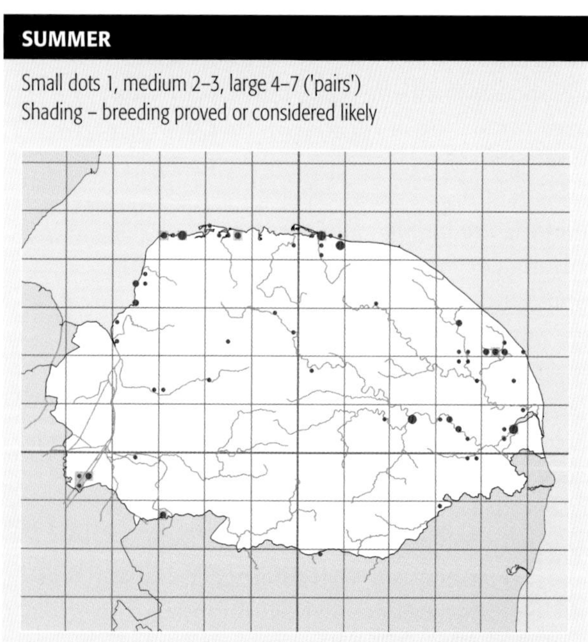

CHANGE SINCE 1980–85

+ Gain ✖ Loss ■ No change

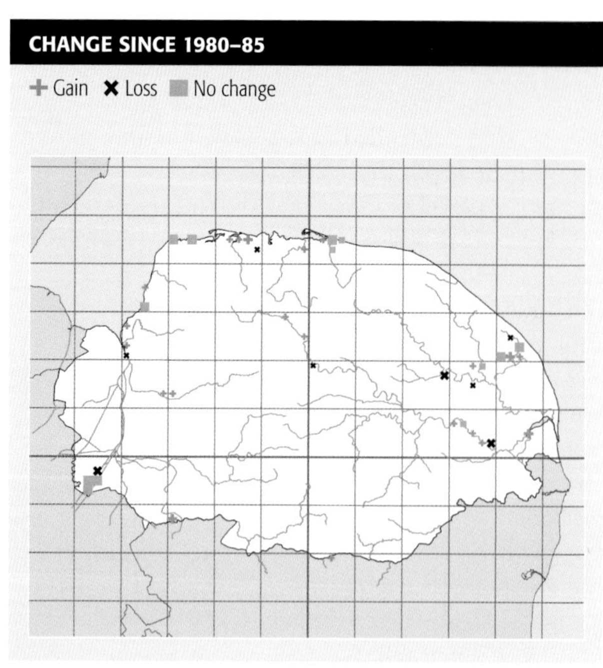

CHRIS KNIGHTS

Hockwold Washes, as they were at Cley, Hickling Broad and Berney Marshes. All six locations that hosted the species in each year of the NBA were reserves with controlled access. Other inland locations in which the species was recorded included a gravel pit, a small farm reservoir and a beet factory settling pool.

'At least one pair bred or attempted to breed in Norfolk in each of the NBA summers, with a maximum of five pairs in 2001.'

The Garganey is one of the earliest summer migrants to arrive back in Britain and is often recorded in March. A few March records have been included on the map. The number of Norfolk sites at which Garganey was recorded in the spring or summer each year was remarkably consistent, varying between 18 and 23. Far more single drakes were recorded in the spring than remained during the summer and the highest counts of drakes were seven at Berney Marshes and five at Titchwell, Cley, Kelling WM and Whitlingham Lane CP. Every year single drakes or pairs were detected at a selection of other, scattered, potentially suitable breeding sites but did not remain to nest. The true distribution for any one year is therefore less extensive than the NBA map, which covers eight summers, may suggest.

Garganey are rare in Britain during the winter months, but one at Cley on 12th December 2006 was the seventh county record in winter, and the first for ten years.

Shoveler

Anas clypeata

NBA 1999–2007	SUMMER: ALL/BREEDING	WINTER
TETRADS OCCUPIED	106 (7%) / 51 (3%)	146 (10%)
SUMMER/WINTER ONLY	35	75
MEAN PER OCCUPIED TETRAD	4 / 7	29
SUMMED MAX COUNTS	450 / 357	4,240
POPULATION ESTIMATE	50–150 bp	1,500–2,000

PREVIOUS ATLASES	SQUARES OCCUPIED	1999–2007	LOSSES	GAINS
1968–72 (10 KM)	45 (73%)	19 (31%)	28	2
1980–85 (TETRAD)	107 (7%)	51 (3%)	86	30
1980–85 (10 KM)	32 (52%)	19 (31%)	20	7
1981–84 WINTER (10 KM)	34 (55%)	42 (68%)	5	13
1988–91 (10 KM)	27 (44%)	19 (31%)	13	5

THE SHOVELER, with its characteristic large, broad, spatulate bill, is a specialist feeder on zooplankton, and is mobile enough to take advantage of local abundances of its food supply as they arise.

Although Shoveler will tolerate brackish waters, most are found inland on marshy pools, areas of open fresh water fringed by reeds or other emergent vegetation and in the dykes criss-crossing grazing marshes. They feed by filtering out food particles whilst skimming the surface of the shallow margins, often swimming in circles in small groups.

According to both *Stevenson* and *Riviere* it was an abundant breeder in Broadland, the Brecks and parts of north Norfolk during the 19th and early 20th centuries but, as elsewhere in western Europe, numbers have fallen since the 1950s. As many of the more ephemeral wetlands have been drained, most of Norfolk's breeding pairs are now restricted to the protected reserves, of which there are many in the county.

The NBA summer map shows that the main concentrations remain along the north Norfolk coast and in Broadland, as well as on the Ouse Washes, but nowadays there are fewer on the Breckland meres. Breeding is never easy to prove and the situation in the summer is complicated by the presence of many non-breeding birds. For example, in 2005, a reserve record of 54 pairs of Shovelers at Holkham NNR produced only

SUMMER

Small dots 1, medium 2–3, large 4–50 ('pairs')
Shading – breeding proved or considered likely

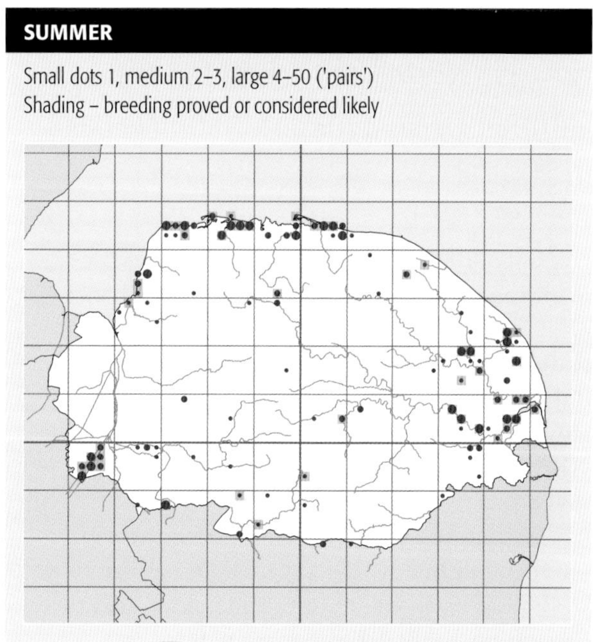

WINTER

Small dots 1–4, medium 5–17, large 18–560 (birds)

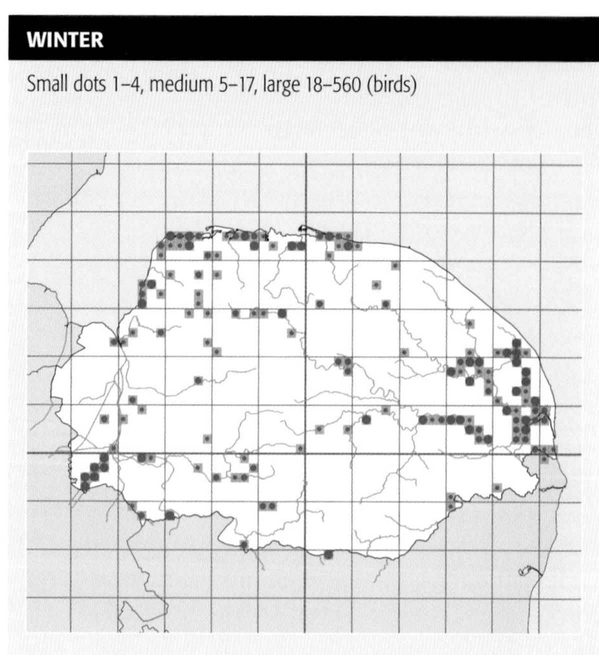

DAVID TIPLING

13 broods, while only a single brood was seen from 25 summering pairs at Holme in 2000. The species is also characterised by marked annual variations in the number of potential breeding pairs at any specific site. Again this is well demonstrated by the Holkham population, which was as low as 27 pairs in 2002, but double that number three years later and averaged 47 pairs between 2000 and 2005. A similar situation exists at Welney, where the numbers of breeding pairs fluctuate according to the springtime water levels. Other sites holding good numbers of potential breeding pairs included Titchwell, Berney and the mid-Yare RSPB reserves. The species bred for the first time on Scolt Head in 2001.

CHANGE SINCE 1980–85

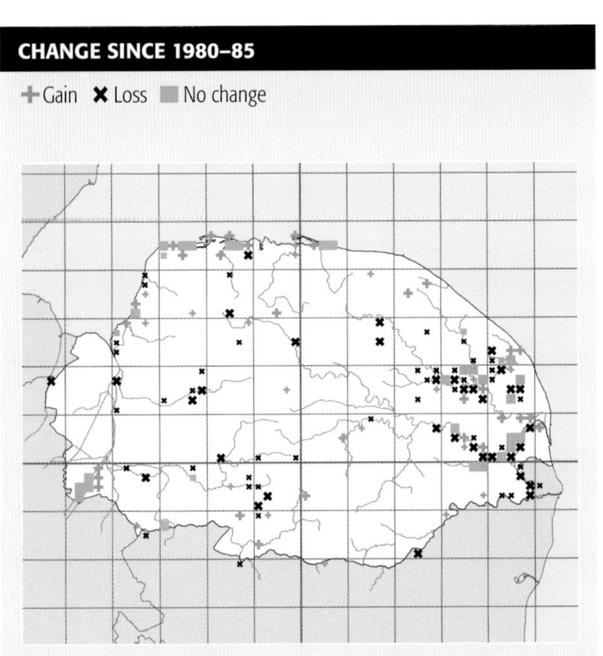

Up to half the British breeding population migrates south in autumn to be replaced by wintering birds from the Continent. Like all wildfowl, Shovelers are more gregarious in winter, although they tend to remain in flocks of no more than 20–30 birds. On occasion, however, much larger concentrations are formed, especially during periods of severe weather, when flocks seek out areas of open, ice-free water. The NBA winter map shows a similar distribution to that in the summer, with the main concentrations in north Norfolk, Broadland and the Ouse Washes. During the NBA winters, many of the Broads held over 100 Shovelers at varying times but Filby Broad consistently was favoured with up to 560 there in January 2002 during a period of particularly severe, freezing weather and 480 in February 2005. Similarly, Breydon Water/Berney was a regular winter stronghold peaking at 679 in February 2003, as was Welney with a maximum count of 249 in January 2005. The highest count in north Norfolk was 196 at Holkham Park.

Comparisons with previous breeding atlases suggests substantial loss of range since 1968–72. Similar numbers of tetrads were occupied in summers 1980–85 and in 2000–07, but in the NBA survey fewer squares were believed to hold breeding pairs. The change map indicates that gains predominated in west Norfolk and losses in Broadland.

Pochard
Aythya ferina

NBA 1999–2007	SUMMER: ALL / BREEDING	WINTER
TETRADS OCCUPIED	90 (6%) / 50 (3%)	156 (11%)
SUMMER/WINTER ONLY	23	89
MEAN PER OCCUPIED TETRAD	3 / 4	50
SUMMED MAX COUNTS	252 / 184	7,822
POPULATION ESTIMATE	30–50 bp	2,000–3,000

PREVIOUS ATLASES	SQUARES OCCUPIED	1999–2007	LOSSES	GAINS
1968–72 (10 KM)	30 (48%)	20 (32%)	15	5
1980–85 (TETRAD)	71 (5%)	50 (3%)	48	27
1980–85 (10 KM)	26 (42%)	20 (32%)	11	5
1981–84 WINTER (10 KM)	44 (71%)	43 (69%)	8	7
1988–91 (10 KM)	32 (52%)	20 (32%)	17	5

THE POCHARD IS ONE of the two most widespread diving ducks in winter in Norfolk. Unlike the Tufted Duck, however, it has not become established as a common breeding species.

Breeding Pochards favour areas of open fresh water with abundant submerged vegetation. Thus they are found on lakes, larger pools, Broads and Breckland meres. Indeed, during the 1980s, the largest numbers breeding in Britain were thought to be in Breckland and Broadland (*1988–91 Atlas*), although the nesting population in these areas was believed to be in decline by then. Unlike many wildfowl, Pochards pair up in spring rather than during the winter months, but the presence of a pair in summer does not necessarily indicate breeding or even attempted breeding. Breeding success is generally low (*1988–91 Atlas*), yet proof of breeding is usually only obtainable when ducklings are seen.

The NBA summer map indicates that the species is a scarce and very localised breeding bird in Norfolk, with the main centre of population in Broadland, and other concentrations at scattered sites in north and central Norfolk, Breckland and the Ouse Washes. The largest summer population during the NBA period was at Holkham NNR, where up to 25 pairs were present, although far fewer actually bred. At Strumpshaw and Breydon Water/Berney the numbers of pairs peaked at seven but at most of the other sites in the county only single pairs were noted. On average 28 broods were recorded annually from 45 pairs in Norfolk during the NBA summers. This compares with a count of 49 pairs on the Flegg Broads alone in 1984 and 19 broods at Holkham NNR in 1997. A countywide survey in 1994 produced a total of 65–68 broods. Despite the decreases

SUMMER

Small dots 1, medium 2–4, large 5–29 ('pairs')
Shading – breeding proved or considered likely

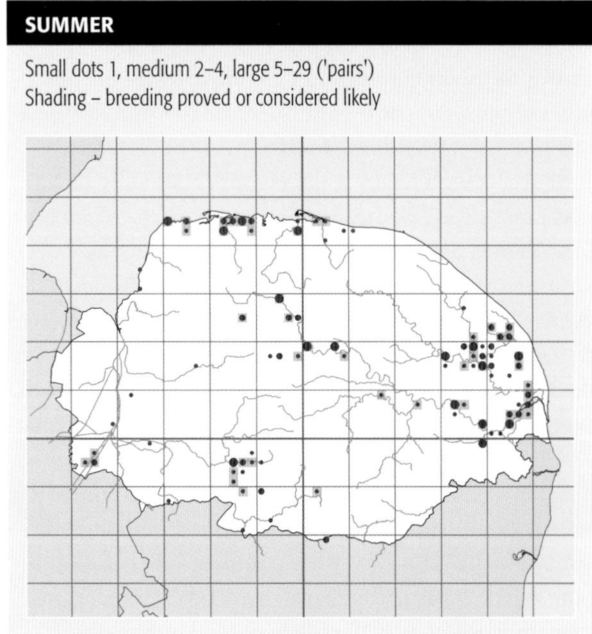

WINTER

Small dots 1–6, medium 7–35, large 36–2,000 (birds)

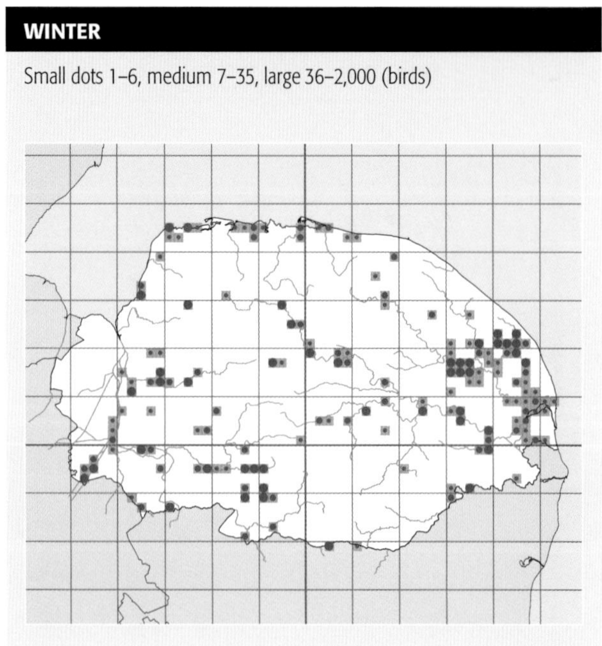

DAVID TIPLING

elsewhere, Pochards bred at Welney in 2000, for the first time for 25 years, and a pair bred for the first time at Cley in 2005.

In winter, Pochards are often found in association with Tufted Ducks on the larger areas of open fresh water, including flooded gravel pits, but are much more selective than that species in their choice of site. The Norfolk breeding population is probably mainly resident, and is augmented by winter visitors from central Europe and Russia. The first continental immigrants are mostly drakes, which begin to arrive to moult as early as June.

CHANGE SINCE 1980–85

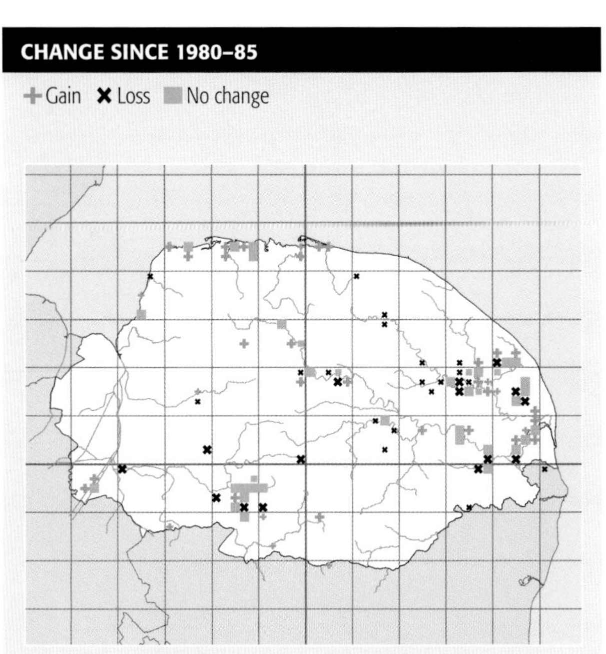

The NBA winter map shows a similar but more widespread distribution than in summer, again with Broadland favoured, as well as many of the inland lakes and gravel pits in the centre and west of Norfolk. Throughout the NBA period, Welney has attracted the largest numbers of Pochards in winter, peaking at 4,062 in February 2000. Here the daily feeds of corn and waste potatoes, supplied primarily for the wild swans, are eagerly awaited by the Pochards, and the reserve also provides the species a secure daytime roost site. In the east of the county, Hickling Broad usually hosts the largest winter concentrations, with a peak of 930 in February 2003, while 240 have been recorded at nearby Horsey Mere. Three-figure counts have also been reported from several other Broads, as well as at Wissington BF, Narborough and Fowl Mere in west Norfolk.

Atlas comparisons are consistent in indicating a loss of breeding range. Gains on the change map are mostly of birds not thought to be breeding, while losses of possible breeders are evident in Broadland and Breckland.

Tufted Duck
Aythya fuligula

NBA 1999–2007	SUMMER: ALL / BREEDING	WINTER
TETRADS OCCUPIED	374 (26%) / 218 (15%)	305 (21%)
SUMMER/WINTER ONLY	149	80
MEAN PER OCCUPIED TETRAD	5 / 7	31
SUMMED MAX COUNTS	1,910 / 1,454	9,508
POPULATION ESTIMATE	200–300 bp	4,000–5,000

PREVIOUS ATLASES	SQUARES OCCUPIED	1999–2007	LOSSES	GAINS
1968–72 (10 KM)	44 (71%)	54 (87%)	1	11
1980–85 (TETRAD)	265 (18%)	218 (15%)	160	113
1980–85 (10 KM)	47 (76%)	54 (87%)	2	9
1981–84 WINTER (10 KM)	54 (87%)	55 (89%)	6	7
1988–91 (10 KM)	53 (85%)	54 (87%)	5	6

THE TUFTED DUCK, which was first reported nesting in Britain in 1849, is now the commonest breeding diving duck. It benefited greatly from the excavation of sand and gravel pits, and their subsequent flooding, which took place in many parts of England during the 20th century, and from the introduction of the non-native zebra mussel *Dreissena polymorpha*, which in many places is its staple food.

Tufted Ducks are highly gregarious for much of the year and pair formation is often delayed until the spring, due in part to the unbalanced sex-ratio that often occurs in winter flocks (*BWP1*). The species also nests much later in the summer than the majority of breeding waterfowl, with most clutches not being laid until mid May or later. Most broods do not appear until July, by which time the NBA set visits had normally been completed, and thus indications of breeding often rested on supplementary records.

During the breeding season, Tufted Ducks inhabit lakes, flooded gravel pits, grazing marsh dykes and slow-flowing rivers, provided there is sufficient surrounding ground vegetation for nesting. The distribution of occupied tetrads on the NBA summer map, although initially appearing to be fairly haphazard, in fact largely follows the courses of the county's rivers, with localised concentrations in Breckland, Broadland and along parts of the north Norfolk coast. As with most duck species, far more Tufted Ducks are present in Norfolk in the

SUMMER

Small dots 1, medium 2–5, large 6–128 ('pairs')
Shading – breeding proved or considered likely

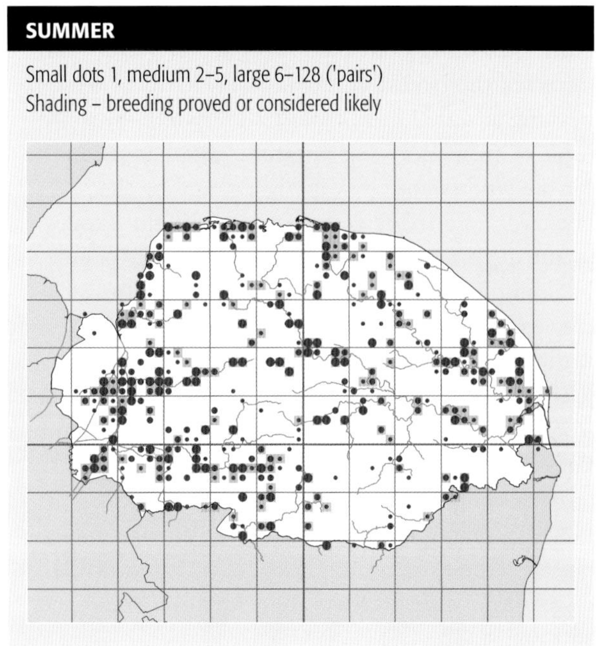

WINTER

Small dots 1–4, medium 5–20, large 21–365 (birds)

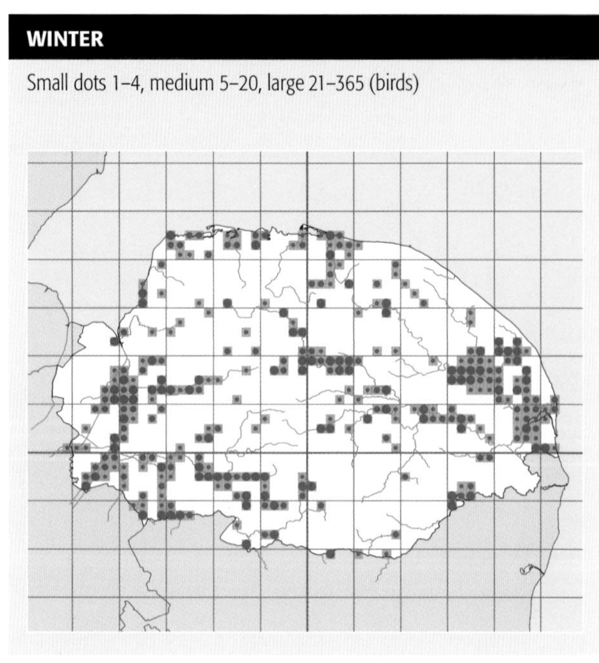

DAVID TIPLING

summer than actually breed. For example at Holkham NNR, where there are many suitable pools and dykes, only about half the pairs of summering Tufted Ducks are subsequently seen with broods. During NBA summers, the maximum counts of potential breeding pairs at favoured sites included 36 at Holkham NNR, 21 at Welney and 20 at Pensthorpe.

CHANGE SINCE 1980–85

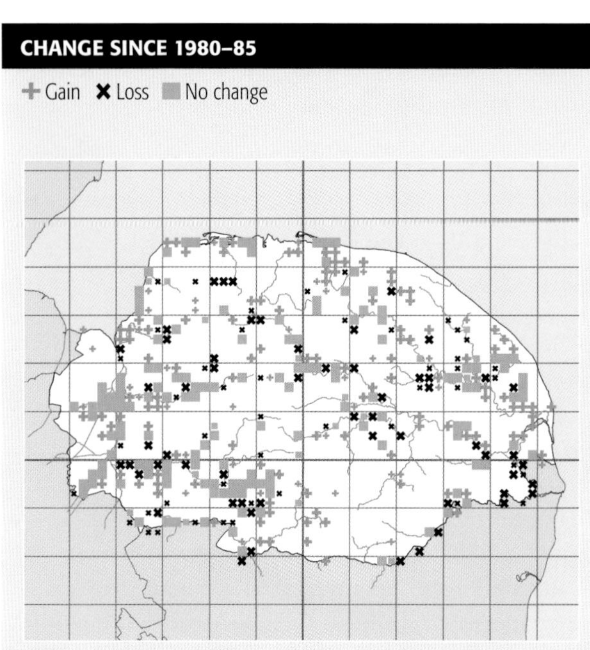

In autumn, the resident Norfolk population of Tufted Ducks is joined by winter visitors from northern Europe and Russia, and wintering flocks are found on parkland lakes, gravel pits, Breckland meres and the Broads. In some more-urban settings they can become quite tame, as they are at Welney, where they join in the feeding frenzy as corn and waste potatoes are fed to the swans. The NBA winter map shows a similar, if more restricted distribution to that in the summer, with clearer concentrations in the Fens, Brecks and Broads, as well as along the valleys of the Rivers Yare and Wensum. The species generally is found in small flocks but concentrations of several hundred may occur where waters remain open during freezing conditions. The largest site counts in NBA winters included 386 along the Great Ouse Relief Channel, 365 at Pensthorpe and 311 at Welney.

National census data show a continuing increase in the breeding population (*Birdtrends*). The comparisons with earlier atlases indicate substantial expansion of summer range since 1968–72. Gains on the change map include tetrads where Tufted Ducks were present but not thought to be breeding. There are also a number of tetrads throughout the county where the species has been lost since 1980–85, perhaps as sites have become unsuitable for the species.

Scaup

Aythya marila

NBA 1999–2007	SUMMER: ALL/BREEDING	WINTER
TETRADS OCCUPIED	4 (<1%) / none	52 (4%)
SUMMER/WINTER ONLY	1	49
MEAN PER OCCUPIED TETRAD	2 / none	5
SUMMED MAX COUNTS	6 / none	267
POPULATION ESTIMATE	1–2 individuals	40–60

PREVIOUS ATLASES	SQUARES OCCUPIED	1999–2007	LOSSES	GAINS
1981–84 WINTER (10 KM)	15 (24%)	25 (40%)	3	13

THE SCAUP IS MAINLY an Arctic-nesting species, visiting Britain from Iceland and from Fenno-Scandia and the Russian tundra. Although it is generally one of the most maritime of the diving ducks that winter in Britain, inland sightings in Norfolk are not infrequent. Especially inland, females and immatures greatly outnumber adult drakes in the county.

It has always been scarce as a winter visitor to the county, except in those years with harsh wintry weather, when several hundred Scaup have been recorded. The principal wintering grounds are the mussel beds or 'scaups' situated in the Wash and off the northwest coast from Snettisham to Titchwell. Elsewhere, occurrences are usually sporadic. The high counts in the Blakeney/Cley area relate to a single party of 22 that were present in Blakeney Harbour on 18th January 2000 and later that day off Cley; normally these sites host one or two Scaup, at most. Historical data suggest there has been no change in this distribution.

DAVID TIPLING

DAVID TIPLING

Scaup are fairly tolerant of brackish or fresh water, and the most reliable site at which to see them is the old gravel pits at the RSPB reserve at Snettisham. During the NBA winters this location generally held the largest flocks, with 22 in February 2000 and 28 in December 2001. Here, as elsewhere, Scaup often associate with other diving ducks, especially Goldeneye. The only other site that hosted more than 20 Scaup was Hunstanton, with up to 26 in the winter of 2000/01.

Inland sightings in Norfolk have become more regular since the 1980s and the map shows that Scaup were recorded more widely inland than any other species of seaduck. Certain localities, including the Great Ouse Relief Channel, Welney, Tottenhill

DAVID TIPLING

WINTER

Small dots 1–2, medium 3–4, large 5–28 (birds)

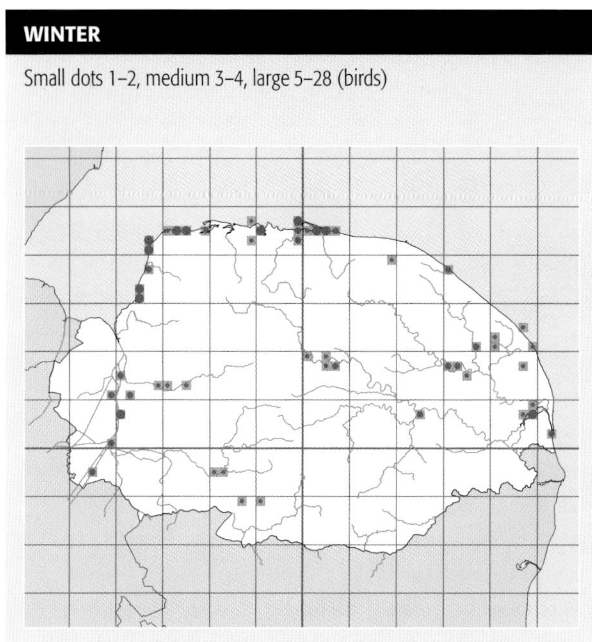

'Scaup has always been scarce as a winter visitor to the county, except in those years with harsh wintry weather, when several hundred birds have been recorded.'

GP and Whitlingham CP, held the species in several of the NBA winters. Most inland records were of singles or small groups briefly present among other diving ducks on the larger waters.

Although the species is essentially a winter visitor, occasional Scaup were recorded at other seasons, notably at Snettisham where one female, possibly injured, remained permanently throughout much of the NBA period, joined at times by a second bird in the summer of 2005.

Eider

Somateria mollissima

NBA 1999–2007	SUMMER: ALL/BREEDING	WINTER
TETRADS OCCUPIED	15 (1%) / none	45 (3%)
SUMMER/WINTER ONLY	5	35
MEAN PER OCCUPIED TETRAD	6 / none	36
SUMMED MAX COUNTS	85 / none	1,624
POPULATION ESTIMATE	80–100 individuals	200–350

PREVIOUS ATLASES	SQUARES OCCUPIED	1999–2007	LOSSES	GAINS
1968–72 (10 KM)	1 (2%)	none	1	0
1980–85 (TETRAD)	1 (<1%)	none	1	0
1980–85 (10 KM)	1 (2%)	none	1	0
1981–84 WINTER (10 KM)	13 (21%)	12 (19%)	3	2
1988–91 (10 KM)	2 (3%)	none	2	0

DAVID TIPLING

EIDERS ARE REGULAR off Norfolk in winter, and smaller numbers spend all year in the county. Nesting has regularly been suspected, but the first confirmed county breeding record is still awaited.

Writing in the 19th century, *Stevenson* described the Eider as very scarce, just about occurring in every winter and he was able to find only a single instance of oversummering. The status of the species up to 1930 was unchanged according to *Riviere* and he was only able to add one further summer record. However, by 1954, parties of up to 45 were being recorded in every month (Seago 1967).

Eiders are entirely coastal and maritime throughout their lives. By successfully adapting to arctic conditions they are able to remain within the breeding range during the winter. British breeders rarely move more than 200 km and those wintering off the Norfolk coast are believed to be Dutch and Baltic birds. Their chief food consists of molluscs (especially blue mussels) and crustaceans, and they tend to forage for these on an ebbing tide in water no deeper than three metres. As with most of the seaduck, the largest concentrations in Norfolk are found in the Wash and along the northwest coast, between Snettisham and Holkham. For most of the time, the Eiders remain fairly well offshore but on occasion small numbers are seen close inshore or in the north-coast harbours. During the NBA winters, the highest counts were of 200 in Holkham Bay, 180 off Hunstanton and 160 in the Scolt Head/Brancaster Harbour area. These counts were eclipsed, however, by an estimate of 1,500 in the middle of the Wash made from aerial surveys in 2005. How many of these birds were off the Lincolnshire coast is unknown.

Far fewer Eiders were reported off the east Norfolk coast. Up to 20 were recorded off Sea Palling and single-figure counts were not infrequent from here south to Gorleston.

Parties of non-breeding and moulting Eiders were present annually off the Norfolk coast during the NBA

DAVID TIPLING

summer survey, their distribution mirroring that in the winter, but involving far fewer birds. The largest flocks were of 48 off Thornham and 40 off Titchwell. No Eiders were located inland during either the winter or summer recording periods of the NBA.

Possible breeding has been recorded by all previous atlas surveys, including a displaying male noted off the Outer Trial Bank during the *1980–85 NBBS*. Breeding was not considered likely during the NBA summers.

SUMMER

Small dots 1, medium 2–4, large 5–24 ('pairs')

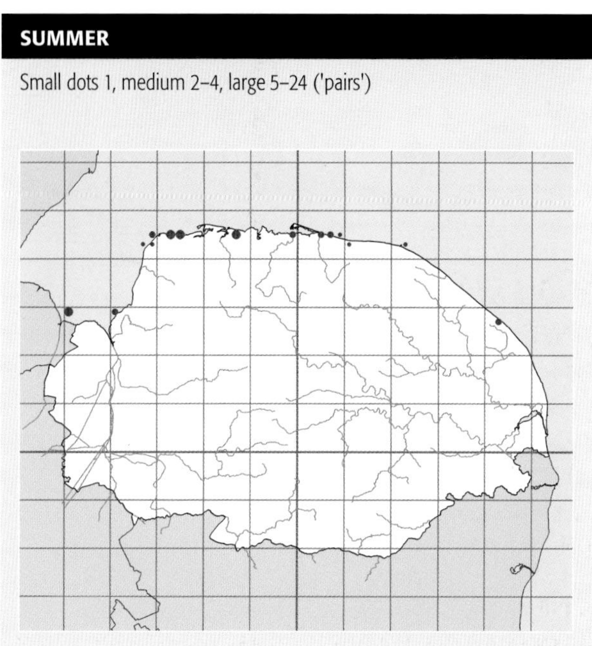

WINTER

Small dots 1–6, medium 7–22, large 23–200 (birds)

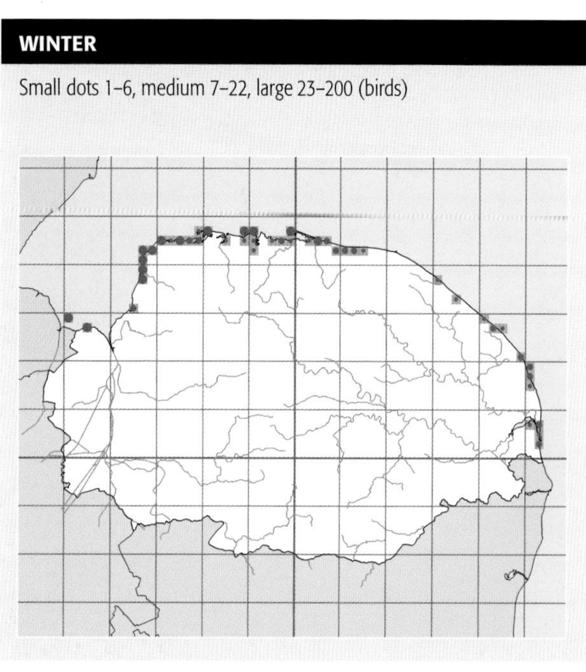

Long-tailed Duck
Clangula hyemalis

NBA 1999–2007	SUMMER: ALL / BREEDING	WINTER
TETRADS OCCUPIED	4 (<1%) / none	27 (2%)
SUMMER/WINTER ONLY	1	24
MEAN PER OCCUPIED TETRAD	1 / none	11
SUMMED MAX COUNTS	4 / none	286
POPULATION ESTIMATE	0–1 individuals	50–100

PREVIOUS ATLASES	SQUARES OCCUPIED	1999–2007	LOSSES	GAINS
1981–84 WINTER (10 KM)	12 (19%)	14 (23%)	4	6

THE LONG-TAILED DUCK, which visits Britain from breeding grounds in the Arctic, is unique amongst European wildfowl in having distinctly different plumages in winter and summer. Most of the British wintering population is found off Scotland and to Norfolk it is a scarce winter visitor.

Since at least the early 1960s the principal wintering area in Norfolk has been off Hunstanton, Holme and Titchwell, a rather more restricted area than for the other species of seaduck. Smaller numbers have also

DAVID TIPLING

been recorded annually in winter as far east as Holkham Bay, but off other parts of the Norfolk coast it is generally very scarce. While on occasion it does consort with flocks of scoters, it tends to feed at a greater distance from the shore and so tends to be under-recorded. It is also more likely to be found in smaller groups of up to a dozen or so birds.

The highest counts during NBA winters were of 62 off Gore Point, Holme, in February 2000 and 100 off Hunstanton/Holme on 16th February 2005. It is a very scarce winter visitor to east Norfolk and the largest party during the NBA period was up to 15 at Winterton in the winter of 1999/2000. Numbers overwintering off the Norfolk coast vary quite widely from year to year. While numbers in Norfolk often peak in March, most Long-tailed Ducks have left the county by April. A few birds were recorded in May, however, including a pair off Scolt Head on 22nd–25th May 2001. During the NBA period three were noted in June: there were singles at Titchwell and Sheringham in 2002, and one remained off Great Yarmouth from 13th April until 5th June 2000.

One or two Long-tailed Ducks were recorded inland in most years during the NBA period, over half in Broadland and most of the others in the region of the Great Ouse. Normally only singletons were present but two were recorded at Breydon Water and at Wiggenhall St Mary Magdalen, and three on Ormesby Broad on 16th–17th January 2000. These inland records were not related to particular weather conditions. A female at Welney made the most protracted stay, from 23rd March to 7th April 2000, and was the only bird recorded inland during the NBA summer recording periods.

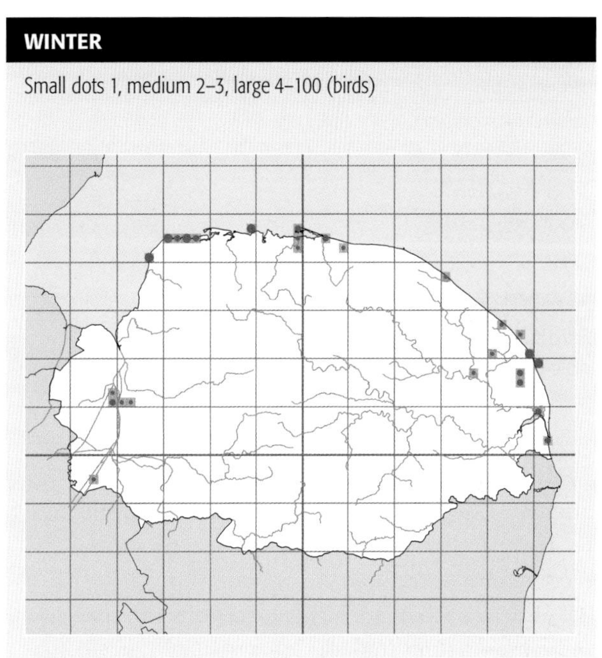

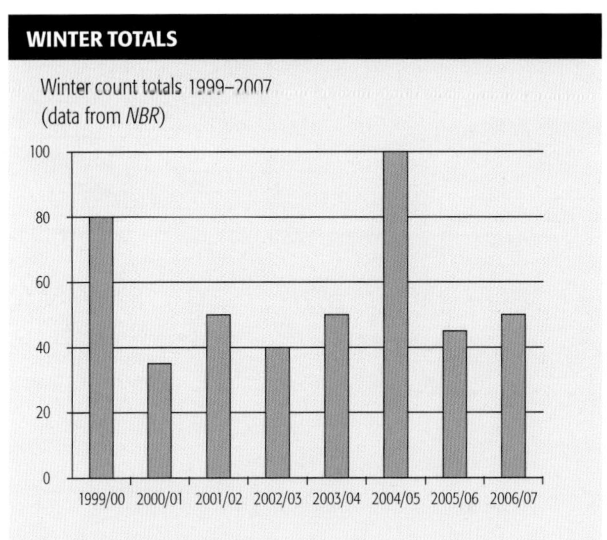

DAVID TIPLING

Common Scoter
Melanitta nigra

NBA 1999–2007	SUMMER: ALL / BREEDING	WINTER
TETRADS OCCUPIED	22 (2%) / none	37 (3%)
SUMMER/WINTER ONLY	10	25
MEAN PER OCCUPIED TETRAD	526 / none	1,193
SUMMED MAX COUNTS	11,565 / none	44,151
POPULATION ESTIMATE	3,000–4,500 individuals	5,000–6,000

PREVIOUS ATLASES	SQUARES OCCUPIED	1999–2007	LOSSES	GAINS
1981–84 WINTER (10 KM)	12 (19%)	14 (23%)	3	5
1988–91 (10 KM)	1 (2%)	none	1	0

THE ALL-DARK Common Scoter is the most numerous seaduck to visit Norfolk and, although predominantly a winter visitor, it is present offshore in every month of the year.

Common Scoter are highly gregarious and spend the winter months in flocks known as 'rafts' in shallow offshore waters. These rafts are generally less than a couple of kilometres from land but at times too distant for shore-based observation. The species tends to favour sandy seabeds where it can feed on molluscs, principally the blue mussel. Thus the distribution map shows the Norfolk population stretching along the north coast from Hunstanton to Sheringham, with only small and often transitory flocks on the east coast. At all localities feeding flocks are typically mobile, drifting with the tide and wind, with groups constantly breaking and re-forming and small parties often taking short flights.

By January, it is usual that most of the smaller flocks have joined together to form loose rafts of several thousand birds, but the favoured sites may vary between winters; for example there were 6,000 off Holme in January 2001 but the following January the main flock, of 8,000, had formed in Holkham Bay. In other years, the main flock moves around the coast as winter progresses or in response to spells of strong onshore winds, for instance 7,000 off Cley in

DAVID TIPLING

December 2001 had relocated to Holkham Bay the following month. Of a British wintering population estimated at 50,000 (*APEP06*), Norfolk may host more than 10% by midwinter. Drakes tend to predominate along the northern North Sea coasts, while females and immatures are commoner among the Norfolk flocks.

The summer coastal distribution is effectively the same as in winter. In some years large flocks remain off the northwest coast well into the late spring, as occurred off Scolt Head in 2005 when 8,000 were present in April and 4,000 in May. Spring flocks presumably include both migrants heading for the breeding grounds in Fenno-Scandia and Russia and birds that will remain all summer, joined in moulting flocks as early as July by males and unsuccessful females returning from the breeding range.

> 'Common Scoter are highly gregarious and spend the winter months in flocks known as 'rafts' in shallow offshore waters.'

There were several records inland but most were made outside the NBA recording periods, with the majority between July and November. No inland birds stayed for more than a day, suggesting that they were simply resting during overland passage. While one or two were recorded each year, multiple sightings were noted on 6th April 2003, when there were 14 at Hockwold Washes and four at Fowl Mere in the southwest and eight at Ranworth Broad and a pair at Hickling Broad in the east of the county.

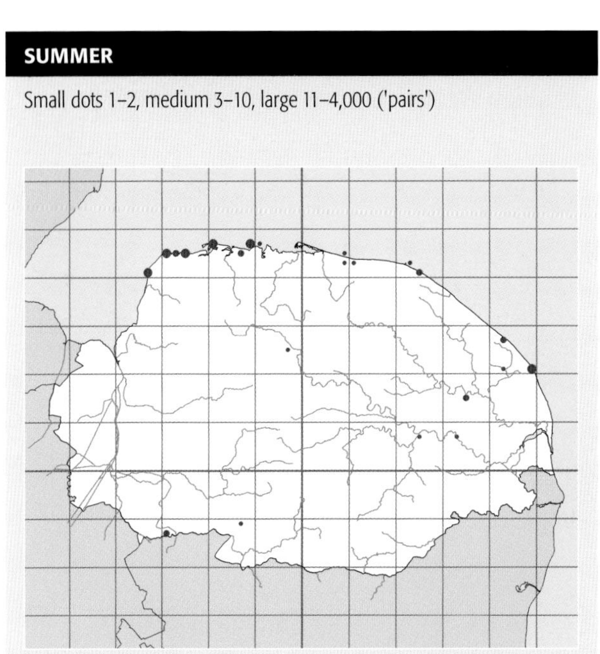

SUMMER

Small dots 1–2, medium 3–10, large 11–4,000 ('pairs')

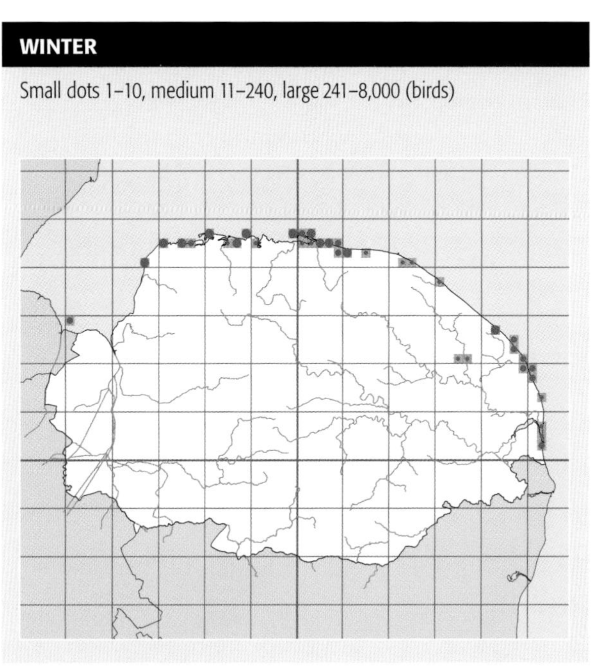

WINTER

Small dots 1–10, medium 11–240, large 241–8,000 (birds)

Velvet Scoter

Melanitta fusca

NBA 1999–2007	SUMMER: ALL / BREEDING	WINTER
TETRADS OCCUPIED	7 (<1%) / none	24 (2%)
SUMMER/WINTER ONLY	1	18
MEAN PER OCCUPIED TETRAD	3 / none	17
SUMMED MAX COUNTS	23 / none	415
POPULATION ESTIMATE	5–10 individuals	50–200

PREVIOUS ATLASES	SQUARES OCCUPIED	1999–2007	LOSSES	GAINS
1981–84 WINTER (10 KM)	10 (16%)	11 (18%)	3	4
1988–91 (10 KM)	1 (2%)	none	1	0

WHILE VELVET SCOTERS can easily be overlooked amongst a large raft of Common Scoters bobbing around on a turbulent sea, they do tend to remain in distinct subgroups and once in flight their white wing flashes make them very obvious. In distribution and behaviour the species is very similar to the Common Scoter but in Norfolk it is far less abundant.

The vast majority of Norfolk's Velvet Scoters are located among flocks of Common Scoters on the coastal stretch from Hunstanton to Weybourne. Normally few are reported from east Norfolk but up to 30 were present in the Horsey/Winterton area in December 2001.

Velvet Scoters tend to winter closer to their northern European breeding areas than do Common Scoters, and the proportion of Velvets in the flocks is accordingly much lower in Norfolk than on more northerly North Sea coasts. Peak numbers occur in late December or early January, although the actual number wintering in the county varies very widely from year to year, with only about 15 in 2000/01 compared with 150 the following winter.

ANDREW MOON

As for Common Scoter, the favoured localities may change from year to year. Notable counts during the NBA period included 120 in Holkham Bay in January 2002 and 59 off Titchwell in December 2004, with 68 off Titchwell in December 2005.

Velvet Scoters are surprisingly rare on inland waters in Britain, but a single drake was noted at Strumpshaw on 22nd January 2002. According to *Stevenson*, the species was not uncommon inland in hard weather during the 19th century.

Lingering parties of Velvet Scoters were recorded with Commons along the north Norfolk coast in April and May, with maximum counts of 15 at Holme on 11th May 2000 and 17 at Titchwell in April 2005. Summering is unusual, but one bird remained in the Holme/Titchwell area throughout June 2002.

WINTER

Small dots 1–4, medium 5–16, large 17–120 (birds)

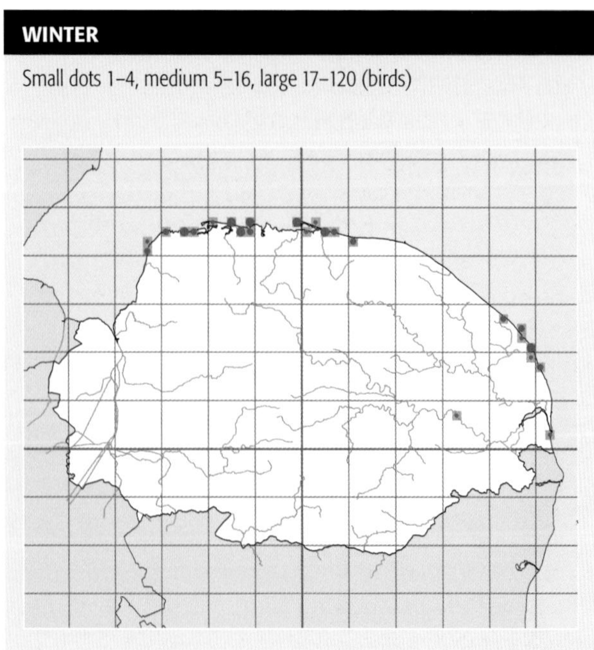

Goldeneye
Bucephala clangula

NBA 1999–2007	SUMMER: ALL/BREEDING	WINTER
TETRADS OCCUPIED	14 (1%) / none	106 (7%)
SUMMER/WINTER ONLY	3	95
MEAN PER OCCUPIED TETRAD	3 / none	13
SUMMED MAX COUNTS	40 / none	1,348
POPULATION ESTIMATE	5–10 individuals	350–400

PREVIOUS ATLASES	SQUARES OCCUPIED	1999–2007	LOSSES	GAINS
1981–84 WINTER (10 KM)	35 (56%)	34 (55%)	9	8
1988–91 (10 KM)	1 (2%)	none	1	0

EDMUND FELLOWES

THE GOLDENEYE IS ONE of the few wintering waterfowl that is equally at home on fresh or salt water, and consequently it has a relatively wide distribution within Norfolk. Goldeneyes are not especially gregarious and are found in small, loose groups rather than large flocks.

Although birds nest as close as Germany at similar latitudes to Norfolk, and the Scottish population is burgeoning, the county presently lies outside the Goldeneye's breeding range, and the species is primarily a winter visitor to Norfolk from Fenno-Scandia and Russia. The vast majority of those seen in the county are females or first-winters, as adult drakes tend to remain further north.

The NBA winter map shows their mixed maritime and inland distribution. The coastal stretch between Snettisham on the Wash and Blakeney in north Norfolk is, however, virtually the only part of the Norfolk coastline that hosts the species. Apart from flying migrants, very few are recorded around the northeast or east coasts of the county. By far the highest counts during the NBA winters were coastal, with maxima of 241 at Titchwell in January 2001 and 185 in the Scolt Head/Brancaster Harbour area in February 2003. The harbours at Thornham and Blakeney peaked at 92 and 87 respectively. Inland, Goldeneyes were recorded from a selection of favoured waters. In the Fens, the Great Ouse Relief Channel was a regular wintering haunt, as were the nearby gravel pits at Tottenhill and Pentney. In central Norfolk, the larger waters along the Wensum valley, such as Sennowe Park Lake, held double-figure counts in most winters, while in east Norfolk many of the Broads hosted small numbers of Goldeneyes. The highest inland counts were 52 at Hickling Broad, 43 on the Great Ouse RC and 40 at Tottenhill GP. In contrast, there are many inland waters in the county where Goldeneyes were surprisingly rare.

While a few Goldeneyes linger on occasion into May, the latest records in the four years 2002 to 2005 were all in the last week of April. There were two June records during the NBA period: one was at a small farm reservoir at Roydon (King's Lynn) in 2000 and a drake visited South Acre GP in 2001.

WINTER

Small dots 1–2, medium 3–12, large 13–241 (birds)

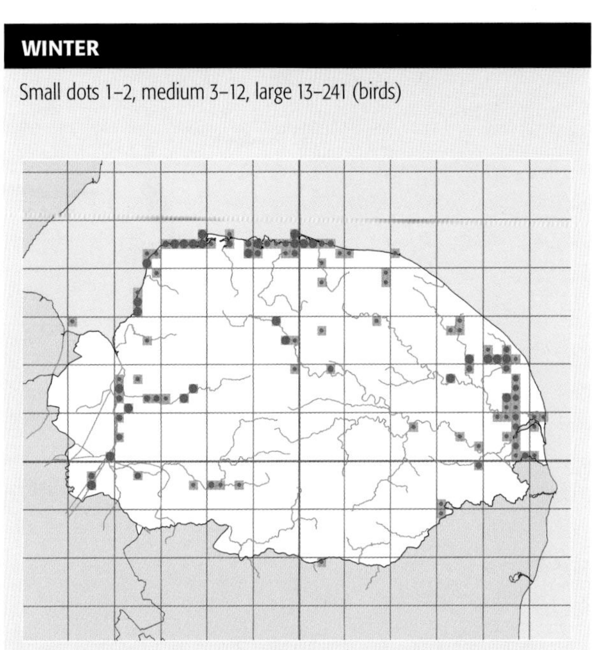

Smew

Mergellus albellus

NBA 1999–2007	SUMMER: ALL / BREEDING	WINTER
TETRADS OCCUPIED	5 (<1%) / none	49 (3%)
SUMMER/WINTER ONLY	1	45
MEAN PER OCCUPIED TETRAD	1 / none	2
SUMMED MAX COUNTS	5 / none	97
POPULATION ESTIMATE	0–1 individuals	5–30

PREVIOUS ATLASES	SQUARES OCCUPIED	1999–2007	LOSSES	GAINS
1981–84 WINTER (10 KM)	13 (21%)	29 (47%)	2	18

WINTERING SMEWS, from their breeding grounds in Finland and the Russian taiga, are widely but thinly distributed in Britain, with highest densities in southeastern counties. Finding a handsome adult drake is surely one of the highlights of a Norfolk winter.

In Norfolk Smews favour fairly large areas of freshwater, where they can pursue their underwater prey, often in the company of Goosanders and Goldeneyes, although they tend to remain in the shallows and close to emergent vegetation. While birds often occur singly, small flocks may

DAVID TIPLING

be found on a few favoured stretches of water. Two localities, Tottenhill GP and Hickling Broad, hosted Smews in every winter during the NBA period. At the former site, where Smews were often present intermittently over a period of several weeks, a maximum of eight birds were recorded in January 2001. During the winter, Smews are often highly mobile, visiting different waters, and the Tottenhill birds were also frequently relocated on the Great Ouse Relief Channel, in the Wiggenhall St Mary Magdalen area. Similarly the Hickling Broad Smews tend to move around the area, visiting Horsey Mere and other waters in the northern Broads. During the NBA period, the highest count in Broadland was of ten at Hickling, also in January 2001.

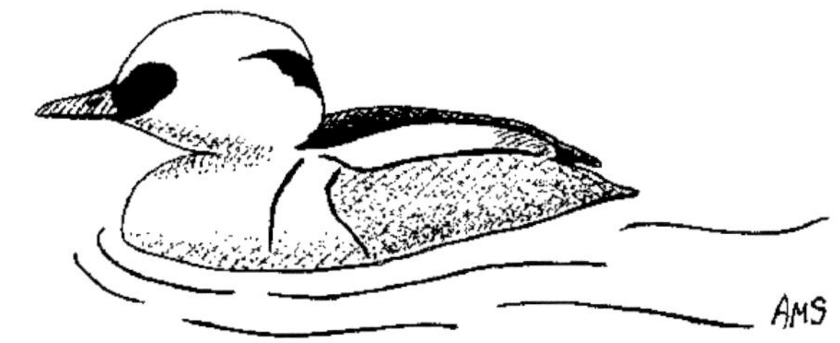

'Influxes of Smews take place in harder weather, mainly in January, presumably as birds are displaced from the near Continent.'

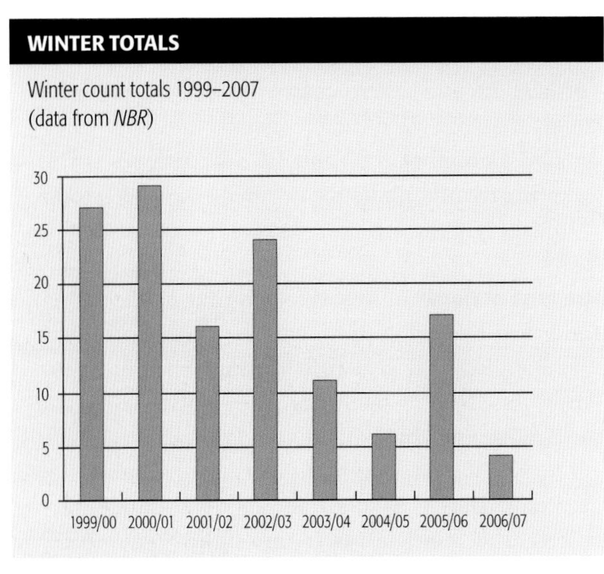

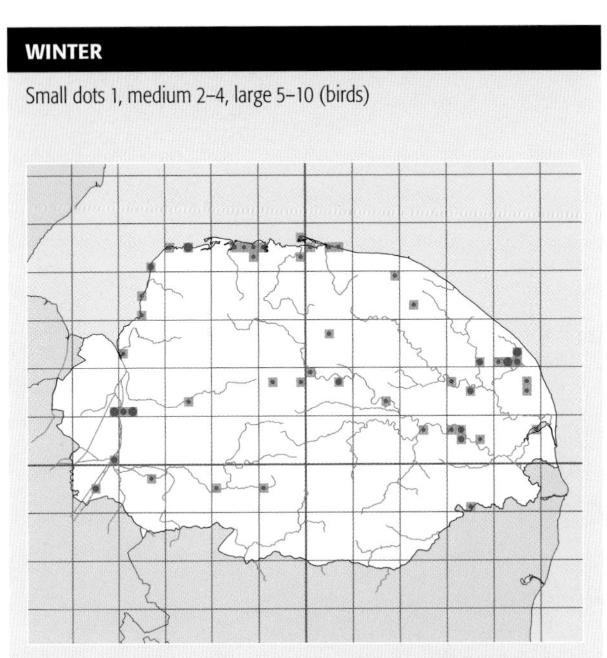

The map shows that as well as these concentrations in the Fens and the Broads, smaller numbers were also reported from coastal pits along the eastern side of the Wash and the sheltered harbours and freshwater reserves in north Norfolk. Many of the inland sightings were made at old gravel workings, those in the middle of the county being concentrated along the Wensum valley.

Influxes of Smews take place in harder weather, mainly in January, presumably as birds are displaced from the near Continent. Females and immatures invariably outnumbered adult drakes and in most winters only one or two adult drakes were reported. However, the two largest January influxes that occurred during the NBA winters, of 25 birds in 2000 and 26 in 2001, involved eight and six adult drakes respectively. An average of 19 Smews per winter was recorded during the NBA period, the counts varying from four to 29. Because the birds are so mobile, it is very difficult to avoid duplication of records in estimating the annual winter populations.

While most Smews have left the county by late February or early March, five stragglers were reported in April, three of which were adult drakes. Another adult drake appeared most unseasonably in June 2003 and toured several Norfolk sites: during its stay it visited Titchwell on 3rd, Welney on 5th, Lopham Fen on 6th–7th and Titchwell again during 8th–19th.

Red-breasted Merganser

Mergus serrator

NBA 1999–2007	SUMMER: ALL / BREEDING	WINTER
TETRADS OCCUPIED	7 (<1%) / none	49 (3%)
SUMMER/WINTER ONLY	1	43
MEAN PER OCCUPIED TETRAD	3 / none	20
SUMMED MAX COUNTS	20 / none	982
POPULATION ESTIMATE	0–5 individuals	100–200

PREVIOUS ATLASES	SQUARES OCCUPIED	1999–2007	LOSSES	GAINS
1981–84 WINTER (10 KM)	18 (29%)	18 (29%)	6	6

THE RED-BREASTED MERGANSER differs from its bulkier cousin the Goosander in being predominantly coastal in its Norfolk distribution.

Both *Stevenson* and *Riviere* described the Red-breasted Merganser as an irregular winter visitor, generally more frequent during periods of hard weather. Nowadays, however, it is fairly common, if rather localised. The bulk of the British breeding population is believed to winter around the coast close to the breeding areas (*Migration Atlas*), and it is thought that those wintering off the Norfolk coast are mainly of Fenno-Scandian and Baltic origin.

The map clearly shows a comparatively compact area of northwest Norfolk that holds the main concentration of birds, between Heacham and Blakeney, with very few recorded in the inner parts of the Wash and around the northeastern and eastern coasts. The only three-figure counts were of 150 in the Heacham/Hunstanton area on 23rd December 2000 and 122 off Titchwell the following month, no doubt involving the same groups of birds.

The vast majority of inland records during the NBA concerned Red-breasted Mergansers along the Fenland drains and rivers. Up to eight were present along the Great Ouse Relief Channel on 14th January 2000 and the river at Ten Mile Bank hosted up to five in January/February 2005. However, numbers involved have been far smaller than in earlier years, without doubt related to the series of mild winters throughout the

DAVID TIPLING

DAVID TIPLING

WINTER

Small dots 1–2, medium 3–10, large 11–150 (birds)

> 'The vast majority of inland records during the NBA concerned Red-breasted Mergansers along the Fenland drains and rivers.'

NBA recording period. There were singles inland in the Breydon Water area, and the furthest inland winter record in east Norfolk came from UEA Broad. A pair was present at Sparham GP on 6th April 2003.

The recent tendency for a few Red-breasted Mergansers to linger in coastal wintering sites into late spring and early summer continued during the NBA period. The highest counts in the summer period were 21 off Scolt Head on 3rd May 2000 and 17 in Blakeney Harbour on 1st May 2004. Occasional birds were reported in June, including a drake that summered at Breydon Water in 2000 and two off Titchwell on 26th June 2005.

Goosander
Mergus merganser

NBA 1999–2007	SUMMER: ALL / BREEDING	WINTER
TETRADS OCCUPIED	11 (<1%) / none	107 (7%)
SUMMER/WINTER ONLY	4	100
MEAN PER OCCUPIED TETRAD	1 / none	5
SUMMED MAX COUNTS	11 / none	513
POPULATION ESTIMATE	0–1 bp	80–150

PREVIOUS ATLASES	SQUARES OCCUPIED	1999-2007	LOSSES	GAINS
1968–72 (10 KM)	none	1 (2%)	0	1
1980–85 (TETRAD)	none	2 (<1%)	0	2
1980–85 (10 KM)	none	1 (2%)	0	1
1981–84 WINTER (10 KM)	25 (40%)	39 (63%)	3	17
1988–91 (10 KM)	none	1 (2%)	0	1

THE GOOSANDER is the largest of the sawbill ducks. During the summer it is a characteristic breeding bird of upland rivers, while in winter it frequents inland areas of open fresh water.

Spreading southwards from Scotland, the species first colonised England in 1941, since when it has

DAVID TIPLING

continued to expand its breeding range, especially in western England and in Wales. To Norfolk it is mostly a midwinter visitor, birds arriving mainly from Fenno-Scandia and the Baltic States in December and January.

In Norfolk, Goosanders frequent rivers, lakes, gravel pits and the Broads, especially favouring the Fenland drains. The NBA winter map clearly shows the concentration along the course of the River Ouse, where the highest numbers in the county are normally recorded. In January 2002 up to 45 were present on the Great Ouse Relief Channel, while 43 were counted at Denver Sluice in December 2005. As Goosanders prefer to fish in water that is no deeper than four metres (*1981–84 Winter Atlas*), they tend to move to the rivers by day, returning to the safety of old gravel workings, such as Pentney and Tottenhill, where the water is deeper, to roost at night. Other areas in the county that regularly hosted wintering Goosanders during the NBA period, with maximum counts, included Thetford Nunnery Lakes (26), the pools and gravel pits at Sparham (18) and UEA Broad (17). Elsewhere single-figure counts, generally involving only one or two birds, were the norm. Apart from birds in flight and clearly on migration, few were recorded around the coast.

British breeders probably do not move far from their natal areas in winter, but hard-weather movements and influxes into southern England involve both British and continental birds. During just such a spell of cold weather and snow in January and early February 2005, an influx of 100–120 Goosanders occurred in Norfolk, with records from many areas of open water within the county.

'To Norfolk it is mostly a midwinter visitor, birds arriving mainly from Fenno-Scandia and the Baltic States...'

Goosanders are rare birds in Norfolk during the summer, although there were at least three sightings in May/June 2005, including one at Potter Heigham from 6th May to early June. In Thetford, occasional summer sightings since the 1990s on the Thet and the Little Ouse culminated in observation of a brood of young in 2006, first seen and probably hatched in adjacent Suffolk, and finally in Norfolk's first proven breeding in 2007. In that year, a female appeared with eight newly hatched young on the Little Ouse near Thetford town centre on 17th May: at least five of these were raised to independence and could often be observed feeding with the tame ducks at Nuns' Bridges (Balmer 2008). These are the first breeding records for East Anglia.

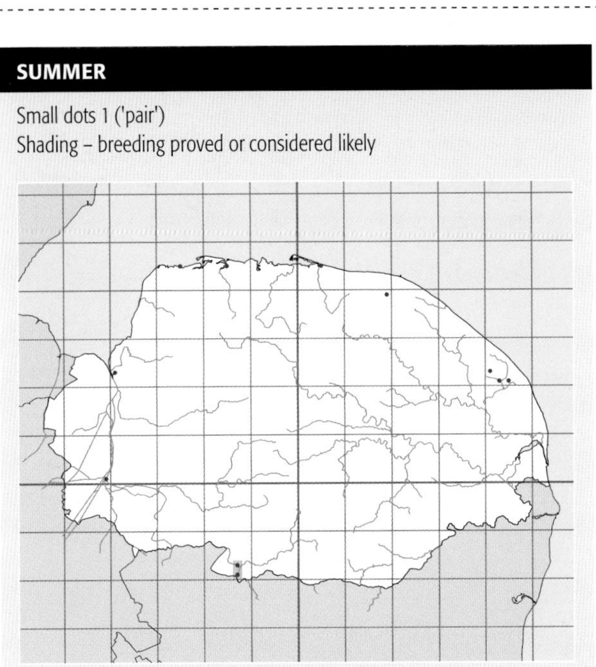

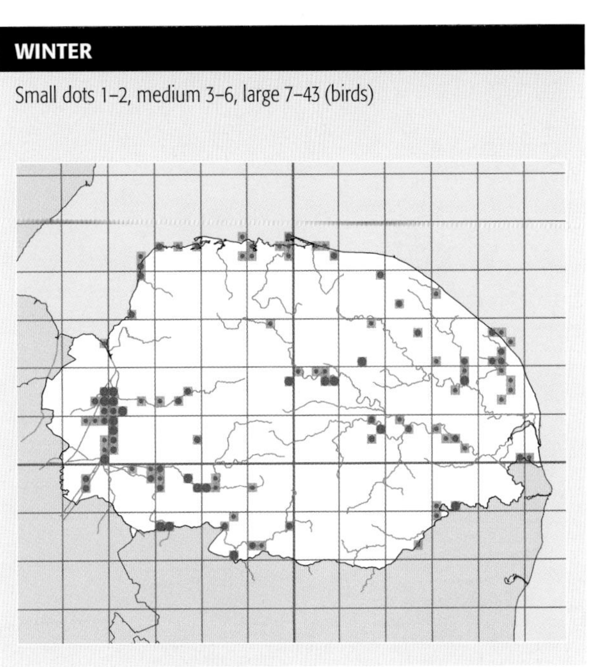

Ruddy Duck

Oxyura jamaicensis

NBA 1999–2007	SUMMER: ALL / BREEDING	WINTER
TETRADS OCCUPIED	68 (5%) / 21 (1%)	41 (3%)
SUMMER/WINTER ONLY	44	17
MEAN PER OCCUPIED TETRAD	2 / 4	5
SUMMED MAX COUNTS	166 / 83	189
POPULATION ESTIMATE	15–20 bp	40–50

PREVIOUS ATLASES	SQUARES OCCUPIED	1999–2007	LOSSES	GAINS
1968–72 (10 KM)	none	14 (23%)	0	14
1980–85 (TETRAD)	3 (<1%)	21 (1%)	3	21
1980–85 (10 KM)	3 (5%)	14 (23%)	3	14
1981–84 WINTER (10 KM)	3 (5%)	21 (34%)	1	19
1988–91 (10 KM)	5 (8%)	14 (23%)	4	13

THE RUDDY DUCK, with its distinctive silhouette and colours, has become a familiar bird to most Norfolk birdwatchers but, with the success of the ongoing cull, the species is currently in steep decline.

It was as recently as 1960 that North American Ruddy Ducks first began to breed regularly in England, following the release of full-winged young birds from the Slimbridge wildfowl collection in the 1950s. The species soon established a stronghold in the Midlands, from where

it expanded to colonise much of Britain. Breeding in the county was first confirmed in the Brecks at Stanford in 1988. The next definite breeding record was not until seven years later, but in the following years it slowly established itself as a scarce resident.

Ruddy Ducks first appear at their breeding sites in March and April, having spent the winter months in small flocks on larger, more open areas of water. During the summer they favour small, reed-fringed freshwater pools and meres, which are fairly shallow and have plenty of emergent vegetation, such as reeds, rushes and reed mace. It is here that the drake performs his bizarre 'bubbling' display and the floating nest is anchored amongst the reeds. Ruddy Ducks are extremely reluctant to fly, preferring to escape detection by diving, and in this and their nesting habits they are more similar to grebes than to other ducks.

The summer NBA map shows loose clusters of occupied tetrads, which conform to the habit of Ruddy Ducks breeding in small groups. The main concentrations were on the reserves along the north Norfolk coast, in Breckland and in the Broads, with up to eight pairs at Holme and

DAVID TIPLING

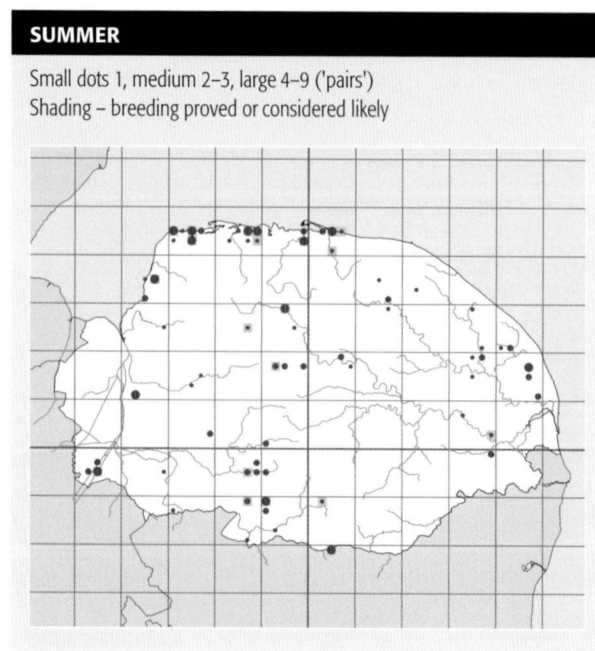

SUMMER

Small dots 1, medium 2–3, large 4–9 ('pairs')
Shading – breeding proved or considered likely

DAVID TIPLING

nine at the Holkham NNR. However, due to their habit of choosing small, often inaccessible pools on which to nest, and the fact that the ducklings remain hidden in the reeds for several weeks, proof of successful breeding was obtained in comparatively few tetrads. Breeding is often very late in the summer and the young may not appear until August or September, by when atlas fieldwork is generally over.

WINTER

Small dots 1, medium 2–3, large 4–35 (birds)

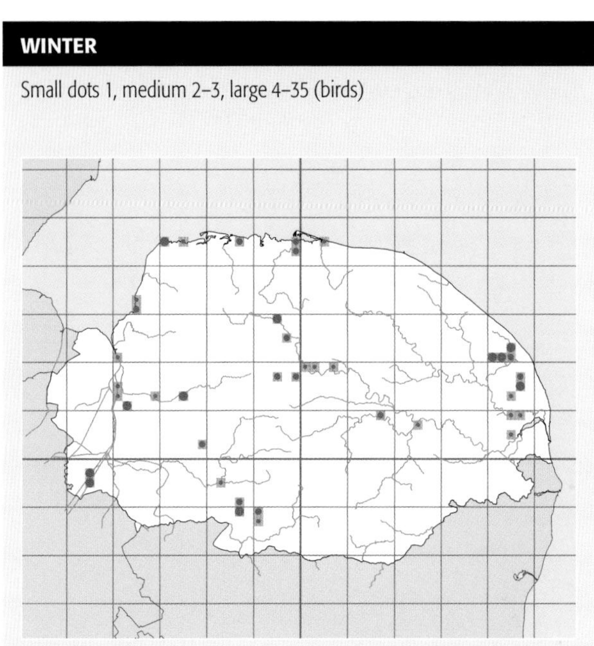

'Ruddy Ducks tend to breed later in the summer and the young may not appear until August or September.'

During NBA summers the number of breeding pairs reported in the county varied from nine to 22.

Ruddy Ducks fly almost exclusively at night and typically move undetected, after the breeding season, to larger, open areas of fresh water, where they remain in loose flocks throughout the winter. The winter map shows clusters of records in the Fens, Breckland, central Norfolk and the Broads, but the north coast was largely deserted at that season. During NBA winters, the largest gatherings were invariably at Tottenhill GP, where a county record of 35 was noted in December 2000. Other double-figure counts have been of up to 14 at Pentney GP, 18 at Welney, 13 at Fowl Mere, 15 at Pensthorpe and 11 at Hickling Broad. At this season, almost 40% fewer tetrads hosted the species than in the summer.

The control measures undertaken throughout Britain to protect European White-headed Ducks *Oxyura leucocephala* from this non-native invader are proving very successful. The NBA maps do not reflect the species' status in 2010, which is already that of a rare visitor to the county.

Red-legged Partridge
Alectoris rufa

NBA 1999–2007	SUMMER: ALL/BREEDING	WINTER
TETRADS OCCUPIED	1,306 (90%) / 1,277 (88%)	1,188 (81%)
SUMMER/WINTER ONLY	166	48
MEAN PER OCCUPIED TETRAD	6 / 6	19
SUMMED MAX COUNTS	8,236 / 8,191	22,059
POPULATION ESTIMATE	8,000–10,000 bp	50,000–80,000

PREVIOUS ATLASES	SQUARES OCCUPIED	1999–2007	LOSSES	GAINS
1968–72 (10 KM)	62 (all)	62 (all)		
1980–85 (TETRAD)	1,194 (82%)	1,277 (88%)	110	193
1980–85 (10 KM)	62 (all)	62 (all)		
1981–84 WINTER (10 KM)	62 (all)	62 (all)		
1988–91 (10 KM)	62 (all)	62 (all)		

THE RED-LEGGED PARTRIDGE was introduced from France into Britain during the 18th century but it was not until the early part of the 19th century that a self-sustaining population was established in Norfolk. By 1960, the species was already more numerous in the county than the Grey Partridge. Annual releases of young birds into shooting estates have increased more than eightfold in the UK since 1980, to around 6.5 million birds (PACEC 2006), and it is likely that the trend in Norfolk has been similar. Releases of the closely related Chukar *A. chukar* and of Chukar–Red-legged hydrids, once common in the county, have been illegal since 1992.

Red-legged favour drier situations than Grey Partridges and thus Norfolk, with its extensive agriculture, sandy and chalky soils and comparatively low rainfall, provides ideal conditions. Although they are commonest on agricultural land, especially where sugar beet is grown (*1988–91 Atlas*), they are also found in a wider variety of habitats than are Grey Partridges, including heathland, orchards, coastal dunes (such as Scolt Head and Blakeney Point), open areas of woodland, and even suburban parks and gardens. Being largely vegetarian and less dependent on insects, the species has coped better than Grey Partridges since the increased use of insecticide sprays on farms.

The NBA summer map shows an almost identical

SUMMER

Small dots 1–3, medium 4–7, large 8–51 ('pairs')
Shading – breeding proved or considered likely

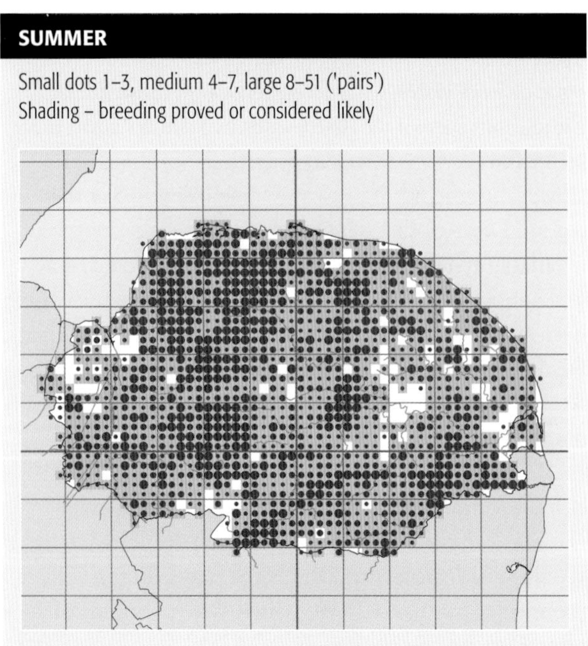

WINTER

Small dots 1–8, medium 9–20, large 21–200 (birds)

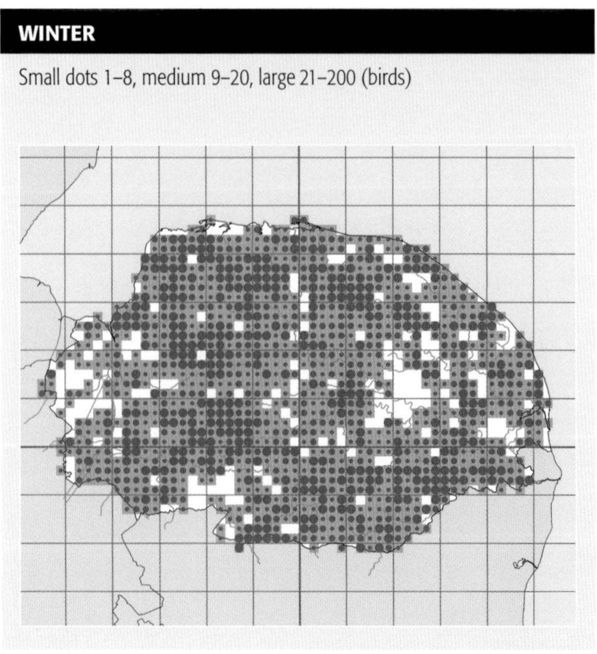

DAVID TIPLING

pattern to that obtained in the *1980–85 NBBS*, the only areas where the species was absent being in the more built-up areas of Norwich and parts of Broadland and Thetford Forest. Northwest Norfolk has many shooting estates and the NBA summer map confirms that this part of the county holds the highest concentration of breeding Red-legged Partridges. Breeding-season surveys carried out in 2003 located 396 pairs on Brancaster Thompson Farms and 229 on the West Barsham Estate. However, the highest count in a single tetrad was of 51 breeding pairs near Brettenham in the Brecks, while over 40 pairs were counted in two tetrads in the Wighton/Walsingham area of northwest Norfolk.

CHANGE SINCE 1980–85

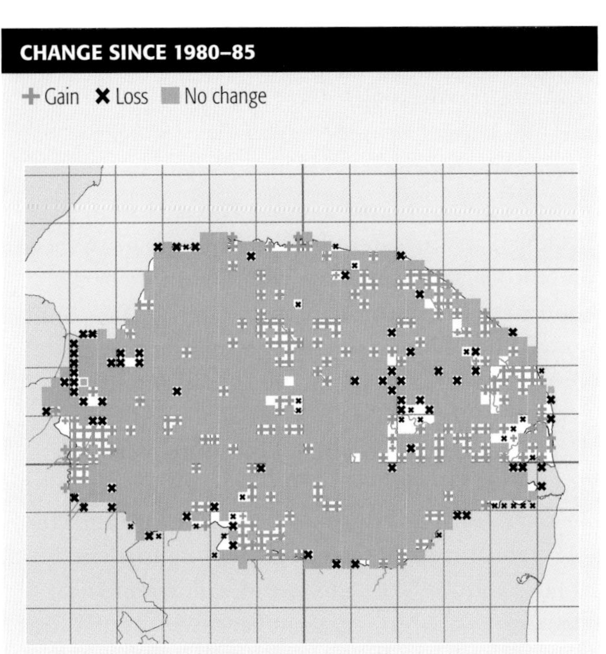

Data from the NBA summer fieldwork indicate that an average of six pairs of Red-legged Partridges were located in tetrads occupied by the species. Allowing for birds missed, this means that the county breeding population must be in excess of 8,000 pairs.

Red-legged Partridges are sedentary and the NBA winter map confirms a very similar widespread distribution to that during the summer. The three highest tetrad counts in winter (167–200) were all on the Shadwell estate, just to the east of Thetford but totals in excess of 100 were obtained from tetrads in all parts of the county.

Changes since the *1980–85 NBBS* are mostly infilling of breeding range, which is especially evident in the Fens west of Downham Market. Owing perhaps to changing patterns of releases, there are also a few tetrads from which the species has been lost.

Grey Partridge
Perdix perdix

NBA 1999–2007	SUMMER: ALL/BREEDING	WINTER
TETRADS OCCUPIED	602 (41%) / 572 (39%)	514 (35%)
SUMMER/WINTER ONLY	254	166
MEAN PER OCCUPIED TETRAD	3 / 3	8
SUMMED MAX COUNTS	1,578 / 1,546	4,196
POPULATION ESTIMATE	1,500–2,500	8,000–12,000

PREVIOUS ATLASES	SQUARES OCCUPIED	1999–2007	LOSSES	GAINS
1968–72 (10 KM)	62 (all)	62 (all)		
1980–85 (TETRAD)	542 (37%)	572 (39%)	259	289
1980–85 (10 KM)	60 (97%)	62 (all)	0	2
1981–84 WINTER (10 KM)	58 (94%)	62 (all)	0	4
1988–91 (10 KM)	60 (97%)	62 (all)	0	2

THE GREY PARTRIDGE is the most widespread partridge in the western Palaearctic, although the population has been declining throughout its range since the early 1950s (*BWP2*). In England, this has been one of the fastest-declining bird species, with a loss of 75% of breeding numbers during 1982–2007 alone (*Birdtrends*). Game-rearing practices favour the species' introduced competitors, the Pheasant and the Red-legged Partridge, and encourage the predators of ground-nesting birds, such as Carrion Crows. Pesticide use, however, has been the main cause of long-term decline.

Grey Partridges favour areas of grassland or other vegetation with patches or strips of taller, denser cover. Such conditions are found on fields of cereals and other crops, on grassy meadows and pastures, and on heaths and commons. The presence of a ready supply of insects is necessary for the survival of chicks during the first two weeks of their life. The use of herbicides has reduced the amount of non-crop vegetation on which the insects can feed, which in turn has adversely affected the survival of Grey Partridge chicks. Careful husbandry of Grey Partridge populations now includes the provision of unsprayed headlands around arable fields and the creation of beetle banks.

DAVID TIPLING

The NBA summer map clearly shows that Norfolk's Grey Partridge population is strongest in the northwest of the county, with smaller pockets of higher numbers in other cereal-growing areas. Indeed, the density of Grey Partridges in northwest Norfolk has been amongst the highest in the world due to specific conservation measures that have been put in place on many of the large shooting estates. The 375 pairs on the West Barsham estate in 2003 constituted the highest density of wild Grey Partridges in Britain.

During the NBA survey, declines were still being recorded in the Brecks and northwest Norfolk. For instance, at Warham only 91 breeding pairs were present in 2000 compared with 500 in 1994. In contrast, a managed estate in the west of the county noted a doubling of the number of breeding pairs from 30 in 2004 to 64 in 2005, resulting in an autumn count of 323 Grey Partridges. All 25 tetrads with double-figure counts of breeding pairs were in northwest Norfolk, with maximum counts of 36 and 24 pairs south of Fring and 23 pairs near Flitcham.

Winter coveys of Grey Partridges consist largely of family groups, the adults and young remaining together until breaking up in February as territories become established. These coveys usually comprise

DAVID TIPLING

SUMMER

Small dots 1, medium 2–3, large 4–36 ('pairs')
Shading – breeding proved or considered likely

WINTER

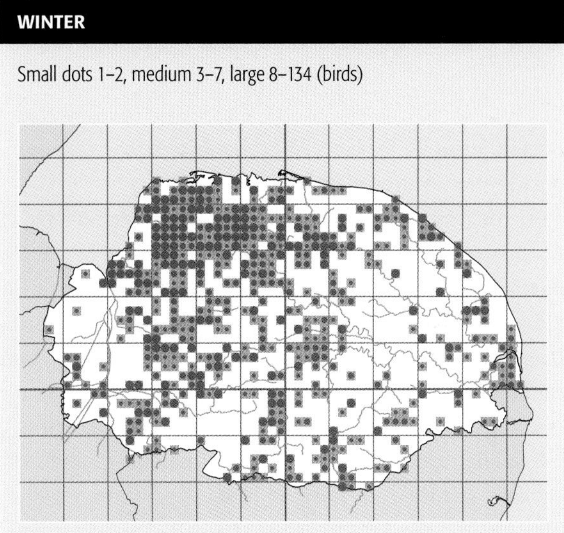
Small dots 1–2, medium 3–7, large 8–134 (birds)

CHANGE SINCE 1980–85

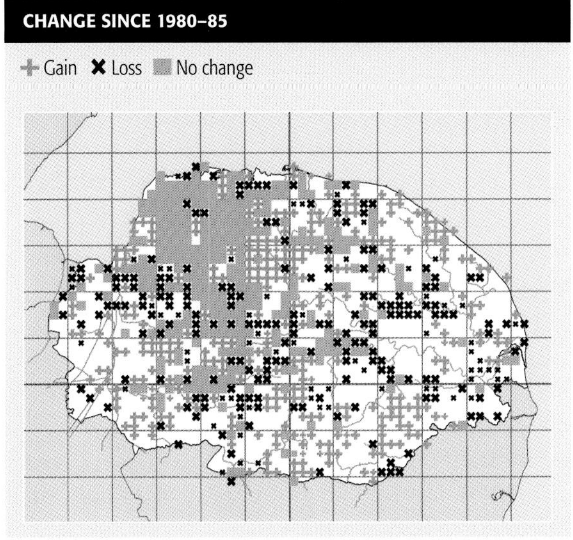
+ Gain ✖ Loss ■ No change

'Careful husbandry of Grey Partridge populations now includes the provision of unsprayed headlands around arable fields and the creation of beetle banks.'

up to about 15 birds, although a single covey of 30 birds was recorded on Massingham Heath. Grey Partridges are one of the most sedentary birds in Britain, some pairs spending their entire life in the same few fields (*1981–84 Winter Atlas*). Therefore it is not surprising that the NBA winter and summer maps show a very similar pattern of distribution, with the northwestern quarter of Norfolk most favoured. The three tetrads with the highest winter counts were the same as in the summer, holding 134, 98 and 81 birds respectively, and all of the 22 tetrads in which 27 or more Grey Partridges were recorded were situated in northwest Norfolk.

It is encouraging that there has been no overall loss of range since previous atlases: in fact a slight increase in occupied squares has been recorded, perhaps partly the result of more thorough coverage for NBA in some parts of the county than in the earlier surveys. Grey Partridges are most easily and most accurately surveyed from a vehicle at dawn or dusk, whereas counts carried out on foot may miss up to three-quarters of the birds present.

Quail

Coturnix coturnix

NBA 1999–2007	SUMMER: ALL / BREEDING	WINTER
TETRADS OCCUPIED	117 (8%) / 36 (2%)	3 (<1%)
SUMMER/WINTER ONLY	114	none
MEAN PER OCCUPIED TETRAD	1 / 2	1
SUMMED MAX COUNTS	162 / 72	3
POPULATION ESTIMATE	20–50 singing males	0–1

PREVIOUS ATLASES	SQUARES OCCUPIED	1999–2007	LOSSES	GAINS
1968–72 (10 KM)	17 (27%)	24 (39%)	9	16
1980–85 (TETRAD)	38 (3%)	36 (2%)	34	32
1980–85 (10 KM)	20 (32%)	24 (39%)	10	14
1981–84 WINTER (10 KM)	none	2 (3%)	0	2
1988–91 (10 KM)	24 (39%)	24 (39%)	15	15

ABBIE MARLAND

SCARCE, IRRUPTIVE, AND rarely seen, the Quail is one of Norfolk's most enigmatic birds.

Formerly a common and widespread species in Britain, it sustained a major decline during the first half of the 19th century, followed by a partial recovery from the 1940s onward. Nowadays, its numbers are limited by agricultural intensification and by hunting pressure while on migration through the Mediterranean region. Larger numbers occur in some years, but the reasons for these influxes are not fully understood. Many that reach Britain are thought to be birds that have already bred in southern Europe, or are young raised there earlier in the season, riding the wave of ripening crops that moves northwards across Europe in summer. Such birds do not arrive in Britain until late June or July, when time may be too short to raise another brood.

Records of Quail are overwhelmingly of males giving their distinctive, ventriloquial call, but such records are very difficult to interpret. Persistent calling may be a sign that a male is unpaired, rather than that it is nesting, whereas a bird that is no longer heard may be mated – but more likely it has moved on. The presence of one or two calling birds also acts as an attraction to other later-arriving migrants and so concentrations of birds may form. There is no easy way to census these birds, however; observers must take full account of the birds' potential for movement between bouts of calling, and the distance over which the call can be heard, or numbers are very likely to be overstated.

'Records of Quail are overwhelmingly of males giving their distinctive call.'

During the breeding season, Quail favour wide open spaces with few trees and bushes, and so are most often located in large cultivated fields, especially those planted with winter wheat and clover, and in hay fields. The NBA summer map is naturally a reflection of the localities in which Quail were heard and in only a few instances was breeding proven. It shows a very sparse and scattered distribution but with a small concentration of birds in north Norfolk, especially on the drier chalk soil in the northwest of the county. The large cereal fields in the Choseley area are one of the most reliable sites in Norfolk for hearing Quail during the summer months. In one of the Choseley tetrads, up to ten calling Quail could be heard in the influx year of 2002, while four or five were also present in tetrads at Holme, Sheringham and Feltwell. Even more Quail were recorded in 2005 with 62 males reported from 47 sites, many of which called for extended periods.

Ten Mile Bank hosted four or five between mid May and early September, while one or two were present at Burnham Market from mid May to late July. Surveys of Quail in northwest Norfolk in recent years have shown that males are most vocal just before darkness falls and during the two hours prior to dawn, the birds becoming quiet at the first glimmer of light. On a single night in June 2006, a total of 26 singing males was estimated at Choseley, far more than in any daytime counts.

As the map is a compilation of records made over an eight-year period, it gives a false impression of the distribution of the species in any one year. The number of calling males reported annually varied from 14 to 66 at 11 to 47 localities.

During the 19th century, Quail were present fairly frequently in Norfolk in winter. In recent years, however, it has been a rarity at this time of year with just four records between 1986 and 1997. During the NBA period, there were five reports of Quail between December and January, twice at Sheringham in different winters and once each at Titchwell, Choseley and Brancaster, while up to four flushed during shoots near Sedgeford in November may have overwintered.

The change map is influenced by the lack of any good 'Quail years' during the *1980–85 NBBS*. For a species so erratic in its occurrence it would be unwise to draw any conclusions about range change from comparisons with the previous atlases.

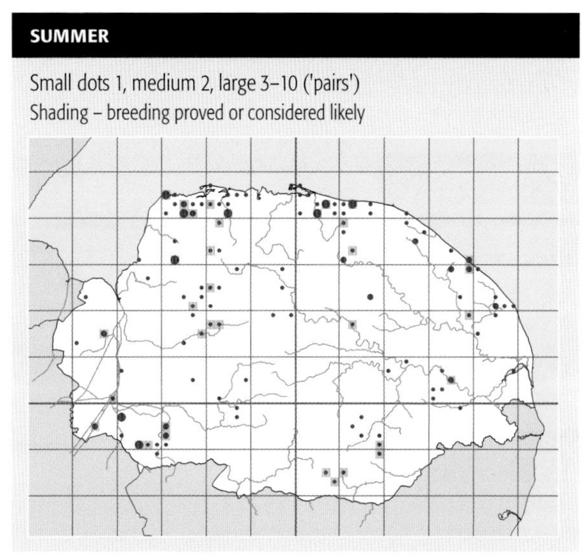

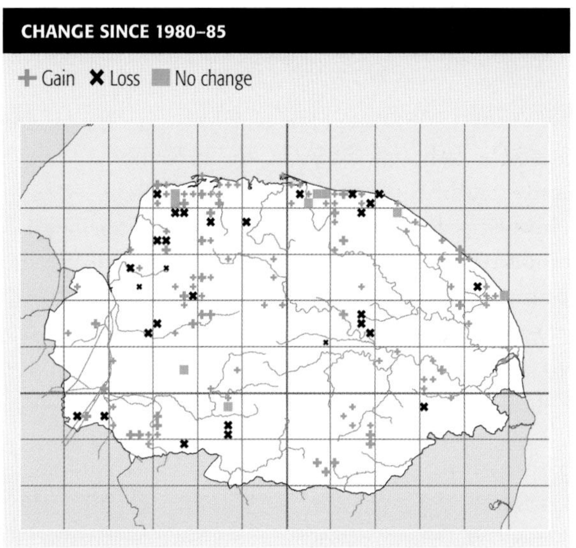

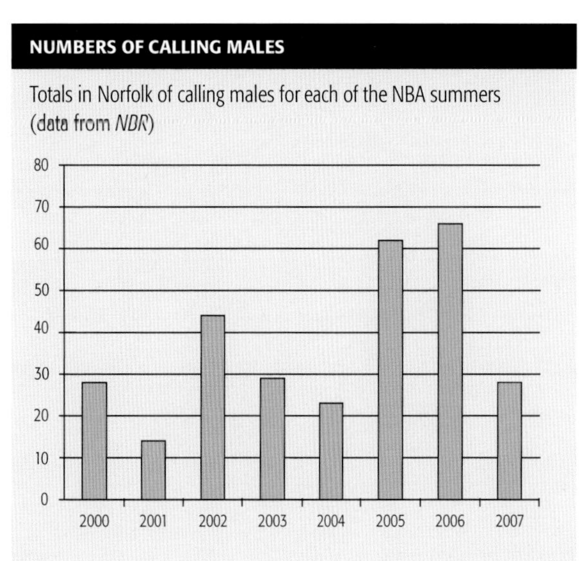

Pheasant

Phasianus colchicus

NBA 1999–2007	SUMMER: ALL/BREEDING	WINTER
TETRADS OCCUPIED	1,390 (95%) / 1,357 (93%)	1,384 (95%)
SUMMER/WINTER ONLY	35	29
MEAN PER OCCUPIED TETRAD	14 / 14	19
SUMMED MAX COUNTS	19,600 / 19,514	26,770
POPULATION ESTIMATE	20,000–30,000 bp	100,000–150,000

PREVIOUS ATLASES	SQUARES OCCUPIED	1999–2007	LOSSES	GAINS
1968–72 (10 KM)	62 (all)	62 (all)		
1980–85 (TETRAD)	1,338 (92%)	1,357 (93%)	54	73
1980–85 (10 KM)	62 (all)	62 (all)		
1981–84 WINTER (10 KM)	62 (all)	62 (all)		
1988–91 (10 KM)	62 (all)	62 (all)		

INTRODUCED BY THE Normans into England almost a thousand years ago, the Pheasant had become well established by the end of the 16th century. Nowadays, Pheasant shooting is big business, with around 35 million poults being released into Britain's countryside each autumn (PACEC 2006). Norfolk has many large shooting estates and it is likely, scaling down from the national figure, that around a million young Pheasants are released annually in the county. For a brief period in autumn, therefore, it is by far the most numerous bird in the county.

The maps demonstrate just how widespread the species is in Norfolk, the Pheasant being, as it was in the *1980–85 NBBS*, the second most widespread non-passerine species after the Woodpigeon. Pheasants inhabit wooded agricultural land and parkland, being found particularly along woodland edges, with the nests generally being along hedgerows or in the periphery of woods. This is reflected in the relative abundance throughout the county, with the highest concentrations in the cereal-growing areas in northwest and southeast Norfolk, and not surprisingly a total absence from the centre of Norwich.

Because of hand-reared releases, predator control and the planting of game cover, shooting estates hold the highest numbers, as is illustrated by a spring count of 3,000 on the Brancaster Thompson farms in 2000. However, naturalised self-supporting populations do exist in the county, as at Scolt Head, where 25 males and 13 broods were counted in 2005. The highest counts of pairs in single tetrads, based on counts of males, were 82 at Woodton and 81 at Shernborne.

The spatial and temporal variations in the plumages

SUMMER

Small dots 1–8, medium 9–16, large 17–82 ('pairs')
Shading – breeding proved or considered likely

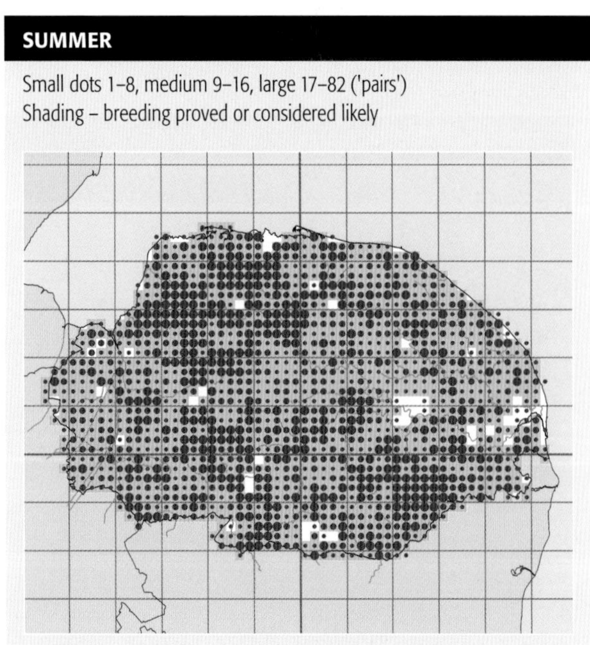

WINTER

Small dots 1–8, medium 9–19, large 20–320 (birds)

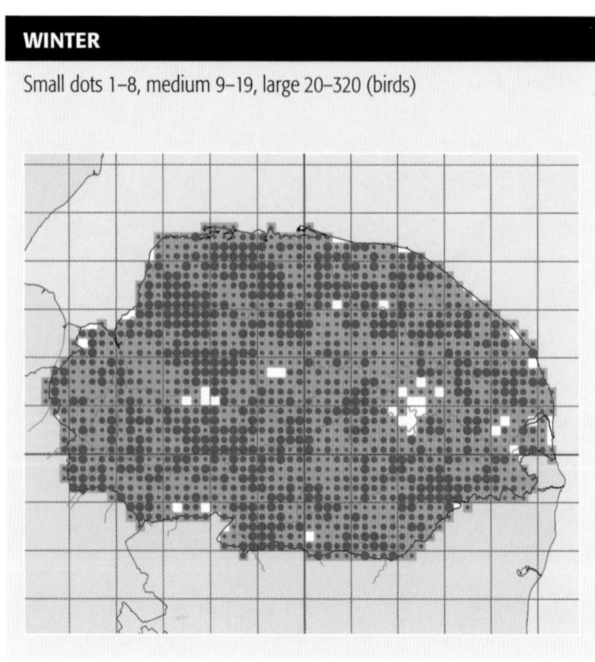

DAVID TIPLING

of Pheasants across the county presumably reflect fashions among managers of shooting estates and the commercial choices that are available to them. In the Shadwell area near Thetford, for example, most males were the type often known as 'Manchurian' in the hatchery catalogues, with extensive powder-blue rumps and much white on the head. During the NBA years, 'Melanistic Mutant' or '*tenebrosus*' Pheasants, which appear black at a distance, became prevalent at an increasing range of locations, and were sometimes reported as Japanese Pheasants *P. versicolor*. Often, releases deliberately include one or two white birds. Away from shooting estates, copper-backed, green-headed males are the norm, with or without the white neck-ring, and it is these that constitute the bulk of the breeding population.

CHANGE SINCE 1980–85

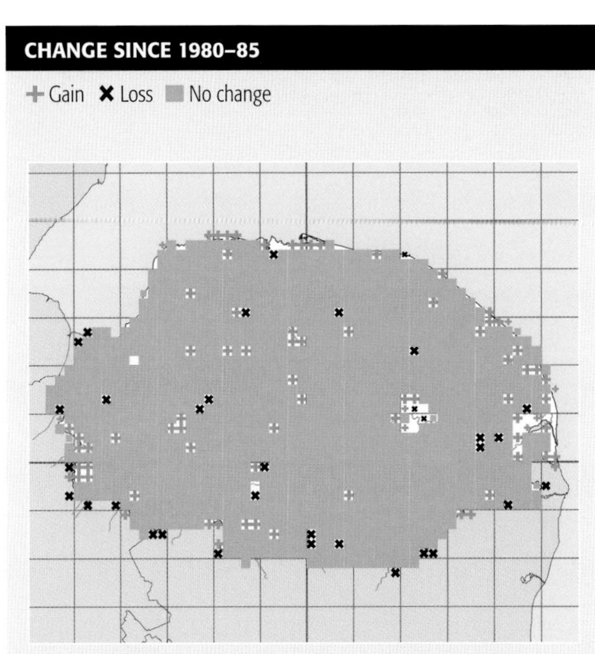

As a resident species, the winter distribution of Pheasants is almost identical to that in the summer, as illustrated by the NBA maps. The species is susceptible to windy, wet and cold weather, and so Pheasants remain in or near sheltered woodland during the winter months. They also inhabit swampy reedbeds. Pheasants tend to be more gregarious during the early months of the winter, although there is a tendency for the two sexes to remain separate. Strips of maize and other seed-rich plants, designed as game cover, shelter the species and also benefit other farmland birds such as finches and buntings. Pheasants are also attracted to recently ploughed fields. All three tetrads in which the winter count exceeded 300 were in the Brettenham area of the Brecks.

The change map indicates that almost all of the tetrads lacking Pheasants in 1980–85 have since been filled. The only parts of the county where Pheasants remained absent were the more urban areas in Norwich and some exposed stretches of the Norfolk coastline; even the Halvergate Marshes hosted a few pairs.

Golden Pheasant

Chrysolophus pictus

NBA 1999–2007	SUMMER: ALL/BREEDING	WINTER
TETRADS OCCUPIED	28 (2%) / 23 (2%)	22 (2%)
SUMMER/WINTER ONLY	18	12
MEAN PER OCCUPIED TETRAD	3 / 3	3
SUMMED MAX COUNTS	72 / 67	66
POPULATION ESTIMATE	20–35 bp	60–80

PREVIOUS ATLASES	SQUARES OCCUPIED	1999–2007	LOSSES	GAINS
1968–72 (10 KM)	11 (18%)	6 (10%)	6	1
1980–85 (TETRAD)	48 (3%)	23 (2%)	35	10
1980–85 (10 KM)	11 (18%)	6 (10%)	6	1
1981–84 WINTER (10 KM)	8 (13%)	10 (16%)	1	3
1988–91 (10 KM)	8 (13%)	6 (10%)	3	1

A MALE GOLDEN PHEASANT, with its dazzling red, orange and yellow plumage, and long, decurved tail, is unmistakable. Despite its bright colours, however, it is easily missed as it slips through dark, tangled undergrowth.

Introduced from central China into Breckland in the late 1880s, Golden Pheasant has retained this stronghold, although numbers have fallen considerably in recent years. In the 1950s, up to 100 were recorded together in Thetford Forest, and by the mid 1960s parties of up to 60 were present in the Hockham/West Tofts area. Since then a decline has occurred, although at the time of the *1980–85 NBBS*, Golden Pheasants were still occupying 48 Norfolk tetrads.

The species' habitat in Breckland is almost exclusively dense, unbrashed coniferous plantations, 10–30 years old. Trees of this age form a dense canopy and allow very little light to enter, as a result there is no ground flora, and this creates the perfect habitat for Golden Pheasants to forage for the insects on which they feed. Cropping rotations within Thetford Forest mean that the locations occupied by Golden Pheasants necessarily change there over time. At East Wretham NR, however, birds are found regularly in blackthorn thickets. At Sandringham, where introductions were made in about 1967, birds find similar bare ground within dense clumps of rhododendron. The estate is making laudable attempts, however, to reduce the coverage of this plant, also from China, which is classed as an alien invasive.

Both summer and winter maps show a main cluster of occupied tetrads to the east and northeast of Thetford, with a smaller area of occupation near Sandringham. It should be borne in mind that these

SUMMER

Small dots 1, medium 2–4, large 5–11 ('pairs')
Shading – breeding proved or considered likely

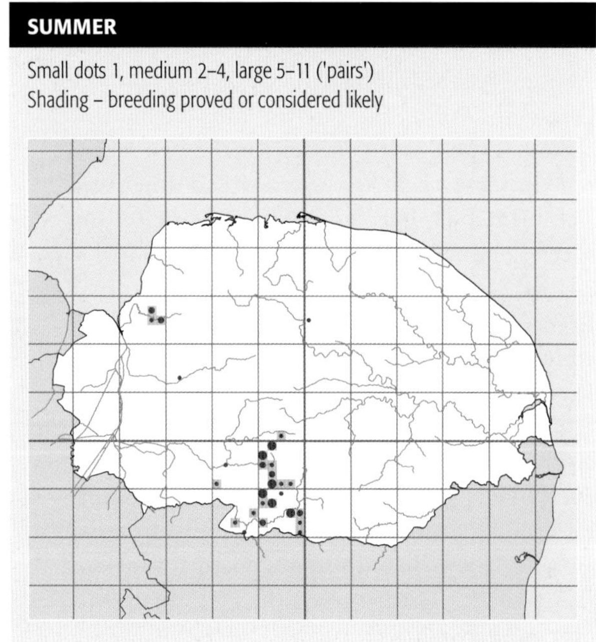

WINTER

Small dots 1, medium 2–5, large 6–14 (birds)

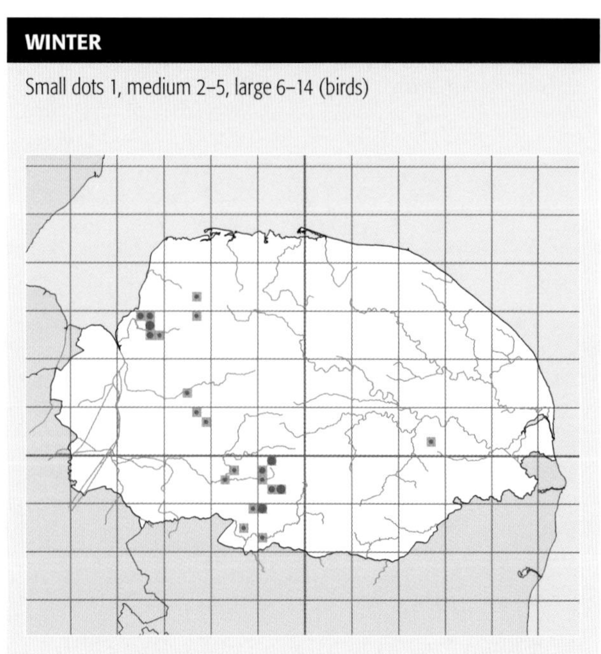

GARY THOBURN

records have been accumulated over an eight-year period from December 1999, and might over-represent the Thetford Forest distribution in any one year.

The most popular sites at which to find Golden Pheasants remain Wayland Wood and Wolferton triangle, and these were the two sites recording the highest counts during the NBA: Wayland Wood held 14 in 2001 and 11 in 2002, and Wolferton eight in 2003. Golden Pheasants are the commonest ornamental pheasant kept in captivity and are thought to be very sedentary. Odd records away from the regular sites almost certainly relate to birds that have escaped from collections, therefore, as surely was a male that frequented a small garden on the outskirts of Thetford for a couple of weeks from late January 2005.

CHANGE SINCE 1980–85

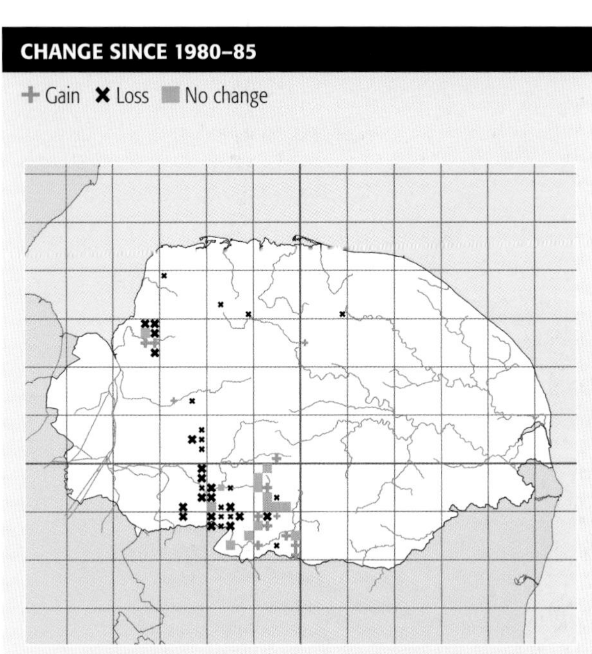

As has been alluded to, Golden Pheasants are far from easy to detect due to their secretive behaviour and the impenetrable habitat they frequent. Many of the records made during the NBA related to males giving their harsh, piercing, deer-like calls. Females are far less frequently seen. In summer, this may be at least in part due to the female remaining on the nest continuously during incubation, leaving neither to eat nor to drink; as a result, she may become covered in spiders' webs (*1988–91 Atlas*)!

The change map shows an interesting pattern of distribution changes in the Sandringham area. Losses west of Thetford have been severe, but some range gain has been noted since 1980–85 in the eastern part of Thetford Forest.

The reasons for the recent decline are not understood (Balmer *et al* 1996). Suggestions have included the cessation of large-scale releases, in-breeding, predation by foxes and a reduction in suitable habitat. Whatever the causes, the Golden Pheasant would be a suitable species for research, as the only viable populations in the wild are in Britain and China, where it is now rare.

Red-throated Diver
Gavia stellata

NBA 1999–2007	SUMMER: ALL/BREEDING	WINTER
TETRADS OCCUPIED	8 (<1%) / none	67 (5%)
SUMMER/WINTER ONLY	3	62
MEAN PER OCCUPIED TETRAD	1 / none	31
SUMMED MAX COUNTS	8 / none	2,053
POPULATION ESTIMATE	0–2 individuals	400–600

PREVIOUS ATLASES	SQUARES OCCUPIED	1999–2007	LOSSES	GAINS
1981–84 WINTER (10 KM)	17 (27%)	17 (27%)	4	4

THE RED-THROATED Diver is the smallest of the three divers that winters off the Norfolk coast, and is by far the most numerous. Birds arrive throughout the autumn, from their freshwater breeding lakes in Scotland and Scandinavia, and winter on tidal, inshore waters.

The map shows that the highest concentrations are found off northeast Norfolk, between Blakeney Point and Winterton. This contrasts with the situation in the 19th century, when hundreds gathered around the herring shoals off Great Yarmouth (*Stevenson*), although the Suffolk coast still holds many hundreds of birds in some winters. Red-throateds are far more numerous in winter than the other divers and feed in loose flocks scattered over a large area of sea. The counting of individual birds is thus not easy,

DAVID TIPLING

particularly in choppy water and when the birds are feeding several kilometres offshore. Once they are at this range, they become impossible to see while swimming and their presence is only apparent once they take flight. On occasion there is an almost constant movement of groups of divers flying to and fro, indicating considerable mobility between sites.

Numbers also fluctuate in response to weather conditions. Onshore winds and rolling seas often produce the highest numbers, as the divers are attracted to sprats and the smaller flatfish, which are also feeding on the sandeels and crustaceans disturbed from the seabed (*1981–84 Winter Atlas*). There is often a marked longshore passage of divers, as birds readjust, having drifted with the current.

The total of Red-throated Divers estimated to be present on the sea from December to February between Blakeney Point and Happisburgh has been remarkably constant, averaging 375 annually from 2000 to 2005 (*NBR*). Maximum site counts have included 200 off Mundesley in January 2001 and 250 off Overstrand in January 2002, and further south 250 off Sea Palling and 400 off Winterton in December 2000. Few of the counts that exceeded 50 were made on set visits to tetrads. It would appear that the average winter population of Red-throated Divers in waters off the Norfolk coast is in the range 400–600.

WINTER

Small dots 1-2, medium 3-12, large 13-400 (birds)

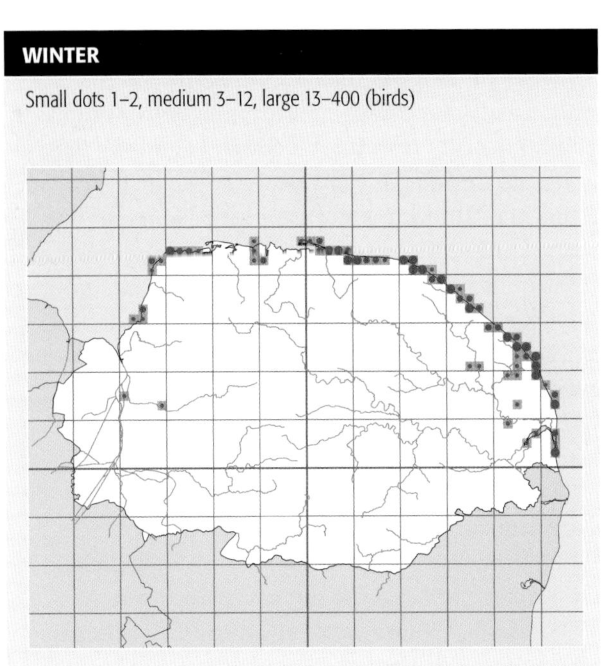

DAVID TIPLING

'The vast majority of Red-throated Divers have left Norfolk waters by April and only a few remain over the summer period.'

Stevenson commented that, during the 19th century, Red-throated Divers were less frequently found inland than the other two species of diver, the reverse of the situation that applies in Norfolk today. Most remain within a few miles of the coast, however, and in south Norfolk the larger species may still predominate – as they do in most inland English counties, despite the Red-throated being far more abundant overall. During NBA winters, ten single Red-throated Divers were recorded inland, seven in Broadland and the others at Saddlebow Relief Channel and Nar Valley Fisheries, where one made an extended stay from 21st February to 16th April 2004. Some inland records involve birds that may not be fully fit, for instance being lightly oiled.

The vast majority of Red-throated Divers have left Norfolk waters by April and only a few were recorded during the NBA summer recording period, even as late as June. However, four birds during the summer period were recorded well inland, all in April.

Black-throated Diver

Gavia arctica

NBA 1999–2007	SUMMER: ALL / BREEDING	WINTER
TETRADS OCCUPIED	5 (<1%) / none	22 (2%)
SUMMER/WINTER ONLY	1	18
MEAN PER OCCUPIED TETRAD	1 / none	2
SUMMED MAX COUNTS	5 / none	38
POPULATION ESTIMATE	0–1 individuals	5–10

PREVIOUS ATLASES	SQUARES OCCUPIED	1999–2007	LOSSES	GAINS
1981–84 WINTER (10 KM)	8 (13%)	13 (21%)	0	5

THE BLACK-THROATED DIVER is intermediate in size and structure between the Red-throated and Great Northern Divers. Although it is the least numerous of the three divers around British coasts in winter, in Norfolk it occurs at about the same frequency as the Great Northern Diver. Peak numbers are recorded in Norfolk in October and November as birds pass through the North Sea from their breeding sites, mainly in Fenno-Scandia and Russia.

Despite an increase in records in Norfolk since the late 1970s (due in part, no doubt, to more observers, improved identification skills and better optical equipment), Black-throated Divers still average fewer than ten birds per winter.

WINTER

Small dots 1, medium 2, large 3–5 (birds)

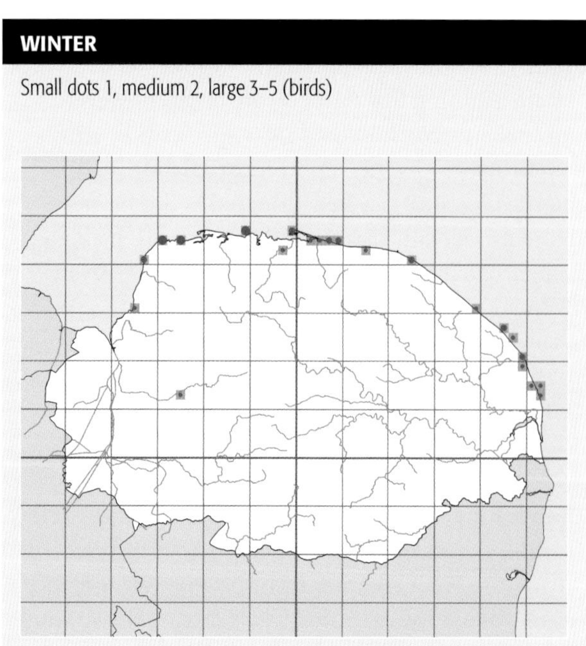

Compared with Red-throated Divers, the map clearly shows that the majority of Black-throated Divers are found on the coastal waters of north Norfolk between Hunstanton and Sheringham, with relatively few off the east coast. There is undoubted duplication of records in the Holme/Titchwell/Scolt Head and Cley/Weybourne/Sheringham areas as birds drift along with the currents. They are not normally gregarious, occurring mostly singly or in groups of two or three. A count of five off Holme on 31st December 1999 was exceptional. Generally fewer than ten individuals are recorded in any one winter.

Both *Stevenson* and *Riviere* stated that Black-throated Divers were more frequent on inland rather than tidal waters. Indeed, 18 out of 24 records given by *Stevenson* were from inland localities. Apart from 1979 when no fewer than 19 were reported inland, only a few are recorded nowadays away from the coast, normally in January/February and only two appeared during the NBA winters. The first involved a bird that landed on a road outside Norwich, was treated at East Winch Animal Hospital and was released at Pentney GP, where it was present on 5th–7th December 2006, and the second was also at Pentney GP on 6th February 2007. In general the species is more likely to be found on larger areas of open water as a longer take-off is needed before the bird becomes airborne.

There were seven records of the species during the NBA summers, probably involving just six birds. Apart from one off Titchwell on 27th May 2000, all were in April and the other sites involved were Hunstanton, Holme, Scolt Head and Cley, the last bird being in full breeding plumage.

Great Northern Diver

Gavia immer

NBA 1999–2007	SUMMER: ALL/BREEDING	WINTER
TETRADS OCCUPIED	5 (<1%) / none	36 (2%)
SUMMER/WINTER ONLY	1	32
MEAN PER OCCUPIED TETRAD	1 / none	2
SUMMED MAX COUNTS	5 / none	71
POPULATION ESTIMATE	0–1 individuals	10–20

PREVIOUS ATLASES	SQUARES OCCUPIED	1999–2007	LOSSES	GAINS
1981–84 WINTER (10 KM)	8 (13%)	13 (21%)	0	5

THE GREAT NORTHERN DIVER is the largest of the three regularly occurring divers in Norfolk and when seen well its heavy build is unmistakable. In Europe, the main wintering areas lie around the coasts of Scotland and Ireland, to where the birds migrate from their northwesterly breeding grounds in Iceland and Greenland. It is a scarce winter visitor to Norfolk.

The map shows a similar distribution to that for Black-throated Diver with most of the Great Northern Divers offshore from north Norfolk between Hunstanton and Cromer. It occurs singly or in groups of two or three, with maximum counts of five off Holme and Morston.

There is undoubted duplication of records in the Holme/Titchwell/Scolt Head and Cley/Weybourne/Sheringham areas as birds drift along with offshore currents. Only four singles were recorded during tetrad set visits, the remainder being supplementary records. Generally fewer than ten individuals were recorded in any one winter. It is known to be more frequent in deeper offshore waters than the other divers, and so there may well be more birds off Norfolk than are visible to watchers onshore.

The majority of the 11 inland records between 1953 and 1999 were in Broadland. There were three inland records during the NBA winters: these were at Blackfleet Broad on 27th December 1999, at Wiggenhall St Mary Magdalen RC from 30th December 2006 to 15th January 2007 and at Barton Broad from 11th January to 16th March 2007.

Occasional Great Northern Divers were noted during the NBA summer recording periods. All were along the north Norfolk coast, some even as late as early May, by which time the birds were in full breeding plumage.

ANDREW MOON

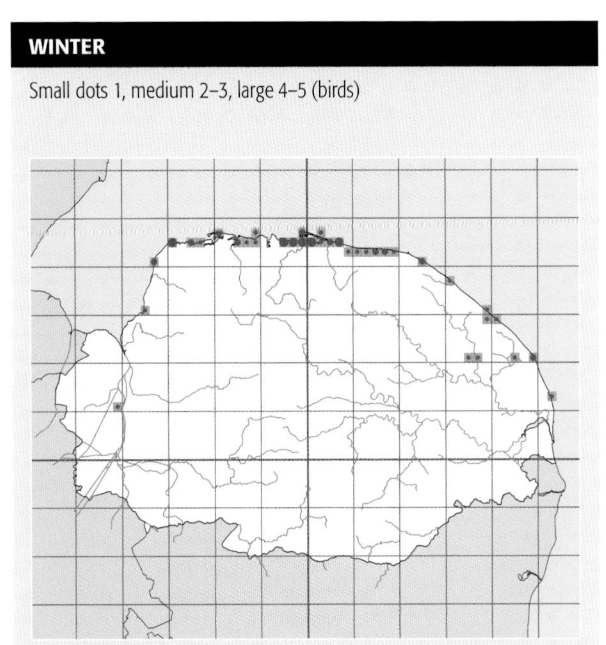

WINTER

Small dots 1, medium 2–3, large 4–5 (birds)

Fulmar
Fulmarus glacialis

NBA 1999–2007	SUMMER: ALL / BREEDING	WINTER
TETRADS OCCUPIED	23 (2%) / 8 (<1%)	19 (1%)
SUMMER/WINTER ONLY	11	7
MEAN PER OCCUPIED TETRAD	7 / 17	25
SUMMED MAX COUNTS	163 / 138	472
POPULATION ESTIMATE	100–140 bp	300–400

PREVIOUS ATLASES	SQUARES OCCUPIED	1999–2007	LOSSES	GAINS
1968–72 (10 KM)	5 (8%)	4 (6%)	2	1
1980–85 (TETRAD)	16 (1%)	8 (<1%)	9	1
1980–85 (10 KM)	5 (8%)	4 (6%)	2	1
1981–84 WINTER (10 KM)	9 (15%)	8 (13%)	3	2
1988–91 (10 KM)	4 (6%)	4 (6%)	1	1

WITH THEIR STIFF-WINGED flight and intermittent glides, Fulmars are a familiar sight around the cliffs of north Norfolk. Their spread around Britain and Ireland from a first toehold on St Kilda during the last 200 years is legendary, and they have been breeding in Norfolk since 1947. From the 1950s to the 1980s, the soft, boulder-clay cliffs between Weybourne and Cromer hosted most of the county's breeding pairs. However, as a result of cliff erosion and mammalian predation, the firmer chalk and carstone cliffs at Hunstanton attracted increasing numbers and are now the site of the county's main nesting colony.

It is never easy to count the number of breeding pairs of Fulmars accurately. The ledges on which they nest are often inaccessible, especially on unstable cliffs, and might not be easy to inspect from either the clifftop or the beach, making the presence of an egg or nestling difficult to ascertain. Although Fulmars do not breed until they are six to even 12 years old, non-breeders visit the colonies during the summer and even occupy and display on potential nesting ledges. Therefore more pairs are present during the summer than are actually breeding. Allowing for these problems, 120 nesting pairs were estimated to be present at Hunstanton in 2005 and 20 pairs between Weybourne and Cromer in the same year. In east Norfolk, Fulmars first bred at Happisburgh in 1978, being recorded there by the *1980–85 NBBS*, and at Scratby in 1995; as a result of human disturbance, however, only the low cliffs at Scratby/California regularly held a few nesting pairs during the NBA summers. Two tetrads in the Stiffkey area were shown as sites of confirmed

DAVID TIPLING

SUMMER

Small dots 1, medium 2–4, large 5–48 ('pairs')
Shading – breeding proved or considered likely

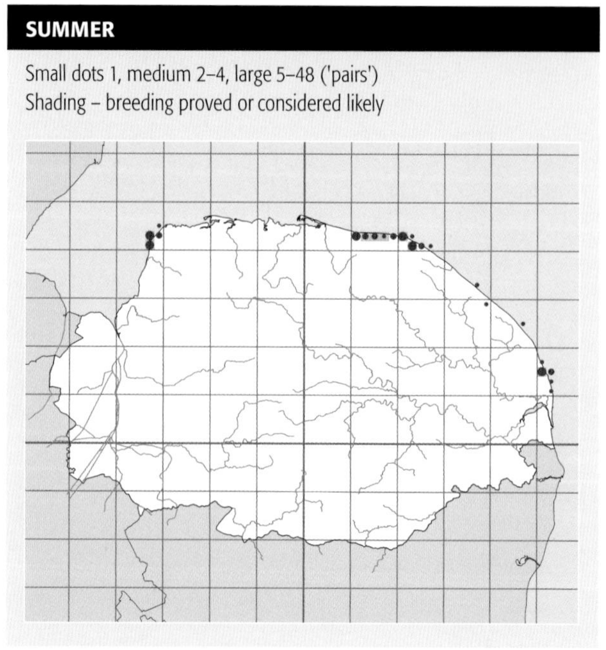

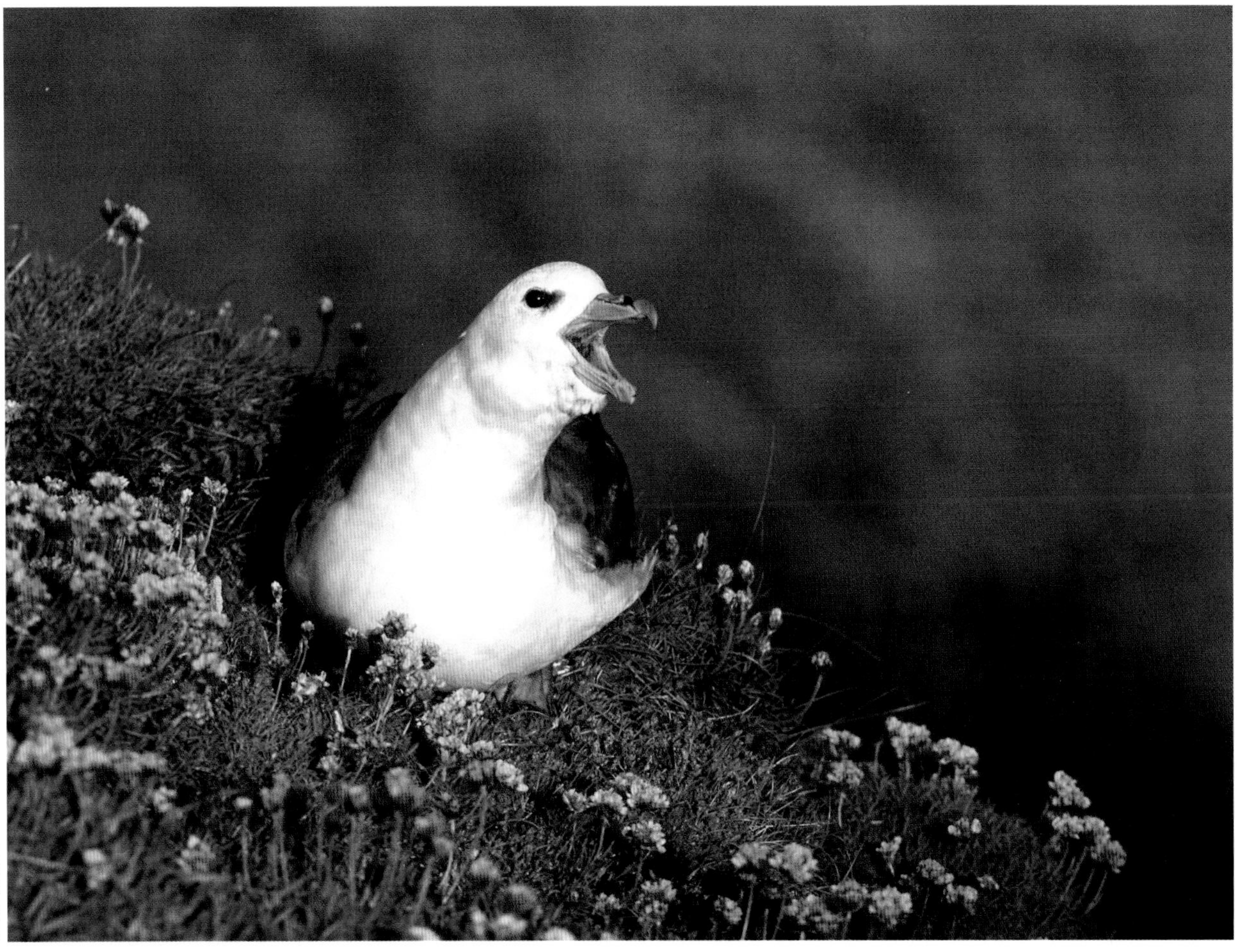

DAVID TIPLING

breeding on the *1980–85 NBBS* map; this error is now corrected in the NBA database.

After breeding, the colonies are deserted while the adults undergo their annual moult at sea. The first birds begin to return in November and by midwinter the breeding colonies are once more fully occupied. Fulmars are the only British seabirds that occupy their nest sites throughout the winter and they defend their territories vigorously even at this time of year. It has been suggested that the breeding population of a colony can be assessed by counting the occupied ledges in December, but winter counts are known to include young non-breeders as well as birds that will later breed at other colonies. This would appear to be borne out by winter counts, with an NBA maximum of 300 at Hunstanton in January 2003. The winter distribution closely matched that of the summer months.

WINTER

Small dots 1, medium 2–4, large 5–300 (birds)

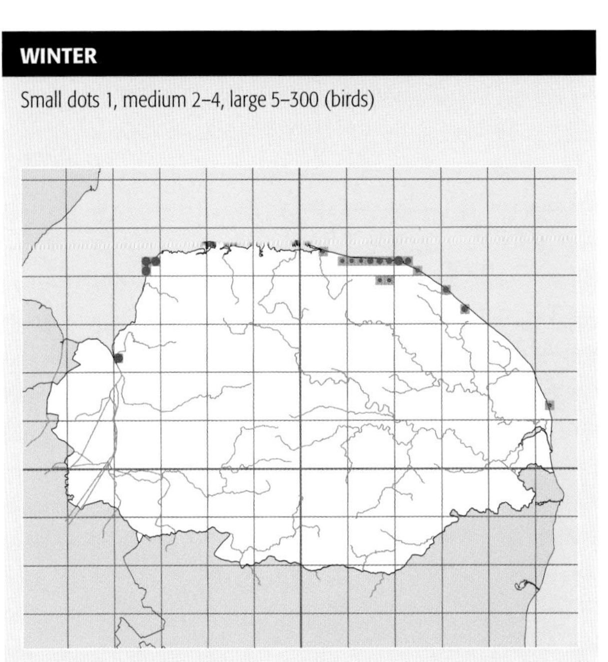

Being pelagic birds, Fulmars would not be expected to occur inland. Nevertheless, a few inland birds were recorded during the NBA period. Most were of single birds not far from the coast between May and August. However, ten were between Lynn Point and King's Lynn Fisher Fleet on 27th February 2002 and one flew over Aylmerton in January 2003. Birds passing at sea or seen only in flight have generally not been mapped.

Cormorant
Phalacrocorax carbo

NBA 1999–2007	SUMMER: ALL / BREEDING	WINTER
TETRADS OCCUPIED	202 (14%) / 4 (<1%)	414 (28%)
SUMMER/WINTER ONLY	48	260
MEAN PER OCCUPIED TETRAD	4 / 31	10
SUMMED MAX COUNTS	741 / 124	4,161
POPULATION ESTIMATE	75–120 bp	1,000–1,500

PREVIOUS ATLASES	SQUARES OCCUPIED	1999-2007	LOSSES	GAINS
1968–72 (10 KM)	none	4 (6%)	0	4
1980–85 (TETRAD)	none	4 (<1%)	0	4
1980–85 (10 KM)	none	4 (6%)	0	4
1981–84 WINTER (10 KM)	46 (74%)	57 (92%)	1	12
1988–91 (10 KM)	1 (2%)	4 (6%)	0	3

THE CORMORANT IS A familiar bird on almost any extensive area of open water in Norfolk, especially outside the breeding season. Since the species began to nest again in the county in 1988, careful observation has confirmed that the majority of birds now recorded in Norfolk during both the summer and winter are of the continental race *sinensis*, whereas previously most were assumed to belong to the nominate North Atlantic race *carbo*. Although *carbo* is traditionally a rock-nesting race, with colonies scattered around the British coast from the Isle of Wight clockwise to Flamborough, it now also breeds in many of the inland tree-nesting colonies established in England by *sinensis* since 1981.

Cormorants inhabit both saltwater and freshwater habitats, but in Norfolk breeding occurs only in treetop colonies, usually adjacent to fresh water. The NBA summer map shows a well-scattered, if rather sparse, distribution throughout the county, birds being present in the harbours, saltmarsh creeks and coastal reserves along the north Norfolk coast, in Broadland, on parkland lakes, flooded gravel pits and in the Fens, especially along the waterways of the Great Ouse. The species definitely nested only at Holkham GM, Narford and Didlington during the eight NBA summers, although breeding was also suspected at Sennowe Park in 2006.

Although tree-nesting, usually in heronries, was taking place at Reedham and Fritton up to the early years of the 19th century, Cormorants ceased to breed in Norfolk at about that time and did so only occasionally until four pairs nested at Narford in 1988. There were three nests

SUMMER

Small dots 1, medium 2–3, large 4–162 ('pairs')
Shading – breeding proved or considered likely

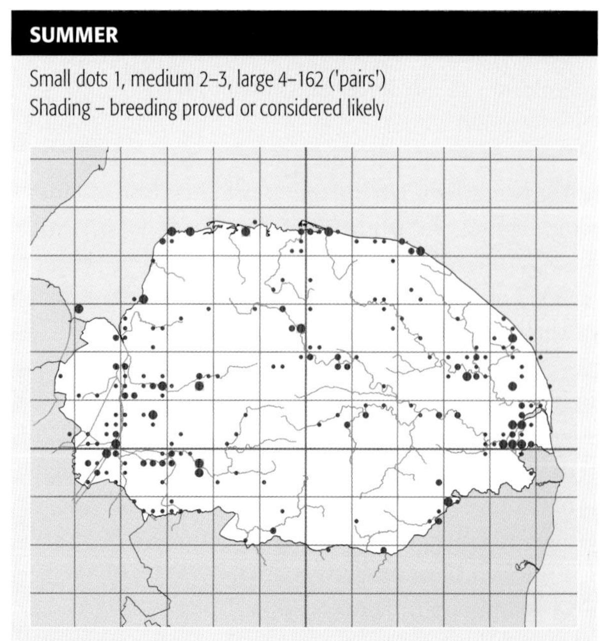

WINTER

Small dots 1–2, medium 3–7, large 8–398 (birds)

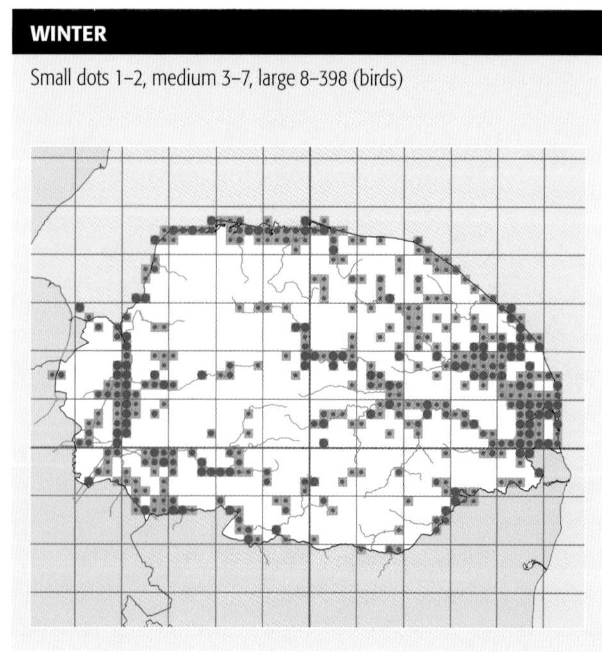

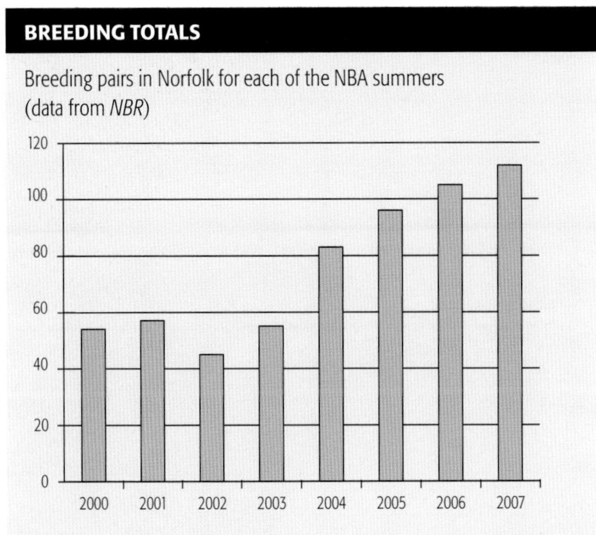

there in 1989 and 14 in 1990, but the colony was not encouraged and no more nests were found until 14 reappeared in 1998. In 1999 there were 29 nests, but the colony was deserted again by 2002, with two nests again in 2004. The species bred at Holkham GM for the first time in 1999, when six pairs nested. By the following year 42 pairs bred, increasing to 88 by 2006. If undisturbed, Cormorants have a high fledging success, as was demonstrated at Holkham in 2003 when most of the 55 pairs raised three young each. Nationally, the inland breeding population is continuing to increase and to spread to new sites (*Birdtrends*). Cormorants feed almost exclusively on fish and they have always therefore come into conflict with fishermen. It is highly likely that the upward trend in Cormorants nesting in Norfolk will continue, despite persecution; culling under licence is now sometimes an option for unwelcoming landowners.

The great majority of summer records do not involve breeding birds. Even at established colonies many non-breeding birds are present, as Cormorants return to their natal colonies when immature but generally do not nest until they are three years old. Summer night-time roosts have also become established at certain localities, gathering in birds from a wide radius. The two largest during the NBA period were at Welney, where up to 543 roosted on power lines, and at Ranworth Broad, where up to 162 roosted on a wooded island.

Although in winter there was formerly a tendency for Cormorants to occupy the British coastline (*1981–84 Winter Atlas*), the NBA winter map demonstrates that, at least in Norfolk, the vast majority are now located on inland waters. As in summer, Cormorants tend to concentrate in winter along the north Norfolk coast, in Broadland, on the gravel pits along the river valleys and in Fenland. At many of these sites large daytime gatherings occur, with birds roosting, preening or just loafing around in the treetops. The highest tetrad counts in winter have included 398 at the Ranworth Broad roost and up to 200 at Welney, while an impressive count of 125 fishing offshore was recorded at Winterton in February 2005 and up to 268 have been counted in the Breydon Water area. The wintering population includes visitors from a wide area, including the near Continent and the Irish Sea, as well as birds from more local breeding populations (*Migration Atlas*).

DAVID TIPLING

Shag

Phalacrocorax aristotelis

NBA 1999–2007	SUMMER: ALL / BREEDING	WINTER
TETRADS OCCUPIED	11 (<1%) / none	50 (3%)
SUMMER/WINTER ONLY	4	43
MEAN PER OCCUPIED TETRAD	1 / none	3
SUMMED MAX COUNTS	14 / none	130
POPULATION ESTIMATE	0–3 individuals	10–60

PREVIOUS ATLASES	SQUARES OCCUPIED	1999–2007	LOSSES	GAINS
1981–84 WINTER (10 KM)	14 (23%)	25 (40%)	3	14

DAVID TIPLING

THE SHAG, WITH its pencil-thin bill, is far less familiar to birdwatchers in Norfolk than its larger cousin the Cormorant. It is a characteristic bird of the rocky habitats of the north and west coasts of Britain, where the adults especially are normally sedentary. To Norfolk, it is a scarce autumn and winter visitor in varying numbers.

During the NBA small numbers were recorded around many parts of the Norfolk coast, as the birds fed in inshore waters or rested, often with wings outstretched, on manmade structures such as groynes. Shags are less gregarious than Cormorants, spending much of their time alone, except at roosts.

Generally, fewer than 15 were recorded in Norfolk in any one winter, although higher numbers are recorded in autumn. Towards the end of January 2005, however, Norfolk witnessed one of the largest 'wrecks' of Shags for a number of years, involving about 60 birds. The first indication was a count of 13 at Hunstanton on 26th January followed the next day by a group of 24 that crash-landed in a garden at Mundford. By 4th February a total of 16 were present along the Great Ouse Relief Channel between Denver Sluice and Stowbridge. It has been suggested that these 'wrecks' occur after stormy nights, usually with strong easterly winds, resulting in some Shags being disturbed from their roosts by the rough seas. They take to the wing, flying in the dark, and are drifted inland by the wind (*1981–84 Winter Atlas*).

Excluding counts made in the first two months of 2005, the maximum site counts were six in Brancaster Harbour in December 2000 and six roosting on the 'baskets' on top of the groyne markers at Sheringham in December 2006. This is one of several sites,

EDMUND FELLOWES

WINTER

Small dots 1, medium 2–4, large 5–24 (birds)

including Hunstanton and Wells Quay, that have hosted Shags more regularly in recent winters. At the latter site one was present for two months from 1st November 2002. The cliffs of Hunstanton and Sheringham have also held roosting Shags; their feathers are less water repellent than those of most other seabirds and they appear to be unable to spend the night at sea (*1981–84 Winter Atlas*).

Not all of the inland records were related to major 'wrecks'. There was a very clear preponderance of records in Fenland along the River Ouse and its relief channels, and others occurred in mid county. Strangely, there were no inland records in Broadland.

Only a small number of Shags were recorded during the NBA summer periods, mostly in April and May, but with one at Blakeney Point on 1st–2nd June 2001. Apart from seven at Great Yarmouth on 1st April 2001, all records involved single birds.

DAVID TIPLING

Bittern
Botaurus stellaris

NBA 1999–2007	SUMMER: ALL/BREEDING	WINTER
TETRADS OCCUPIED	25 (2%) / 8 (<1%)	65 (4%)
SUMMER/WINTER ONLY	5	45
MEAN PER OCCUPIED TETRAD	1 / 2	1
SUMMED MAX COUNTS	30 / 12	83
POPULATION ESTIMATE	10–19 booming males	20–40

PREVIOUS ATLASES	SQUARES OCCUPIED	1999–2007	LOSSES	GAINS
1968–72 (10 KM)	11 (18%)	5 (8%)	6	0
1980–85 (TETRAD)	11 (<1%)	8 (<1%)	5	2
1980–85 (10 KM)	7 (11%)	5 (8%)	3	1
1981–84 WINTER (10 KM)	19 (31%)	24 (39%)	6	11
1988–91 (10 KM)	7 (11%)	5 (8%)	3	1

BEING A SECRETIVE and crepuscular bird, the Bittern is rarely easy to see and often it is its deep booming call, emanating from the depths of a large reedbed, that betrays its presence. A chance encounter with one in flight, low over the tops of the reeds, is always memorable.

Formerly abundant in the marshlands of the Broads and the Fens, the species began a steady decline as a result of wetland drainage and persecution, and by around 1850 it had become extinct as a British breeding bird. Through a more enlightened attitude and by the creation of reserves, Bitterns returned as breeding birds early in the 20th century. Numbers peaked in the 1950s with 80 booming males, of which 60 were in Norfolk. Subsequently they fell again, however, particularly in their Broadland stronghold, where water pollution, pesticides, reed cutting, increased boat traffic and the invasion of introduced coypu *Myocastor coypus* were variously held responsible. In recent years, much research, effort and money has been put into improving and creating breeding habitat for Bitterns and the population is increasing once again.

The Bittern favours extensive stands of *Phragmites* reedbed, although on occasion nests are built in quite small patches of reeds. Areas of open freshwater adjacent to the reeds are another requirement, in which the Bittern can feed on fish (especially eels, rudd and sticklebacks), amphibians, small mammals and large aquatic insects. Even brackish water is tolerated.

Bitterns are polygynous, individual males often attracting several partners. They are strongly territorial from late winter through to midsummer and an average territory occupies about 20 ha, which is also generally the minimum size of reedbed that will attract and hold a booming male. For this reason, the Norfolk breeding population of Bitterns is found in the larger reedbeds in Broadland and along the north Norfolk coast. The number of males heard booming each summer varied from nine in 2000 and 2001 to a peak of 19 in 2004 (representing 35% of the British population), although the presence of a booming male does not necessarily indicate that any females attempted to nest.

In no year in the NBA period were more than two nests known to have been successful, failures being related to inclement weather (both exceptionally wet and dry summers), flooding of the nest or predation. At one site in 2005 the corpse of a Bittern, thought to be a female, was found entangled in a barbed wire fence in April, but the male continued to boom. Elsewhere, in the same year, a male was booming at dusk on 15th March at a new site that was suitable for breeding, but a fortnight later the reedbed had been cut and extensively burned.

In late summer, juvenile Bitterns leave their natal reedbeds to find an alternative site in which to spend the autumn and winter, and so it is important that other suitable areas of reeds that have not been used for breeding are available for these first-year birds. At this time of year, the most important factor is the availability of food, and Bitterns can turn up almost anywhere that can supply suitable prey. Winter numbers are swollen by visitors from the Continent, arriving mainly in December and January, and especially during periods of hard weather. Unusually high numbers were noted during the winter of 2002/03.

During the NBA winters, Bitterns were recorded in 65 tetrads, of which 45 had not been occupied during the summer survey. Maximum counts were at Strumpshaw, where numbers increased steadily throughout February 2003 to peak at six by the end of the month, and at Hickling Broad, with four in January 2004. The winter map shows a much wider distribution of records inland, presumably representing both dispersed local birds and continental immigrants, while the concentration of sightings in Broadland and along the north Norfolk coast are more likely to be resident breeding adults. Bitterns are often more easily seen in winter as they feed along the edges of reeds, especially if they are narrow stands lining dykes or around the edges of lakes, ponds or old gravel pits. Such localities included Pentney and Lynford GPs, Whitlingham Lane and Snettisham CPs, Felbrigg Lake and UEA Broad. Occasionally they are found in inappropriate habitats, particularly during hard weather, such as one by the roadside at Litcham Common in January 2002. Another fed in the open at Kelling WM in early 2006, taking what cover it could amongst the scattered clumps of rushes: it was present for several weeks and appeared to be feeding on toads.

Numbers of boomers were in the low teens during the *1980–85 NBBS*. There was a doubling since 1980–85 in the number of tetrads occupied; however, breeding was considered likely in only a third of the tetrads occupied during the NBA summers.

Since 1980–85 there has been some expansion within both sections of the breeding range in Norfolk. There are also new records in Fenland, reflecting habitat creation in neighbouring counties. It has been suggested, however, that the burgeoning population of Greylag Geese in Broadland may be having a detrimental effect on Bitterns there, by grazing the reeds along the water's edge.

SUMMER

Small dots 1, medium 2, large 3 ('pairs')
Shading – breeding proved or considered likely, dots centralised

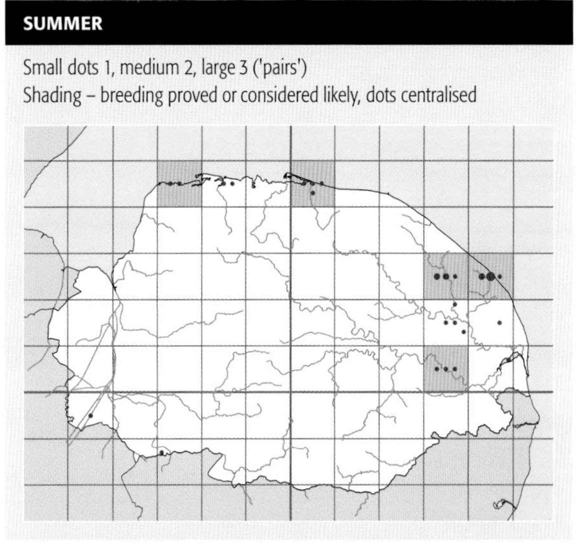

WINTER

Small dots 1, medium 2–3, large 4–6 (birds)

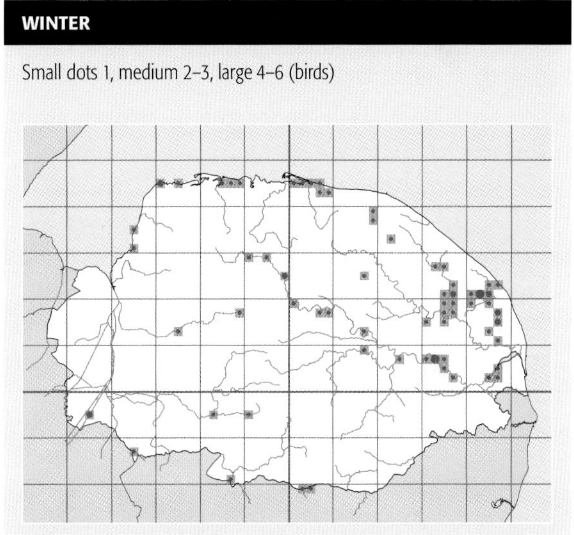

SUMMER TOTALS

Booming males recorded 2000–07
(data from *NBR*)

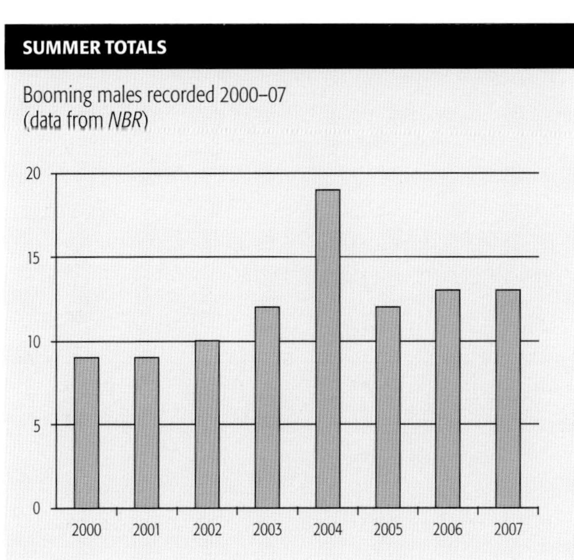

WINTER TOTALS

Winter count totals 1999–2007
(data from *NBR*)

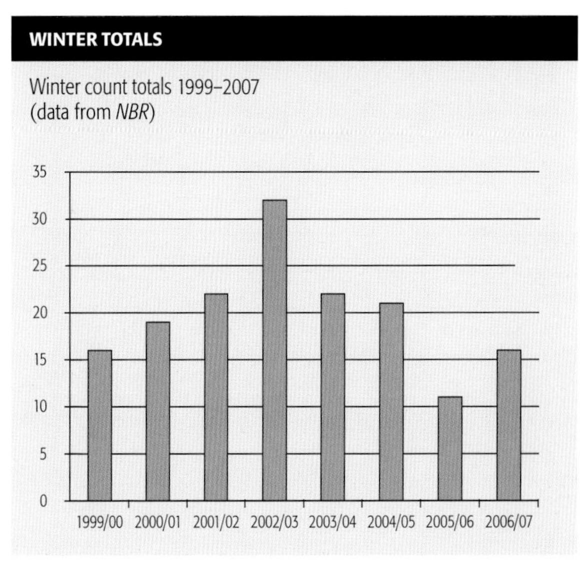

Little Egret

Egretta garzetta

NBA 1999–2007	SUMMER: ALL / BREEDING	WINTER
TETRADS OCCUPIED	77 (5%) / 4 (<1%)	86 (6%)
SUMMER/WINTER ONLY	35	44
MEAN PER OCCUPIED TETRAD	4 / 31	7
SUMMED MAX COUNTS	302 / 125	564
POPULATION ESTIMATE	0–130 bp	50–250

PREVIOUS ATLASES	SQUARES OCCUPIED	1999–2007	LOSSES	GAINS
1968–72 (10 KM)	none	3 (5%)	0	3
1980–85 (TETRAD)	none	4 (<1%)	0	4
1980–85 (10 KM)	none	3 (5%)	0	3
1981–84 WINTER (10 KM)	none	32 (52%)	0	32
1988–91 (10 KM)	none	3 (5%)	0	3

THIS SMALL WHITE heron with its distinctive yellow feet has become a regular feature of many of Norfolk's saltmarshes and coastal wetlands, and is increasingly being seen also on inland sites. It was as recently as 1993/94 that Little Egrets overwintered for the first time in the county, and breeding was first noted in 2002. The changing status of the Little Egret in Norfolk has been described comprehensively by Harold & Bloomfield (2005).

By the end of the NBA period there were six well-scattered breeding locations in Norfolk. For the birds' security, these cannot all be identified on the NBA summer map, although it has already been made public that one of them is at Holkham NNR. From just eight breeding pairs at two sites in 2002, the county breeding total had increased to 128 pairs at six sites by 2007 (*NBR*).

The Little Egret inhabits both fresh and salt waters, feeding around the shallow edges of pools and lagoons, on flooded water meadows, in the tidal creeks and pools on saltmarshes and even along the tideline. Although it breeds colonially and forms communal roosts, the species tends to feed alone. The NBA summer map shows that the main concentrations were along the coastal marshes between Holme and Blakeney in the north and around the inland end of Breydon Water in the east. Smaller clusters of records are also apparent in Broadland, although generally it remained relatively scarce in that area, on the shores of the Wash, and around the Ouse Washes. A few others

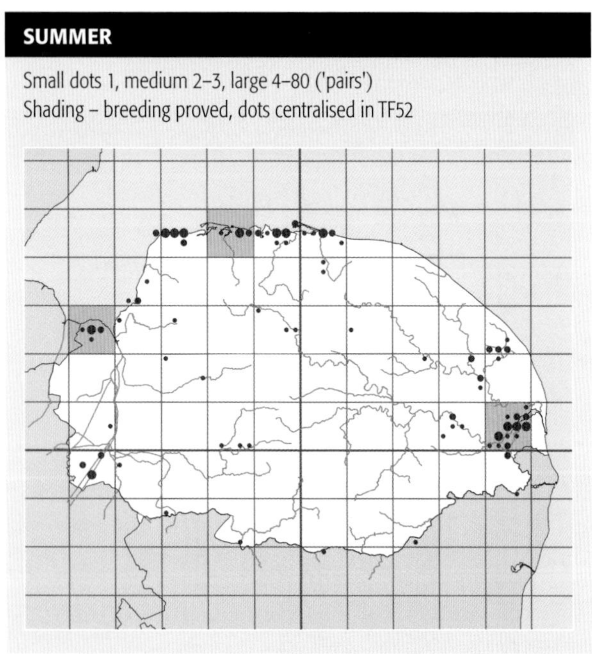

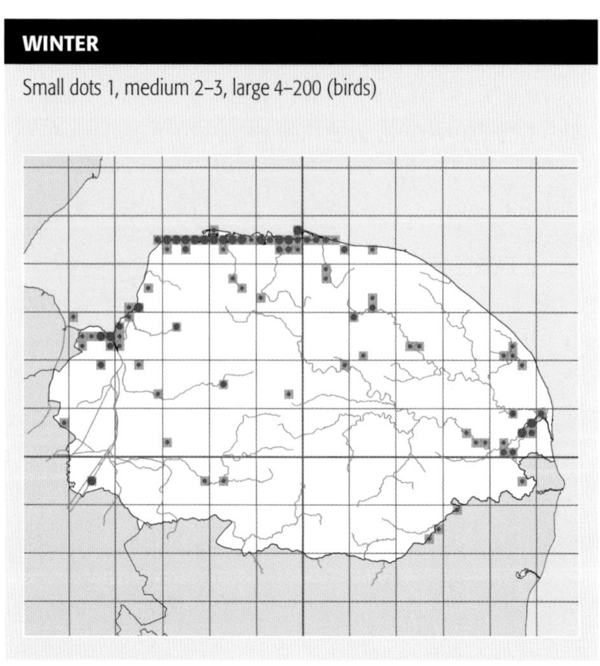

DAVID TIPLING

were noted at scattered inland sites during the summer recording period.

Until about 1990, the vast majority of Little Egrets breeding in Europe migrated south or southwest in autumn, many wintering south of the Sahara, but by the late 1990s it was estimated that up to 20,000 were wintering in France. A post-breeding northward influx into Britain has since developed, with numbers increasing throughout the autumn in Norfolk, peaking in November and then declining during the first three months of the year as some birds return to mainland Europe.

The NBA winter map demonstrates that the main wintering area for the species is along the north Norfolk coast, the saltmarsh creeks and harbours being particularly favoured at this time of year. Aside from night-time roosts, the highest tetrad count was of 32 on Warham SM, while up to 115 have been present in Wells Harbour and 98 were counted at high-tide roosts at Scolt Head and Brancaster Harbour in 2004. Whereas the main night-time roost in north Norfolk was at Titchwell up to the winter of 2001/02, Holkham subsequently attracted far larger numbers, peaking at 212 in November

'By the end of the NBA period there were six well-scattered breeding locations in Norfolk.'

2004 (outside the NBA winter recording period) and up to 200 the following month. In east Norfolk, up to 32 roosted near Breydon Water. Little Egrets were also recorded regularly around the Wash in winter but the only double-figure counts were at Snettisham, where up to 11 were present. In the final two or three NBA winters, Little Egrets were also becoming more regular inland, with scattered records from flooded gravel pits and lakes, often along the river valleys in central and north Norfolk and along the Waveney valley in the southeast.

The rapid colonisation of Norfolk has been facilitated by milder winters but the potential effect of severe winter weather was well illustrated during the early part of 2005, when six dead Little Egrets were found at Holkham. Much suitable habitat remains unoccupied in Norfolk and it is likely that the species will continue its remarkable expansion within the county.

Grey Heron

Ardea cinerea

NBA 1999–2007	SUMMER: ALL/BREEDING	WINTER
TETRADS OCCUPIED	600 (41%) / 32 (2%)	751 (51%)
SUMMER/WINTER ONLY	160	311
MEAN PER OCCUPIED TETRAD	2 / 15	2
SUMMED MAX COUNTS	1,368 / 467	1,793
POPULATION ESTIMATE	300–380 bp	1,500–2,000

PREVIOUS ATLASES	SQUARES OCCUPIED	1999–2007	LOSSES	GAINS
1968–72 (10 KM)	45 (73%)	21 (34%)	25	1
1980–85 (TETRAD)	205 (14%)	32 (2%)	184	11
1980–85 (10 KM)	44 (71%)	21 (34%)	23	0
1981–84 WINTER (10 KM)	58 (94%)	62 (all)	0	4
1988–91 (10 KM)	58 (94%)	21 (34%)	37	0

THE GREY HERON is the largest and most familiar of Norfolk's herons. The county holds a substantial breeding population and also plays host to winter visitors from northern Europe.

During the breeding season, Grey Herons are closely associated with water and trees. They prefer feeding in shallow, fresh water such as rivers, streams, dykes, lakes, pools, Broads, Breckland meres, gravel pits and marshes, but are also found along tidal creeks and on the foreshore. There is a close link between the occupied tetrads and the main river systems in the county, especially the Rivers Bure, Yare and Waveney in the eastern half of Norfolk and the Rivers Nar and Wissey in the west.

Whereas the map confirms that the birds are widespread, nesting localities are few and well scattered. Norfolk's heronries are mostly in tall trees, and at traditional sites often well known to observers. Many heronries are readily located, but solitary pairs or groups of two or three can be easily overlooked, especially when nests are built in dense carr, in reedbeds or in conifers. Nesting birds are believed to feed at distances up to 10 km from their heronry. Birds more distant from one of Norfolk's known heronries during April to June are likely to be mostly non-breeding birds, although some may be nesting at sites as yet unknown, or in a neighbouring county. Since first fledging is often in April, some post-breeding wanderers may

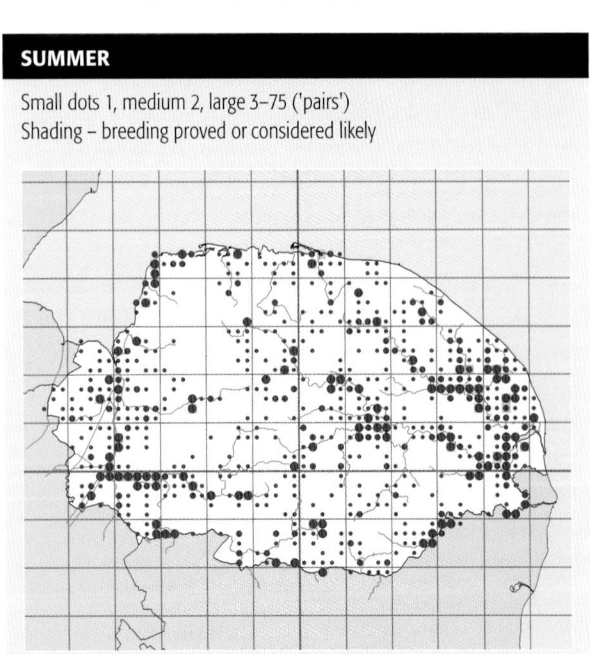

SUMMER

Small dots 1, medium 2, large 3–75 ('pairs')
Shading – breeding proved or considered likely

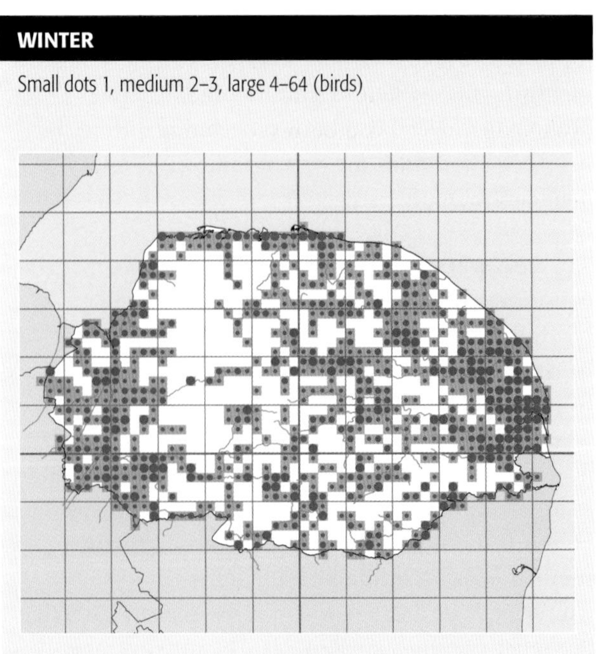

WINTER

Small dots 1, medium 2–3, large 4–64 (birds)

DAVID TIPLING

also have been mapped. During the NBA summers, the highest counts of apparently occupied nests were at Islington, near Tilney High End, with 52 in 2004, and Great Witchingham, with 44 in 2005. The highest midsummer count of birds was at Welney where there were 82 birds in June 2004, no doubt including many newly fledged juveniles.

Many factors can affect the number of nests at an individual site from one year to the next. For example in 2004, there was just one nest at Feltwell Black Dyke, where there had been seven in the previous year, after a new landowner had cleared ditches and felled trees. In the same year, the Great Witchingham heronry fell from 50 nests in 2003 to 16 in 2004, apparently as a result of the herons no longer being fed by the site's owners.

In winter, Grey Herons were even more widespread than during the summer months, with distinct concentrations in the Fens and in Broadland, especially around Breydon Water. As herons often return to their breeding colonies during February, the winter map includes some birds that were already back at heronries. It also includes an unknown number of winter visitors from northern and western Europe. The highest winter counts included 64 at Lenwade in December 2001 feeding on waste from a pet food processing plant, 33 at Hoe and 23 at Banham Moor, attracted by abattoir waste, in February 2005.

Nesting herons throughout the UK have been the subject of annual surveys for the BTO Heronries Census since 1928. Grey Herons are particularly vulnerable to hard winter weather, especially when frozen water restricts access to fish and snow covers other feeding sites. First-winter birds are particularly susceptible as they are less adept at finding food. Heronries Census nest counts fell sharply following the severe winter of 1962/63 but, from that low point, numbers increased to record levels around 2001 (*Birdtrends*).

Although not every heronry is counted in the county every year, there is an exceptional record for some Norfolk sites, particularly in the west of the county where a single observer (Tony Vine) counted most of the known sites over a period of more than 60 years. More-intensive national surveys in 1985 and 2003 both recorded 28 active heronries in Norfolk, with most sites being common to the two surveys: in 2003 these held 363 apparently occupied nests, at an average of 13 nests per heronry, whereas in 1985 only 238 occupied nests were counted. The increase in population matches the upward trend recorded nationally over this period.

Spoonbill
Platalea leucorodia

NBA 1999–2007	SUMMER: ALL/BREEDING	WINTER
TETRADS OCCUPIED	24 (2%) / 1 (<1%)	7 (<1%)
SUMMER/WINTER ONLY	20	3
MEAN PER OCCUPIED TETRAD	2 / 6	1
SUMMED MAX COUNTS	50 / 6	7
POPULATION ESTIMATE	0–1 bp	0–1

PREVIOUS ATLASES	SQUARES OCCUPIED	1999–2007	LOSSES	GAINS
1968–72 (10 KM)	none	1 (2%)	0	1
1980–85 (TETRAD)	none	1 (<1%)	0	1
1980–85 (10 KM)	none	1 (2%)	0	1
1981–84 WINTER (10 KM)	2 (3%)	4 (6%)	1	3
1988–91 (10 KM)	2 (3%)	1 (2%)	1	0

THE EARLIEST DATED reference to the Spoonbill nesting in Norfolk, at Cantley and elsewhere, is contained in an ancient document dated AD 1300 (Dye *et al* 2009) and other historical records show that Spoonbills bred in Norfolk wetlands up to the 17th century (*BoN*). A long-awaited recolonisation finally took place in 2010.

Spoonbills were recorded in each of the NBA summers, but in varying numbers, with a maximum of about 20 in 2002. In that year, there were remarkable counts of 14 at Breydon Water and 11 at Holkham GM, both in June. It is never easy to work out how many Spoonbills are present in the county, however, as singletons and small parties frequently move between localities, even during the course of a day. Spoonbills being conspicuous in flight, as well as on the ground, their movements are often recorded by observers at different points along the route.

Sightings fell into two main areas of Norfolk – the

DAVID TIPLING

DAVID TIPLING

damp grazing marshes and shallow freshwater pools in north Norfolk, and Broadland in the east. The first birds arrived in late March or early April and numbers generally built up in May and June, later arrivals often joining the small groups that were already present. Titchwell, Holkham GM, Cley, Hickling Broad and the Breydon Water/Berney Marsh area held Spoonbills in each of the NBA summers.

In Broadland in 2000, a pair attempted to construct a nest in reeds but unfortunately Coots removed the sticks from the nest as quickly as it was built. Not surprisingly the pair gave up after only a few days. In another NBA summer, a pair was thought to be nesting at a different locality, but no young were reared. It is likely that most of the birds seen in the county are too young to breed: Spoonbills are thought not to reach breeding maturity until 3–4 years old. Summer sightings certainly include many birds lacking the crest and yellow breast patch of a breeding adult, or with the black-tipped wings of immature plumage.

The latest Norfolk Spoonbills are normally recorded in September, but an immature frequented the saltings and tidal creeks between Titchwell and Blakeney Harbour in December 2004, before settling at Holkham GM in January 2005, where it remained until early May.

'Spoonbills were recorded in each of the NBA summers, but in varying numbers, with a maximum of about 20 in 2002.'

SUMMER

Small dots 1, medium 2–3, large 4–6 ('pairs')
Shading – breeding proved or considered likely

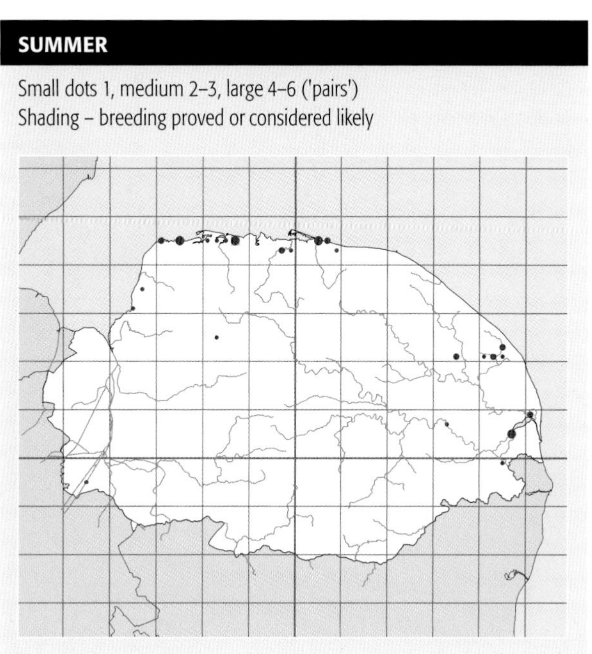

Little Grebe
Tachybaptus ruficollis

NBA 1999–2007	SUMMER: ALL / BREEDING	WINTER
TETRADS OCCUPIED	217 (15%) / 185 (13%)	268 (18%)
SUMMER/WINTER ONLY	115	166
MEAN PER OCCUPIED TETRAD	2 / 2	4
SUMMED MAX COUNTS	424 / 385	1,168
POPULATION ESTIMATE	350–400 bp	1,000–1,200

PREVIOUS ATLASES	SQUARES OCCUPIED	1999–2007	LOSSES	GAINS
1968–72 (10 KM)	51 (82%)	55 (89%)	5	9
1980–85 (TETRAD)	121 (8%)	185 (13%)	82	146
1980–85 (10 KM)	44 (71%)	55 (89%)	3	14
1981–84 WINTER (10 KM)	50 (81%)	52 (84%)	4	6
1988–91 (10 KM)	42 (68%)	55 (89%)	3	16

THE LITTLE GREBE occupies a wide range of wetland habitats within the county, both in open country and in woodland settings. The main requirements are luxuriant underwater vegetation and emergent plants on the surface. Provided these are present, Little Grebes will nest on small pools, at secluded corners on larger lakes and gravel pits, and along marshland dykes. A pair has even nested on a garden pond at Corpusty, successfully rearing four young.

Although Little Grebes are rather secretive birds during the breeding season and are experts at concealment, they are far more vocal than other grebes. The far-carrying trills of pairs duetting often give away their presence and, provided suitable waters were visited, most breeding pairs were probably located. The NBA summer map shows that the species is widely but sparsely distributed around the county, with concentrations in north Norfolk, in the Brecks and around Breydon Water. The larger Broads fail to attract Little Grebes during the summer, although they do host gatherings in the winter. Similarly, few pairs were found in the Fens.

The highest tetrad counts of breeding pairs were along the north coast, with 14 at Burnham Overy and 12 at Burnham Norton and Holkham FM, with 12 also in the Brecks at East Wretham. Whereas 20 pairs were breeding in the Breydon Water area in 2001, this fell to no more than ten in the later years of the NBA. Progressively fewer breeding pairs were reported to the county recorders over the years of NBA fieldwork, suggesting a possible decline in the Norfolk population. Data gathered for the NBA suggest that about

SUMMER

Small dots 1, medium 2, large 3–14 ('pairs')
Shading – breeding proved or considered likely

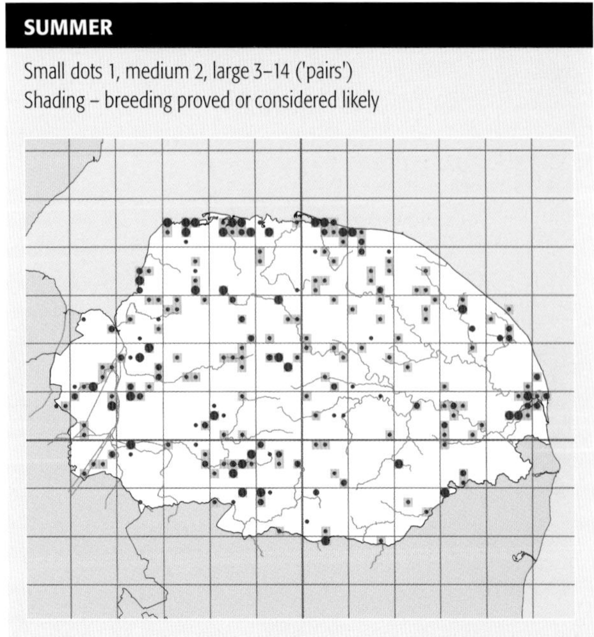

WINTER

Small dots 1, medium 2–4, large 5–39 (birds)

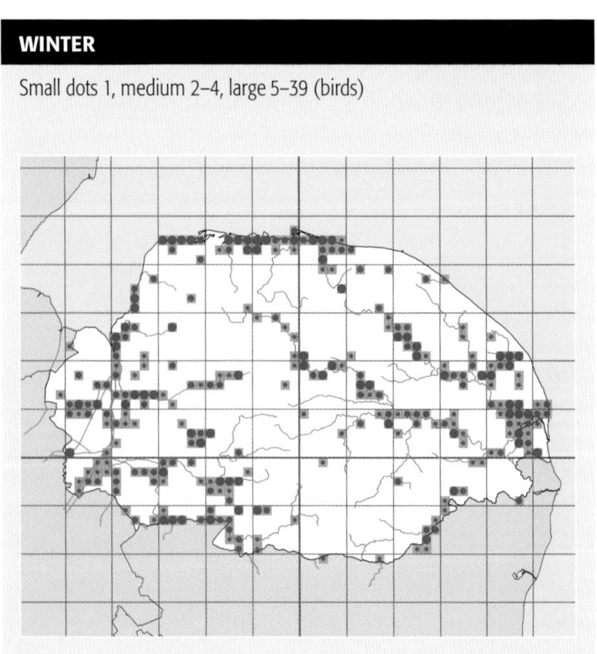

DAVID TIPLING

350–400 pairs of Little Grebes breed in Norfolk, a total which is within the range of 5–10 pairs per occupied 10-km square that was estimated by the *1988–91 Atlas*.

Little Grebes are more gregarious during the winter and small, loose gatherings occur on some of the more open and exposed areas of fresh water, and on coastal brackish and saline waters, the coastal dykes being especially favoured in spells of cold winter weather. Some breeding sites hold birds throughout the year, unless a freeze makes this impossible. Although almost half of the summer tetrads were not occupied in winter, Little Grebes were more widespread in the winter period, especially along the river valleys. As in summer, however, the coastal strip of north Norfolk and the Wash is favoured, as are the gravel pits south of King's Lynn, the Brecks and the Breydon Water area, while some of the larger Broads, such as Hickling, also host good winter numbers. The highest tetrad winter counts included 39 at Snettisham, 35 at Swanton Morley GPs and 31 at Hockwold Washes. Winter numbers are almost certainly increased by a few continental immigrants.

CHANGE SINCE 1980–85

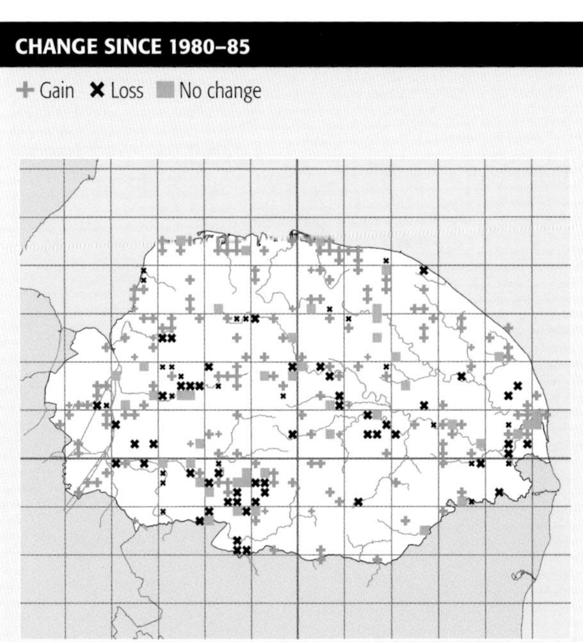

Comparing the map with the *1980–85 NBBS*, it is apparent that a dropping water table may have made some Breckland meres and pingos temporarily unsuitable during the NBA period. However, more tetrads were occupied in north Norfolk than in 1980–85, especially in the Holkham area. Breeding first occurred on the Holkham FM in 1982 and, as appropriate wetland management was undertaken, the numbers of breeding Little Grebes steadily increased. During most NBA summers, about 40 pairs bred on the Holkham NNR with up to ten additional pairs on Holkham Lake.

Great Crested Grebe

Podiceps cristatus

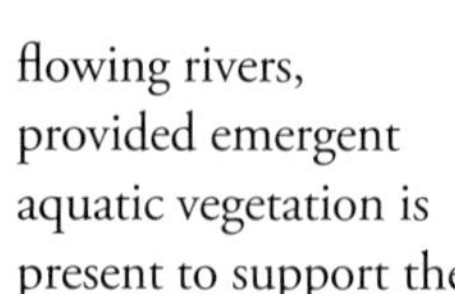

NBA 1999–2007	SUMMER: ALL / BREEDING	WINTER
TETRADS OCCUPIED	208 (14%) / 159 (11%)	196 (13%)
SUMMER/WINTER ONLY	68	56
MEAN PER OCCUPIED TETRAD	3 / 3	5
SUMMED MAX COUNTS	564 / 486	939
POPULATION ESTIMATE	450–500 bp	1,000–1,500

PREVIOUS ATLASES	SQUARES OCCUPIED	1999–2007	LOSSES	GAINS
1968–72 (10 KM)	39 (63%)	40 (65%)	5	6
1980–85 (TETRAD)	149 (10%)	159 (11%)	59	69
1980–85 (10 KM)	39 (63%)	40 (65%)	5	6
1981–84 WINTER (10 KM)	46 (74%)	45 (73%)	8	7
1988–91 (10 KM)	45 (73%)	40 (65%)	8	3

THE GREAT CRESTED Grebe is the largest Palaearctic grebe. It is a bird of lowland waters and has expanded its range in northwest Europe as old gravel workings have become flooded. It almost became extinct as a British breeding bird during the second half of the 19th century as it was slaughtered for its feathers, but recovered once it became fully protected by law.

During the summer, Great Crested Grebes frequent shallow freshwater lakes, flooded gravel pits and slow-flowing rivers, provided emergent aquatic vegetation is present to support the nest. The NBA summer map shows a clear concentration in Broadland, with scattered pairs on parkland lakes, gravel pits along the River Nar and the other river valleys in the county, on the Great Ouse and its relief channels, and on some of the Breckland meres. In Broadland, pairs nest in the more sheltered bays around the Broads and in the ronds bordering some of the quieter rivers. Although the birds can be surprisingly tolerant of boat traffic and human presence, nests may be swamped by the wave action from boats, while water skiing and other similar activities can disturb breeding pairs. The highest numbers of pairs in a tetrad during the years of the NBA were 27 at Barton Broad, 17 at Nar Valley Fisheries and 16 at Wroxham Broad, while the Hickling Broad complex has held up to 32 pairs. The presence of birds in breeding plumage does not necessarily indicate, however, that nesting has been attempted.

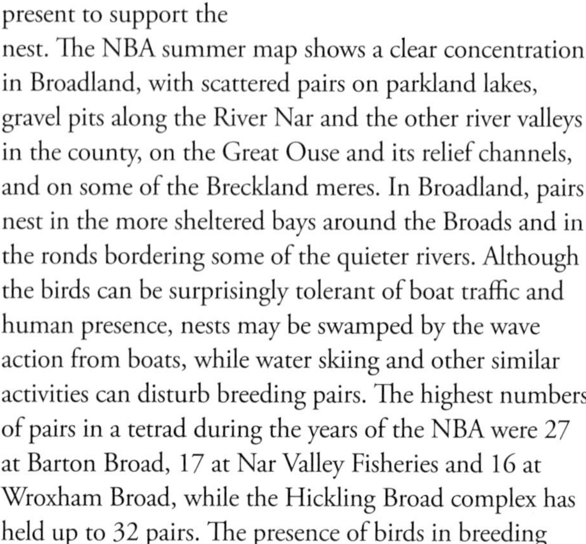

A county census of Great Crested Grebes in 1998 produced a total of 705 adult birds in Norfolk, of which 422 were in Broadland (Seago 1999).

SUMMER

Small dots 1, medium 2–3, large 4–27 ('pairs')
Shading – breeding proved or considered likely

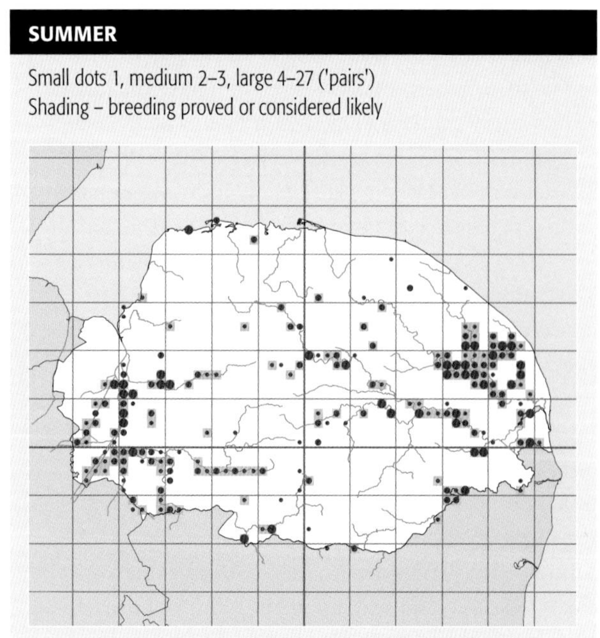

WINTER

Small dots 1–2, medium 3–6, large 7–50 (birds)

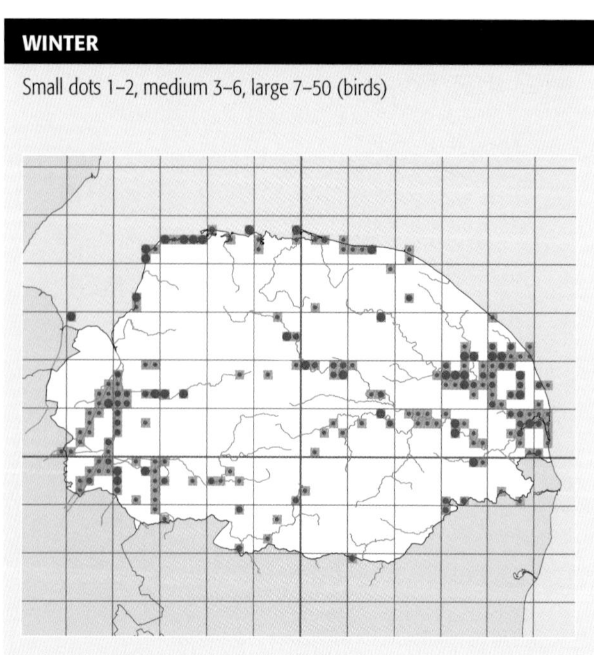

DAVID TIPLING

'In Broadland, pairs nest in the more sheltered bays around the Broads and in the ronds bordering the quieter rivers.'

While some pairs of Great Crested Grebes remain on their breeding territories throughout the year, if the winter weather permits this, others disperse to coastal waters as winter progresses and temperatures fall. At this time of year, they may be found, usually singly or in small loose groups, on sheltered inshore waters, estuaries, such as Breydon Water, or on coastal pools. While the NBA winter and summer maps show many similarities, with the two main concentrations in Broadland and along the river systems south of King's Lynn, the inshore coastal waters and harbours between Hunstanton and Sheringham also host good numbers during the winter. The highest counts during the NBA winters included 50 at Holme and 30 at Hunstanton and between Thornham and Scolt Head on the north coast, 35 at Barton Turf in the Broads and 31 along the Great Ouse Relief Channel in the Fens. Influxes of continental Great Crested Grebes take place into Britain during spells of very hard weather, but how many of these immigrants reach Norfolk is unknown.

CHANGE SINCE 1980–85

+ Gain ✖ Loss ■ No change

Comparison with previous atlas data shows conflicting evidence of range change in Norfolk. There was a net loss of five 10-km squares since 1988–91. The change map on the other hand indicates expansion at tetrad level since 1980–85, especially in Broadland and the Fens.

Red-necked Grebe

Podiceps grisegena

NBA 1999–2007	SUMMER: ALL/BREEDING	WINTER
TETRADS OCCUPIED	5 (<1%) / none	39 (3%)
SUMMER/WINTER ONLY	2	36
MEAN PER OCCUPIED TETRAD	1 / none	2
SUMMED MAX COUNTS	5 / none	61
POPULATION ESTIMATE	0–1 individuals	10–20

PREVIOUS ATLASES	SQUARES OCCUPIED	1999–2007	LOSSES	GAINS
1981–84 WINTER (10 KM)	12 (19%)	23 (37%)	2	13

THE RED-NECKED GREBE, a smaller, stockier version of the more familiar Great Crested Grebe, is a scarce winter visitor and passage migrant to Norfolk. It is the least gregarious of all the European grebes and is the only one that does not regularly breed in Britain.

It occurs sparingly in winter on sheltered coastal waters, as well as on areas of open water inland. The distribution map shows that it is most numerous along the north Norfolk coast, as was the case during the *1981–84 Winter Atlas*. More Red-necked Grebes are seen on autumn passage in Norfolk, between August and November, than are present during the winter months. However, occasional midwinter influxes have been noted during periods of hard weather on the Continent, most notably in February 1979.

About 200 Red-necked Grebes overwinter in Britain (*APEP06*), of which almost 10% are found in Norfolk. The number present varies from year to year, with just four in the winter of 2003/04 compared with about 22 in 2005/06. Generally they are found singly or in groups of two or three, but up to nine were present in Holkham Bay in January 2002. As Red-necked Grebes are fairly conspicuous birds on the open areas of water that they frequent, few are likely to have been missed.

During the 19th century most Red-necked Grebes were found on inland waters, particularly

DEAN EADES

WINTER TOTALS

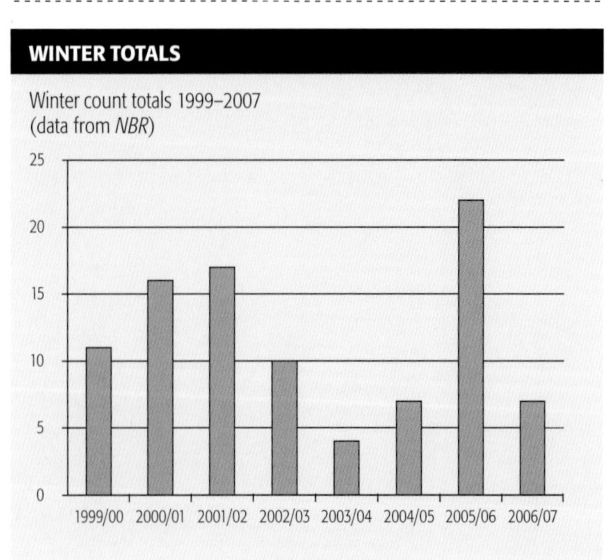

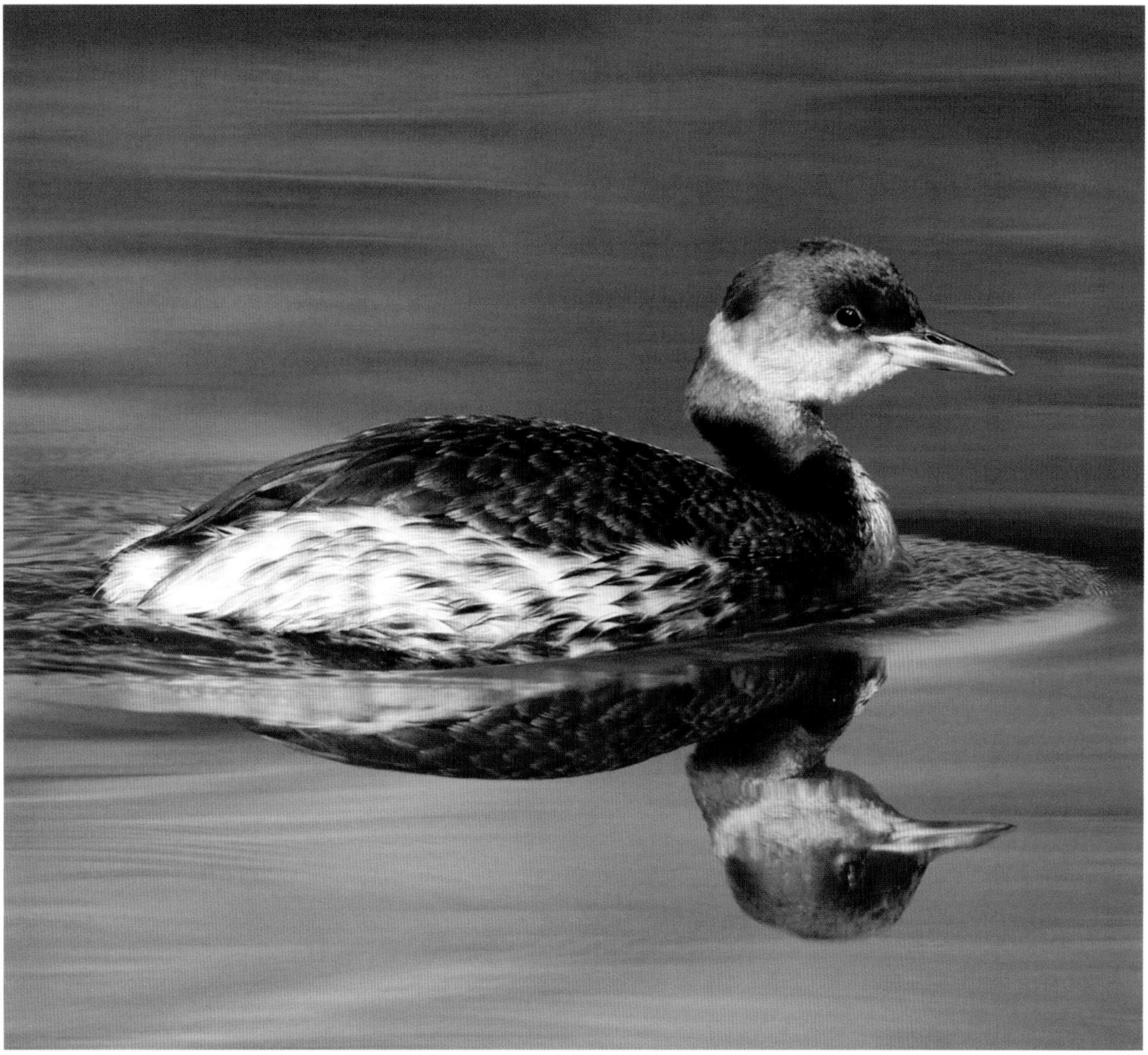

DEAN EADES

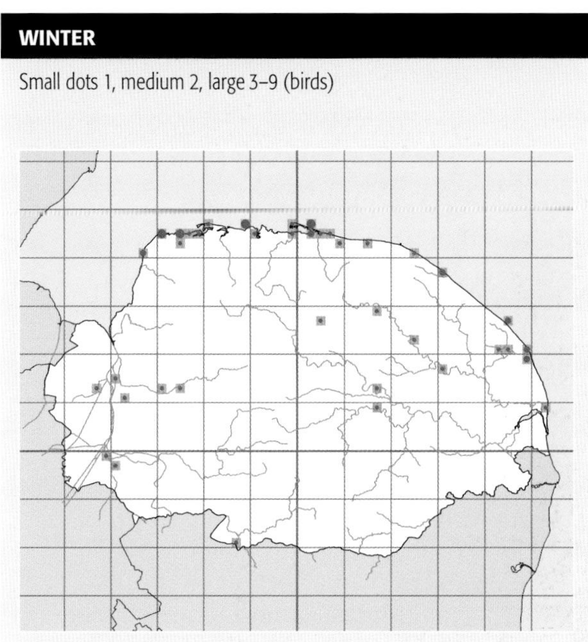

WINTER

Small dots 1, medium 2, large 3–9 (birds)

'Most wintering Red-necked Grebes have left British waters by the end of March but four were recorded during the NBA summer recording periods.'

in Broadland (*Stevenson*). In the NBA period one or two were recorded inland each winter, favoured localities being the Broads, on gravel pits or on the Rivers Ouse and Bure. On occasion, inland birds make prolonged stays, as did one at Blickling Park Lake from 15th January to 17th February 2003.

Most wintering Red-necked Grebes have left British waters by the end of March but four were recorded during the NBA summer recording periods, with the latest at Hunstanton on 1st May 2001.

Slavonian Grebe

Podiceps auritus

NBA 1999–2007	SUMMER: ALL/BREEDING	WINTER
TETRADS OCCUPIED	3 (<1%) / none	34 (2%)
SUMMER/WINTER ONLY	1	32
MEAN PER OCCUPIED TETRAD	1 / none	2
SUMMED MAX COUNTS	3 / none	68
POPULATION ESTIMATE	0–1 individuals	15–30

PREVIOUS ATLASES	SQUARES OCCUPIED	1999-2007	LOSSES	GAINS
1981–84 WINTER (10 KM)	8 (13%)	14 (23%)	2	8

THE SLAVONIAN GREBE is a scarce winter visitor and passage migrant to Norfolk from the Baltic region and Russia.

It is the most maritime of our grebes in winter, favouring sheltered inshore waters. Its Norfolk distribution is not dissimilar to that of Red-necked Grebe but it is even more concentrated in the coastal waters of north Norfolk between Hunstanton and Cley. **Slavonian Grebes** tend to gather in Holkham Bay in late autumn and early winter, before moving westwards along the coast to spend the midwinter period off Holme and Titchwell. Again like Red-necked Grebes, they are usually found singly or in small groups. The highest counts during the NBA winters were nine off Titchwell during 9th–12th December 2003 and seven off Holme on 16th January 2002. About 725 Slavonian

JIM ALMOND

IAN COOK

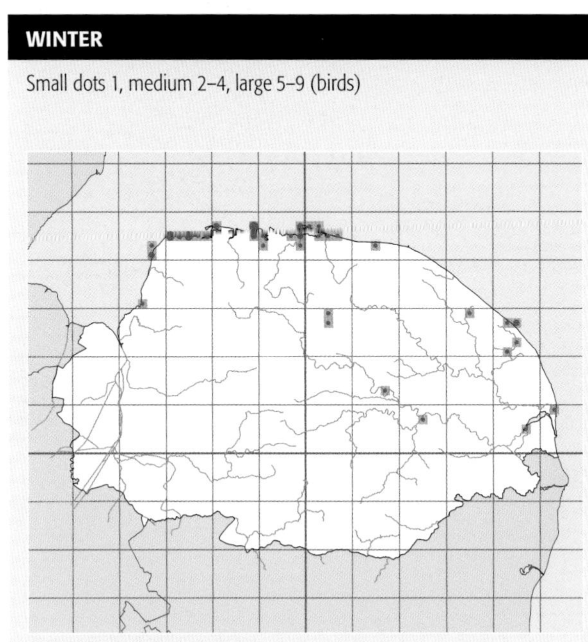

'Slavonian Grebes tend to congregate in the coastal waters of north Norfolk between Hunstanton and Cley.'

Grebes spend the winter in Britain (*APEP06*), but only around 15–30 of these are thought to be in Norfolk.

Fewer Slavonian than Red-necked Grebes were found inland, but again the Broads and old gravel workings were favoured. None of these inland birds remained at the same site for more than two weeks.

Six Slavonian Grebes were reported during the NBA summers: one in breeding plumage graced Hickling Broad from 25th April to 7th May 2001, while another found on the tideline at East Runton on 26th May 2001 had been dead for several days.

Black-necked Grebe
Podiceps nigricollis

NBA 1999–2007	SUMMER: ALL / BREEDING	WINTER
TETRADS OCCUPIED	10 (<1%) / none	18 (1%)
SUMMER/WINTER ONLY	7	15
MEAN PER OCCUPIED TETRAD	1 / none	1
SUMMED MAX COUNTS	11 / none	22
POPULATION ESTIMATE	0–2 individuals	3–4

PREVIOUS ATLASES	SQUARES OCCUPIED	1999–2007	LOSSES	GAINS
1981–84 WINTER (10 KM)	6 (10%)	11 (18%)	4	9

TREVOR GUNBY

THE BLACK-NECKED GREBE has never been proved to breed in Norfolk, although there was an unsubstantiated claim of breeding on a Breckland mere in 1931. Neither is the county a major part of the British winter range, which is concentrated on a few, well-sheltered southern and southwestern localities. However, the species has been recorded annually in the county since 1953, with peak numbers between the mid 1950s and mid 1960s on the inshore waters of the Wash, when a maximum of 35 was noted off Hunstanton in December 1961. Recently, numbers have been much lower, and rather more have been recorded on spring and autumn passage than during the winter months.

'The Black-necked Grebe has never been proved to breed in Norfolk.'

During the NBA winters, Black-necked Grebes were reported from only 18 tetrads between December and February, and one third of the localities were inshore coastal waters. The remaining records were from open areas of fresh water inland and all but one involved single birds. Sites included parkland lakes and old gravel workings. The only multiple record concerned up to three birds that remained at Hickling Broad for several weeks in January/

SUMMER

Small dots 1, medium 2 ('pairs')

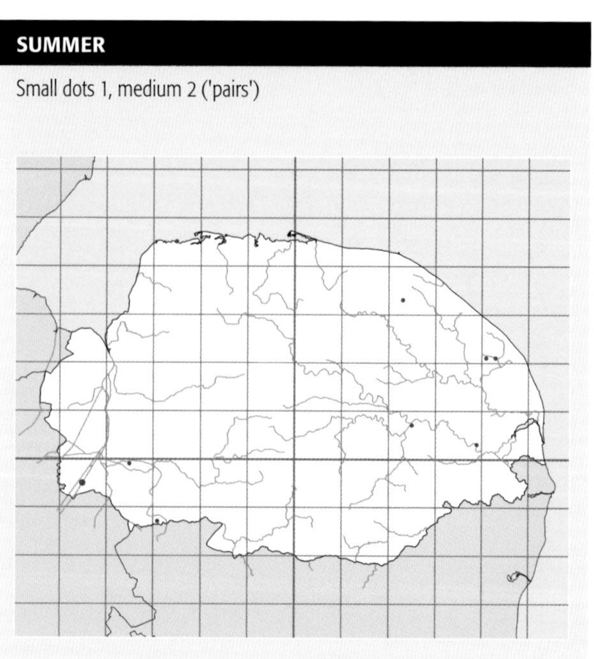

STEVE RAY

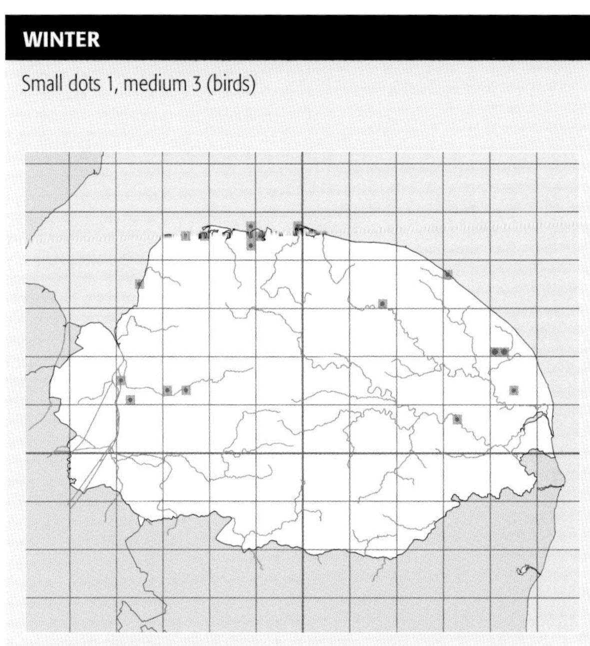

WINTER

Small dots 1, medium 3 (birds)

February 2006. Another long-staying individual returned to Holkham Park Lake for three consecutive winters up to the winter of 2000/01.

The summer map also shows only a few, well-scattered tetrads that hosted Black-necked Grebes, mainly individuals on spring passage in April or May. In the breeding season small, shallow, well-vegetated pools are favoured. Pair formation among Black-necked Grebes often occurs during stopovers while on spring migration. Several of the records made during the summer NBA period involved two together, including a pair displaying at Whitlingham Lane CP on 10th May 2004. Welney hosted more spring Black-necked Grebes than any other site, with ones or twos in 2000, 2004 and 2005, and two pairs in 2002. Up to two were also present intermittently at Cantley BF in June/July 2000. As sporadic nesting may occur almost anywhere (*1988–91 Atlas*), it is not beyond the realms of possibility that Black-necked Grebe may one day be added to the list of Norfolk's breeding birds.

Honey-buzzard
Pernis apivorus

NBA 1999–2007	SUMMER: ALL / BREEDING	WINTER
TETRADS OCCUPIED	7 (<1%) / 2 (<1%)	none
SUMMER/WINTER ONLY	7	none
MEAN PER OCCUPIED TETRAD	1 / 2	none
SUMMED MAX COUNTS	8 / 3	none
POPULATION ESTIMATE	2–3 bp	none

PREVIOUS ATLASES	SQUARES OCCUPIED	1999–2007	LOSSES	GAINS
1968–72 (10 KM)	1 (2%)	2 (3%)	1	2
1980–85 (TETRAD)	3 (<1%)	2 (<1%)	3	2
1980–85 (10 KM)	2 (3%)	2 (3%)	2	2
1988–91 (10 KM)	2 (3%)	2 (3%)	1	1

GIVEN THAT THE Honey-buzzard is well adapted to warm, dry, continental climates, and is abundant on the opposite shore of the North Sea, it is surprising that Norfolk is not among the British strongholds of this species. It is a very secretive woodland bird, related more closely to the kites than to buzzards, that has very variable plumage: like Buzzards, some are pale and others very dark.

Honey-buzzards are summer visitors to Europe, usually arriving during May. It is a rare breeding bird in Britain with around 50 pairs present during the breeding season (*APEP06*), not all of which actually nest. Provided both birds survive, pairs of Honey-buzzards often return to the same patch of woodland in successive summers, although the actual nest-site may vary. They are often long-lived birds and a pair in Hampshire remained faithful to their breeding site for 23 years (Elms 2005).

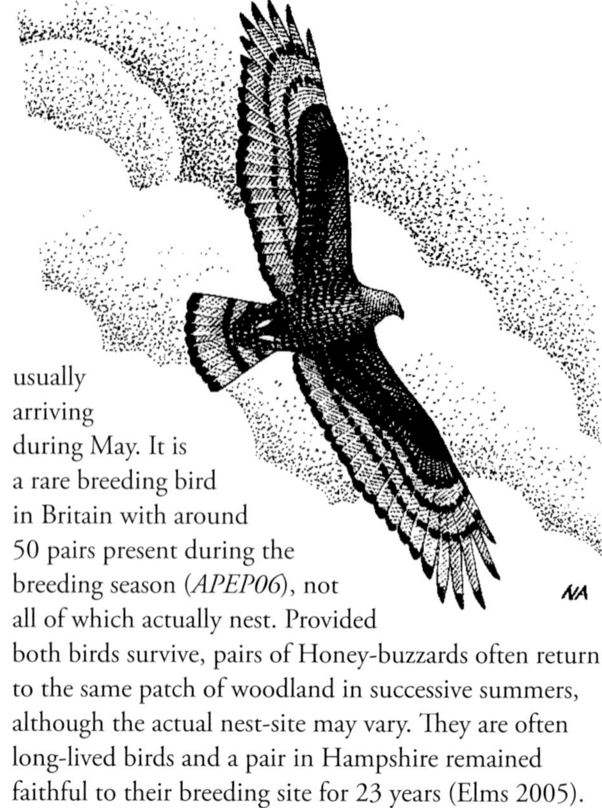

DAVE MANSELL

Honey-buzzards favour extensive woodland with glades, clearings or rides, where they can search the ground for bees' and wasps' nests that they excavate in order to feed on the larvae and pupae, which they also gather to feed their nestlings. Their breeding is timed so that they are feeding their young when wasp larvae are most abundant. Low temperatures and high rainfall in summer adversely affect wasp density, which in turn

SUMMER

Small dots 1, medium 2 ('pairs')
Shading – breeding proved or considered likely, dots centralised

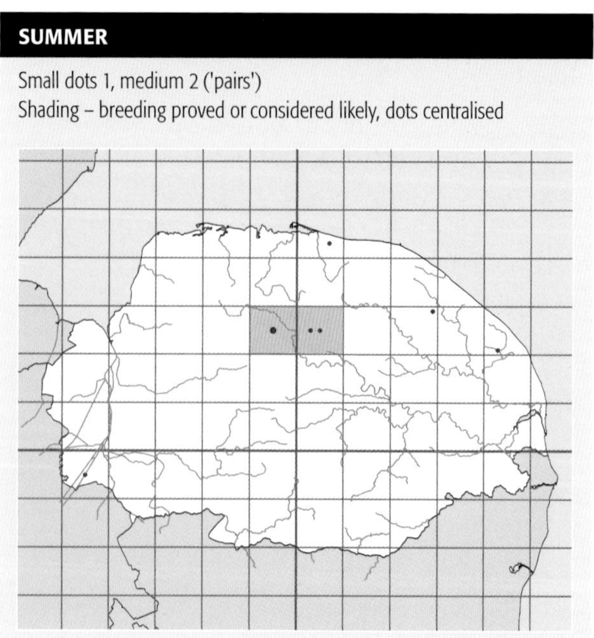

DAMIAN WATERS

can reduce the breeding success of the Honey-buzzard (*1988–91 Atlas*).

The species first nested successfully in Norfolk, at Felbrigg, in 1974 but despite one or two pairs being present in the county in most of the summers since then, successful breeding has been proved in only nine of the subsequent years, either in the Swanton Novers/Fulmodeston area or at Sennowe Park. During the NBA period, one pair returned each year to this same general area but was only successful in three of the years. Up to four additional adults summered in the county each year and breeding was possible at up to two other sites. The provision of two Raptor Watch Points by Natural England has helped birdwatchers to enjoy the spectacle of these magnificent raptors displaying in May and June. However, it may be that the constant presence of people and of parked cars discourages the Honey-buzzards from displaying in the immediate area (Williamson 2005). Other Honey-buzzard sightings, which average about ten annually in May and June, refer to passing migrants (most of which are not mapped).

Honey-buzzards have always been harassed by egg collectors. While their mimicry of Buzzard plumages may help to protect them from fiercer raptors, it makes the species more vulnerable to persecution by ignorant gamekeepers who mistakenly believe the birds are a threat to shooting interests. Quite possibly it is these factors that have so far prevented the growth of the Norfolk population.

It has been suggested that one reason the Norfolk Honey-buzzards have moved breeding territories in recent seasons is that they are intolerant of the aggression shown towards them by Buzzards, which are usually on eggs by the time that the Honey-buzzards first return in the late spring (Williamson 2005).

Red Kite
Milvus milvus

NBA 1999–2007	SUMMER: ALL / BREEDING	WINTER
TETRADS OCCUPIED	45 (3%) / none	28 (2%)
SUMMER/WINTER ONLY	38	21
MEAN PER OCCUPIED TETRAD	1 / none	1
SUMMED MAX COUNTS	45 / none	28
POPULATION ESTIMATE	5–10 individuals	2–5

PREVIOUS ATLASES	SQUARES OCCUPIED	1999–2007	LOSSES	GAINS
1981–84 WINTER (10 KM)	3 (5%)	17 (27%)	2	16

THIS SHOWY, graceful raptor, with its strongly forked tail and buoyant, effortless flight, is slowly increasing its profile as a Norfolk bird.

Once a widespread and familiar scavenger throughout Britain's towns and villages, the Red Kite declined catastrophically during the late 18th and 19th centuries, such that by 1920 only about a dozen breeding pairs remained in central Wales. After a reintroduction programme was started in 1989, the species bred again for the first time in both England and Scotland in 1992. Since then the breeding population has increased steadily and by summer 2000 over 400 pairs were estimated to be present.

As in the rest of Britain, persecution and egg collecting caused the demise of the Red Kite in Norfolk with the last breeding pair being observed in about 1830. It remained a very rare bird in the county for many years and not one was recorded between 1881 and 1958; since 1986, however, the species has been noted annually. A pair, possibly of continental origin, bred successfully just over the county border

SUMMER

Small dots 1 ('pair')

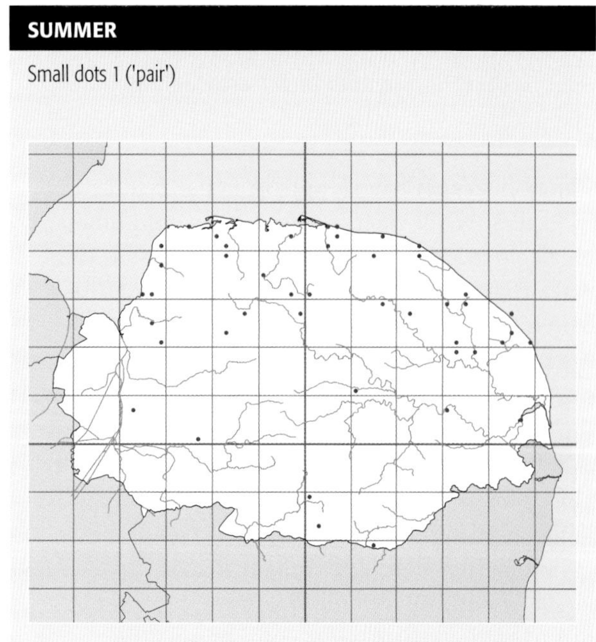

WINTER

Small dots 1 (bird)

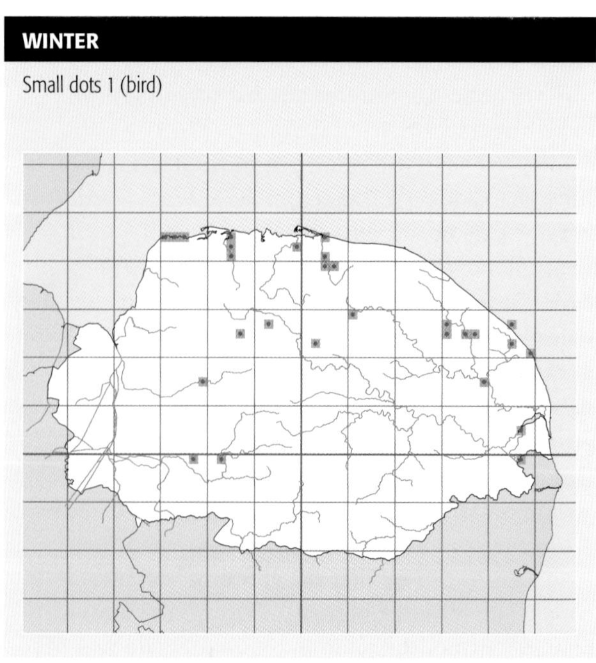

DAVID TIPLING

in northeast Suffolk in 1996 and 1997, but Red Kites did not begin to recolonise Norfolk until after the NBA period.

Although about 25 were reported annually during the NBA summer recording periods, the vast majority were birds simply flying over on passage and are not included in the NBA summer map. Those that have been plotted were birds that either remained for more than a day or were seen to be hunting in the area. The map shows that very few were present in the southern half of the county and about half were at or near coastal localities, suggesting that these too involved largely migrants. An unusually heavy passage occurred in May 2004, including five together over Swanton Novers and four flying south at Winterton. It is likely that some of the spring records involve birds from the Continent, although several carrying wing tags clearly originated from the reintroduction programme.

'Red Kites did not begin to recolonise Norfolk until after the NBA recording period.'

Red Kites in north and central Europe are mainly migratory but an increasing number since the 1950s have, like the Welsh birds, remained over winter (*BWP2*). The winter distribution in Norfolk is similar to that in summer, although winter numbers were smaller; a strong seasonal pattern has yet to emerge. One or two were recorded during each of the NBA winters, and as for the summer, the map shows that they were mainly in the northern half of the county. All winter records referred to single birds and almost without exception to birds seen on only a single date.

Marsh Harrier
Circus aeruginosus

NBA 1999–2007	SUMMER: ALL / BREEDING	WINTER
TETRADS OCCUPIED	283 (19%) / 85 (6%)	137 (9%)
SUMMER/WINTER ONLY	187	41
MEAN PER OCCUPIED TETRAD	1 / 2	3
SUMMED MAX COUNTS	360 / 143	385
POPULATION ESTIMATE	90–120 nesting females	80–120

PREVIOUS ATLASES	SQUARES OCCUPIED	1999–2007	LOSSES	GAINS
1968–72 (10 KM)	5 (8%)	22 (35%)	1	18
1980–85 (TETRAD)	46 (3%)	85 (6%)	20	59
1980–85 (10 KM)	14 (23%)	22 (35%)	2	10
1981–84 WINTER (10 KM)	8 (13%)	30 (48%)	2	24
1988–91 (10 KM)	24 (39%)	22 (35%)	8	6

DAVID TIPLING

THE MARSH HARRIER, the largest and bulkiest of the harriers, has made a remarkable recovery as a British breeding bird during the last 35–40 years. It was formerly widespread in Britain but, as a result of wetland drainage, egg collecting and shooting, numbers fell drastically and the species had ceased to breed in England by the end of the 19th century. The Broads were recolonised in the 1920s but, after spreading into other parts of East Anglia, the species declined once more in the 1960s, due to pesticide poisoning. By 1971 only a single breeding pair remained in Britain, at Minsmere in Suffolk, since when the species has made a remarkable recovery and many Marsh Harriers are now resident in Norfolk throughout the year.

Traditionally, Marsh Harriers have been associated with extensive reedbeds and areas of shallow fresh water. Since the 1980s, however, they have been breeding in smaller reedbeds and in arable fields. The recolonisation of Norfolk was almost certainly aided by the dispersal of Marsh Harriers from the Dutch polders, where the breeding population expanded rapidly after land reclamation, only to decline once the marshland was dry enough for agriculture. By the mid 1990s, up to 69 females were nesting in Norfolk and over 100 young were fledging in some years.

As a nationally rare species still vulnerable to disturbance and persecution, breeding localities, though numerous in the county, are disguised on the summer map. Clearly distinct areas in northwest and east Norfolk held the majority of birds during the summer months, with roughly equal numbers in each of these two areas. In the north, pairs nested in many of the coastal reedbeds between Titchwell and Salthouse, and inland and around the Wash in fields of arable crops. In east Norfolk, the extensive reedbeds on the reserves in Broadland and along the Yare valley, almost as far inland as Norwich, held the majority of breeding pairs. Suitable wetland sites along the valleys of the Rivers Wensum and Waveney also hosted a few nesting pairs. Compared with the *1980–85 NBBS*, when Marsh Harriers were recorded in 46 tetrads, the number of tetrads in which the species was present during the NBA had increased sixfold to 283, although the vast majority of these did not hold breeding pairs. Some records refer to spring migrants, which are evident across the county in April and May.

A full breeding survey of Marsh Harriers in Britain in 2005 produced a total of 360 nesting females from which 800 young fledged. The Norfolk contribution to these totals was 102 nests producing 222 young, with 80% of the nests in reedbeds and 20% in crops or on rough grassland. Holkham NNR has generally held the highest count of nests, peaking at 14 in 2004.

Fundamental to the continuing population expansion in Norfolk has been the adoption of arable crops as a nesting habitat. The first young to fledge successfully from such a site, anywhere in Britain, were raised in a field of winter barley in northwest Norfolk in 1982. Autumn-sown cereals provide a crop of suitable height by the following spring for nesting Marsh Harriers (Williamson 2003a). As the changeover from spring to autumn sowing has progressed, so the amount of potential habitat for breeding harriers has increased. A Marsh Harrier quartering arable land is now a familiar sight in many parts of the county. However, nesting in crops is not without its dangers: nests can be carelessly destroyed during agricultural operations, they are more vulnerable to the attentions of egg thieves and mammalian predators, and the harriers' presence is not always welcomed by gamekeepers. Crop rotations may often force a change of territory location between years.

Prior to the 1980s, it was estimated that probably no more than ten Marsh Harriers (mostly females) were overwintering in Britain, mainly in East Anglia, the vast majority flying south in the autumn to winter around the Mediterranean or in northwest Africa (*1981–84 Winter Atlas*). Since 1982, however, the number wintering in Norfolk has increased at least tenfold and it is now not unusual to see females, immatures and even adult males quartering reedbeds, saltmarshes or arable fields in the middle of winter. The NBA winter map shows a mainly coastal distribution with the majority in Broadland and smaller numbers along the north Norfolk coast. Daytime counts of up to ten Marsh Harriers were recorded from five tetrads in Broadland.

The most reliable method of estimating the number of wintering Marsh Harriers in Norfolk is to coordinate the counts at the various known roost sites in north Norfolk and Broadland. Hampshire (2006) found that the best method at the well-known Stubb Mill roost at Horsey was to count birds leaving the roost at dawn. The Brayden Marshes, as viewed from Stubb Mill, in use as a winter roost by Marsh Harriers, Hen Harriers and Merlins since the mid 1950s, has remained the main roost in Broadland; peak numbers there increased during the NBA winters from 18 in December 1999 to 70 in January 2006 and 91 in December 2006. Other wetland sites in the Broads and along the river valleys are also used as winter roosts, as are the reedbeds in north Norfolk. It is likely that about 100 Marsh Harriers, mostly from local breeding populations, currently winter in Norfolk.

SUMMER

Small dots 1, medium 2, large 3–7 ('pairs')
Shading – breeding proved or considered likely

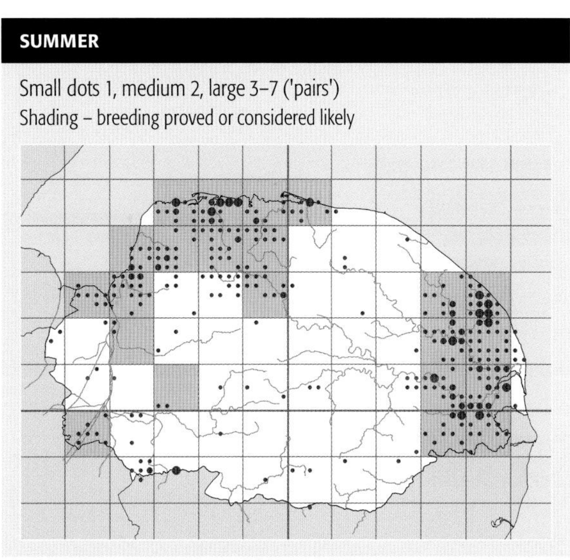

WINTER

Small dots 1, medium 2–3, large 4–91 (birds)

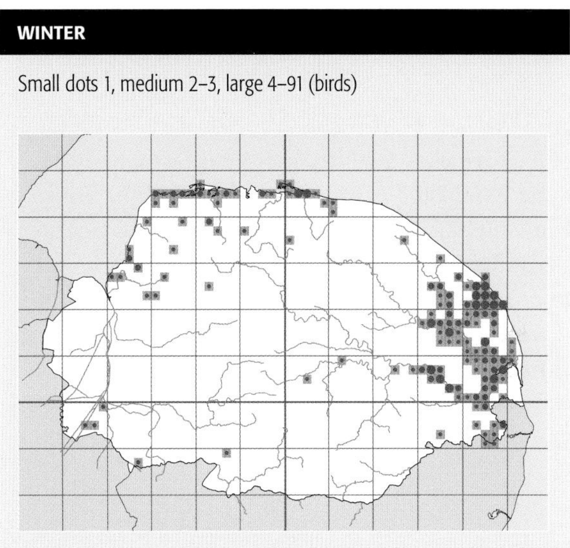

BREEDING TOTALS

Nesting females in Norfolk for each of the NBA summers (data from *NBR*)

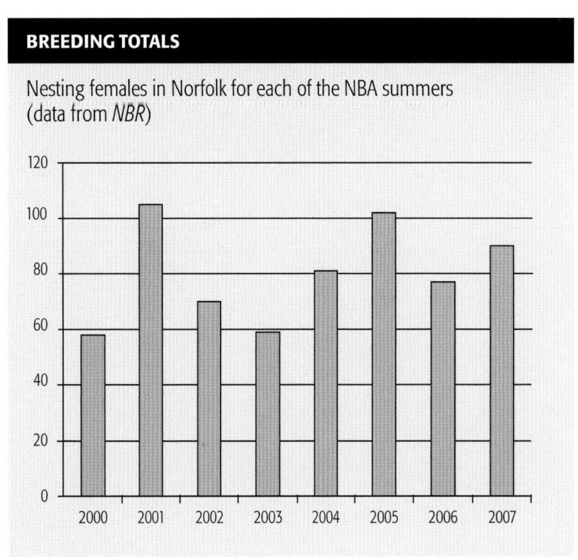

Hen Harrier

Circus cyaneus

NBA 1999–2007	SUMMER: ALL/BREEDING	WINTER
TETRADS OCCUPIED	27 (2%) / none	181 (12%)
SUMMER/WINTER ONLY	8	162
MEAN PER OCCUPIED TETRAD	1 / none	1
SUMMED MAX COUNTS	28 / none	257
POPULATION ESTIMATE	0–2 individuals	30–35

PREVIOUS ATLASES	SQUARES OCCUPIED	1999–2007	LOSSES	GAINS
1968–72 (10 KM)	1 (2%)	none	1	0
1980–85 (TETRAD)	1 (<1%)	none	1	0
1980–85 (10 KM)	1 (2%)	none	1	0
1981–84 WINTER (10 KM)	46 (74%)	36 (58%)	14	4
1988–91 (10 KM)	5 (8%)	none	5	0

AN ADULT MALE Hen Harrier, with its striking pale grey, white and black plumage is one of the most handsome winter visitors to Norfolk, while the brown females and immatures, known as 'ringtails', with their white rumps, are no less attractive in their own way.

Up to the late 19th century, Hen Harriers bred throughout Britain, but during the 20th century numbers declined due to illegal killing (which regrettably continues to this day on grouse moors), egg collecting and habitat loss. Nowadays, British breeding Hen Harriers are confined to moorland, heather-covered hillsides and young forestry plantations in the far north and west.

In Norfolk, Hen Harriers formerly bred in the wetlands of the Fens and Broads, the last confirmed nesting being at Horsey in 1861. However, during the last 40 years, the species has been suspected of breeding, or at least attempting to breed, in the county on several occasions, including an apparent record of confirmed breeding in northwest Norfolk in 1972 (*1968–72 Atlas*), to which, in the absence of any local information, some doubt must attach. During the NBA period, males or pairs were recorded displaying over reedbeds on several occasions in the late spring or summer and a pair probably attempted to breed in 2002. The remaining records refer to Hen Harriers on spring passage, which sometimes continues into the second half of May. One was even predating Oystercatcher chicks on Blakeney Point on 18th June 2000.

It is as a winter visitor to Norfolk that the Hen Harrier is best known. Increasing numbers have been overwintering in East Anglia since the late 1970s. At this time of year, Hen Harriers, generally singly, are to be found quartering open areas of land, such as arable farmland, heaths, coastal grazing marshes, saltmarshes and reedbeds. The majority of records refer to females or immatures. The NBA winter map shows that, like Marsh Harrier, this species concentrates in northwest Norfolk and in Broadland. There are also smaller concentrations around the Wash and in the area of Massingham Heath.

During the late afternoon, Hen Harriers begin to gather at traditional winter roost sites, each generally holding no more than about half a dozen birds. These communal roosts are sited in reedbeds, on saltmarshes and on heathland, but as the birds are very easily disturbed they must be observed only from a distant vantage. Some, such as those at Titchwell, Warham Greens, Cley and Stubb Mill are well watched, whereas others are best left totally undisturbed. As Hen Harriers disperse widely during the daytime, the winter population can be estimated

DAVID TIPLING

only from coordinated roost counts; during the NBA period, an average of 30–35 birds were present in January/February. The highest roost counts were of 12 at Warham Greens and nine at Stubb Mill.

> 'During the NBA period, males or pairs were recorded displaying over reedbeds on several occasions.'

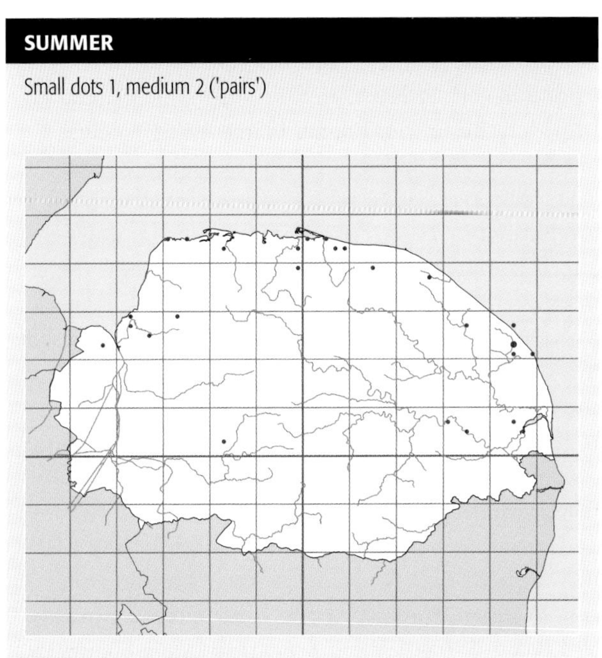

SUMMER

Small dots 1, medium 2 ('pairs')

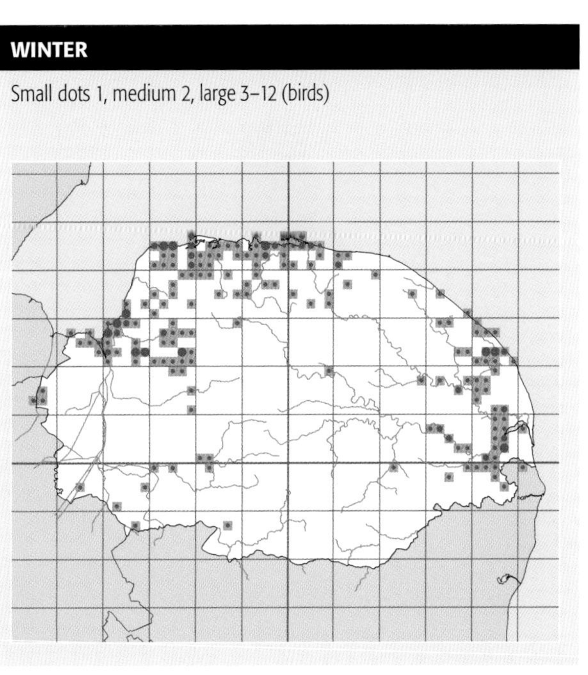

WINTER

Small dots 1, medium 2, large 3–12 (birds)

Montagu's Harrier
Circus pygargus

NBA 1999–2007	SUMMER: ALL / BREEDING	WINTER
TETRADS OCCUPIED	30 (2%) / 4 (<1%)	none
SUMMER/WINTER ONLY	30	none
MEAN PER OCCUPIED TETRAD	1 / 1	none
SUMMED MAX COUNTS	31 / 5	none
POPULATION ESTIMATE	2–6 nesting females	none

PREVIOUS ATLASES	SQUARES OCCUPIED	1999–2007	LOSSES	GAINS
1968–72 (10 KM)	7 (11%)	2 (3%)	5	0
1980–85 (TETRAD)	6 (<1%)	4 (<1%)	6	4
1980–85 (10 KM)	3 (5%)	2 (3%)	1	0
1988–91 (10 KM)	8 (13%)	2 (3%)	6	0

THE DELIGHTFUL Montagu's Harrier has probably always been the scarcest of the three British breeding harriers. There was a marked contraction in range during the 19th century, due to illegal killing by gamekeepers, egg collecting and land reclamation. Following a partial recovery in the first half of the 20th century, numbers once again fell sharply from the late 1950s onwards, possibly related to the effects of organochlorine pesticides (until these were banned) and the Sahelian drought that affected their winter survival in West Africa (*1988–91 Atlas*).

In Norfolk, breeding pairs were confined to the eastern parts of the Broads by the middle of the 19th century, although the species has not nested in that part of the county since 1973. As well as wetland habitats, Montagu's Harriers have always occupied drier situations, such as gorse-covered heaths and young forestry plantations, but it was not until 1968 that two nests were constructed in wheat fields near the Wash, the first record of crop nesting by the species in Britain. Since then, most British pairs have bred in winter wheat, barley or oilseed rape (*1988–91 Atlas*).

DAVID TIPLING

For the birds' security, breeding localities have been disguised on the NBA summer map. The general area in which the species breeds in northwest Norfolk has been public knowledge for the last couple of years, however, and a raptor watch point has been established by cooperation between the landowner and Natural England. Most of the records on the map refer to hunting birds or to birds on spring passage. The first spring records of Montagu's Harriers all fell between 12th and 19th April during the eight NBA years, with pairs often returning together or within a few hours of each other.

The summer of 2000 was the first since 1982 in which Montagu's Harriers failed to breed in Norfolk, and breeding was not re-established until 2003. It was thought that the birds formerly breeding near the Wash had translocated to Lincolnshire, possibly as a result of insufficient prey being available in

DAVID TIPLING

SUMMER

Small dots 1, medium 2 ('pairs')
Shading – all 10-km squares with records, dots centralised

'...it was not until 1968 that two nests were constructed in wheat fields near the Wash, the first record of crop nesting by the species in Britain.'

earlier years, leading to poor fledging success. Since 2003 up to four or more pairs have bred annually in Norfolk. Non-breeding birds have also been present, probably including the young from the previous summer, as ringing has indicated that birds tend to return to breed in their natal areas. Through observations of individuals with distinctive wing moult patterns, it is known that some birds wander widely across the county during the summer months.

A dark-morph bird was recorded over Cley, Weybourne and Sheringham on 8th June 2003 and was only the seventh Norfolk record of this form.

Goshawk

Accipiter gentilis

NBA 1999–2007	SUMMER: ALL/BREEDING	WINTER
TETRADS OCCUPIED	20 (1%) / 5 (<1%)	97 (7%)
SUMMER/WINTER ONLY	2	79
MEAN PER OCCUPIED TETRAD	1 / 1	1
SUMMED MAX COUNTS	20 / 5	98
POPULATION ESTIMATE	6–10 bp	15–35

PREVIOUS ATLASES	SQUARES OCCUPIED	1999–2007	LOSSES	GAINS
1968–72 (10 KM)	none	5 (8%)	0	5
1980–85 (TETRAD)	3 (<1%)	5 (<1%)	3	5
1980–85 (10 KM)	2 (3%)	5 (8%)	2	5
1981–84 WINTER (10 KM)	6 (10%)	43 (69%)	1	38
1988–91 (10 KM)	8 (13%)	5 (8%)	6	3

WHILE THERE CAN BE no doubting the size and bulk of a female Goshawk, a male is little bigger than a female Sparrowhawk, and given a brief view identification may not always be straightforward.

Goshawks probably bred regularly in Britain until the 19th century, when as a result of persecution and deforestation they became extinct as British breeding birds. It was not until 1968 that the species once again bred in Britain, since when its recolonisation has been aided by escaped or released falconers' birds. Indeed, the first breeding record for Norfolk since the 19th century, in the Brecks in 1975, involved a female carrying a falconer's bell.

British Goshawks inhabit extensive areas of coniferous, deciduous and mixed woodland, in which they spend the majority of their time below the canopy, except when displaying. Thus, despite their large size, Goshawks can be remarkably elusive, and are easily overlooked. Females tend to remain within their nesting territory for most of the year, while males and juveniles wander more widely. However, once a nesting territory has been established it may be occupied by the pair for up to five months before laying commences (*BWP2*).

SUMMER

Small dots 1 ('pair')
Shading – all 10-km squares with records, dots centralised

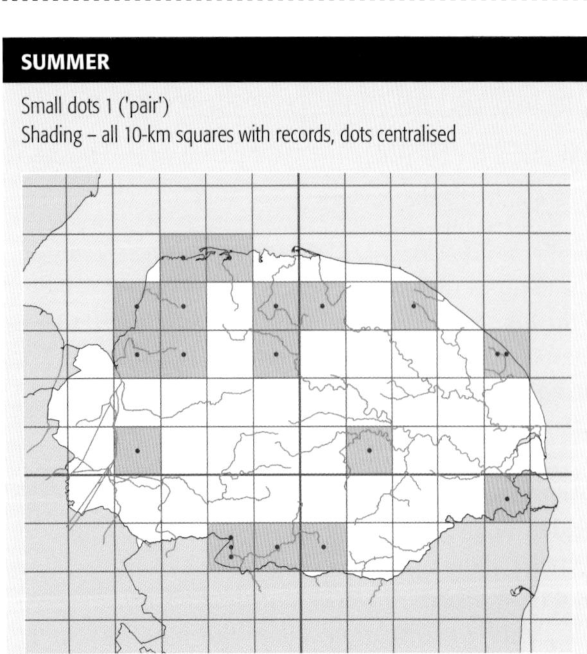

WINTER

Small dots 1, medium 2 (birds)
Shading – all 10-km squares with records, dots centralised

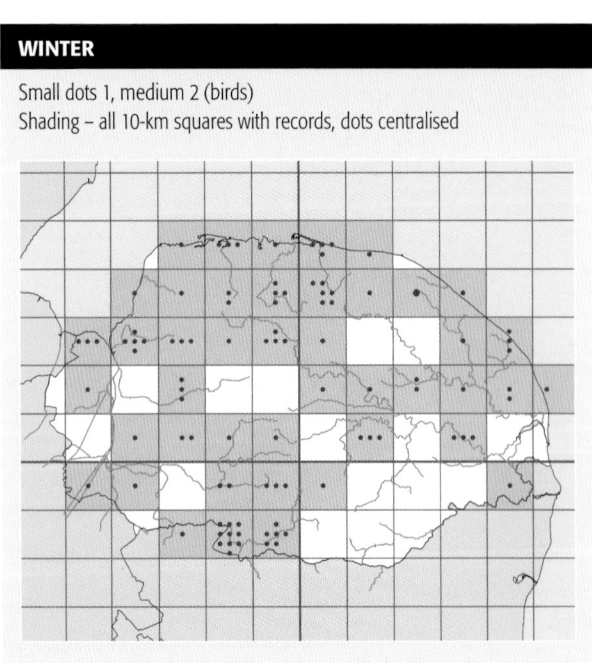

DAVID TIPLING

Since the initial recolonisation, rather little expansion of the county's breeding population has occurred, despite the growth of the British population to around 400 pairs (*APEP06*). NBA records fell short of the eight 10-km squares found to be occupied during the *1988–91 Atlas*. Despite the enormous area of apparently ideal Goshawk habitat in Thetford Forest, no more than about five pairs are believed to nest there, at a much lower density than in similar habitats elsewhere in Britain.

The number of localities where displaying males or pairs have been recorded each year remained in single figures throughout the NBA period, with a maximum of eight in 2003. While most sites have only hosted single pairs, one held three displaying males, and at another site six Goshawks were seen in the air together. Breckland no longer hosts the majority of these displaying birds. An exceptional bird frequented Welney throughout May 2002 and was even observed soaring with Marsh Harriers: in the absence of any suitable woodland in the Fens, it roosted each night in a thorn bush in the middle of the marsh.

'Despite the enormous area of apparently ideal Goshawk habitat in Thetford Forest, no more than about five pairs are believed to nest there...'

As the Goshawk remains such a rare breeding bird in Norfolk, is easily disturbed and may attract the attention of egg collectors and of unscrupulous falconers and gamekeepers, the NBA map is deliberately vague as to breeding localities. The winter distribution is much wider, encompassing many one-off sightings of birds out of breeding habitat. Some winter sightings may have been of continental visitors.

Sparrowhawk
Accipiter nisus

NBA 1999–2007	SUMMER: ALL/BREEDING	WINTER
TETRADS OCCUPIED	763 (52%) / 562 (39%)	936 (64%)
SUMMER/WINTER ONLY	194	367
MEAN PER OCCUPIED TETRAD	1 / 1	1
SUMMED MAX COUNTS	877 / 670	1,282
POPULATION ESTIMATE	700–800 bp	1,000–1,500

PREVIOUS ATLASES	SQUARES OCCUPIED	1999–2007	LOSSES	GAINS
1968–72 (10 KM)	44 (71%)	62 (all)	0	18
1980–85 (TETRAD)	128 (9%)	562 (39%)	59	493
1980–85 (10 KM)	43 (69%)	62 (all)	0	19
1981–84 WINTER (10 KM)	46 (74%)	62 (all)	0	16
1988–91 (10 KM)	59 (95%)	62 (all)	0	3

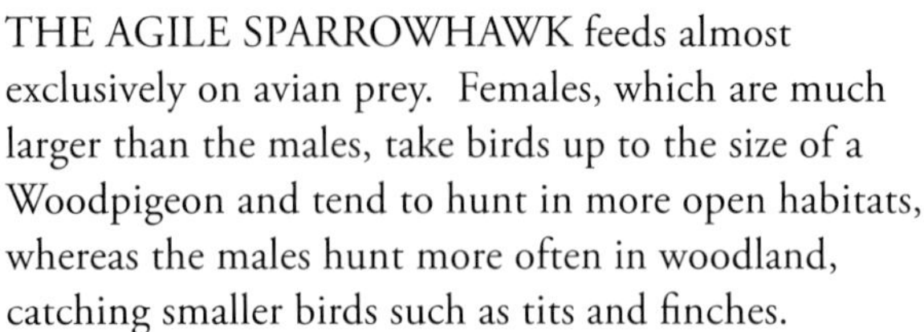

THE AGILE SPARROWHAWK feeds almost exclusively on avian prey. Females, which are much larger than the males, take birds up to the size of a Woodpigeon and tend to hunt in more open habitats, whereas the males hunt more often in woodland, catching smaller birds such as tits and finches.

Historically, Sparrowhawk shooting and nest destruction was rife in Norfolk, to protect game interests, and prior to 1914 the species was very scarce. With keepering in decline during and following the war periods, the species recovered strongly and by 1950 it was very common and widespread around the county, only to decline again due to poisoning by organochlorine pesticides, as did many species at the top of their food chain. Sparrowhawks were affected so catastrophically by pesticides that there was no definite proof of any breeding at all in Norfolk between 1954 and 1960, although birds were still being seen in Breckland, Broadland and on parts of the north coast. Once these chemicals were banned in the early 1960s, a further recovery took place and, remarkably, Sparrowhawks had recolonised the whole county by about 1990. The species is still unpopular in powerful quarters, however, and there is evidence of renewed illegal killing on some shooting estates.

The Sparrowhawk nests mostly in coniferous and mixed woodland, but also in farmland copses and even in gardens. The presence of one or more breeding pairs is often betrayed by their aerial displays over the nesting territories in March and April. The NBA summer map shows just how widespread the species has become, the comparatively treeless Fens being the only part of the county where sightings were relatively scarce. Not all Sparrowhawks present in summer are breeding birds, however, and non-breeders may even be as numerous as those that are nesting (*1988–91 Atlas*). While occupied tetrads held an average of just one pair, four pairs were recorded in one Thetford Forest tetrad and three pairs were reported from several other tetrads well scattered around the county.

During winter, adult Sparrowhawks may hunt well away from their summer territories, while younger birds also tend to move further afield (*1981–84 Winter Atlas*). Small numbers from the Fenno-Scandian population join local birds for the winter. A wider distribution is well demonstrated by the NBA winter map, with birds spreading further into the Fens and the more open arable areas of central and northwest Norfolk. Sparrowhawks are normally seen singly in winter and the highest tetrad counts during winter fieldwork for the NBA were of six at both Woodton and Anmer.

During the *1980–85 NBBS*, the species was still scarce as a breeding bird in Norfolk and was recorded in only 9% of the tetrads compared with the 39% in which breeding was considered likely during the NBA. The change map, produced from the original NBBS record cards, is a vivid illustration of the spread of the species throughout the county since the 1980s.

DAVID TIPLING

'The NBA summer map shows just how widespread the species has become, the comparatively treeless Fens being the only part of the county where sightings were relatively scarce.'

It is now not unusual to see Sparrowhawks hunting along hedgerows and shelterbelts, over arable fields and saltmarshes. Many urban and suburban gardens are also visited by Sparrowhawks, usually males, in search of small birds gathering at feeding stations. Similarly, finches and buntings attracted to game cover strips often become victims. In December 2004, a Sparrowhawk regularly frequented the Pied Wagtail roost at Thickthorn Services on the outskirts of Norwich, while one that flew through the Starling roost at Weybourne Hope reedbed took a Water Rail, only to release it apparently unharmed a couple of minutes later.

SUMMER

Small dots 1, medium 2, large 3–4 ('pairs')
Shading – breeding proved or considered likely

WINTER

Small dots 1, medium 2, large 3–6 (birds)

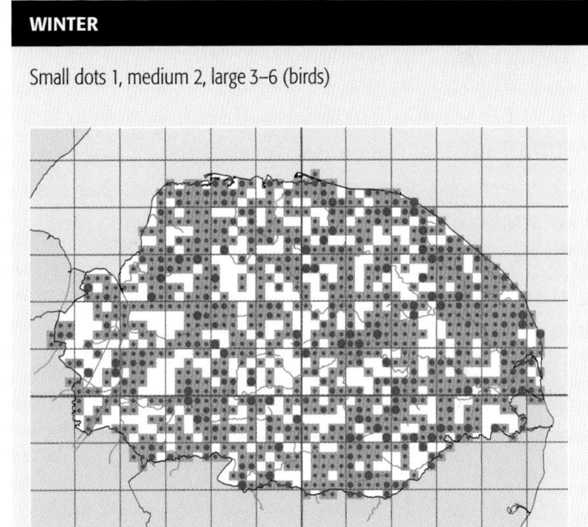

CHANGE SINCE 1980–85

+ Gain ✖ Loss ■ No change

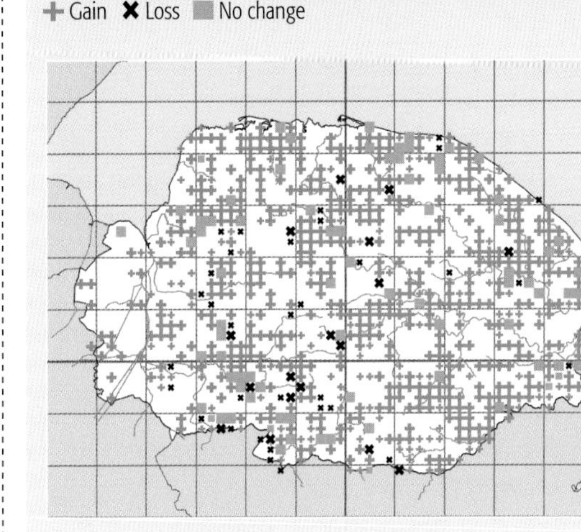

Buzzard

Buteo buteo

NBA 1999–2007	SUMMER: ALL/BREEDING	WINTER
TETRADS OCCUPIED	265 (18%) / 113 (8%)	242 (17%)
SUMMER/WINTER ONLY	148	125
MEAN PER OCCUPIED TETRAD	1 / 1	2
SUMMED MAX COUNTS	301 / 133	411
POPULATION ESTIMATE	25–50 bp	150–250

PREVIOUS ATLASES	SQUARES OCCUPIED	1999–2007	LOSSES	GAINS
1968–72 (10 KM)	4 (6%)	39 (63%)	1	36
1980–85 (TETRAD)	1 (<1%)	113 (8%)	0	112
1980–85 (10 KM)	1 (2%)	39 (63%)	0	38
1981–84 WINTER (10 KM)	10 (16%)	56 (90%)	1	47
1988–91 (10 KM)	2 (3%)	39 (63%)	0	37

IN RECENT DECADES the British population of Buzzards has shown one of the highest rates of growth of any bird in the country, and by 2001 it was arguably Britain's commonest diurnal raptor (*Birdtrends*). During the NBA period, the Buzzard's status within Norfolk strengthened greatly, though it still remains relatively scarce.

During the last 200 years, the species has had a very chequered history, being widespread in Britain up to the early years of the 19th century, only to decline due to extensive killing, particularly on the heavily keepered estates. The species' situation was aided by the lack of keepering during and between the two World Wars, but it once more declined in the 1950s due to the use of organochlorine pesticides and the myxomatosis outbreak that severely reduced its main prey, the rabbit. The reasons for its marked spread eastwards in the southern half of England in recent decades are not fully understood.

Buzzards generally nest in broad-leaved woodland, and are easily located as they soar and display over their breeding territories. They hunt over open country, including farmland, heathland and pastures. The NBA summer map shows a fairly wide scattering of records from most areas except the Fens, but with a concentration in the northwest of the county. Here the many scattered woods set amongst parkland and open arable land provide an ideal habitat for the species. Indeed, at many locations up to two pairs of Buzzards were present in summer, while in four

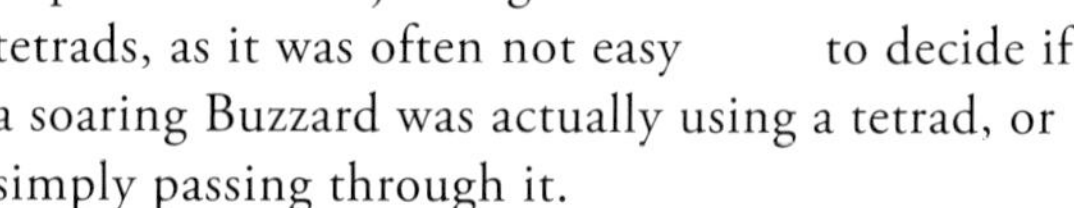

tetrads three pairs were displaying and in one tetrad four pairs. However, there was undoubtedly much duplication in adjoining tetrads, as it was often not easy to decide if a soaring Buzzard was actually using a tetrad, or simply passing through it.

During the ***1968–72 Atlas***, the species was recorded in only four 10-km squares in Norfolk and it was not until the mid 1980s that occasional pairs of Buzzards began to spend the summer in the county. The first successful breeding since the 19th century was recorded in 1992, although a pair built a nest in a west Norfolk locality in 1984 but no eggs were laid (*1980–85 NBBS*). During the summers of 1994 and 1995, 20 Buzzards were hand reared and released in the county as part of a study of the species' habitat requirements. What effect this had on the subsequent recolonisation of Norfolk by Buzzards is unknown, but by 1998 up to 12 breeding pairs were present. Since then the number of breeding Buzzards in the county has steadily increased, with 25 confirmed breeding pairs in 2005; in addition another 22 pairs were present and may well have bred. Distribution at the tetrad scale was changing markedly in Norfolk throughout the NBA period, and the maps probably best represent the distribution in the middle years, with some further spread by 2007. Undoubtedly, some of the spring records refer to Buzzards that were simply passing through the county as they returned to their continental breeding areas, passage continuing into the second half of May.

Breeding Buzzards are very susceptible to disturbance and it is also likely that illegal persecution of breeding pairs continues on some of the county's shooting estates. In the majority of areas, though, gamekeepers were aware of breeding Buzzards and were directly responsible for their protection and successful breeding.

'British Buzzards are sedentary, with probably most nesting pairs remaining within their breeding territories...'

SUMMER

Small dots 1, medium 2, large 3–4 ('pairs')
Shading – breeding proved or considered likely

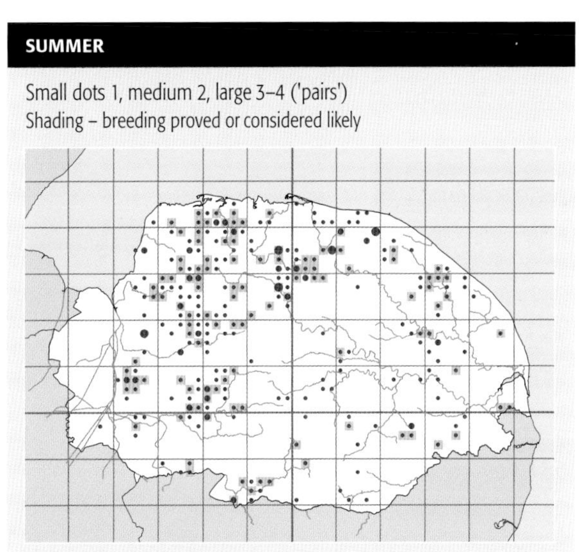

WINTER

Small dots 1, medium 2, large 3–10 (birds)

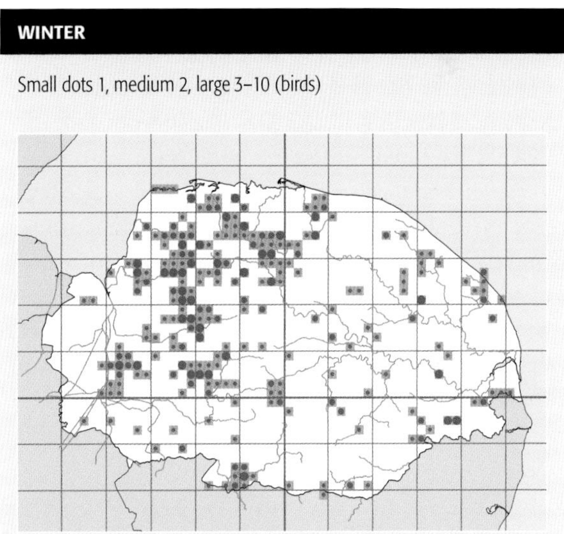

BREEDING TOTALS

Breeding pairs in Norfolk for each of the NBA summers (data from *NBR*)

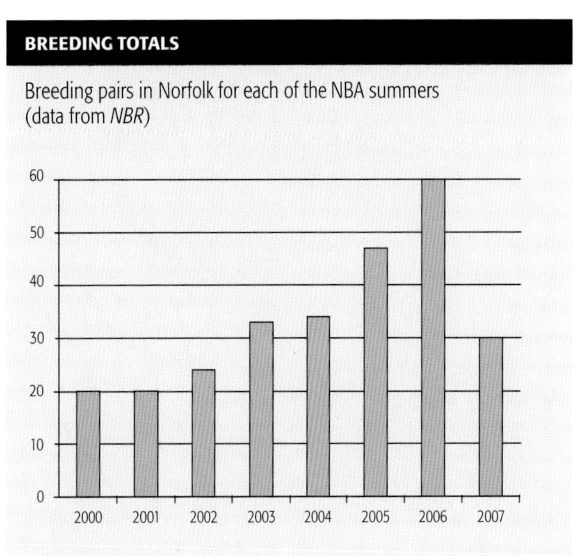

British Buzzards are sedentary, with probably most nesting pairs remaining within their breeding territories throughout the year, and as a result the NBA winter map is very similar to that in the summer. In northwest Norfolk, and in the Brecks, five or six Buzzards were recorded in several tetrads, while up to ten were reported near Holt, nine at Great Massingham and eight at both Swanton Novers and Little Snoring, especially on fine, late-winter days, as the birds began to exhibit pre-breeding territorial behaviour. Some of the gatherings may well have involved family parties from the previous summer. The winter map is in direct contrast to that in the *1981–84 Winter Atlas*, where the majority of records were from around the coast of northeast Norfolk and may well have involved continental birds.

Unusual examples of winter behaviour included one feeding behind a plough at Brograve Level in January 2000 and another feeding on a swan carcass at Welney in December 2005.

Rough-legged Buzzard
Buteo lagopus

NBA 1999–2007	SUMMER: ALL/BREEDING	WINTER
TETRADS OCCUPIED	4 (<1%) / none	57 (4%)
SUMMER/WINTER ONLY	4	57
MEAN PER OCCUPIED TETRAD	1 / none	1
SUMMED MAX COUNTS	4 / none	64
POPULATION ESTIMATE	none	1–4

PREVIOUS ATLASES	SQUARES OCCUPIED	1999–2007	LOSSES	GAINS
1981–84 WINTER (10 KM)	15 (24%)	20 (32%)	7	12

ONCE THE MOST regular *Buteo* in Norfolk, this species is now vastly outnumbered by the county's resident Buzzards.

Despite the fact that they have been recorded annually in Norfolk since 1978, it seems possible that they have become less common since the time of *Stevenson*, who writing in the 19th century described them as regular winter visitors, but in varying numbers. Rough-legged Buzzards visiting Britain are from the Fenno-Scandian breeding population, the numbers fluctuating in response to the levels of Arctic rodents, in particular lemmings. In good lemming years, more Rough-legged Buzzards fledge and, if there is also a marked southward movement, an influx into eastern Britain can result. The last influx into Norfolk, in the early part of 1998, pre-dated the NBA fieldwork. Occasional individuals, some returning regularly to the same parts of Norfolk over several winters, appear independently of influx years.

During the NBA period, few Rough-legged Buzzards reached Britain. An average of just two birds was recorded in each of the winters, with a maximum of only four or five in the winter of 2003/04. Rough-legged Buzzards have a large hunting range during the course of a winter, wandering widely in search of the rabbits on which they feed. Their mobility is reflected in the wide distribution of records on the map, considering how few birds were actually present.

Rough-legged Buzzards favour the more remote, inaccessible open areas of the county with an abundance of rabbits, such as heathland, coastal fields and extensive grazing marshes. Another feature of many wintering areas was the presence of conifer plantations, often quite small, in which the birds could roost. During the NBA period, two areas each hosted Rough-legged Buzzards on a regular, if not annual, basis: Massingham and Grimston Heaths, and the Haddiscoe Marshes. In January/February

CHRIS KNIGHTS

WINTER

Small dots 1, medium 2, large 3 (birds)

'During the NBA period, two areas each hosted birds on a regular basis: Massingham and Grimston Heaths and the Haddiscoe Marshes.'

2004, up to three could be watched hunting together in the Massingham/Grimston/Flitcham area, while the only other multiple occurrence was of two at Burnham Market in December 2003.

Overwintering Rough-legged Buzzards have normally left Norfolk by the end of March. During the first half of most of the NBA summer recording periods, however, variable numbers of spring passage birds were recorded, with the latest on 15th May 2005. In 2000 not one was recorded in April or May, whereas 12–13 spring sightings were reported in both 2003 and 2004.

Osprey
Pandion haliaetus

NBA 1999–2007	SUMMER: ALL/BREEDING	WINTER
TETRADS OCCUPIED	53 (4%) / none	none
SUMMER/WINTER ONLY	53	none
MEAN PER OCCUPIED TETRAD	1 / none	none
SUMMED MAX COUNTS	53 / none	none
POPULATION ESTIMATE	0–2 individuals	none

THE SPECTACLE OF an Osprey plunging feet first into the water to catch its prey is a moment to savour. In Norfolk this raptor is essentially a passage migrant, but lingering birds occurred in most of the NBA years, and even some midsummer sightings, and one day it could be added to Norfolk's breeding avifauna.

Its extinction in Britain in 1916, and successful recolonisation of Scotland in the mid 1950s has been well documented. Its subsequent expansion, aided by an introduction at Rutland Water, took the British population to 148 pairs by 2002 (*APEP06*).

Breeding Ospreys require access to a regular supply of medium-sized fish that can be obtained from near the surface of fresh, brackish or salt water. In Scotland, the majority of nests are in Scots pines but they sometimes take advantage of specially constructed artificial platforms. In Norfolk, many sites would appear to be suitable for breeding Ospreys.

The summer map shows that, during the NBA period, Ospreys were recorded at many well-scattered localities. The vast majority of these sightings were of spring migrants simply passing through the site on their way to Scotland or Scandinavia, albeit fishing or at least making an unsuccessful hunt. Others passed through the county but may not appear on the map, as they were not specifically using the tetrad in which they were seen. Those recorded in April were likely to have been older, experienced Ospreys heading for an established territory, whereas on average second-summer birds follow about a month later (*BWP2*).

Each year, one or two Ospreys lingered in the county for more than just a few days, and on two occasions two birds were involved: at Ranworth and Cockshoot Broads for a week from 13th May 2000 and at Rockland Broad, where one remained from 26th April to 16th May 2005, and was joined by a second bird on 5th–6th May. Many sightings of an Osprey were made at various sites in the Wensum valley between June and early August 2001. As well as in Broadland, Ospreys were recorded at gravel pits

DAVID TIPLING

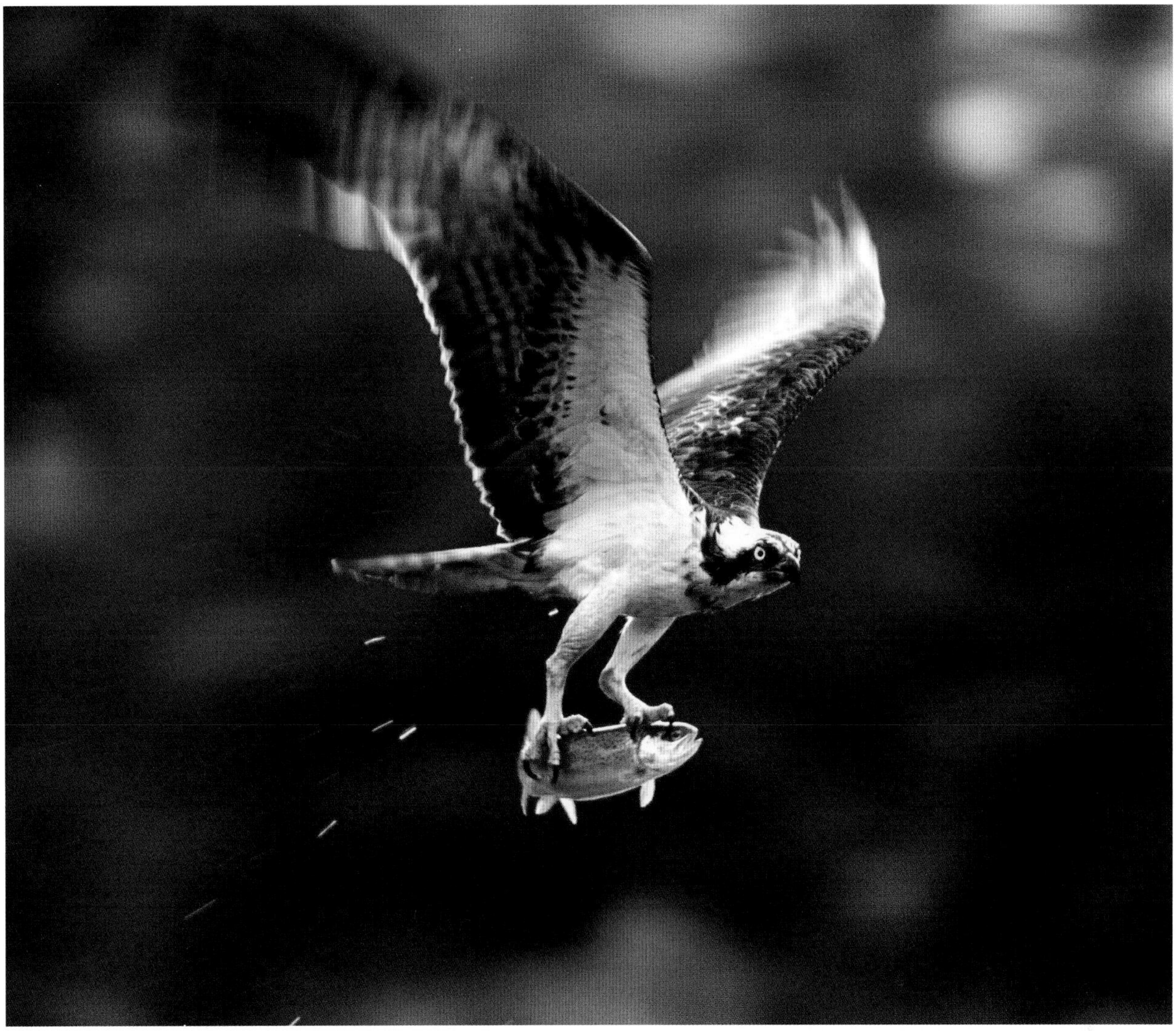

DAVID TIPLING

SUMMER

Small dots 1 ('pair')

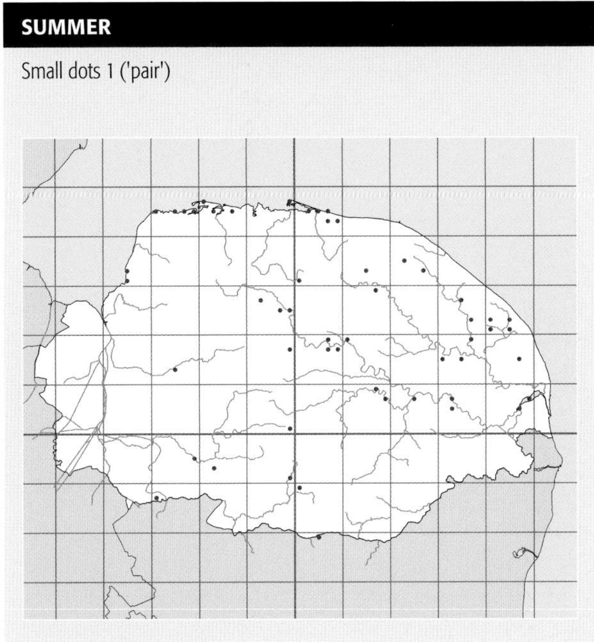

'The summer map shows that, during the NBA period, Ospreys were recorded at many well-scattered localities.'

and parkland lakes, but at few of the Breckland meres. Coastal brackish waters and north coast harbours were also occasionally visited by passing Ospreys during the summer periods. There are no previous atlas data for the county.

Trial nests are generally built in the year prior to first egg-laying, and if the pair are subsequently successful in fledging young, others are attracted to the area and a loose colony may well form (*1988–91 Atlas*). Ospreys have been recorded annually in Norfolk since 1953, and with the increasing number of spring migrants in recent years, peaking at 45 in 2004, it is a realistic hope that they may nest in the county before too long.

Kestrel

Falco tinnunculus

NBA 1999–2007	SUMMER: ALL / BREEDING	WINTER
TETRADS OCCUPIED	1,146 (79%) / 926 (63%)	1,235 (85%)
SUMMER/WINTER ONLY	122	211
MEAN PER OCCUPIED TETRAD	1 / 1	2
SUMMED MAX COUNTS	1,586 / 1,344	2,297
POPULATION ESTIMATE	1,000–1,500 bp	2,000–3,000

PREVIOUS ATLASES	SQUARES OCCUPIED	1999–2007	LOSSES	GAINS
1968–72 (10 KM)	62 (all)	62 (all)		
1980–85 (TETRAD)	1,047 (72%)	926 (63%)	356	235
1980–85 (10 KM)	62 (all)	62 (all)		
1981–84 WINTER (10 KM)	62 (all)	62 (all)		
1988–91 (10 KM)	62 (all)	62 (all)		

THE KESTREL HAS probably always been the most widespread and numerous raptor in Norfolk, although it did decline significantly during the early 1960s due to the effects of pesticides ingested through its prey. Once the organochlorines that were responsible had been banned, Kestrels quickly regained their former status.

Kestrels are found wherever there are open areas, such as parkland, farmland, heathland, commons, saltmarshes and dunes, over which they can hunt for the small mammals, especially voles, which form their main prey. They nest in trees, both along hedgerows and in woods, on ledges, in cliff holes and occasionally on tall buildings. It is therefore not surprising that the NBA summer map shows that it is very widespread throughout the county. However, pairs may hunt for food well away from the actual nest site and so their presence in a tetrad may not always indicate that they bred there.

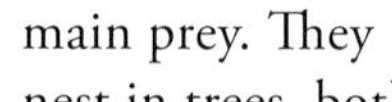

Kestrels are far less frequent visitors to gardens than are Sparrowhawks. Although Kestrels are scarce in central Norwich, they are found on the outskirts of the city and also breed in Great Yarmouth, where five pairs were present in each of two tetrads during the NBA summer fieldwork: these were at Martham and

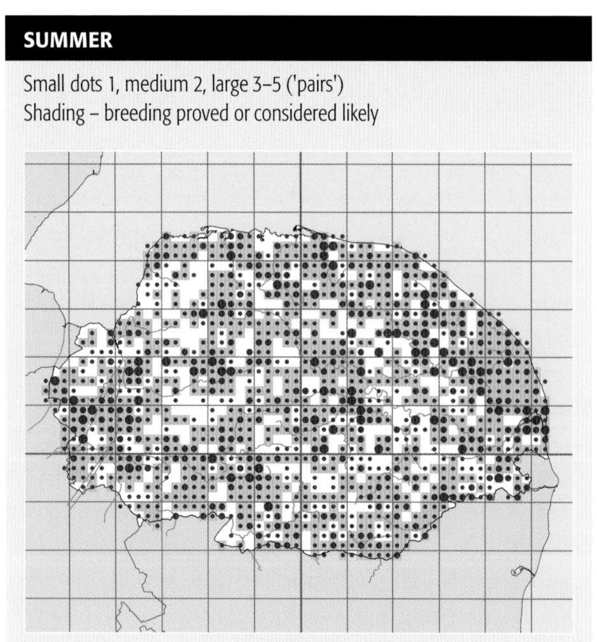

SUMMER

Small dots 1, medium 2, large 3–5 ('pairs')
Shading – breeding proved or considered likely

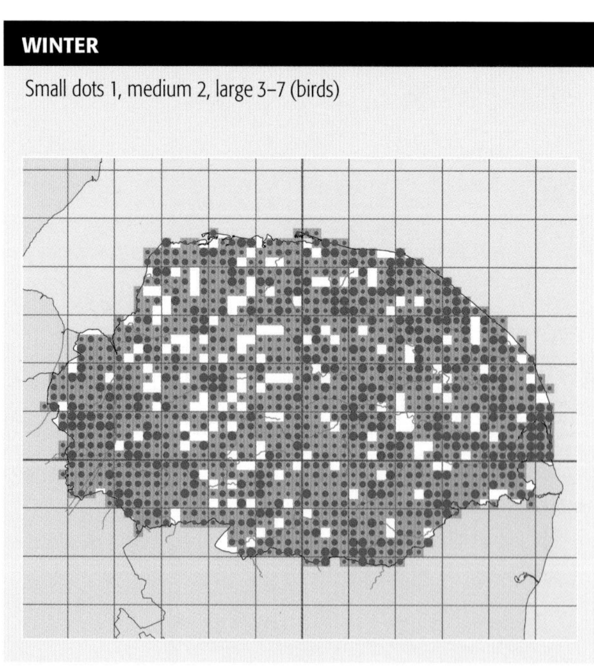

WINTER

Small dots 1, medium 2, large 3–7 (birds)

DAVID TIPLING

the North Denes area of the town, the latter birds possibly attracted by the large colony of Little Terns on the beach. At this ternery, Kestrel predation on hatchlings has been a significant factor in the high failure rates recorded, especially in 2001. Although birds do not feature highly in the list of items of prey taken by Kestrels, one was regularly noted taking Redshanks at Burnham Overy in 2004 and in June one was seen carrying an adult Little Tern. There is a healthy population of Kestrels is in the Stanford TA where, in 2005, 14 pairs (11 of which were breeding in nest boxes) successfully raised 55 young.

Kestrels in southeast England tend to be sedentary and pairs may remain within their breeding territories throughout the year, but the winter population in Norfolk is augmented by visitors from upland areas of Britain, as well as from the Continent. The NBA winter map shows the species to be even more widespread than in summer, with generally higher counts in the individual tetrads. Although Kestrels tend to be solitary, individual birds are often attracted to areas with concentrations of voles, such as grazing marshes, and three tetrads held up to seven birds: Cley/Wiveton, Buckenham Marshes and West Caister. Juveniles, in particular, are susceptible to harsh winter weather, when voles are harder to find.

CHANGE SINCE 1980–85

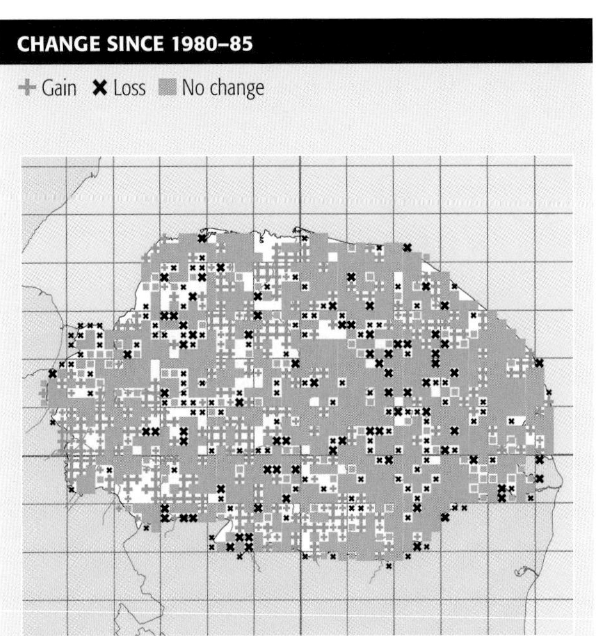

Comparison with previous atlases provides very little evidence of any expansion or contraction of range in Norfolk. The change map shows a mixture of gains and losses throughout the county, except in the Fens, where there has been a marked expansion of range since 1980–85.

Merlin
Falco columbarius

NBA 1999–2007	SUMMER: ALL / BREEDING	WINTER
TETRADS OCCUPIED	34 (2%) / none	158 (11%)
SUMMER/WINTER ONLY	7	131
MEAN PER OCCUPIED TETRAD	1 / none	1
SUMMED MAX COUNTS	37 / none	182
POPULATION ESTIMATE	none	15–25

PREVIOUS ATLASES	SQUARES OCCUPIED	1999–2007	LOSSES	GAINS
1980–85 (TETRAD)	1 (<1%)	none	1	0
1980–85 (10 KM)	1 (2%)	none	1	0
1981–84 WINTER (10 KM)	23 (37%)	48 (77%)	2	27

THIS SMALL DASHING falcon is a winter visitor and passage migrant in Norfolk, although it has been recorded in every month of the year. The British breeding population has undergone a long-term decline, due to continuing persecution, habitat loss and pesticide pollution, from which a recovery is now in progress (*Birdtrends*).

The Merlin breeds on moorland and other upland areas, and most populations are migratory; the wintering birds in southeast England are most likely to be from Scandinavia (*Migration Atlas*). It hunts small birds, particularly Skylarks, over open country and in Norfolk favours coastal fields, freshwater marshes, saltings, dunes and heaths. This preference is reflected in the NBA winter map, which shows clusters of records along the north Norfolk coast from Holme to Sheringham, in Broadland, over the heaths at Massingham and

EDMUND FELLOWES

CHRIS KNIGHTS

Grimston, on the Wash saltmarshes, and in the Welney area. In recent years, records from other sites well inland have no longer become exceptional, with sightings of Merlins hunting over arable fields. They usually hunt alone, but may roost or even hunt with other birds of prey such as Hen Harriers. During the NBA winters, a maximum of three Merlins, excluding roost counts, was noted at both Titchwell and Scolt Head.

For the last 30 years, Merlins have been counted at the half-a-dozen or so roost sites in the county, situated in marram dunes, heathland, freshwater marshes, saltings and willows (in the Fens). As winter roosts are sensitive to disturbance, the locations are not generally made public. As the birds hunt over extensive ranges by day, co-ordinated counts at these roosts is the only reliable method of estimating the county's wintering population. The maximum counts at the two widely known roost sites near Stubb Mill, Hickling, and at Warham Greens have been eight (two bushes holding four Merlins each in December 2005) and three respectively. Allowing for a few birds not using the communal roosts, 15–25 Merlins would appear to have wintered in Norfolk during the NBA period.

WINTER

Small dots 1, medium 2, large 3–8 (birds)

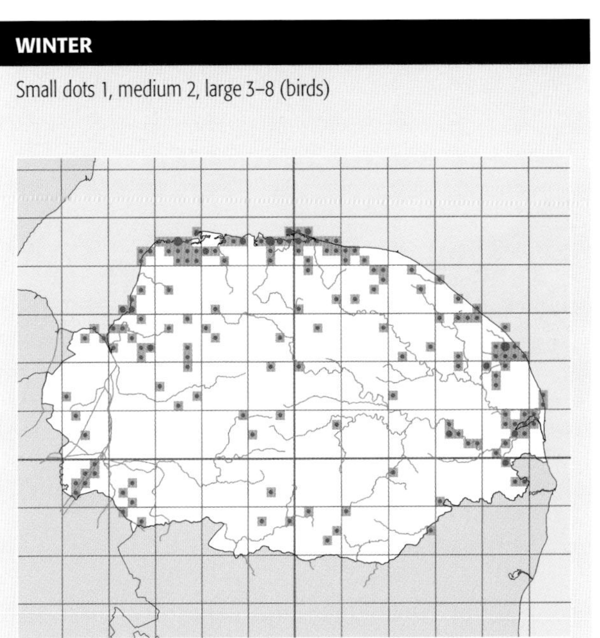

Most wintering Merlins have left the county by the end of March, although a few are reported in April and occasionally in May. In each of the years 2003–05, the species was also recorded in June, with the latest at Holme on 26th June 2004. The vast majority of reports of Merlins during the NBA summers were around the coast.

Hobby

Falco subbuteo

NBA 1999–2007	SUMMER: ALL/BREEDING	WINTER
TETRADS OCCUPIED	237 (16%) / 50 (3%)	none
SUMMER/WINTER ONLY	237	none
MEAN PER OCCUPIED TETRAD	1 / 1	none
SUMMED MAX COUNTS	274 / 64	none
POPULATION ESTIMATE	40–70 bp	none

PREVIOUS ATLASES	SQUARES OCCUPIED	1999–2007	LOSSES	GAINS
1968–72 (10 KM)	1 (2%)	26 (42%)	1	26
1980–85 (TETRAD)	7 (<1%)	50 (3%)	7	50
1980–85 (10 KM)	5 (8%)	26 (42%)	2	23
1988–91 (10 KM)	24 (39%)	26 (42%)	12	12

THE LONG, SLENDER wings of the Hobby give it a Swift-like appearance, an impression that is accentuated by its rapid glides and elegant aerobatics as it pursues its flying prey.

Like many raptors, Hobbies declined significantly during the 19th century due to persecution and egg collecting. Both *Stevenson* and *Riviere* described the species as an irregular breeder and there were only three recorded instances of successful breeding in Norfolk during the first half of the 20th century. Although a pair nested in 1983 and 1984, it was not until the next year that young were reared, the first record of successful breeding since 1951. Three pairs nested in the county in 1986, since when there has been a slow but steady increase in Hobbies summering and breeding in Norfolk.

Hobbies are summer visitors to Europe from southern Africa, and are highly dependent on aerial insect prey. The first in spring are generally recorded in Norfolk in mid April, with the main arrival occurring during May. They favour open areas of low vegetation with lines of trees or small areas of woodland, often near expanses of

CHRIS KNIGHTS

fresh water, where dragonflies are abundant. Heathland with clumps of pines and farmland bordering woodland or with mature hedgerow trees are both ideal breeding habitats.

While the NBA summer map indicates a wide distribution in the county, it is a compilation of records made over an eight-year period and may exaggerate the abundance and distribution of the species in any one year. Since nesting Hobbies are prone to disturbance and remain vulnerable to unwanted attention, the nesting distribution is not shown at tetrad level. Although Hobbies may be encountered almost anywhere within Norfolk, they are most abundant in Broadland and in the Brecks. In the summer of 2000, sightings of Hobbies in the latter area were considered to be as common as those of Sparrowhawks or Kestrels, while 2005 was an exceptionally good year and a total of 12 pairs nested in the Brecks, all in old Carrion Crows' nests in Scots pines, fledging at least 31 young (Hoblyn 2006). Several sites in Broadland attract good numbers of Hobbies, the highest counts during the years of NBA fieldwork including 25 at Hickling Broad in June 2005, nine at Strumpshaw and six at Rockland Broad. Elsewhere, 30 were noted at Hockwold Washes in the Fens in May 2004, while up to seven were recorded at both Sennowe Park and Houghton Park.

Male Hobbies do not breed until they are two years old, and females are probably not fertile until that age (*BWP2*). In recent years, increasing numbers of first-summer Hobbies have oversummered in Norfolk (Williamson 2000) and these non-breeding birds have undoubtedly accounted for many of the NBA records. During the nesting period, Hobbies tend to be unobtrusive except during courtship displays and while feeding the young (*1988–91 Atlas*), when they are most likely to be taking avian prey, especially hirundines and Swifts.

BREEDING TOTALS

Breeding pairs in Norfolk for each of the NBA summers (data from *NBR*)

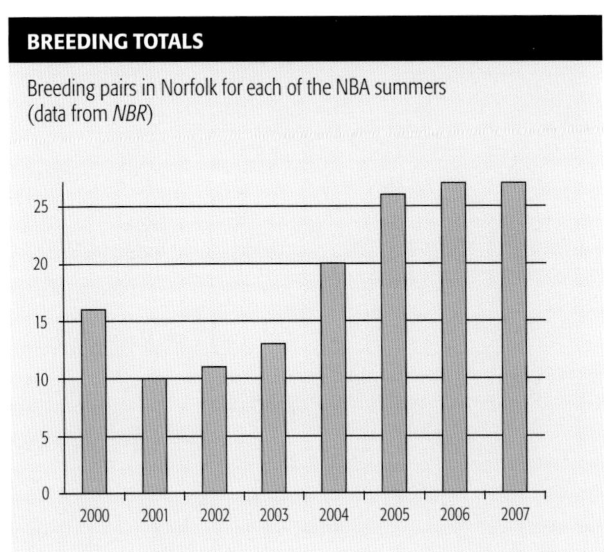

SUMMER

Small dots 1, medium 2, large 3–8 ('pairs')
Shading – breeding proved or considered likely

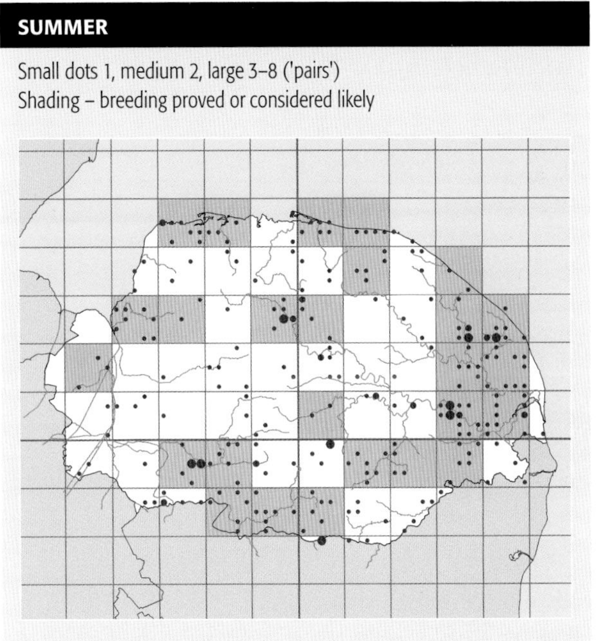

'The first in spring are generally recorded in Norfolk in mid April, with the main arrival occurring during May.'

Nesting birds range very widely when hunting, and passage migrants and non-breeders might be observed almost anywhere. It is thus very difficult to assess whether Hobbies recorded away from known breeding areas might indicate a pair nesting in the tetrad in which they were seen, and the population assessment is necessarily speculative. During the NBA period the number of nesting pairs being reported to the county recorders showed a clear increasing trend, rising to 27 by 2006 (*NBR*). NBA found a cumulative total of 64 likely breeding pairs in 50 tetrads. Given the secretive nature of the species, we feel that as many as 40–70 pairs may have nested in Norfolk each summer in the NBA period.

Peregrine

Falco peregrinus

NBA 1999–2007	SUMMER: ALL/BREEDING	WINTER
TETRADS OCCUPIED	36 (2%) / none	146 (10%)
SUMMER/WINTER ONLY	11	121
MEAN PER OCCUPIED TETRAD	1 / none	1
SUMMED MAX COUNTS	36 / none	172
POPULATION ESTIMATE	0–2 individuals	15–25

PREVIOUS ATLASES	SQUARES OCCUPIED	1999–2007	LOSSES	GAINS
1981–84 WINTER (10 KM)	7 (11%)	48 (77%)	0	41

DAVID TIPLING

PEREGRINES FORMERLY BRED in Norfolk, Hunstanton cliffs being a traditional site that was last used in 1815, but the species had disappeared as a breeding species in the county by the middle of the 19th century. Nowadays, it is known as a winter visitor and passage migrant, although overwintering has only become regular since the mid 1980s. Normally nesting on cliffs and crags, Peregrines now breed in several British cities on cathedrals and other tall, inaccessible buildings. A new colonisation of the county is eagerly awaited.

The species declined during the 19th and 20th centuries as a result of human persecution, but far more catastrophic was the effect of contamination from organochlorine pesticides during the 1950s. Once these chemicals had been banned in the early 1960s, Peregrines began to recover and the breeding population in the UK rose to around 1,400 pairs by 2002 (*Birdtrends*).

The NBA winter map demonstrates that two main areas of the county are favoured: the coastal marshes along the north Norfolk and Wash coastline and Broadland, although a considerable number of sightings were noted at well-scattered inland sites elsewhere.

SUMMER

Small dots 1 ('pair')

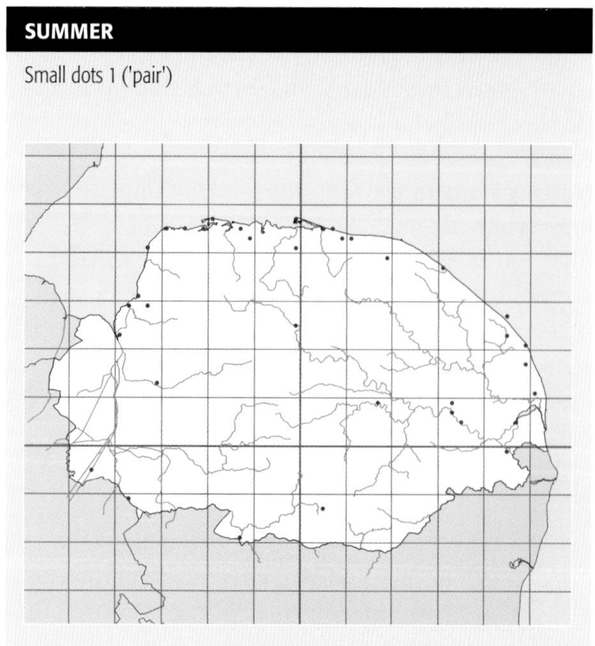

WINTER

Small dots 1, medium 2, large 3–4 (birds)

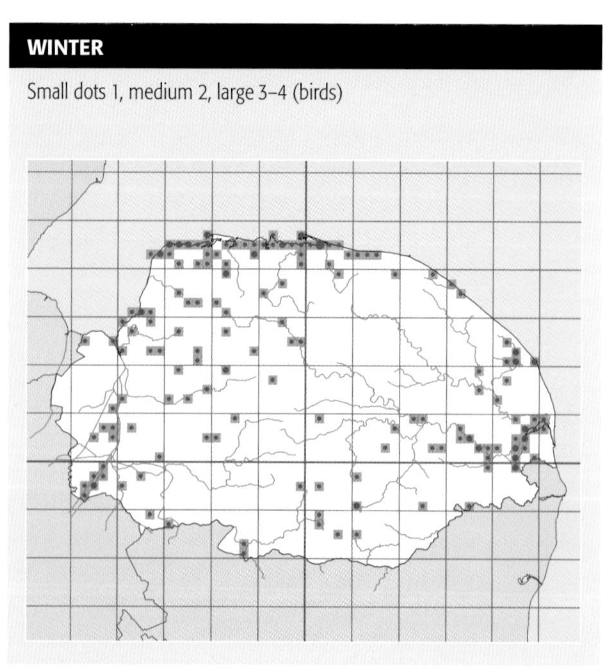

DAVID TIPLING

In northwest Norfolk, Peregrines regularly overwinter along various stretches of the coast, each section holding up to three birds. The favoured areas are Wolferton/Snettisham, Hunstanton/Titchwell, Scolt Head/Brancaster Harbour and Holkham/Cley. In east Norfolk, up to three have also wintered regularly in the Breydon Water/Berney/Fritton area (roosting on the Haddiscoe pylons at night) and two in the Horsey/Heigham Holmes area and in the Yare valley. Up to two have been recorded at Welney in the Fens. Inland, Peregrines appear to favour the flock ranges of Golden Plovers. The highest day-counts have been five at Stiffkey on 31st January 2004 and four at Blakeney GM on 10th December 2001.

Many of the Peregrines that overwinter in Norfolk are first-winter birds that have dispersed from their natal areas in the north and west of Britain, or are visitors from Scandinavia, and others are adults presumably returning to former haunts. Many establish temporary home ranges during the winter months, which are used in successive years. Feral Pigeons and dovecote birds are major food items for breeding Peregrines, but this changes during the winter months, when waders and ducks feature more prominently in their diet.

While most of the Peregrines have left Norfolk by late April, passage birds are recorded in May and one or two are even noted in June in most years. The vast majority are recorded on only a single date but one lingered at Titchwell from 7th to 15th May 2000. The NBA summer map shows that most of those noted during the summer recording period were at coastal locations, supporting the assumption that they were largely birds on passage.

Comparison with the *1981–84 Winter Atlas* demonstrates the extent of winter range gain in Norfolk, from 11% of 10-km squares in that survey to 77% during the NBA period.

Water Rail
Rallus aquaticus

NBA 1999–2007	SUMMER: ALL/BREEDING	WINTER
TETRADS OCCUPIED	58% (4%) / 44 (3%)	177 (12%)
SUMMER/WINTER ONLY	21	140
MEAN PER OCCUPIED TETRAD	3 / 4	3
SUMMED MAX COUNTS	202 / 188	488
POPULATION ESTIMATE	100–200 bp	500–800

PREVIOUS ATLASES	SQUARES OCCUPIED	1999–2007	LOSSES	GAINS
1968–72 (10 KM)	33 (53%)	16 (26%)	20	3
1980–85 (TETRAD)	54 (4%)	44 (3%)	46	36
1980–85 (10 KM)	30 (48%)	16 (26%)	22	8
1981–84 WINTER (10 KM)	35 (56%)	48 (77%)	4	17
1988–91 (10 KM)	17 (27%)	16 (26%)	8	7

THE SKULKING HABITS of the Water Rail mean that its characteristic calls, recalling squealing pigs and known as sharming, and given most often between dusk and dawn, are heard far more often than the bird is seen.

As a breeding species in Norfolk, it was common in wetland sites in the 19th century, but declined as a result of drainage and by 1930 was far more localised, with the bulk of the population in Broadland. The

species continued to decline during the second half of the 20th century although this trend appears to have halted.

During the summer, the Water Rail inhabits freshwater swamps, marshes and fens with fairly tall, dense vegetation, especially stands of *Phragmites*, while flooded and overgrown old gravel pits are also occupied by breeding pairs. The NBA summer map shows a sparse and well-scattered distribution, with the main concentration in Broadland, where it has been for at least the last 80 years. Water Rails were also recorded at several of the reserves along the north Norfolk coast but at very few sites in the Fens. There were many in the reedbeds at Lopham Fen; this site is at the head of the Waveney valley and apparently well isolated from other known breeding sites in Norfolk. By their secretive nature and the fact that they are more vocal at night, it is likely that Water Rails were missed at some less frequently visited sites.

Nocturnal censuses of calling birds at reserves shows how densely occupied some favoured sites

SUMMER

Small dots 1, medium 2–3, large 4–55 ('pairs')
Shading – breeding proved or considered likely

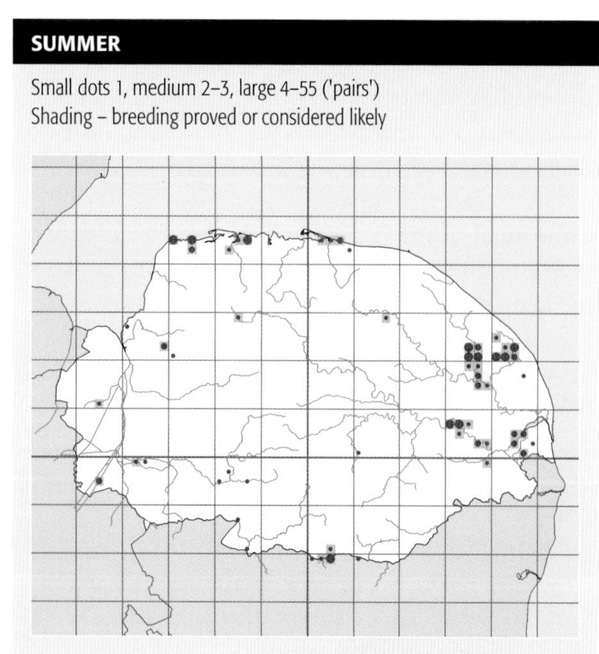

WINTER

Small dots 1, medium 2–3, large 4–31 (birds)

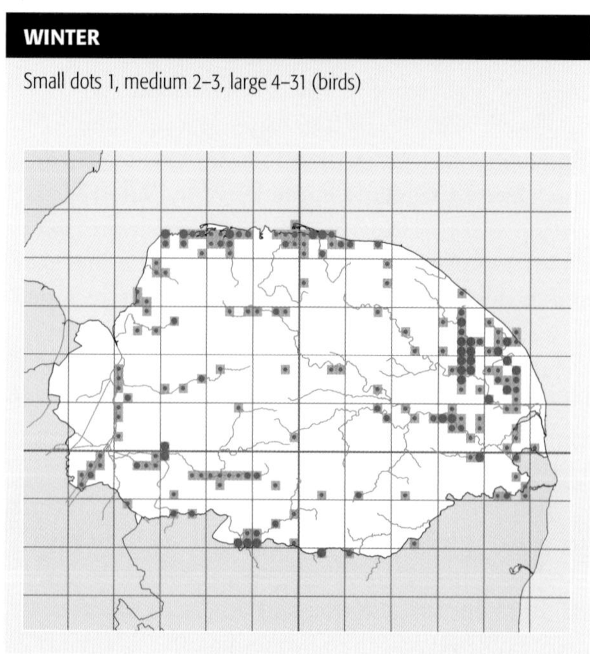

DAVID TIPLING

can be. For example at Strumpshaw in 2004, no fewer than 55 territory-holding pairs were located. In other recent years, 20 pairs have been estimated at Holkham NNR, 17 at Hickling and 10–14 at Surlingham. An estimated 17 pairs at Lopham Fen in 2007 included birds in the smaller Suffolk section of the reserve (Green 2007).

The British population of Water Rails is largely resident but immigrants from northern Europe arrive in the autumn. During periods of severe winter weather, especially persistent frost after heavy snowfalls, birds may be found in a variety of atypical habitats, such as open ditches and even gardens, and this is reflected in the much wider distribution as shown on the NBA winter map. As in the summer, there are obvious concentrations in the reedbeds in Broadland and along the north Norfolk coast between Holme and Kelling, but in addition many Water Rails were noted at inland locations throughout the county. Many of these sites were along the river valleys, where birds fed amongst the riverside vegetation or in the adjoining drainage ditches. Other places holding wintering Water Rails included old gravel pits, sewage treatment works and beet-factory settling ponds. Although Water Rails tend to be solitary during the winter, some surprisingly high counts were made, including 30 at Surlingham Broad and 20 elsewhere in the Broads at Catfield Fen, Hickling and Strumpshaw, and at Holme on the north Norfolk coast.

CHANGE SINCE 1980–85

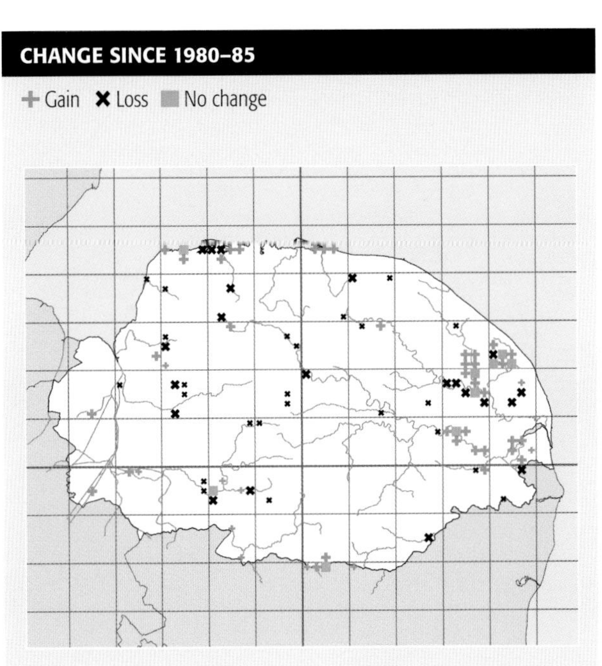

Water Rails probably have few predators deep in the heart of the reedbeds but a Sparrowhawk, which had swept through a Starling roost at Weybourne Hope reedbed, was seen to take one; it was then dropped and released, however, apparently unharmed.

Comparison with the results from earlier atlases suggests that range changes have been relatively minor. The change map indicates that some losses have occurred in inland Norfolk since the *1980–85 NBBS*, but there are gains notably at Lopham Fen, where its habitat has been extensively restored, in the Cley area, and in the Broads and Fenland.

Moorhen
Gallinula chloropus

NBA 1999–2007	SUMMER: ALL/BREEDING	WINTER
TETRADS OCCUPIED	1,216 (83%) / 1,189 (81%)	1,169 (80%)
SUMMER/WINTER ONLY	118	71
MEAN PER OCCUPIED TETRAD	5 / 5	10
SUMMED MAX COUNTS	5,684 / 5,650	12,191
POPULATION ESTIMATE	8,000–10,000 bp	20,000–30,000

PREVIOUS ATLASES	SQUARES OCCUPIED	1999–2007	LOSSES	GAINS
1968–72 (10 KM)	62 (all)	62 (all)		
1980–85 (TETRAD)	1,188 (81%)	1,189 (81%)	134	135
1980–85 (10 KM)	62 (all)	62 (all)		
1981–84 WINTER (10 KM)	62 (all)	62 (all)		
1988–91 (10 KM)	62 (all)	62 (all)		

ABLE TO NEST BY the tiniest of ponds, the Moorhen is a widespread and numerous bird of fresh waters throughout the county.

During the breeding season, Moorhens are found in most areas of open fresh water bordered by bankside or emergent vegetation, particularly favouring those sheltered by woodland or tall emergent plants. Although their distribution overlaps that of the Coot along the margins of lakes and rivers, Moorhens tend to avoid more open, disturbed water. Unlike Coots, they also occupy the tiny pools, only a few metres across, that are a common feature of nearly all of Norfolk's farmland.

The NBA summer map shows that Moorhens occur very widely throughout the county, but rather sparsely in the northern half of the Fens. The species was also absent from parts of the Brecks, in particular around Beachamwell and the extensive areas of woodland between Mundford and Methwold, as well as from Terrington Marsh, the chalkier soils around the Docking area and the northern part of Norwich.

Although it was generally not difficult to detect Moorhens during the summer, many drainage ditches in the Fens were inaccessible due to standing crops and lush bankside vegetation. One Fenland observer commented that the species was surprisingly scarce in the tetrads he covered, attributing this to the lack of trees or shrubs for nesting in by the dykes, leaving nests vulnerable to ground predators such as rats (N. Owens, pers comm). The clearing of bankside vegetation is known to reduce the number of breeding Moorhens. They also form an important part of the diet of American mink *Mustela vison*, which first appeared

SUMMER

Small dots 1–2, medium 3–5, large 6–38 ('pairs')
Shading – breeding proved or considered likely

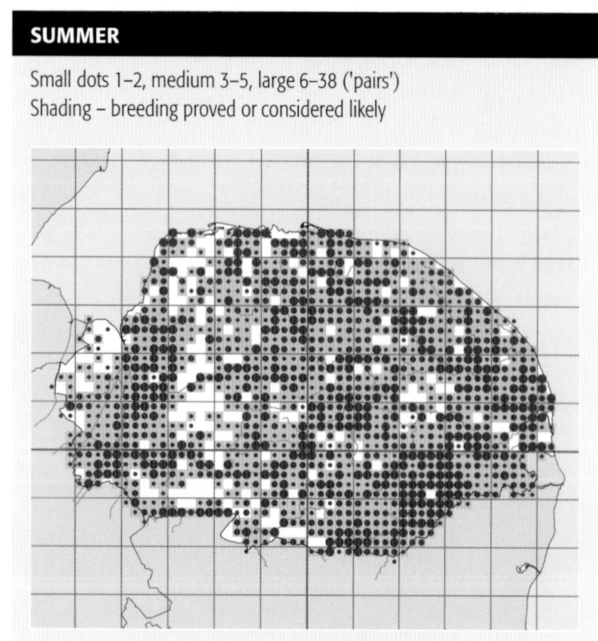

WINTER

Small dots 1–4, medium 5–11, large 12–109 (birds)

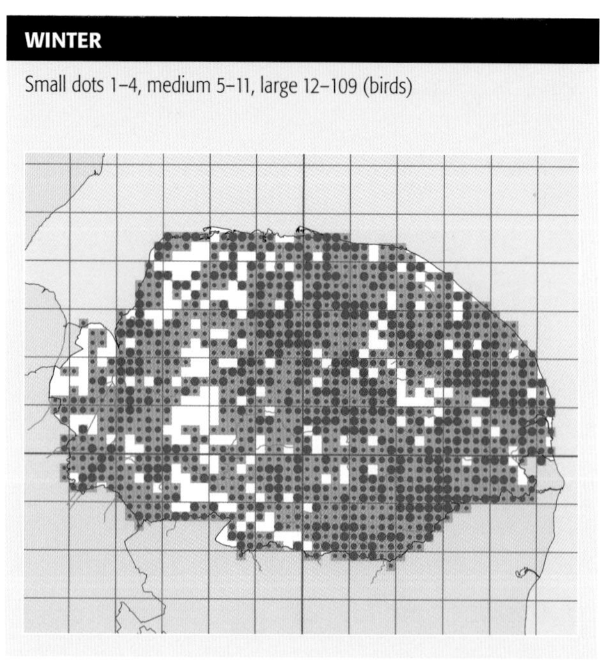

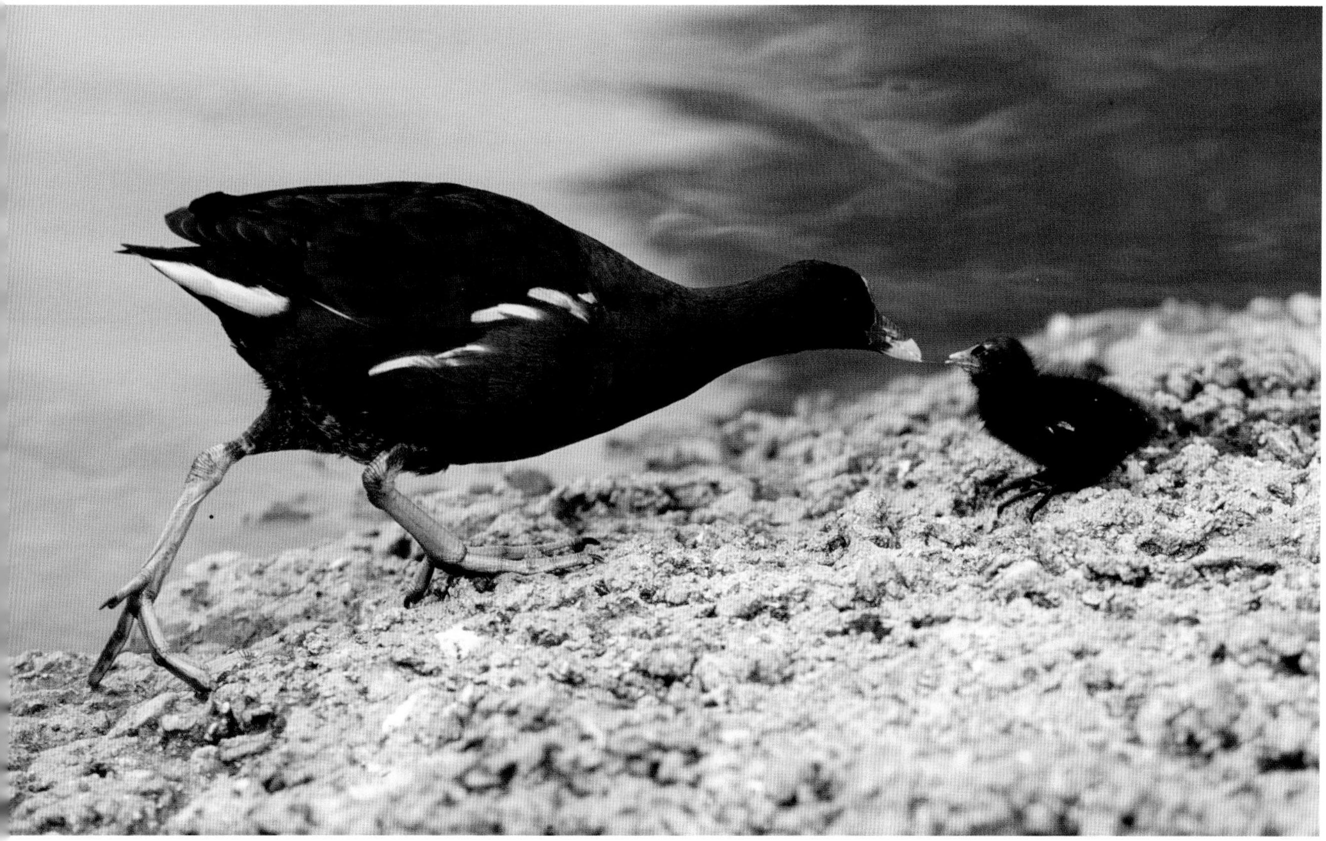

DAVID TIPLING

in the wild in Britain in the 1950s, and one observer believed that this predator was responsible for the virtual disappearance of Moorhens from the Tud valley.

Throughout the NBA summers, Holkham NNR consistently held the highest numbers of breeding birds, varying from 83 to 110 pairs annually. The breeding population at Cley has fallen from 48 pairs in 1993 to 12 in recent years. Moorhens are known to nest in bushes or low trees by the waterside, as well as on the ground, but a nest built two metres off the ground in a Lawson cypress tree in a pondless garden in Blakeney was most unusual.

CHANGE SINCE 1980–85

+ Gain ✖ Loss ■ No change

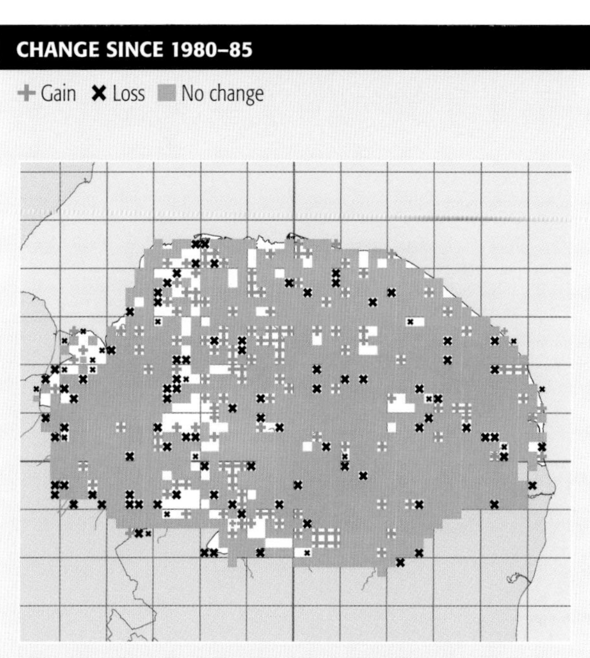

Although some pairs remain within their territories throughout the year, many adults and first-winter birds form loose winter flocks based on farmland ditches or around the margins of larger bodies of water, such as the Broads and parkland lakes. Winter numbers are augmented by visitors from further north and east in Europe, where the species is more migratory. The NBA winter map shows an almost identical distribution to that in the summer, however, but with more localised concentrations of birds. The highest site counts during the years of the NBA were all made in north Norfolk, with 102 at Holkham NNR, 109 at Cley and 103 at Blakeney GM, where no fewer than 60 were present on one occasion within an enclosure for pinioned wildfowl.

The overall distribution statistics indicate no range change since previous atlases. The change map, however, suggests that infilling has occurred within some of the groups of tetrads from which Moorhens were not recorded in 1980–85.

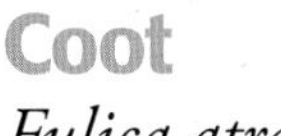

Coot

Fulica atra

NBA 1999–2007	SUMMER: ALL/BREEDING	WINTER
TETRADS OCCUPIED	468 (32%) / 410 (28%)	426 (29%)
SUMMER/WINTER ONLY	125	83
MEAN PER OCCUPIED TETRAD	5 / 6	41
SUMMED MAX COUNTS	2,535 / 2,461	17,283
POPULATION ESTIMATE	1,800–2,500 bp	15,000–20,000

PREVIOUS ATLASES	SQUARES OCCUPIED	1999–2007	LOSSES	GAINS
1968–72 (10 KM)	53 (85%)	60 (97%)	0	7
1980–85 (TETRAD)	383 (26%)	410 (28%)	154	181
1980–85 (10 KM)	56 (90%)	60 (97%)	1	5
1981–84 WINTER (10 KM)	58 (94%)	60 (97%)	1	3
1988–91 (10 KM)	57 (92%)	60 (97%)	1	4

THE COOT HAS ALWAYS been a common and widespread water bird in Norfolk, the county's breeding population increasing as gravel extraction proliferated during the 20th century.

Compared with the Moorhen, it favours larger expanses of open freshwater, albeit fairly shallow with surrounding emergent or floating vegetation. Thus it is found on the Broads, parkland lakes, gravel pits, Breckland lakes and meres, reed-fringed drainage dykes on the coastal reserves and even on some slow-moving rivers. The NBA summer map shows that it is a common and widespread species throughout low-lying areas of the county, being absent only from the more arable areas in northwest, south and central Norfolk, as well as parts of Fenland and the Brecks. Clear concentrations exist in Broadland and on the north Norfolk coastal reserves.

Annual surveys at Holkham NNR suggest that numbers probably reached a peak during the 1990s, with 176 pairs in 1995 and a maximum of 154 during the years of NBA fieldwork. The number of breeding pairs at Welney peaked at 205 in 2000, but many of the nests failed due to predation as the floods receded from May onwards. In Broadland, up to 79 pairs were recorded at Ormesby Broad and, in the Nar valley, West Acre held up to 67 pairs.

While some pairs remain within their territories throughout the year, many move to larger areas of open water to moult, from June onwards, where they remain throughout the winter, often grazing the surrounding grassland as well as diving for food. While the NBA winter distribution is almost identical

SUMMER

Small dots 1, medium 2–4, large 5–79 ('pairs')
Shading – breeding proved or considered likely

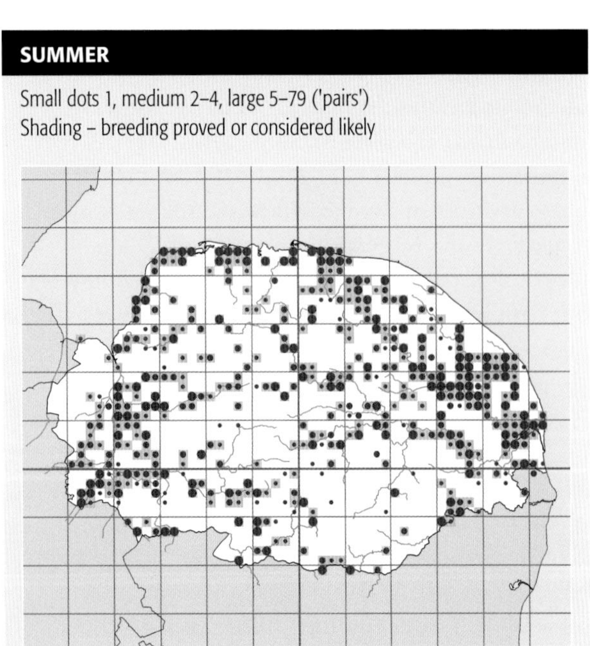

WINTER

Small dots 1–3, medium 4–16, large 17–825 (birds)

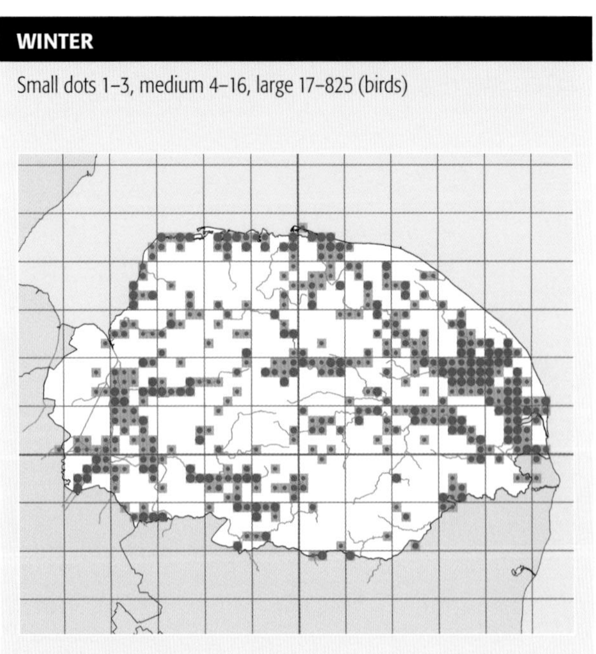

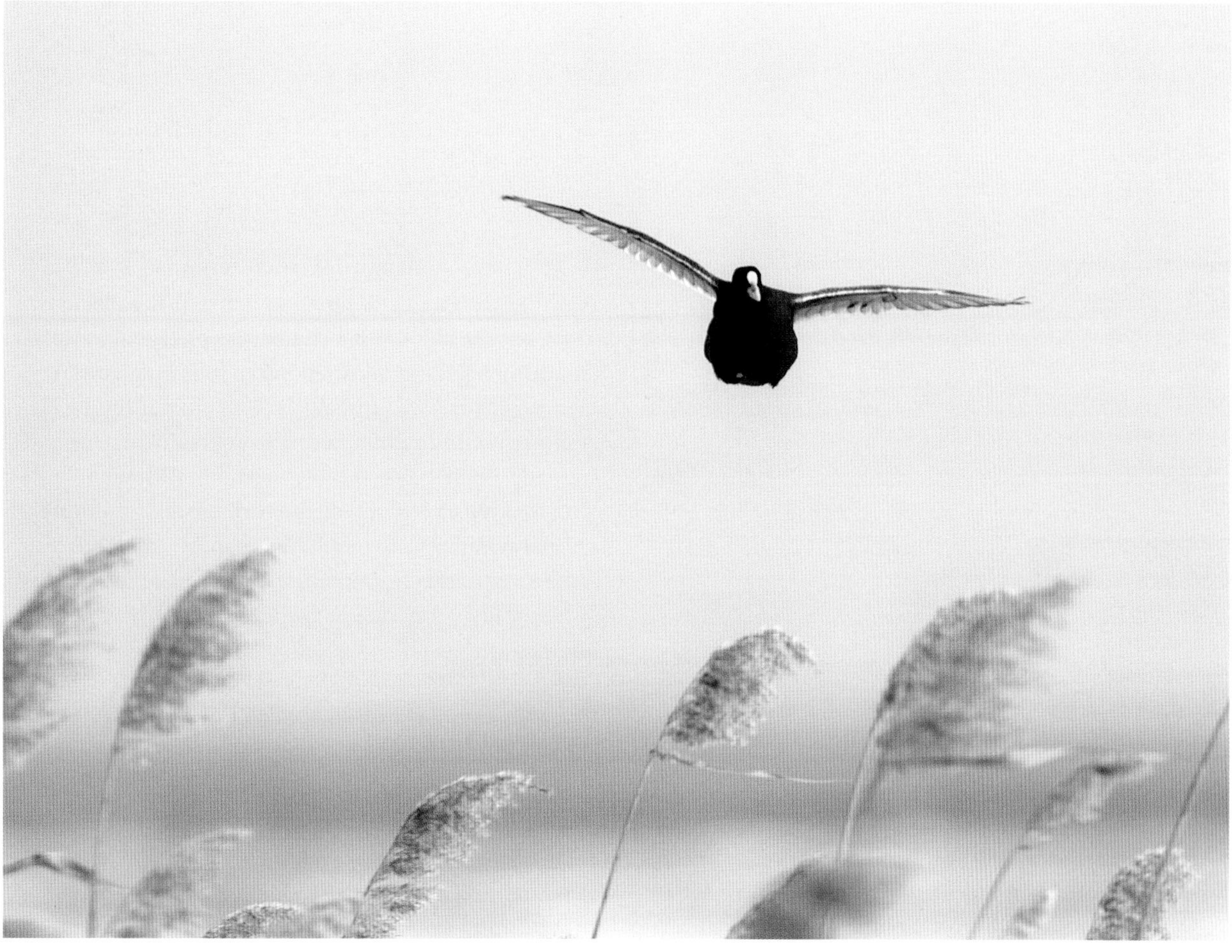

DAVID TIPLING

'The summer map shows that Coot is a common and widespread species throughout low-lying areas...'

CHANGE SINCE 1980–85

+ Gain ✖ Loss ■ No change

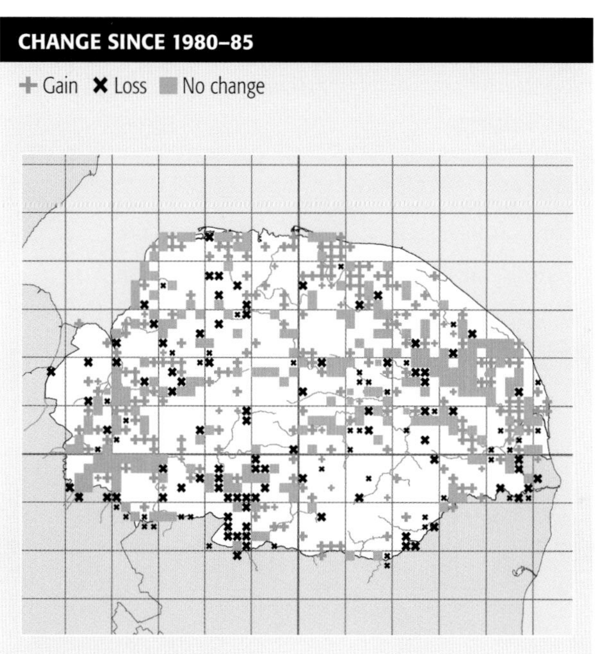

to that in the summer, it shows a clearer concentration of numbers in Broadland, where Hickling Broad has been a favourite wintering site for Coots since at least the early 19th century. Considerable numbers still assemble here with a peak count during the NBA winters of 5,300 in December 1999. Elsewhere in Broadland, Breydon Water has held almost 1,500 of which over 700 have gathered on Berney Marshes. On the outskirts of Norwich, 825 were recorded at Colney GP.

During periods of severe weather, particularly if inland waters become frozen, Coots move to brackish coastal sites and even estuaries. The north and east European populations are migratory and cold weather on the Continent may result in movements into Britain of these birds at any time during the winter.

The breeding distribution is similar to that recorded during the *1980–85 NBBS*, although some extension of range is evident, especially in the northeast of the county. A concentration of tetrad losses in Breckland suggests that the meres, some of which have very variable water levels, were generally in poor condition for Coots during the NBA period.

Crane

Grus grus

NBA 1999–2007	SUMMER: ALL/BREEDING	WINTER
TETRADS OCCUPIED	17 (1%) / 4 (<1%)	15 (1%)
SUMMER/WINTER ONLY	9	7
MEAN PER OCCUPIED TETRAD	2 / 1	12
SUMMED MAX COUNTS	28 / 4	187
POPULATION ESTIMATE	2-9 bp	11-36

PREVIOUS ATLASES	SQUARES OCCUPIED	1999–2007	LOSSES	GAINS
1968–72 (10 KM)	none	1 (2%)	0	1
1980–85 (TETRAD)	1 (<1%)	4 (<1%)	0	3
1980–85 (10 KM)	1 (2%)	1 (2%)		
1981–84 WINTER (10 KM)	2 (3%)	4 (6%)	0	2
1988–91 (10 KM)	1 (2%)	1 (2%)		

THE CRANE BREEDS from Fenno-Scandia and the northern part of central Europe eastwards to central Siberia. As a result of hunting and wetland drainage in the Middle Ages, the European range and population of Cranes began to decrease. During the last 30–40 years, however, it has begun to reoccupy some of its former haunts and, since 1981, at least one pair has bred or attempted to breed in Norfolk, the first in Britain for many centuries.

Cranes need large undisturbed wetlands in which to breed and, as the nest is built on the ground, the nest-site has to be inaccessible to potential ground predators. For this reason the birds select soft, waterlogged, marshy ground, the nest being built up well above the water table.

After arriving in Norfolk in the autumn of 1979, a pair remained and attempted to breed in Broadland in 1981 but the chick that hatched was predated. However, successful breeding occurred in the following year. At least two pairs bred annually in Norfolk during the NBA summers, with in 2006 five pairs definitely nesting and four additional pairs possibly breeding. Although Cranes are gregarious for much of the year, breeding pairs are generally solitary and have large nesting territories. Nest failure may result from predation by Marsh Harriers or Bitterns, but foxes are the greatest threat at both the egg and nestling stages.

The NBA summer map does not show the breeding distribution at tetrad level, although the general nesting location is widely known. Each spring singles, pairs or small groups of Cranes are recorded flying west around the Norfolk coast, before returning to the Broads the same day or a few days later. Some remain to feed on marshland in north Norfolk, where they have been mapped. The other occupied tetrads include one that took up residence at Pensthorpe, having been attracted by the captive birds there, and birds that bred at Lakenheath Fen, across the border in Suffolk, in 2007.

In winter, Cranes feed in open, but preferably inaccessible, fields and grazing marshes. The NBA winter map shows that as in summer, they are concentrated in a small part of northeastern Broadland. The Norfolk

WINTER TOTALS

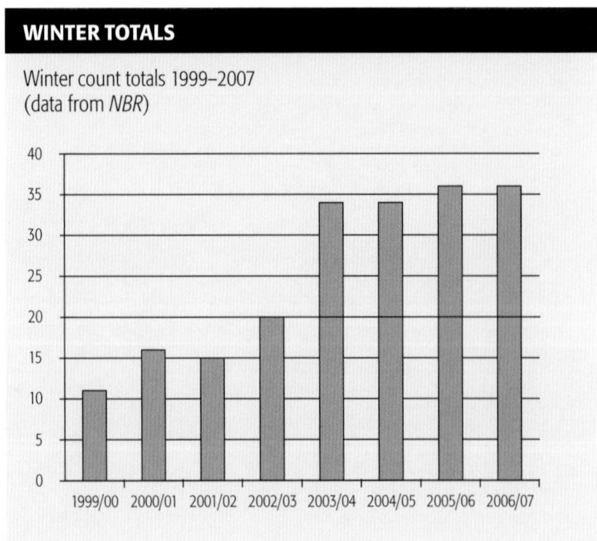

DAVID TIPLING

winter population exceeds the total of local adults and their offspring. This was especially true during the winter of 2004/05, when the Broadland flock reached 24 in December 2004 but had increased to 34 by January 2005. A party of three seen arriving off the sea at Scolt Head in September 2004 suggests a Scandinavian origin for at least some of these extra birds. The following winter, a juvenile that was present in Broadland in December was thought to be from one of the pairs that had bred in Yorkshire in 2005.

An almost sequential pattern of growth in winter peak numbers in Norfolk was evident during the NBA period.

SUMMER

Small dots 1, medium 2, large 3–7 ('pairs')
Shading – breeding proved, dots centralised within 20-km square

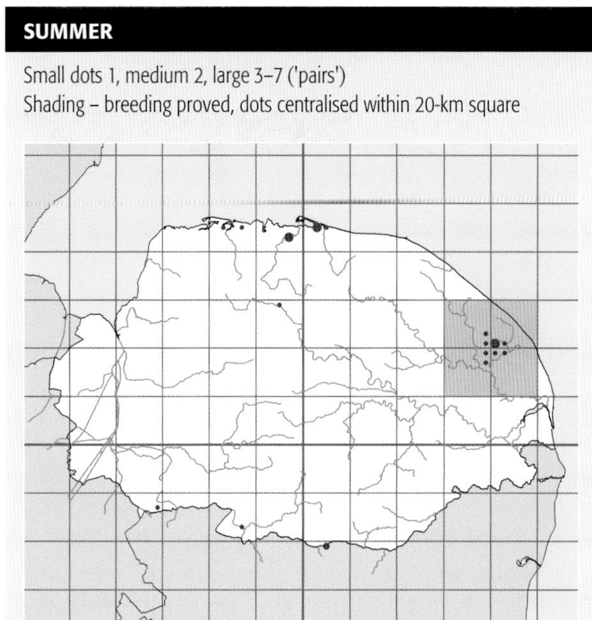

WINTER

Small dots 1–3, medium 4–12, large 13–34 (birds)

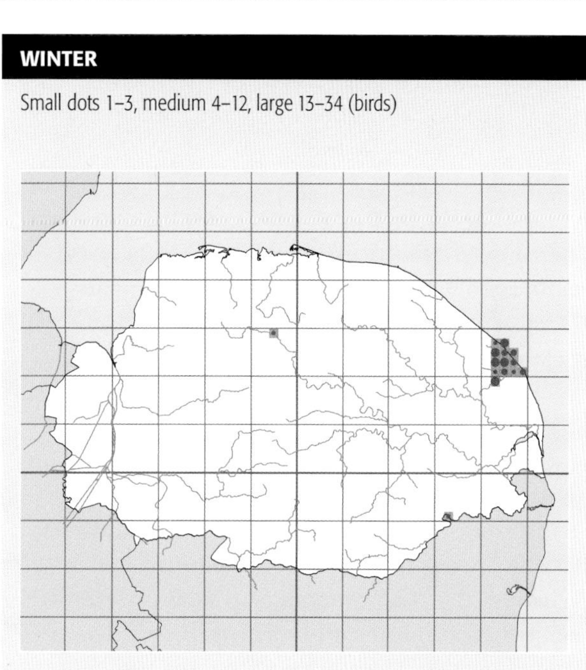

Oystercatcher
Haematopus ostralegus

NBA 1999–2007	SUMMER: ALL / BREEDING	WINTER
TETRADS OCCUPIED	626 (43%) / 411 (28%)	147
SUMMER/WINTER ONLY	501	22
MEAN PER OCCUPIED TETRAD	6 / 8	154
SUMMED MAX COUNTS	3,879 / 3,386	22,710
POPULATION ESTIMATE	400–500 bp	8,000–9,000

PREVIOUS ATLASES	SQUARES OCCUPIED	1999–2007	LOSSES	GAINS
1968–72 (10 KM)	18 (29%)	56 (90%)	1	39
1980–85 (TETRAD)	218 (15%)	411 (28%)	71	264
1980–85 (10 KM)	36 (58%)	56 (90%)	0	20
1981–84 WINTER (10 KM)	20 (32%)	42 (68%)	3	25
1988–91 (10 KM)	47 (76%)	56 (90%)	2	11

DAVID TIPLING

THE OYSTERCATCHER'S NAME suggests a bird of the coast, where indeed it is conspicuous on many of Norfolk's beaches and estuaries. In the last few decades, however, it has spread to many inland sites, where they nest on grazing marshes, open pasture and arable land.

In Britain, as in other western European countries, breeding Oystercatchers increased and became more widespread during the 20th century, particularly after 1940. During the *1968–72 Atlas*, the species was nesting inland throughout much of Scotland and northwest England but in East Anglia was virtually confined to the coast. By the *1988–91 Atlas*, inland breeding had spread to many parts of eastern England, including Norfolk.

Around the coast, Oystercatchers feed on marine molluscs in the intertidal zone, as well as on softer-bodied invertebrates that they obtain from both marine and terrestrial substrates. Breeding pairs, therefore, need to be within a reasonable distance of such food sources and nests are located on shingle beaches, among dunes and on saltmarshes. As a result of increasing disturbance from holidaymakers, the vast majority of coastal Oystercatchers now nest on nature reserves. Breeding Oystercatchers are largely absent from the coast of northeast Norfolk, where beaches are narrower and more disturbed.

Inland, the NBA summer map shows an almost complete distribution at tetrad level in northwest Norfolk, with extensive concentrations also in Broadland and in unforested parts of Breckland. Elsewhere in the county, the breeding distribution closely follows Norfolk's major rivers. Inland sites are generally deserted after late July until the birds return in late winter or early spring.

During the breeding season, Oystercatchers draw attention to themselves by their noisy piping displays and it is unlikely that many pairs will have been missed. Some records, however, will undoubtedly be of passing migrants or of birds nesting in adjacent tetrads. The NBA summer map also shows the spring flocks that gather on the Wash in April and May, often involving over 2,000 birds.

Earlier surveys of breeding Oystercatchers revealed 190 pairs in Broadland in 1995 and 530 pairs around the coast from the Wash to Cley in 1997, which included 200 pairs on Blakeney Point alone. It is not known how many of these pairs were actually nesting, however. During the NBA summers, numbers at Blakeney Point peaked at 154 pairs in 2003 with 148 pairs the following year; however, in each of these years hardly any eggs hatched, due to predation by Common Gulls. If this continues, recruitment to the colony will clearly not take place and numbers are bound to fall. The only other site to hold over 100 breeding pairs was Scolt Head, where there were up to 108 pairs. Elsewhere around the coast, breeding failures were the result of human disturbance and ground predators, while predation of the young by Marsh Harriers occurred annually at Holkham NNR.

In 1996, Oystercatchers were first suspected of breeding on the flat roof of the Asda superstore adjacent to Breydon Water and this habit has continued in recent years, but with varying success (Dye 2003). A pair also nested on the flat roof of a small hangar at the deserted airbase at Sculthorpe for the first time in 2002 (Bloomfield 2003b), while displaying birds were noted on roofs at the Bircham Newton Training Centre in 2004. A nest at Thornham Harbour in 2002 was on top of a tree stump.

Oystercatchers are gregarious in winter, although they often feed alone or in small groups, gathering into large flocks at the high-tide roosts. The NBA winter map shows the mainly coastal distribution of the species at this time of year. The vast majority of birds were found along the north and west coasts between the Wash and Blakeney, with smaller gatherings in the Breydon Water area. During the NBA winters, the highest counts all involved high-tide roosts and included up to 6,440 at Snettisham, 2,585 at Ousemouth, 1,500 at Wolferton and 1,350 at Holme. While many juvenile British-bred Oystercatchers winter in western France and Iberia, a large proportion of the population of Norway winters around the Wash (*Migration Atlas*). The number of wintering birds varies in relation to the available stocks of cockles and mussels, and the species is also very vulnerable to starvation during periods of prolonged severe weather. Counts made for the Wetland Bird Survey in recent years indicate a substantial reduction in the number of Oystercatchers overwintering around the Norfolk coast compared with the late 1980s and early 1990s.

The few Oystercatchers recorded inland during the NBA winters were mostly either birds making short feeding forays from the coast, or birds returning to their breeding sites before the end of February.

A comparison with the distribution recorded during the *1980–85 NBBS* shows the marked spread inland in the last 20 years and in particular a colonisation of south Norfolk, from where the species had been almost entirely absent in the earlier survey. The increase of winter range, from 32% to 68% of 10-km squares, follows from the spread of breeding, because some birds have already returned to their breeding sites before the end of the winter period.

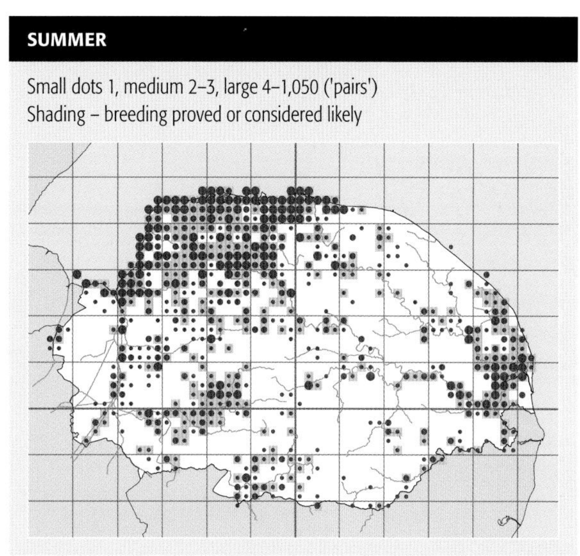

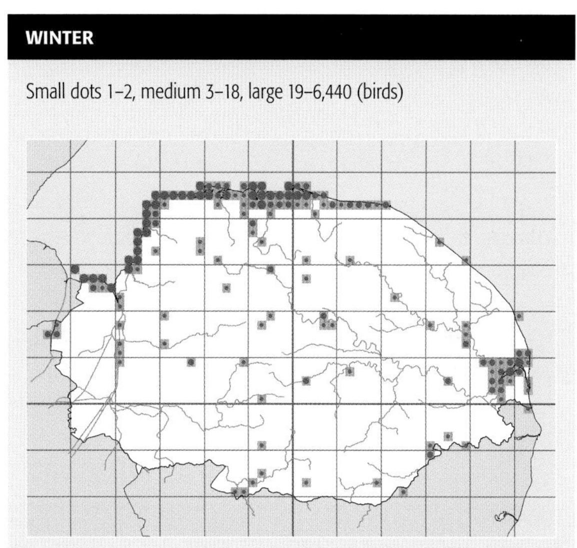

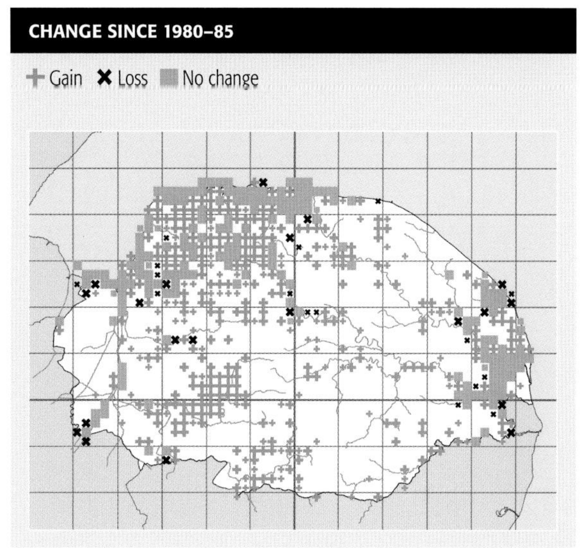

Avocet

Recurvirostra avosetta

DAVID TIPLING

NBA 1999–2007	SUMMER: ALL / BREEDING	WINTER
TETRADS OCCUPIED	68 (5%) / 41 (3%)	18 (1%)
SUMMER/WINTER ONLY	55	5
MEAN PER OCCUPIED TETRAD	19 / 25	59
SUMMED MAX COUNTS	1,279 / 1,018	1,066
POPULATION ESTIMATE	300–500 bp	200–350

PREVIOUS ATLASES	SQUARES OCCUPIED	1999–2007	LOSSES	GAINS
1968–72 (10 KM)	1 (2%)	15 (24%)	1	15
1980–85 (TETRAD)	6 (<1%)	41 (3%)	0	35
1980–85 (10 KM)	4 (6%)	15 (24%)	0	11
1981–84 WINTER (10 KM)	4 (6%)	10 (16%)	0	6
1988–91 (10 KM)	9 (15%)	15 (24%)	2	8

THE AVOCET BECAME extinct as a breeding bird in England during the first half of the 19th century, with the last nesting pair in Norfolk being noted at Salthouse in about 1824. As a result of habitat changes and bird protection schemes, England was recolonised in the 1940s, probably from the Netherlands and Denmark. It was not until 1977, however, that the species bred successfully in Norfolk, for the first time in the 20th century – this time at Cley, only a short distance from the site of the last nesting over 150 years earlier.

During the breeding season they favour brackish lagoons with low, sparsely vegetated islands that have gently sloping banks, generally within a short distance of the coast. In north Norfolk, these conditions are found at many of the managed coastal reserves, where protection, at least from human disturbance, can be provided.

The map shows that Avocets were recorded during the summer in 68 tetrads, compared with just six at the time of the *1980–85 NBBS*, such has been the scale of the spread of this species during the two intervening decades. Since the *1988–91 Atlas*, the number of 10-km

SUMMER

Small dots 1–2, medium 3–12, large 13–181 ('pairs')
Shading – breeding proved or considered likely

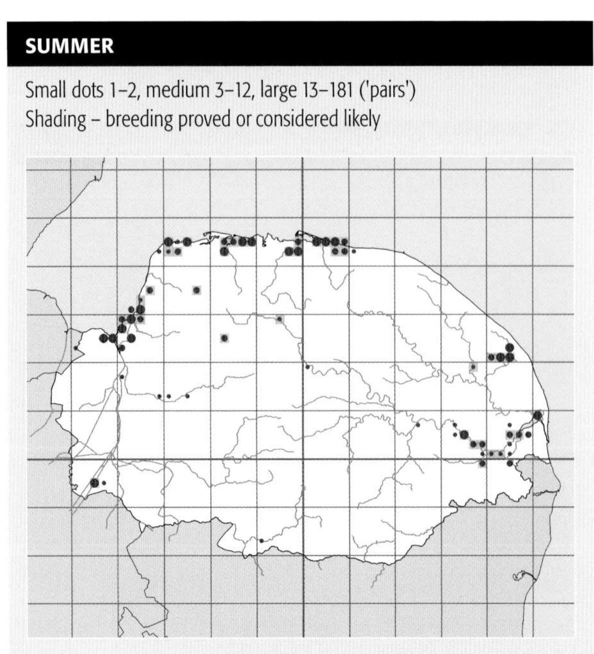

WINTER

Small dots 1–2, medium 3–69, large 70–268 (birds)

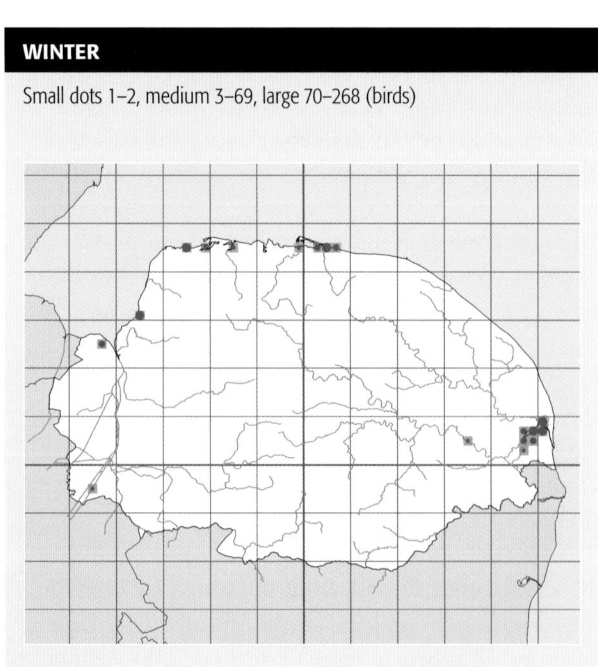

squares occupied has doubled, with much of this change representing colonisation of inland sites, mainly those where soft, muddy habitats mimic the coastal conditions.

Data gathered in Suffolk in the 1970s and 1980s showed that, as the number of breeding pairs of Avocets increased, so the number of young reared per pair declined (Hill 1988). The same scenario has been played out in Norfolk and, particularly in the last few years, many pairs have failed to raise even a single youngster. The causes have varied between locations, but have included seasonal flooding, mammalian predation (foxes and stoats) and avian predators, including Coots and Kestrels. But perhaps the most significant has been the predation on eggs and young at Cley by Grey Herons that caused an almost total breeding failure during 2005–07. Unfortunately egg collectors have also taken their toll in north Norfolk. Despite all these problems, most Norfolk colonies have continued to expand and new sites have been colonised. Birds at new colonies generally produce more young than those at longer-established sites, and this may help explain how the county's breeding population was able to rise from around 300 pairs in 2000 to about 500 pairs in 2005. Passage birds and other non-breeders also swell the summer population.

More than 50 pairs each were recorded during the NBA summers at Snettisham, Titchwell, Holkham and Cley, with smaller numbers at many other suitable localities as far east as Kelling WM. In east Norfolk, several smaller colonies have become established in Broadland, as far inland as Cantley BF, while in the Breydon Water area 53 pairs were breeding by 2000. In 2005, 48 pairs were also nesting at Welney in the Fens. Occasional Avocets turn up elsewhere inland during the spring and summer, at other freshwater sites, such as old gravel pits. At Wissington BF, a pair hatched two chicks in 2004, taking advantage of temporary low water levels in the main pit.

The increase in breeding population has been outstripped by the rate of rise in wintering birds in the county. Avocets are migratory in the northern part of their breeding range but the recent spell of mild winters has encouraged more to remain in North Sea countries outside the breeding season. Increasing numbers have overwintered in England since the late 1970s, with the vast majority in the estuaries along the Channel and southern North Sea coasts and only a few Norfolk records (*1981–84 Winter Atlas*). It was not until 1995/96 that Avocets first wintered in numbers in Norfolk, at Breydon Water, peaking at 76. Since then, and during the NBA winters, the Breydon Water area has remained the wintering stronghold, with a maximum of 268. The only other locations to hold Avocets regularly in December or January were Cley, where a maximum of 34 was reported, and, in the later years of the NBA recording period, Titchwell. However, by late February spring passage has commenced and the winter map shows these passage birds at other sites along the north Norfolk coast and in the Wash, with peak counts of 130 at Snettisham, 87 at Titchwell and 90 at Cley.

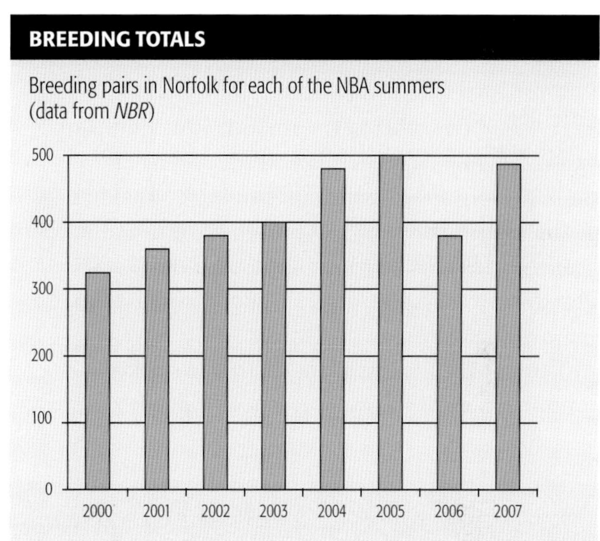

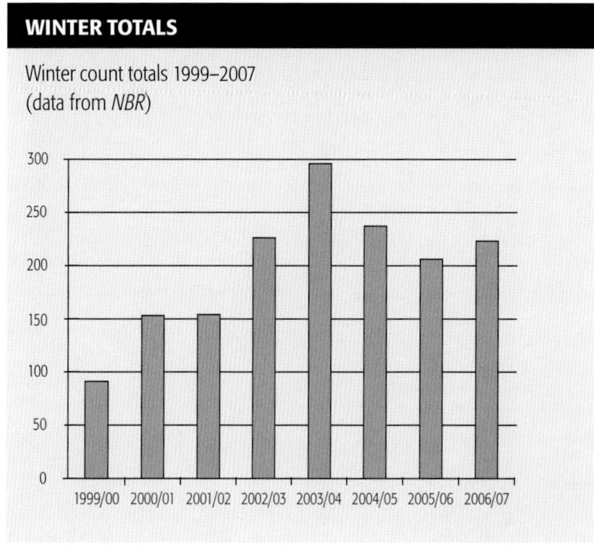

Stone-curlew

Burhinus oedicnemus

NBA 1999–2007	SUMMER: ALL/BREEDING	WINTER
TETRADS OCCUPIED	73 (5%) / 46 (3%)	3 (<1%)
SUMMER/WINTER ONLY	71	1
MEAN PER OCCUPIED TETRAD	1 / 2	6
SUMMED MAX COUNTS	100 / 72	19
POPULATION ESTIMATE	90–130 bp	3–10

PREVIOUS ATLASES	SQUARES OCCUPIED	1999–2007	LOSSES	GAINS
1968–72 (10 KM)	18 (29%)	10 (16%)	9	1
1980–85 (TETRAD)	33 (2%)	46 (3%)	14	27
1980–85 (10 KM)	8 (13%)	10 (16%)	1	3
1981–84 WINTER (10 KM)	1 (2%)	3 (5%)	1	3
1988–91 (10 KM)	9 (15%)	10 (16%)	1	2

THE STONE-CURLEW, with its cryptic plumage, strong legs and large eyes, is well adapted to its skulking, terrestrial, crepuscular and nocturnal habits. At one time it was such a characteristic bird of the open heaths and Brecks that it was known as the Norfolk Plover. Nowadays the species is largely confined to southwest Norfolk.

Throughout Europe a long-term and marked contraction in its range has resulted from the intensification of arable farming. This has been reflected in England, where the highest numbers now remain in Breckland and on Salisbury Plain. In Breckland, the spread of forestry plantations and the myxomatosis epidemic that started in the 1950s have also contributed to its decline.

Stone-curlews inhabit undisturbed dry ground; they favour heathland and pastures with a close-cropped turf that have been grazed by rabbits or sheep. In Norfolk, however, most pairs now nest on arable land. Up to 28 pairs nested in Stanford TA during NBA summers, mostly on arable, perhaps because heathland there is now in poor condition. Elsewhere in Breckland, pairs bred in fields of spring-sown

DAVID TIPLING

SUMMER

Small dots 1, medium 2, large 3–5 ('pairs')
Shading – breeding proved or considered likely, dots centralised

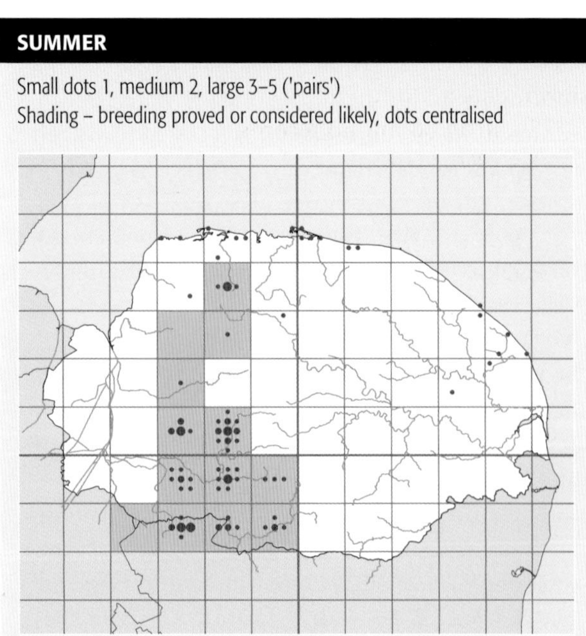

CHRIS KNIGHTS

crops, such as sugar beet, barley and maize, and even in larger open areas created within forestry. For reasons of security, the breeding distribution is shown only at 10-km level. Breeding occurred in TF72 and TL68 but no records were made available for the NBA database.

During the eight years of NBA fieldwork, the Norfolk breeding population has been carefully stewarded by the RSPB and the county population has increased from 88 pairs in 2000 to 131 pairs in 2006, with 129 pairs in 2007. Nearly all are within the Brecks but up to 10 pairs now breed in the north of the county.

Stone-curlews are summer visitors to England, the first birds arriving back at their breeding sites early in March, with the main arrival in April. Most of the records on the NBA summer map away from the breeding areas are of coastal migrants. Apart from two together at Cley, all involved single birds and most were present for one day only.

'Most of the records on the NBA summer map away from the breeding areas are of coastal migrants.'

Stone-curlews from northern and eastern Europe winter in North Africa or south of the Sahara. Occasional wintering in Britain has a long history, but currently appears to be exceptional. During the NBA winters, however, up to 13 were present on occasion in December in the Hilborough area. There were winter records also from two further tetrads, one of which had not been occupied in the breeding season.

Comparison with the *1968–72 Atlas* suggests that some range loss may have occurred in the north and east of the county. Since 1980–85, however, many more tetrads have been occupied in Breckland, despite the loss of several heathland tetrads in Stanford TA.

Little Ringed Plover
Charadrius dubius

NBA 1999–2007	SUMMER: ALL / BREEDING	WINTER
TETRADS OCCUPIED	64 (4%) / 40 (3%)	none
SUMMER/WINTER ONLY	64	none
MEAN PER OCCUPIED TETRAD	2 / 2	none
SUMMED MAX COUNTS	133 / 88	none
POPULATION ESTIMATE	25–40 bp	none

PREVIOUS ATLASES	SQUARES OCCUPIED	1999–2007	LOSSES	GAINS
1968–72 (10 KM)	9 (15%)	24 (39%)	3	18
1980–85 (TETRAD)	52 (4%)	40 (3%)	41	29
1980–85 (10 KM)	23 (37%)	24 (39%)	11	12
1988–91 (10 KM)	21 (34%)	24 (39%)	10	13

LITTLE RINGED PLOVERS were first known to breed in England in Hertfordshire in 1938. Since then they have spread as a breeding species to many parts of Britain, with 400 pairs in 1972 and up to 1,000 by 1988–91. The species first bred in Norfolk at Stowbridge in 1960, and remains a scarce and localised breeding bird. Although a few pairs use traditional sites from year to year, favouring fairly shallow fresh water and particularly gravel pits, many of the observations of nesting birds during this survey were in tetrads not used in 1980–85. Any lightly vegetated floodwater, even if ephemeral, may be graced with a spring visit or even a breeding attempt.

The NBA summer map shows a scattered and sparse inland distribution, with coastal records confined to the northwest. While very many of the breeding birds are located at gravel pits, those still being worked as well as disused sites, others have nested around beet-

SUMMER

Small dots 1, medium 2, large 3–12 ('pairs')
Shading – breeding proved or considered likely

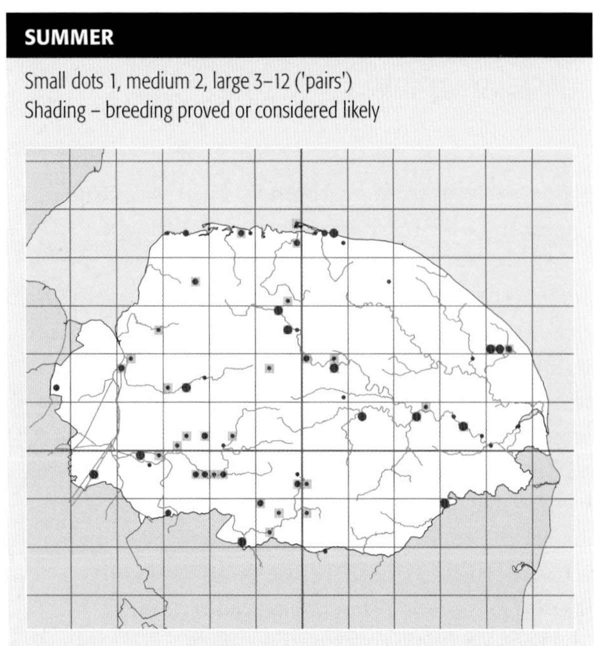

CHANGE SINCE 1980–85

+ Gain ✖ Loss ■ No change

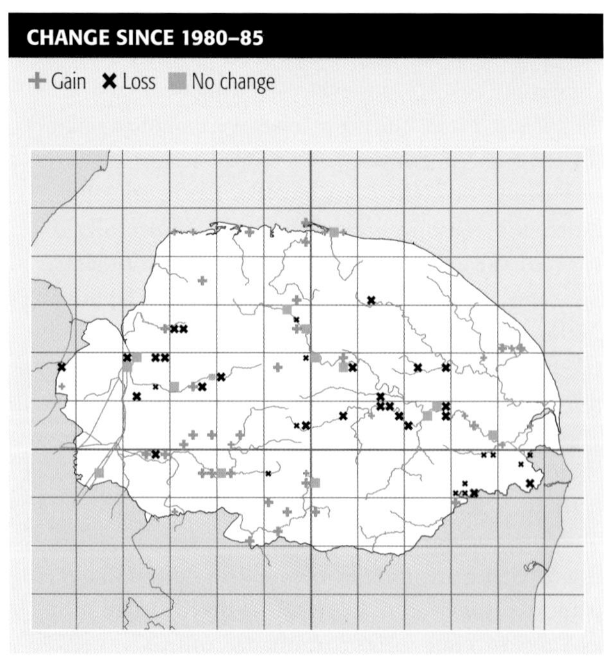

DAVID TIPLING

factory settling ponds, flooded riverside meadows and even on arable fields among crops of sugar beet, carrots and onions.

Breeding failure is usually the result of disturbance, predation or a change of water levels. Since 2001, breeding success at Welney has been greatly improved by the use of protective cages over the nests, which allow access to the incubating birds but deter Coots, Moorhens and mammalian predators. In fact, it has been so successful that Welney now holds the highest number of breeding Little Ringed Plovers at any single site in the county, with 25 young fledging from 12 pairs in 2002. At Blakeney Point in 2005, groups of two or three birds were noted displaying and nest scraping but breeding did not progress further. Where both species are present, territorial Ringed Plovers usually drive away their smaller relatives. Some NBA records may refer to birds on spring passage.

> 'The species first bred in Norfolk at Stowbridge in 1960, and remains a scarce and localised breeding bird.'

There is little evidence of change in the Norfolk breeding population over the last two decades. The distribution at tetrad level was concentrated in mid county during the *1980–85 NBBS*, and is now more dispersed, but Little Ringed Plovers were recorded in 3–4% of the county's tetrads in both surveys.

Ringed Plover
Charadrius hiaticula

NBA 1999–2007	SUMMER: ALL/BREEDING	WINTER
TETRADS OCCUPIED	81 (6%) / 62 (4%)	66 (5%)
SUMMER/WINTER ONLY	35	20
MEAN PER OCCUPIED TETRAD	5 / 6	19
SUMMED MAX COUNTS	428 / 360	1,269
POPULATION ESTIMATE	150–210 bp	300–400

PREVIOUS ATLASES	SQUARES OCCUPIED	1999–2007	LOSSES	GAINS
1968–72 (10 KM)	27 (44%)	19 (31%)	13	5
1980–85 (TETRAD)	95 (7%)	62 (4%)	50	17
1980–85 (10 KM)	31 (50%)	19 (31%)	14	2
1981–84 WINTER (10 KM)	19 (31%)	17 (27%)	5	3
1988–91 (10 KM)	33 (53%)	19 (31%)	16	2

RINGED PLOVERS ARE characteristic birds of wide sandy beaches but, partly as a result of human competition for this type of habitat during the summer months, it is declining alarmingly as a breeding species in Norfolk.

The species has always had a chequered history, at least in east Norfolk, where it had become extinct by 1870 due to persecution and egg collecting; but by the end of the 19th century a few pairs had once more returned to breed. The county stronghold has always been along the sand and shingle beaches of north and west Norfolk. Increasing numbers of holidaymakers are now using these beaches, to the detriment of the breeding Ringed Plovers. At some places, protective measures can be taken, such erecting temporary fencing, but this does not stop foxes and stoats or aerial predators, such as crows or gulls, from taking the breeding adults, eggs and young. Possibly due to increasing disturbance on the beaches, more pairs began to nest on nearby arable land from about 1950. Elsewhere, 400 pairs bred in the Norfolk and Suffolk Brecks in the early years of the 20th century, but as a result of agriculture and forestry in that area only a handful remained there by 1970.

The summer map shows that the majority of pairs were found from Snettisham on the eastern side of the Wash around the north Norfolk coast as far east as Weybourne. Coastal pairs nest above the high-water mark on Norfolk's sand and shingle beaches, and at some sites amongst vegetated sand dunes. Small numbers were also located along the beaches of east Norfolk, while other pairs nested on manmade scrapes and lagoons at the reserves at Snettisham, Titchwell and

SUMMER

Small dots 1, medium 2–4, large 5–33 ('pairs')
Shading – breeding proved or considered likely

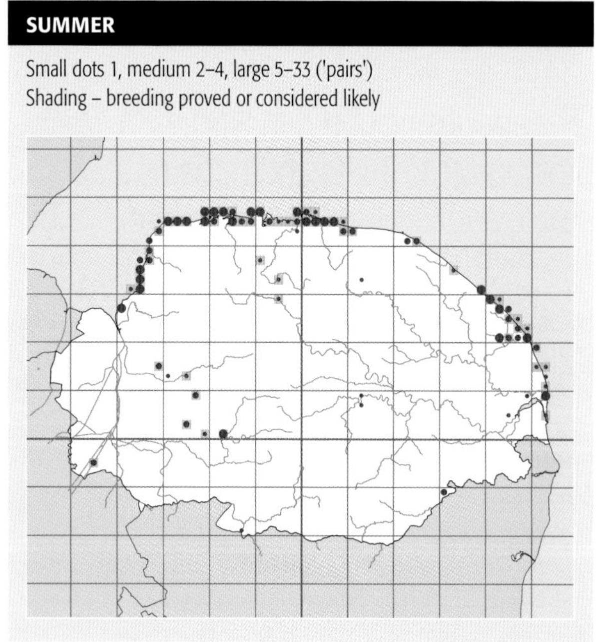

WINTER

Small dots 1–3, medium 4–21, large 22–91 (birds)

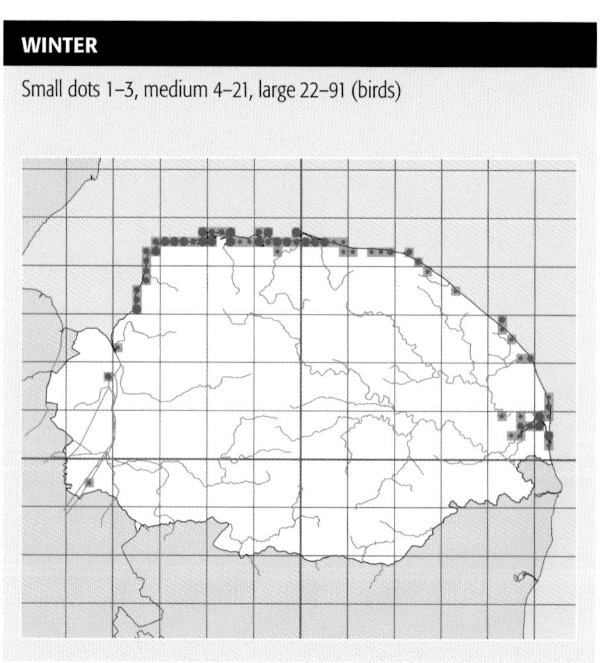

DAVID TIPLING

Cley, and a few pairs were found on arable fields just inland from the beach. Ringed Plovers were located in 16 genuinely inland tetrads during the NBA summers, with a maximum of six pairs in the Hilborough/Gooderstone area and three at Welney; this compares with almost 30 inland tetrads during the *1980–85 NBBS*, when the species nested much more widely in the Brecks and the Fens.

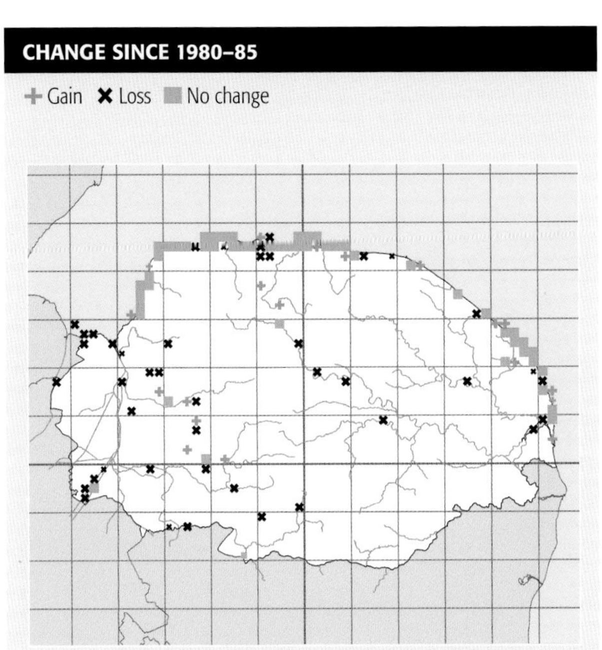

Counts in spring are complicated by the number of passage birds in the county, most being nominate *hiaticula* bound for Canada, Greenland, Iceland or southern Fenno-Scandia (*Migration Atlas*). During the NBA springs, the highest count was of 700 at Snettisham in 2004. May counts at Scolt Head/Brancaster Harbour exceeded 300 in most years, with a maximum of 450 in 2005. At Breydon Water, counts regularly exceeded 300 in the early years of the NBA, peaking at 486 in 2001, but since 2004 have not reached three figures. Spring migrants have also been noted inland in May, including 43 at Welney in 2000 and 125 at Rush Hills, Hickling Broad, in 2004. May flocks have not generally been included in the NBA database, and so in the main the totals represent breeding pairs, although small numbers of passage migrants may have been included at some sites.

The winter map clearly demonstrates that Ringed Plovers are almost exclusively coastal at this time of year. Occurring singly or in loose flocks, they frequent the same wide open stretches of sand as do the breeding birds, but are also found feeding on intertidal muddy sand around the saltings, estuaries and harbours, particularly in north Norfolk and at Breydon Water. These are probably largely winter visitors from further north in Britain or from the near Continent, Norfolk's breeding population having mostly moved off west or south during the autumn. The highest counts during the NBA winters were of 168 at Scolt Head/Brancaster Harbour, 80–90 at Holme, Wells and Blakeney Harbour, and 112 at Breydon Water. Numbers normally peaked in January or February, with an average of around 350 Ringed Plovers in the county at this season during the NBA period. Some of Norfolk's breeding Ringed Plovers return as early as February and might therefore appear on the winter map.

During the 1984 national breeding Ringed Plover survey 541 pairs were mapped in Norfolk, which was identified as the most important county in England, holding 6% of the UK population. By 1993 this total had declined to 429 pairs and, by 2005, Norfolk's population was estimated at 200 pairs or below, less than half the number of breeding Avocets (*NBR*). Even at Scolt Head, a highly inaccessible site, the breeding population had fallen from 180 pairs in 1984 to 57 in 2005.

The change map shows little indication of shrinkage in the coastal range since 1980–85, but the losses of breeding tetrads in Breckland and the Fens, where the species is now rare, are clearly evident. Comparison with the 10-km atlases also shows losses, of both breeding and winter range.

Golden Plover
Pluvialis apricaria

NBA 1999–2007	SUMMER: ALL/BREEDING	WINTER
TETRADS OCCUPIED	49 (3%) / none	475 (33%)
SUMMER/WINTER ONLY	16	442
MEAN PER OCCUPIED TETRAD	46 / none	580
SUMMED MAX COUNTS	2,268 / none	275,567
POPULATION ESTIMATE	0–10 individuals	35,000–50,000

PREVIOUS ATLASES	SQUARES OCCUPIED	1999–2007	LOSSES	GAINS
1981–84 WINTER (10 KM)	55 (89%)	60 (97%)	1	6

WITH THEIR SPANGLED golden-brown upperparts, Golden Plovers are attractive birds at any time of the year but particularly so in breeding plumage, when they sport a contrasting black face and black underparts.

Golden Plovers breed on northern tundra and uplands, and are passage migrants and winter visitors to Norfolk, probably mostly from Fenno-Scandian or Russian breeding grounds. During the winter they form dense flocks, often in the company of Lapwings. Flocks feed on extensive areas of grassland, especially permanent pastures, or among winter cereals or sugar beet, while ploughed land is favoured for roosting. Beet fields are particularly attractive once the beet has been lifted and the surface soil disturbed by the harvesting operations.

The NBA winter map shows the species to be well distributed in the more agricultural parts of the county in central and southeast Norfolk. There are also large numbers of Golden Plovers on the north coast reserves and in the Breydon Water area; here the flocks gather on the intertidal mudflats, saltings and coastal grazing marshes. Mason & Macdonald (1999b) considered that estuaries are more important for foraging than was realised and have suggested that warmer autumns resulting from climate change may make traditional feeding areas in cereal fields unsuitable due to rapid crop growth. Their earlier research also showed that Golden Plovers avoided cereal fields where the blade height was greater than 9 cm, whereas Lapwings would tolerate 11 cm (Mason & Macdonald 1999a). Golden Plovers use traditional wintering areas, often returning to specific fields in consecutive winters, despite being highly mobile within a range of up to 10 km or so during the course of the winter, or even of a single day;

SUMMER

Small dots 1–5, medium 6–30, large 31–530 ('pairs')

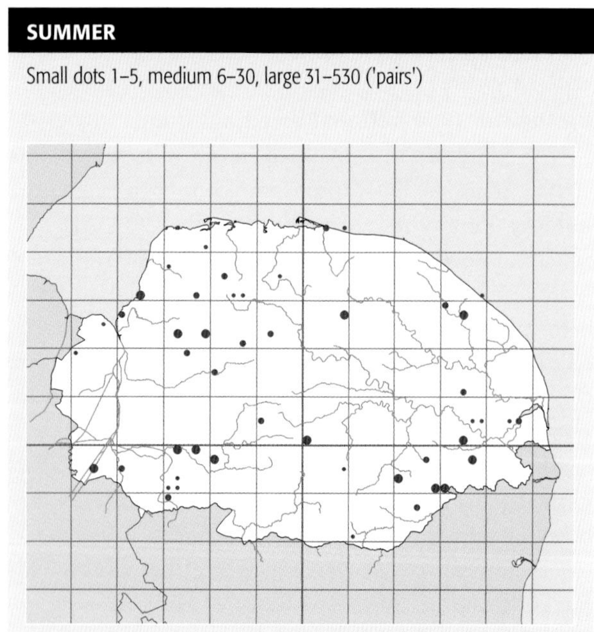

WINTER

Small dots 1–42, medium 43–300, large 301–6,900 (birds)

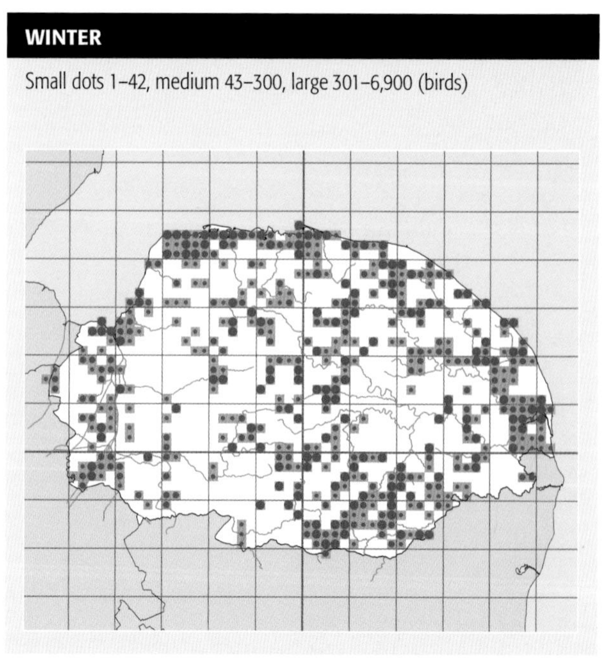

DAVID TIPLING

the distribution of flock ranges appeared to change rather little during the NBA period.

In recent years, the largest numbers of Golden Plovers in the county, by far, have been at Breydon Water, with an amazing record count of 30,940 in February 2005. Counts in north Norfolk have included up to 6,000 at Titchwell and 5,000 in Blakeney Harbour and at Salthouse, with 5,500 on the Wash at Snettisham and in the Brecks 5,600 in the Stanford TA and 5,300 at East Wretham. By contrast, there were large areas of farmland in east and in west Norfolk that the species did not use, perhaps because they were unsuitable or through the birds' preference for traditional sites. Golden Plovers, which are exceptionally wary of aerial predators, avoid the vicinity of woodland cover and are rarely seen in the forested regions of Breckland.

The tetrad counts include many duplicate records, but it is likely that 35,000–50,000 birds are normally present. Hard weather elsewhere can

'In recent years, the largest numbers of Golden Plovers in the county, by far, have been at Breydon Water, with an amazing record count of 30,940 in February 2005.'

result in further immigration into the county, while Golden Plovers move south and west if severe weather persists in Norfolk.

Winter visitors diminish rapidly in numbers in February. Often after a distinct interval, smaller flocks reappear in April and early May, occasionally admixed with Dotterel. These are clearly passage migrants, unconnected with the winter flocks, and presumably heading for more northerly or more mountainous parts of the breeding range. The summer map shows that such migrants occur widely across the county, with a less clumped distribution than is shown by the winter birds.

Grey Plover

Pluvialis squatarola

NBA 1999–2007	SUMMER: ALL / BREEDING	WINTER
TETRADS OCCUPIED	23 (2%) / none	68 (5%)
SUMMER/WINTER ONLY	7	52
MEAN PER OCCUPIED TETRAD	71 / none	138
SUMMED MAX COUNTS	1,626 / none	9,368
POPULATION ESTIMATE	150–200 individuals	1,500–2,500

PREVIOUS ATLASES	SQUARES OCCUPIED	1999–2007	LOSSES	GAINS
1981–84 WINTER (10 KM)	14 (23%)	19 (31%)	3	8
1988–91 (10 KM)	2 (3%)	none	2	0

THE GREY PLOVER, with its mournful call so characteristic of the open mudflats, is a common winter visitor and passage migrant to Norfolk from its breeding grounds in high-Arctic Siberia, with some non-breeders remaining all summer.

Throughout the winter, Grey Plovers can be found feeding on intertidal mudflats and to a lesser extent along the muddy foreshore of Norfolk's saltmarshes. The map shows the highest concentration of birds around the Wash, and the extensive mudflats exposed at low tide between Wells and Blakeney Harbour. While feeding, Grey Plovers are often solitary or in small groups of two or three, as their feeding method relies upon not disturbing prey temporarily present at the surface of the mud (*1981–84 Winter Atlas*). They roost in large parties, along with dense flocks of Knot and Dunlin at high tide. It is these roosting flocks that account for the largest tetrad counts.

During the NBA winters the two highest counts were both in the Wash, with 1,546 at Terrington and 1,942 at Snettisham. Along the north Norfolk coast, peak counts decreased eastwards, from 729 at Holme

SUMMER

Small dots 1, medium 2–15, large 16–700 ('pairs')

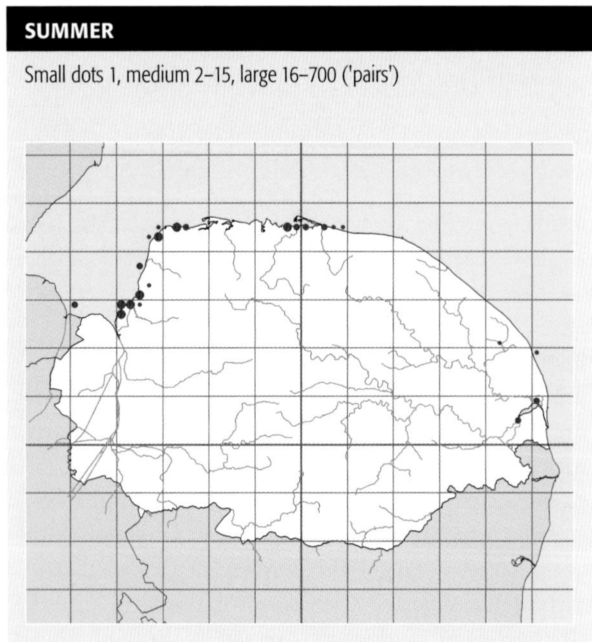

WINTER

Small dots 1–2, medium 3–57, large 58–1,942 (birds)

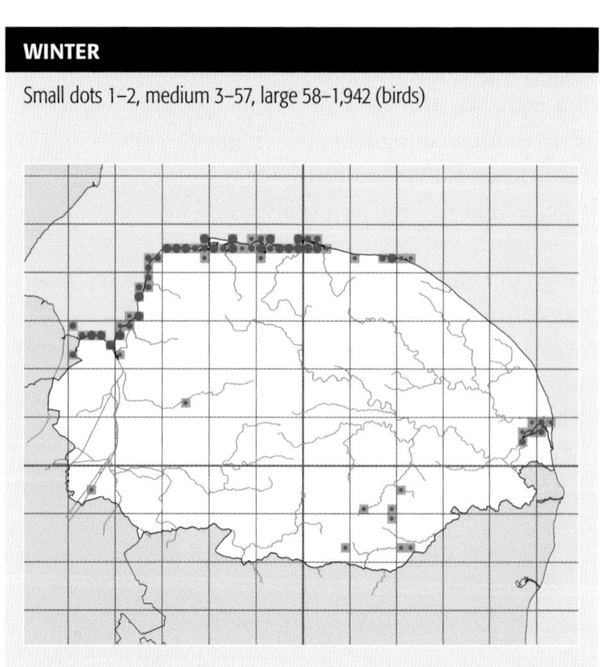

DAVID TIPLING

to 200 in Blakeney Harbour. Not a single Grey Plover was reported on any of the sandy beaches between Cromer and the mudflats of Breydon Water, where Grey Plovers reached a maximum of about 45 birds during the winter period.

Occasional single Grey Plovers were encountered inland during the NBA winters. A series of records of one bird with Golden Plover flocks in the arable area of south Norfolk between Diss and Long Stratton over several winters probably involved just one or maybe two returning individuals. The only multiple sighting on farmland with Golden Plovers concerned five near Brancaster.

Higher numbers of Grey Plover are recorded around the Wash on passage than are present in the winter and this was reflected in counts of up to 3,200 at Snettisham in April and May. The distribution during the NBA summers included some birds, mainly first-years, that remained on the wintering grounds all summer but also spring migrants, of which some appeared at inland sites. For instance, Grey Plovers were recorded almost annually at Welney, with a maximum of nine in May 2000, and two or three were reported most years at Rush Hills on Hickling Broad. Such migrants are mapped only where they appeared to be using the tetrad in which they were seen.

'The map shows the highest concentration of birds around the Wash, and the extensive mudflats exposed at low tide between Wells and Blakeney Harbour.'

DAVID TIPLING

Lapwing
Vanellus vanellus

NBA 1999–2007	SUMMER: ALL/BREEDING	WINTER
TETRADS OCCUPIED	752 (52%) / 571 (39%)	967 (66%)
SUMMER/WINTER ONLY	188	403
MEAN PER OCCUPIED TETRAD	5 / 6	300
SUMMED MAX COUNTS	3,931 / 3,458	289,909
POPULATION ESTIMATE	750–1,000 bp	40,000–50,000

PREVIOUS ATLASES	SQUARES OCCUPIED	1999–2007	LOSSES	GAINS
1968–72 (10 KM)	62 (all)	57 (92%)	5	0
1980–85 (TETRAD)	761 (52%)	571 (39%)	388	198
1980–85 (10 KM)	59 (95%)	57 (92%)	4	2
1981–84 WINTER (10 KM)	62 (all)	62 (all)		
1988–91 (10 KM)	58 (94%)	57 (92%)	3	2

DESPITE A MARKED reduction in numbers since the early 1960s, the Lapwing remains our most numerous and most widespread breeding and wintering wader.

CBC and BBS data indicate a halving in the UK breeding population during the period 1982–2007, and Lapwing is one of the most strongly declining bird species in Europe (*Birdtrends*). Much permanent pasture has been converted to arable land, crops are sprayed more frequently during the spring and early summer, and many crops are now sown in the autumn rather than the spring: all these factors have reduced the capacity of the countryside to host breeding Lapwings. Pairs avoid nesting in fields of crops that are over 15 cm tall, a height that is already exceeded in early spring by winter wheat and winter barley.

During the breeding season, Lapwings favour lowland farmland and fresh marshes, especially if areas of fresh water are nearby. For nesting, they require large open areas with all-round visibility to detect the approach of any potential danger. Patches of bare ground or short vegetation are also required for feeding, while newly hatched young are often taken to marshy ground to feed. Their noisy aerial displays mean that NBA observers probably missed few potential breeding pairs.

Apart from parts of Broadland and the Breydon Water area, where higher densities also occurred, the NBA summer map shows that Lapwings were sparsely distributed in the east of the county and absent from large areas north and south of Norwich. Distribution was more complete in west Norfolk but with large unoccupied areas in the Fens as well as an absence from Thetford Forest.

> 'Lapwings are mainly migratory and Britain is the most northerly regular wintering area in Europe.'

During the NBA period, the highest concentrations of breeding Lapwings were confined to wetland reserves in the county. All three-figure counts of breeding pairs were on such reserves, with 160 at Welney, 129 at Berney, 106 at Holkham NNR and 104 at Buckenham. These numbers compare with 147 pairs at Welney and 240 at Holkham in 1996. But even at these sites breeding success may be very low. Flooding in the late spring at Welney in 2000 resulted in very few young being fledged, while in other years unusually dry springs have had the same adverse effect. At Berney, no predator control was carried out between 2001 and 2003, resulting in considerable loss of Lapwings to foxes. Since re-instituting measures to control such predators, breeding success has improved. Similar controls are used at Holkham NNR and Welney with good effect, while other heavily keepered estates, such as those at Gooderstone and Hilborough, apparently have relatively stable Lapwing populations.

Some observers found that fields holding likely breeding pairs on the first summer visit had been ploughed by the second visit and no Lapwings were present. Conversely, Continental immigrants, including failed breeders or perhaps even successful adults and fledged young, were present at some sites by the time of the second visit in late June but had not bred locally. The map may therefore exaggerate the true extent of breeding in the county.

Lapwings are mainly migratory and Britain is the most northerly regular wintering area in Europe. During the winter, the birds are highly gregarious and are found on flooded meadows and marshland, arable land and areas of short grassland, such as airfields. The NBA winter map shows that they are widely distributed throughout the county, being absent only from parts of the Brecks and isolated pockets elsewhere. Flocks gather at traditional sites but they are also opportunistic, feeding on sugar beet fields both during and after lifting, and also at open pig units. Like Golden Plovers, they often use ploughed fields as roosting sites. Immigration of Continental birds takes place during periods of hard weather, while emigration from the county occurs if severe weather persists here. At some sites, late-winter counts may well have included flocks of passage birds returning to the Continent, while at others the wintering birds might have already departed by early February.

In recent years, Breydon Water has become a site of international importance for wintering Lapwings, with counts peaking at 29,136 in January 2005. In the same month, Welney held 12,038, while other five-figure counts during the NBA winters included 16,065 at Ouse Mouth in January 2006. Other major winter gatherings included 8,000 at Buckenham, 7,280 at Terrington and 5,000 at Heigham Holmes. Lapwings are highly mobile during the course of the winter and thus it is extremely difficult to assess Norfolk's wintering population.

All comparisons with previous breeding atlases illustrate decline. At the time of the *1980–85 NBBS* it was noted that Lapwings were absent from parts of northeast and south Norfolk, but the area now unoccupied is considerably more extensive; the change map shows many losses, particularly in the east and on the fringes of the Fens and in Breckland. It is likely, too, that wintering numbers, currently estimated at 40,000–50,000, have fallen as a result of population decrease in continental Europe.

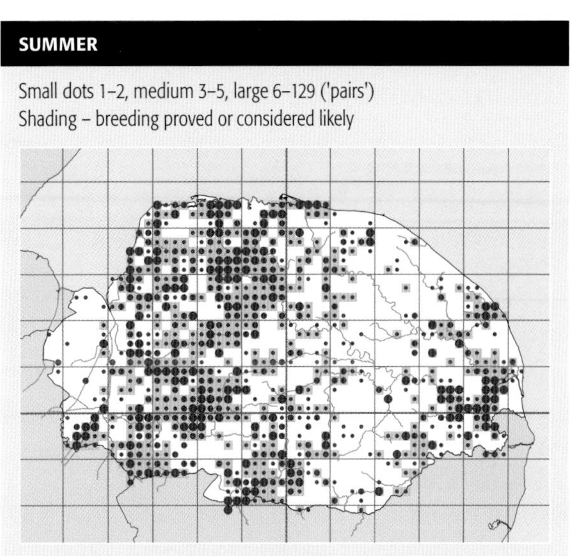

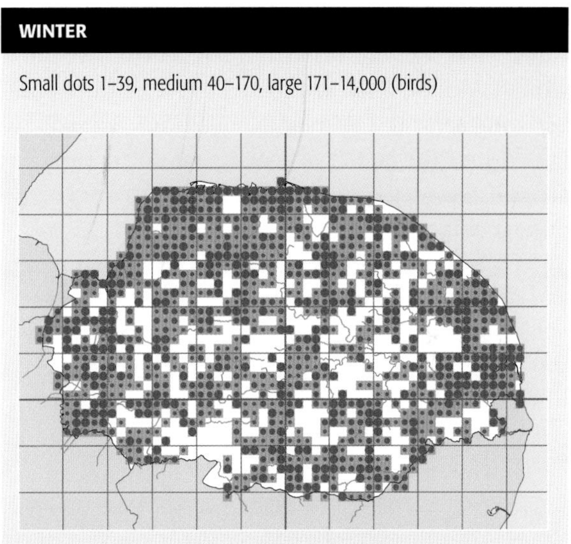

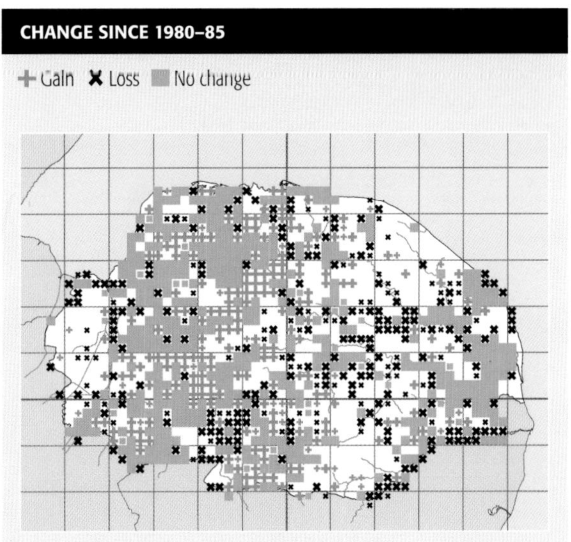

Knot
Calidris canutus

NBA 1999–2007	SUMMER: ALL / BREEDING	WINTER
TETRADS OCCUPIED	19 (1%) / none	45 (3%)
SUMMER/WINTER ONLY	6	32
MEAN PER OCCUPIED TETRAD	1,085 / none	2,804
SUMMED MAX COUNTS	20,606 / none	126,182
POPULATION ESTIMATE	1,000–3,000 individuals	40,000–80,000

PREVIOUS ATLASES	SQUARES OCCUPIED	1999–2007	LOSSES	GAINS
1981–84 WINTER (10 KM)	12 (19%)	13 (21%)	2	3

A LARGE FLOCK OF KNOT performing their amazing aerial manoeuvres, like distant wisps of smoke, is a sight not to miss during a cold Norfolk winter. Although the numbers of this visitor from breeding areas in Greenland and eastern Canada have fallen since the late 1960s, many tens of thousands are still recorded on winter counts or occur as passage migrants.

Knots are highly gregarious birds, both feeding and roosting in dense flocks. In Britain, they are concentrated around most of the major estuaries, with the Wash holding by far the greatest winter numbers throughout the NBA period and being of primary international importance for the species. Observers for the Wetland Bird Survey made counts of up to 140,000 Knots on the Wash during the NBA period, shared between Norfolk and Lincolnshire.

During winter the flocks are highly mobile, both within and between estuaries (*1981–84 Winter Atlas*), and this is reflected in the varying counts made in Norfolk during the course of a single winter. The high-tide roost at Snettisham is often spectacular, and during the NBA winters a maximum of 45,000 Knots was recorded here, in December 2004. Elsewhere, up to 7,500 were reported at Terrington Marsh.

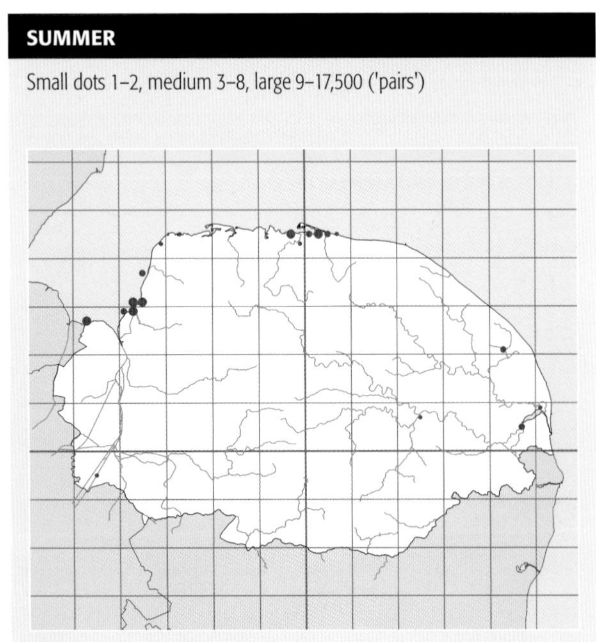

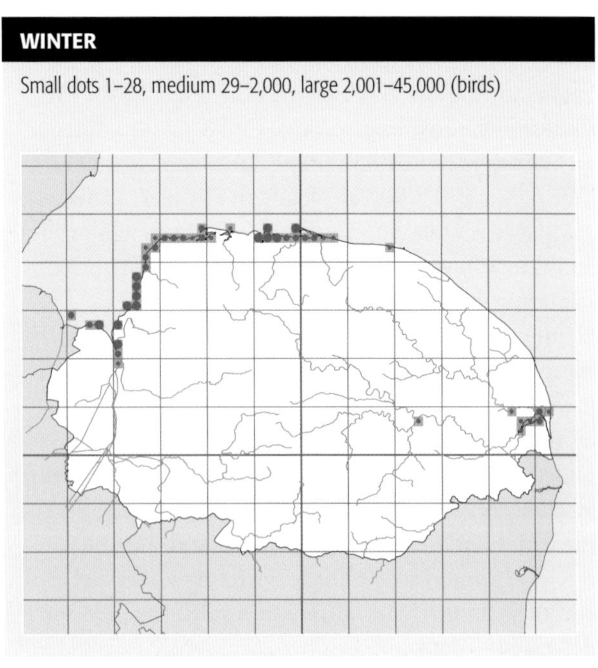

DAVID TIPLING

The north Norfolk saltmarshes and intertidal mudflats also host large numbers of Knots, particularly during periods of cold weather. Maximum counts during the NBA included 4,000 in the Scolt Head/ Brancaster Harbour area, 6,300 in Wells Harbour and 7,250 off Warham Greens. In north Norfolk, excluding birds in flight, only one record was made east of Salthouse during the NBA winters. In east Norfolk, the extensive low-tide mudflats at Breydon Water regularly held several hundred Knots in winter, peaking at 700 in December 2002.

Flocks often roost on fields a short distance inside the seawall. Otherwise, Knots are very rare inland in winter. During the NBA winters there were only two such records, involving three birds near West Lynn and one at Whitlingham CP. Inland records are more frequent at passage times, however: during the NBA summer periods Knots were recorded annually in May at Rush Hills on Hickling Broad, with a maximum of nine, and up to 16 were present at Welney in early May 2000.

Counts of spring passage or summering birds at Snettisham included 6,000 in May and 10,000 in June, of which perhaps up to 3,000 non-breeders would have remained through the summer.

'Observers from the Wetland Bird Survey made counts of up to 140,000 Knots on the Wash during the NBA period, shared between Norfolk and Lincolnshire.'

Sanderling
Calidris alba

NBA 1999–2007	SUMMER: ALL/BREEDING	WINTER
TETRADS OCCUPIED	27 (2%) / none	61 (4%)
SUMMER/WINTER ONLY	9	43
MEAN PER OCCUPIED TETRAD	30 / none	74
SUMMED MAX COUNTS	819 / none	4,539
POPULATION ESTIMATE	300–350 individuals	800–1,200

PREVIOUS ATLASES	SQUARES OCCUPIED	1999–2007	LOSSES	GAINS
1981–84 WINTER (10 KM)	15 (24%)	15 (24%)	1	1

AN ENTERTAINING SIGHT along many of Norfolk's sandy beaches is of a small group of Sanderlings busily running back and forth at the tide's edge. As they dart in and out of the surf, following the movement of the waves, they pick up the small marine crustaceans on which they feed. They are winter visitors and passage migrants to Norfolk from their high-Arctic breeding areas in northeast Canada, Greenland, Svalbard and Siberia.

The winter map shows that, unlike most other wintering waders, Sanderlings occur around much of the Norfolk coastline and are not dependent on areas of intertidal mud or saltmarshes. They are, however, concentrated around the outer Wash and the northwest Norfolk coast. While feeding, they are generally spread out around the coastline in small groups, but roosts gather at high tide in large, tightly packed flocks.

Counts rarely exceeded 500 during the NBA winters, but Holme held 656 in February 2001, and Titchwell hosted 550 in December 2000 and 750 in February 2003, while 1,100 were present in Holkham Bay in December 2005, feeding among a large wreck of razor shells that had been deposited on the tideline. Other sites that recorded over 400 birds during the NBA winters were Snettisham and Thornham Harbour.

Sanderlings are rarely found away from the beaches but, in the opening months of both 2002 and 2003, up to 30 regularly fed on flooded fields at Waxham. The other atypical site for Sanderlings is Breydon Water where, since records began, birds have been noted feeding on the open mudflats. For reasons not yet understood, numbers have fallen dramatically in recent years and, whereas flocks of over 100 were not unusual in the 1970s and 1980s, the highest counts during the NBA winters barely reached double figures.

Sanderlings are rarely found inland, and there were no reports during the NBA winters and only a few in spring. At both Welney and Rush Hills on Hickling Broad up to six were recorded annually in May, and occasional birds were reported inland at other sites, such as gravel pits. Away from their normal coastal habitat, up to 45 have also fed on the freshwater marsh at Titchwell in May. On both spring and autumn passage, far larger numbers of Sanderlings are recorded in Norfolk than are found in winter; the highest count during the NBA summer periods was of 3,900 at Snettisham in May 2002. Only a few hundred non-breeders are thought to remain through the summer months.

DAVID TIPLING

SUMMER

Small dots 1–2, medium 3–6, large 7–550 ('pairs')

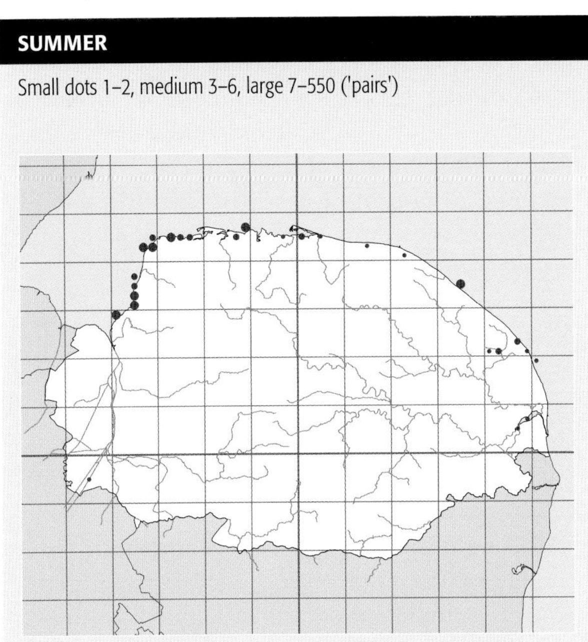

WINTER

Small dots 1–6, medium 7–30, large 31–751 (birds)

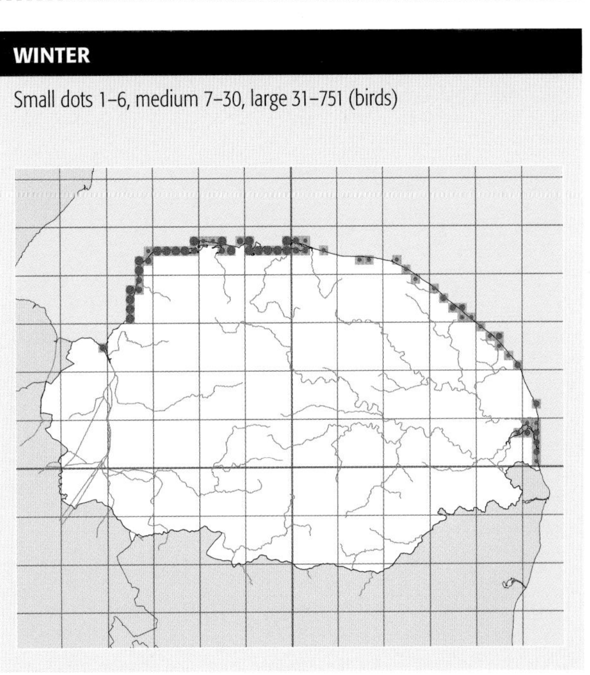

Little Stint

Calidris minuta

NBA 1999–2007	SUMMER: ALL / BREEDING	WINTER
TETRADS OCCUPIED	11 (<1%) / none	8 (<1%)
SUMMER/WINTER ONLY	5	2
MEAN PER OCCUPIED TETRAD	2 / none	2
SUMMED MAX COUNTS	21 / none	18
POPULATION ESTIMATE	1–5 individuals	5–15

PREVIOUS ATLASES	SQUARES OCCUPIED	1999–2007	LOSSES	GAINS
1981–84 WINTER (10 KM)	3 (5%)	7 (11%)	1	5

THE DIMINUTIVE Little Stint is mainly an autumn passage migrant to Norfolk, but in recent years a handful of individuals have been recorded annually also in winter.

The species breeds on the Arctic tundra of Norway and northern Russia, and the European population winters largely in tropical Africa, with variable numbers further north, mainly around the Mediterranean Basin. Little Stints were very rare winterers in Britain prior to the 1930s, but numbers have increased, especially since the 1960s. During the *1981–84 Winter Atlas*, fewer than 30 Little Stints overwintered in Britain, the majority along the south coast.

WINTER

Small dots 1, medium 2–3, large 4–5 (birds)

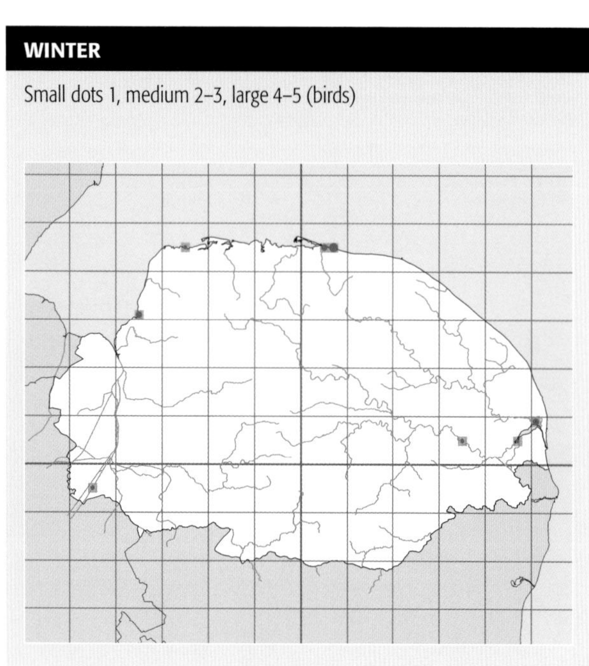

CHRIS COOK

Last century, occasional Little Stints had been recorded in Norfolk in winter with a maximum of three at Wisbech SF in December 1964 and 1968. The species was recorded in just three 10-km squares during the *1981–84 Winter Atlas*, all in northwest Norfolk. Little Stints were recorded in all eight NBA winters, in a total of eight tetrads, with peaks of nine birds in winter 2000/01 and 13 in 2001/02; no more than three were noted in other winters. The favoured sites were Snettisham, with a maximum of five on 14th January 2001, Cley/Salthouse, peaking at seven in December 2001, and Breydon/Berney Marshes with up to three, also peaking in December 2001. Away from the coast and coastal estuaries, up to two were also recorded at Welney (in three winters) and once at Buckenham Marshes.

Small numbers of spring passage migrants were reported annually during the NBA summer recording period, and occasional individuals may summer in the county.

Purple Sandpiper

Calidris maritima

NBA 1999–2007	SUMMER: ALL / BREEDING	WINTER
TETRADS OCCUPIED	3 (<1%) / none	24 (2%)
SUMMER/WINTER ONLY	1	22
MEAN PER OCCUPIED TETRAD	1 / none	2
SUMMED MAX COUNTS	3 / none	55
POPULATION ESTIMATE	none	5–25

PREVIOUS ATLASES	SQUARES OCCUPIED	1999–2007	LOSSES	GAINS
1981–84 WINTER (10 KM)	10 (16%)	10 (16%)	3	3

BEING PRIMARILY A WADER of rocky shores, it is not surprising that Purple Sandpipers are very scarce winter visitors to Norfolk. Their confiding and approachable nature means that it is unlikely that many were missed during the NBA periods.

***Stevenson,* writing in** the 19th century, stated that they occurred regularly in winter and yet *Riviere* in 1930 described them as being only occasional, and so it appears likely that they may have been prone to long-term fluctuations. Certainly, numbers in Norfolk have varied considerably during the last 50 years, peaking at over 100 in February 1987 compared with a maximum of only 23 during the NBA winters. In most winters since 2000, single-figure totals have become the norm. Purple Sandpipers winter further north than any of the other Arctic-breeding waders, Britain being in the southern part of the wintering range. Numbers have fallen nationally, as well as locally, in recent years, and it has been suggested that climatic warming may be partly responsible for this downward trend.

The distribution map is a reflection of those parts of the county where at least some natural or artificial rocky shoreline exists, such as the carstone outcrop between Heacham and Hunstanton and, at low tide, at Titchwell and West Runton. Whereas the eastern side of the Wash was formerly the favoured area to find Purple Sandpipers in winter, as in the *1981–84 Winter Atlas*, the east coast of Norfolk between Eccles and Waxham was the area holding the most during the NBA period, with maximum counts of ten between Eccles and Sea Palling, and six at Waxham.

As well as rocky shores, Purple Sandpipers may also be found on wooden groynes and the substructure of piers and jetties, which are also exposed to vigorous wave action. The new rocky breakwaters protecting the northeast coast have provided additional suitable habitat in recent years. Here the birds can seek out the molluscs and other marine invertebrates upon which they feed. Although they show strong winter site fidelity, an average of only eight birds have overwintered in Norfolk during the last five years. Therefore it is difficult to know where to search for them, although in recent winters Titchwell has generally hosted one or two. Purple Sandpipers have only ever been found at two inland sites in Norfolk (*BoN*), although a dozen have been recorded at Breydon Water since 1950, two of which were on 31st January 2005.

A few spring sightings were reported in each of the NBA summer periods, with Scolt Head claiming more records than any other site. Generally only single birds were involved but there were seven at Sea Palling on 8th May 2001 and two at Scolt Head on 19th May 2003, while away from the shore two even fed on the freshwater marsh at Titchwell on 16th May 2005. One at Eccles/Sea Palling on 27th June 2003 was only the sixth Norfolk record for that month and the first since 1977.

WINTER

Small dots 1, medium 2–3, large 4–7 (birds)

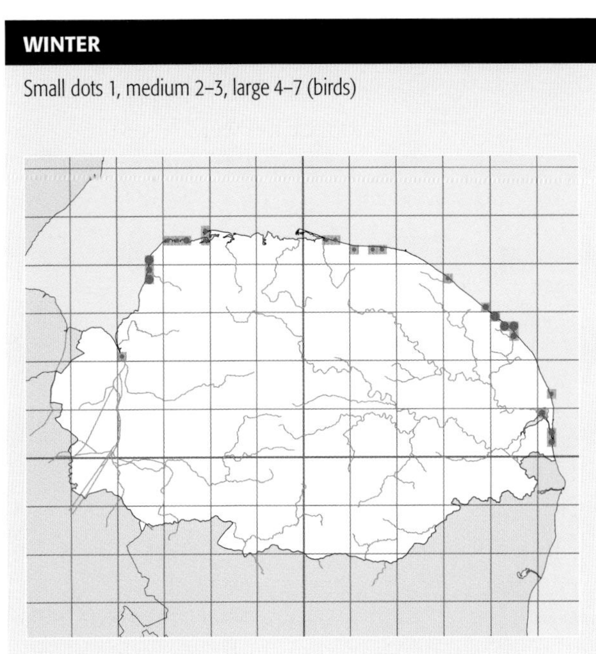

Dunlin

Calidris alpina

NBA 1999–2007	SUMMER: ALL/BREEDING	WINTER
TETRADS OCCUPIED	33 (2%) / none	85 (6%)
SUMMER/WINTER ONLY	12	64
MEAN PER OCCUPIED TETRAD	166 / none	783
SUMMED MAX COUNTS	5,464 / none	66,570
POPULATION ESTIMATE	100–200 individuals	17,000–40,000

PREVIOUS ATLASES	SQUARES OCCUPIED	1999–2007	LOSSES	GAINS
1981–84 WINTER (10 KM)	23 (37%)	21 (34%)	5	3
1988–91 (10 KM)	3 (5%)	none	3	0

DURING THE WINTER the Dunlin is the most abundant coastal wader in Britain, and in many places in Norfolk it is one of the commonest and most familiar.

Dunlins are highly gregarious and pass the winter in large, dense flocks that feed busily on the extensive mudflats that are exposed at low tide around the Wash and Breydon Water, and in the harbours of north Norfolk. Unlike Knot, this species also makes ready use of the muddy creeks and channels of the saltings. The map shows that the largest winter concentrations occurred around the Wash, where peak numbers occur before the NBA season began, during the autumn moult. Largest numbers of Dunlins were found at the high-tide roosts, Snettisham being particularly favoured, where a maximum of 15,200 was present in February 2000. Further west at Terrington, 10,700 were recorded in the same month. Despite these high counts, Dunlin are almost always outnumbered on the Wash by Knot.

Dunlins are largely absent from the northeast Norfolk coast between Salthouse and Breydon

SUMMER

Small dots 1, medium 2–23, large 24–2,550 ('pairs')

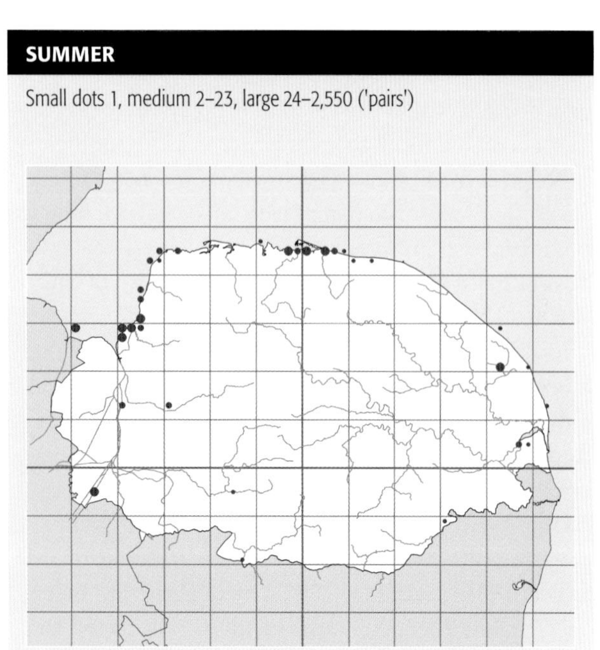

WINTER

Small dots 1–14, medium 15–400, large 401–15,196 (birds)

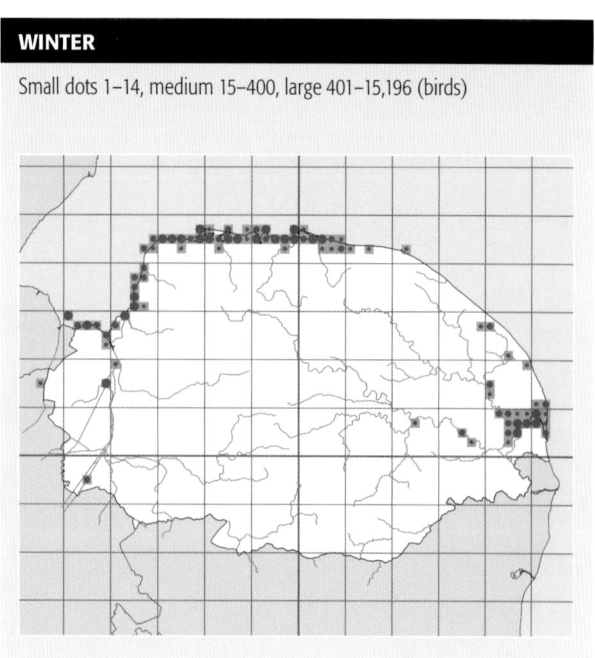

DAVID TIPLING

Water, where sandy shores predominate. At the latter site, large numbers congregate to feed on the extensive intertidal mud, as well as on the surrounding freshwater grazing marshes, particularly at Halvergate. Although numbers have been in decline in east Norfolk for a number of years, 6,280 were recorded in the Breydon Water/Berney area in December 2001. Overwintering Dunlins have been decreasing throughout the county, even within the NBA period, with peaks of 38,500 in 1999/2000 but just 17,000 in 2004/05.

As the map illustrates, wintering Dunlins are predominantly coastal. The only inland sites to hold more than a handful regularly during the NBA winters were Welney, with a maximum of 192 in February 2005, and Buckenham Marshes, with 143 in December 2002.

Dunlin that winter in Norfolk are primarily from Russia (nominate *alpina*), but other races, mainly *arctica* from northeast Greenland and *schinzii* mainly from Iceland and northern Britain, also occur, especially at passage times (*Migration Atlas*).

'Overwintering Dunlins have been decreasing throughout the county, even within the NBA period...'

During the NBA summers, the highest numbers were in the Wash at Terrington and Snettisham, where maxima of 13,400 and 7,700 were counted respectively in May 2000. Of these, no more than a few hundred are thought to spend the whole summer in the county. Spring migrants in small numbers also occurred inland, especially in the west of the county.

Ruff

Philomachus pugnax

NBA 1999–2007	SUMMER: ALL / BREEDING	WINTER
TETRADS OCCUPIED	26 (2%) / none	59 (4%)
SUMMER/WINTER ONLY	8	41
MEAN PER OCCUPIED TETRAD	15 / none	27
SUMMED MAX COUNTS	394 / none	1,594
POPULATION ESTIMATE	0–5 individuals	275–375

PREVIOUS ATLASES	SQUARES OCCUPIED	1999–2007	LOSSES	GAINS
1968–72 (10 KM)	1 (2%)	none	1	0
1980–85 (TETRAD)	2 (<1%)	none	2	0
1980–85 (10 KM)	2 (3%)	none	2	0
1981–84 WINTER (10 KM)	12 (19%)	16 (26%)	2	6
1988–91 (10 KM)	6 (10%)	none	6	0

MALE RUFFS, WITH their distinctive, variably coloured ruffs and ear tufts, are still to be seen in Norfolk springs performing their communal, lekking displays, but sadly the species no longer nests in the county.

Formerly the species bred in many parts of England. After an interval of 41 years, nesting was proved once again, at the Ouse Washes in 1963. In 1971, 21 nests were located there, including some in the Norfolk section of the Washes, and a few bred at Welney up to 1977, but breeding has not been proven in Norfolk since then.

During the breeding season Ruffs inhabit wet, grassy meadows, in which the very secretive females, known as Reeves, conceal their nests. Males take no part in nest construction, incubation or parental duties, only consorting with the females when they mate at the leks. Proof of breeding is extremely hard to obtain. The NBA summer map shows that the species is confined to a few scattered localities in Norfolk, most of which are simply used by Ruffs on spring passage to breeding grounds in Fenno-Scandia or Russia. However, during the NBA springs, lekking was noted at Salthouse, where up to 12 males were at the lek, and Welney, but no birds were

SUMMER

Small dots 1–4, medium 5–16, large 17–55 ('pairs')

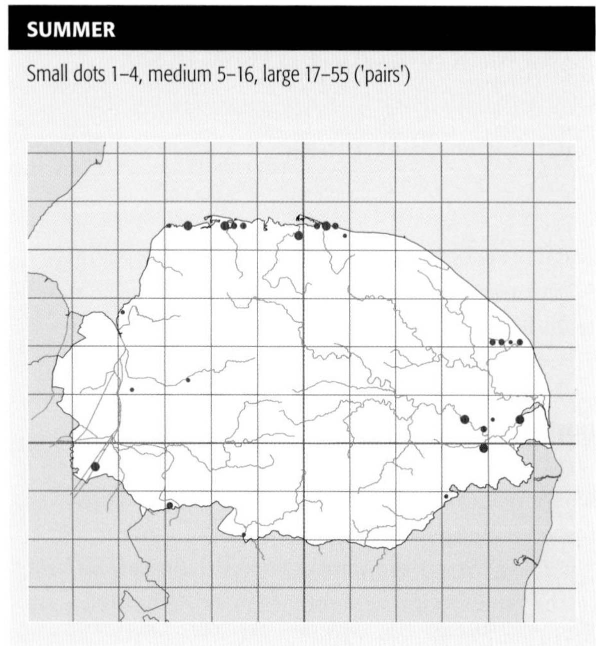

WINTER

Small dots 1–5, medium 6–23, large 24–176 (birds)

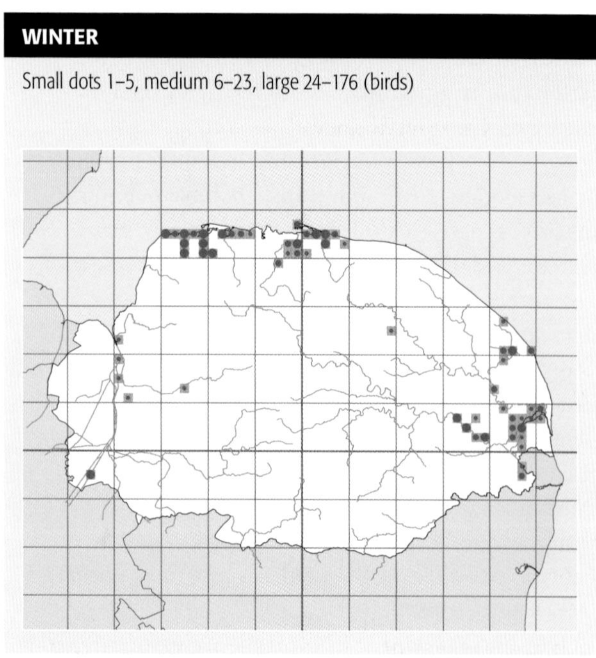

DAVID TIPLING

present after early June and so almost certainly these also involved passage birds still moving north. The highest spring counts, involving at least 100 birds, were made at Titchwell, Cley and Welney.

Ruffs are highly migratory, wintering in sometimes-vast gatherings in West Africa. Wintering in Britain was first recorded in Cambridgeshire in 1934/35. Although they have wintered in Norfolk for the last 50 years, it is only comparatively recently that the winter population has been in three figures. At this time of the year, they frequent dry grassland, stubble fields, freshly ploughed arable land and occasionally tidal mudflats, returning to wetlands to roost at night. The NBA winter map shows that there are a few discrete areas in which nearly all of the county's wintering Ruffs were found. In north Norfolk, one population remains centred on Titchwell, spreading to arable fields at Choseley and as far inland as Docking, to the grazing marshes at Holme,

'Although Ruff have wintered in Norfolk for the past 50 years, it is only comparatively recently that the winter population has been in three figures.'

Brancaster and Burnham Norton, and occasionally onto the tidal mudflats at Brancaster Harbour. Another group remains in the Blakeney/Cley area. In Broadland, regular wintering groups are found in the Breydon Water/Berney area and the Yare valley, while, in the Fens, Welney often hosts the largest winter gatherings in the county. During the NBA period, an average of 330 Ruffs wintered annually in Norfolk, representing about half of the British total, including peak counts of 176 at Welney, 162 at Titchwell, 155 at Breydon Water/Berney, 80 at Cley and 50 at Strumpshaw.

Jack Snipe

Lymnocryptes minimus

NBA 1999–2007	SUMMER: ALL/BREEDING	WINTER
TETRADS OCCUPIED	10 (<1%) / none	57 (4%)
SUMMER/WINTER ONLY	1	48
MEAN PER OCCUPIED TETRAD	1 / none	2
SUMMED MAX COUNTS	10 / none	97
POPULATION ESTIMATE	none	100–150

PREVIOUS ATLASES	SQUARES OCCUPIED	1999–2007	LOSSES	GAINS
1981–84 WINTER (10 KM)	22 (35%)	26 (42%)	10	14

JACK SNIPE ARE scarce winter visitors to Norfolk and, owing to their secretive habits, rarely seen. An encounter with a Jack Snipe normally comes as a complete surprise, as it rises silently from the observer's feet. They are typically solitary birds, inhabiting areas of damp, muddy marshland with short, yet dense vegetation. They also feed on flooded fields, water meadows and damp commons, and along the banks of streams and dykes but, although often found with Snipe, Jack Snipe are far more selective in their feeding places. Regular haunts provide a background that matches the bird's pale yellow camouflage stripes: fallen reed stems are ideal.

The source of Norfolk's passage migrants and winter visitors is likely to be northern Fenno-Scandia and western Russia. The first in autumn usually appear in mid September. Probably most Jack Snipe seen in the county during autumn move on towards France or Spain, however, and do not remain for the winter.

The NBA winter map shows the species to be sparsely distributed throughout the county, with clusters of records from the wetland reserves along the north Norfolk coast and in Broadland. The wetlands in the Fens also contributed a few records, as did the river valleys in south Norfolk. None were recorded in the more arable parts of central Norfolk. Most tetrads hosted single birds but some had two or three, while three sites held five or more on the same date: Cantley BF (seven), East Ruston Fen (six) and Whitlingham Lane CP (five).

The majority of Jack Snipe are found by being disturbed while feeding or resting, rather than being spotted on the ground. One on a brackish mere in the Fens was detected only when a fox flushed it! However, they are one of the few species whose presence can be detected retrospectively by the series of crescent-shaped patterns of holes left in the mud where they have been

JIM ALMOND

'The source of Norfolk's passage migrants and winter visitors is likely to be northern Fenno-Scandia and western Russia.'

probing. Given that the species is so secretive, and that many areas of apparently suitable habitat could not be visited, it is likely that the map under-represents the true distribution. On the other hand, observations at accessible sites confirm that this is indeed a very scarce bird in the winter months.

Jack Snipe return to their northern European breeding areas in March and April, and a few singles were noted during the early part of the summer recording period, all but one of the ten tetrads involved also contributing sightings in the winter.

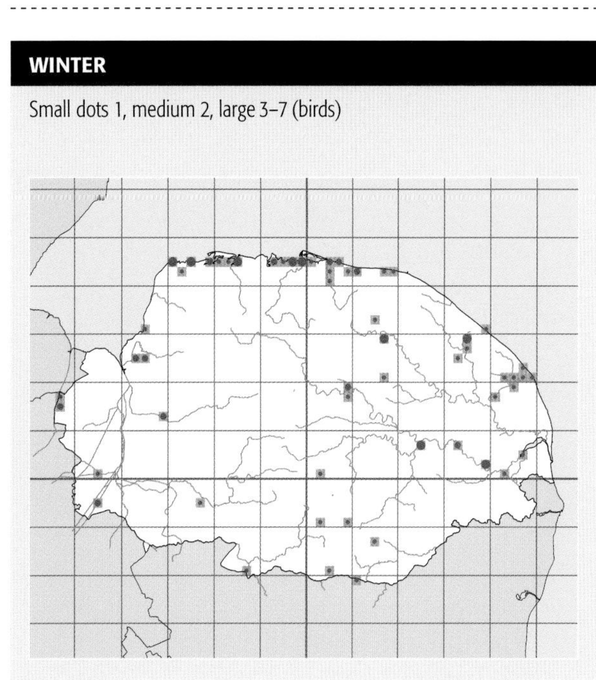

WINTER

Small dots 1, medium 2, large 3–7 (birds)

Snipe

Gallinago gallinago

NBA 1999–2007	SUMMER: ALL/BREEDING	WINTER
TETRADS OCCUPIED	136 (9%) / 62 (4%)	473 (32%)
SUMMER/WINTER ONLY	45	382
MEAN PER OCCUPIED TETRAD	3 / 4	14
SUMMED MAX COUNTS	379 / 242	6,491
POPULATION ESTIMATE	60–120 bp	3,000–6,000

PREVIOUS ATLASES	SQUARES OCCUPIED	1999–2007	LOSSES	GAINS
1968–72 (10 KM)	60 (97%)	27 (44%)	34	1
1980–85 (TETRAD)	322 (22%)	62 (4%)	282	22
1980–85 (10 KM)	53 (85%)	27 (44%)	28	2
1981–84 WINTER (10 KM)	62 (all)	61 (98%)	1	0
1988–91 (10 KM)	48 (77%)	27 (44%)	23	2

THE SNIPE IS A characteristic bird of bogs and shallowly flooded grasslands, both habitats providing its requirements of soft mud for probing and adjacent patches of tussocky vegetation for cover. Its former wide British breeding range has been much reduced, but the species remains familiar as a winter visitor.

Since the 1950s, many areas of wetland across lowland Britain have been drained for use as arable land, while earlier grazing and higher stocking rates have adversely affected breeding success, because of increased trampling, at sites that remain (*1988–91 Atlas*). Snipe have disappeared as breeding birds from many sites where the habitat appears unchanged. In Norfolk, the species was absent from only two 10-km-squares during the *1968–72 Atlas*, but from 14 by the *1988–91 Atlas* and from 35 by the NBA period.

During the breeding season, male Snipe draw attention to themselves by their drumming display and '*clipper*' calls, and so it is unlikely that many territorial birds would have been missed during NBA fieldwork. The NBA summer map shows a very sparse and scattered distribution. Breeding pairs are now

SUMMER

Small dots 1, medium 2–4, large 5–31 ('pairs')
Shading – breeding proved or considered likely

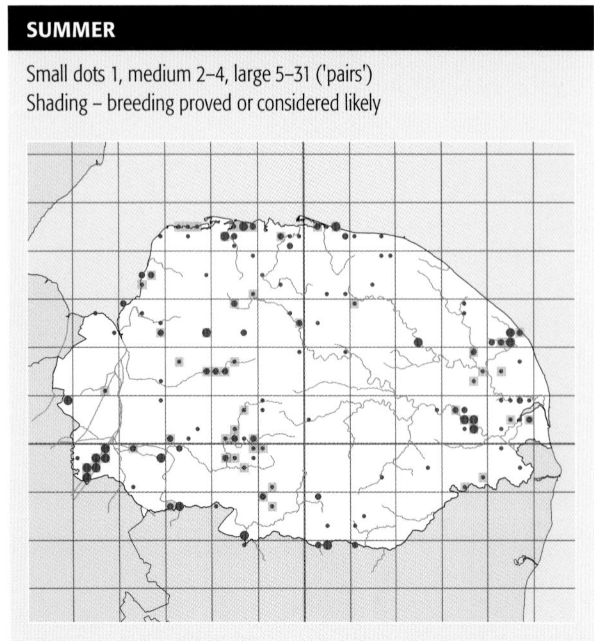

WINTER

Small dots 1–2, medium 3–9, large 10–267 (birds)

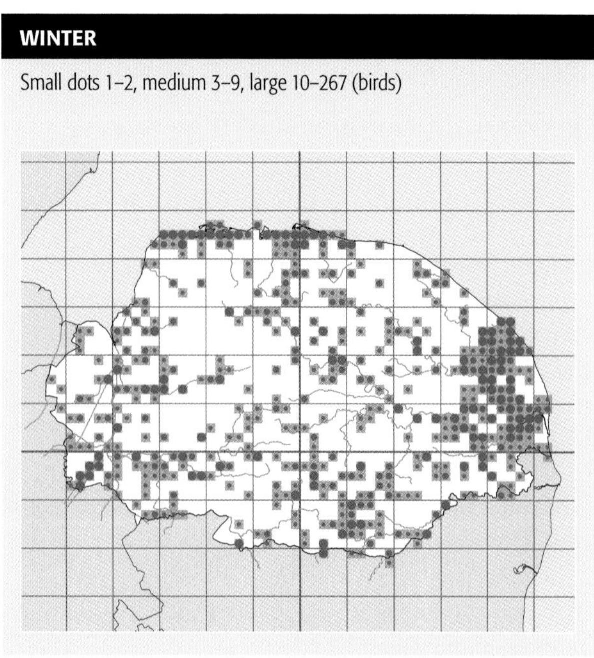

DAVID TIPLING

almost entirely confined to protected wetland reserves, such as Welney, Berney Marshes, the Yare valley and the northern Broads. The highest concentration of drumming Snipe during the years of NBA fieldwork was in the Fens at Welney, where 71 territories were counted in 2003 and 68 in 2005. In Broadland, a maximum of 31 pairs was recorded in the Martham area with 14 at Buckenham Marshes. Holkham NNR held the most drummers in north Norfolk peaking at 17 in 2004.

NBA observers considered that breeding was likely in only 62 of the county's tetrads during 2000–07. There has undoubtedly been a marked fall in the number of breeding pairs in the county since a comprehensive survey undertaken in 1982 revealed a minimum of 500 drumming Snipe in Norfolk (representing 23% of the English and Welsh populations), of which 173 were present at Welney.

Snipe are far more widespread and numerous in the winter than in summer, because of immigration mainly from Fenno-Scandia and Russia. During the winter, Snipe are found in a much broader range of localities and habitats than are used for breeding. Concentrations occur in the Fens, at Breydon Water and in other parts of Broadland and on the coastal and freshwater marshes along the north Norfolk coast. Other localities that attract them are old gravel workings, sewage farms, along the muddy fringes of streams and rivers, flooded water meadows and even arable land. This was demonstrated by a group of 27 that was flushed from a ploughed field near Stokesby during NBA fieldwork and a count of 240 at Sea Palling in December 2001, during a blizzard when snow lay deep on the ground. The highest counts during the NBA winters included 350 at Breydon Water, 267 at Burnham Overy Marshes, 250 at Repps and 230 in the Scolt Head/ Brancaster Harbour area.

CHANGE SINCE 1980–85

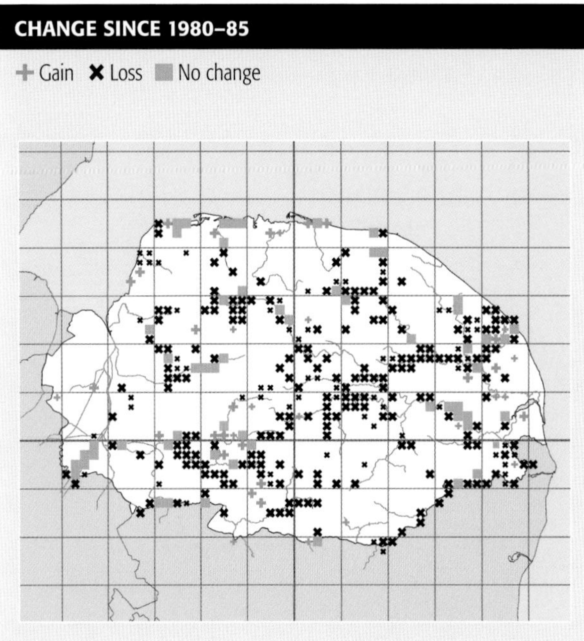

Comparison with previous breeding atlases tells a sorry tale of severe range loss, which is evident all across lowland Britain. The change map reveals the extent of losses since the *1980–85 NBBS*. Breeding Snipe were then recorded at a wide scattering of sites in inland Norfolk, especially along the river valleys, which no longer hold the species.

Woodcock

Scolopax rusticola

NBA 1999–2007	SUMMER: ALL / BREEDING	WINTER
TETRADS OCCUPIED	197 (14%) / 182 (12%)	483 (33%)
SUMMER/WINTER ONLY	75	361
MEAN PER OCCUPIED TETRAD	2 / 2	3
SUMMED MAX COUNTS	432 / 415	1,415
POPULATION ESTIMATE	200–300 roding males	5,000–10,000

PREVIOUS ATLASES	SQUARES OCCUPIED	1999–2007	LOSSES	GAINS
1968–72 (10 KM)	48 (77%)	38 (61%)	16	6
1980–85 (TETRAD)	230 (16%)	182 (12%)	146	98
1980–85 (10 KM)	50 (81%)	38 (61%)	14	2
1981–84 WINTER (10 KM)	51 (82%)	58 (94%)	2	9
1988–91 (10 KM)	38 (61%)	38 (61%)	9	9

WITH ITS CREPUSCULAR habits and mainly solitary nature, the Woodcock is one of the most enigmatic of Norfolk's birds. It remains a common winter visitor, valued in some quarters for sport shooting, but there is growing evidence across Britain for a major decline in breeding numbers and distribution.

During the breeding season, Woodcocks favour damp deciduous or mixed woods with variable shrub cover and woodland rides. They also inhabit coniferous woodland, including young forestry plantations. The nest scrape is well concealed by low vegetation or at the base of a tree, and the incubating female is extremely well camouflaged. The presence of breeding birds is generally revealed by the male's distinctive roding flights at dusk.

The NBA summer map shows a fairly wide, if rather scattered distribution, with the stronghold in Breckland and other localised concentrations in the woods around the Sandringham area, along the Cromer to Holt ridge and in Broadland. The highest localised concentration in the summer period was in the Hoveton tetrad, with 16 pairs (roding males), followed by 12 near Thetford and at Coltishall. It is likely that the Norfolk breeding population numbers in the region of 250 roding males.

Although the majority of British Woodcocks are

SUMMER

Small dots 1, medium 2–3, large 4–16 ('pairs')
Shading – breeding proved or considered likely

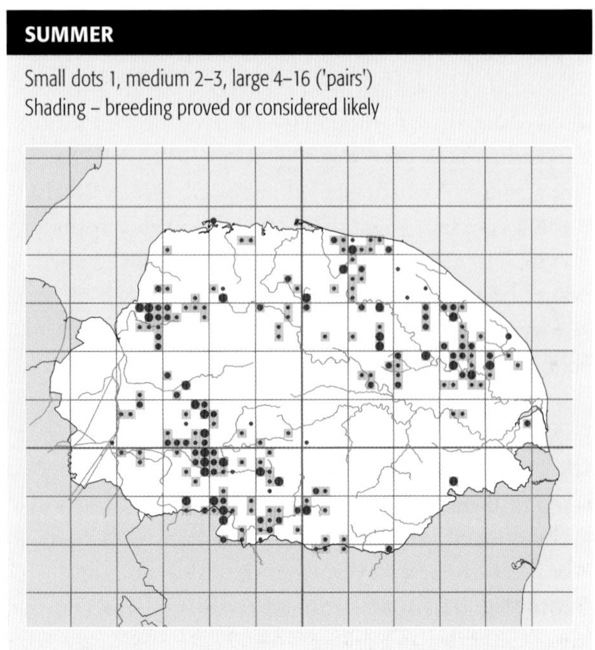

WINTER

Small dots 1, medium 2–3, large 4–70 (birds)

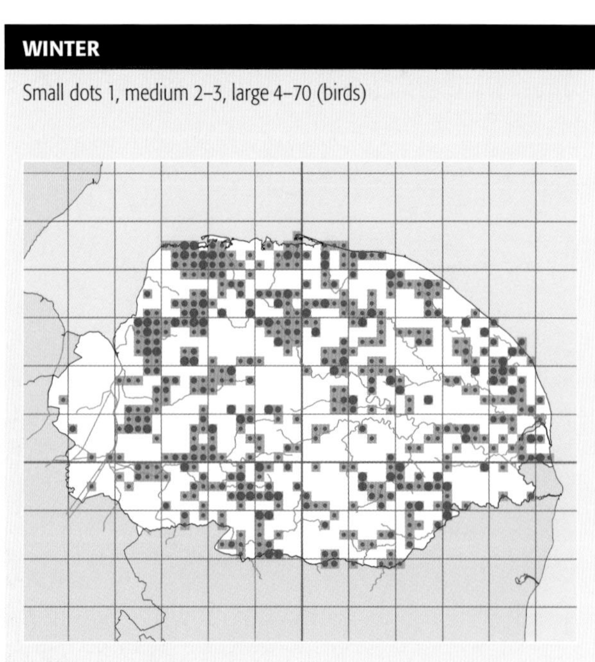

DAVID TIPLING

probably resident, winter visitors arrive from Fenno-Scandia and other parts of northern Europe. While the majority arrive in late autumn, severe weather on the Continent may result in immigration later in the winter. At this season Woodcocks feed in a far wider variety of habitats, and during NBA fieldwork were reported from roadside ditches, grass verges and even gardens, especially during periods of hard weather. They usually roost in woodland by day, feeding in open fields at night, but even during daytime may occasionally be disturbed from stubble or a crop planted as game cover.

This wider distribution is reflected in the NBA winter map, although as in the summer many records are concentrated in the more wooded parts of the county. None were detected in the lower parts of Fenland. The highest counts were all made during shoots, as birds were flushed by the beaters, and included 300 at Holkham in late December 2004, 70 near Brancaster and 68 at Repps. The maximum tetrad counts made during set visits by NBA fieldworkers were 24 at Repps and 18 at Houghton. As in the summer, observers would have missed many birds that did not flush, and a high proportion of records were from chance encounters on supplementary visits. Estimating Norfolk's total winter population during the NBA period is very difficult but it probably lay within the range 5,000–10,000 birds.

CHANGE SINCE 1980–85

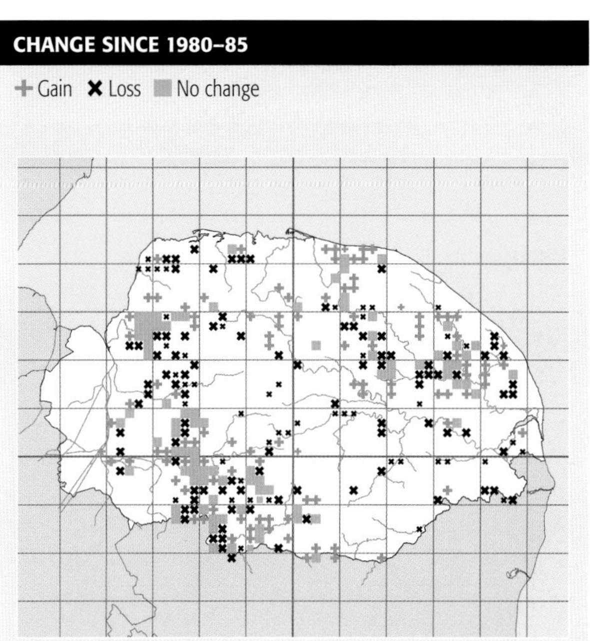

A loss of breeding range of ten Norfolk 10-km squares occurred between the *1968–72* and *1988–91 Atlases*. The change map shows that considerable further range loss at tetrad level has occurred since the *1980–85 NBBS*. Isolated localities then occupied across mid Norfolk have almost all been lost, and the main pockets of remaining distribution have each lost ground during the two decades preceding the NBA survey.

Black-tailed Godwit

Limosa limosa

NBA 1999–2007	SUMMER: ALL / BREEDING	WINTER
TETRADS OCCUPIED	32 (2%) / 1 (<1%)	36 (2%)
SUMMER/WINTER ONLY	15	19
MEAN PER OCCUPIED TETRAD	76 / 750	181
SUMMED MAX COUNTS	2,437 / 750	6,511
POPULATION ESTIMATE	0–5 bp	3,500–4,500

PREVIOUS ATLASES	SQUARES OCCUPIED	1999–2007	LOSSES	GAINS
1968–72 (10 KM)	7 (11%)	1 (2%)	6	0
1980–85 (TETRAD)	5 (<1%)	1 (<1%)	4	0
1980–85 (10 KM)	2 (3%)	1 (2%)	1	0
1981–84 WINTER (10 KM)	8 (13%)	15 (24%)	1	8
1988–91 (10 KM)	6 (10%)	1 (2%)	5	0

DAVID TIPLING

THE BLACK-TAILED GODWIT is a large, graceful wader for which Britain has a special international importance, as host to almost the entire population of the Icelandic race on passage or in winter.

The species was formerly quite widespread as a nesting bird in eastern England, but became extinct as a breeding species in the early 19th century due to wetland drainage, egg collecting and shooting, and it was not until the 1930s that it began to breed sporadically again in the Fens. By 1952, it was breeding regularly on the Ouse Washes, which remained the main breeding site until 1991. Elsewhere in Norfolk, breeding was attempted at Cley in 1964 but it was not until four years later that two pairs nested there, only for all the young to be taken by stoats. Similarly, in 1969 and 1970, two pairs nested but no young successfully fledged. Subsequently, breeding has occurred at other sites.

During the breeding season Black-tailed Godwits favour areas of damp grassland, preferably grazed, placing the nest on a grassy hummock or on slightly raised ground. There appears to be no shortage of suitable areas in Norfolk where the species could breed, but it remains a very rare breeding bird within the county. The NBA summer map shows that Black-tailed Godwits were recorded in a few well-scattered localities around the Wash, along the north Norfolk coast, in east Norfolk and at Welney in the Fens. However, at all but one of these sites, non-breeding migrant or oversummering birds were involved. Since 2001 up to five pairs have bred annually at one inland location, successfully raising up to six young each year, except for 2005 and 2007 when breeding failed completely. All the breeding pairs are of the continental nominate race *limosa*.

Black-tailed Godwits are migratory, and birds of the nominate race winter mainly in West Africa. The Icelandic breeding population *islandica* winters in western Europe, however, and in increasing numbers nowadays in Britain and neighbouring countries. Norfolk's winter visitors are highly gregarious, favouring muddy estuaries, shallow brackish

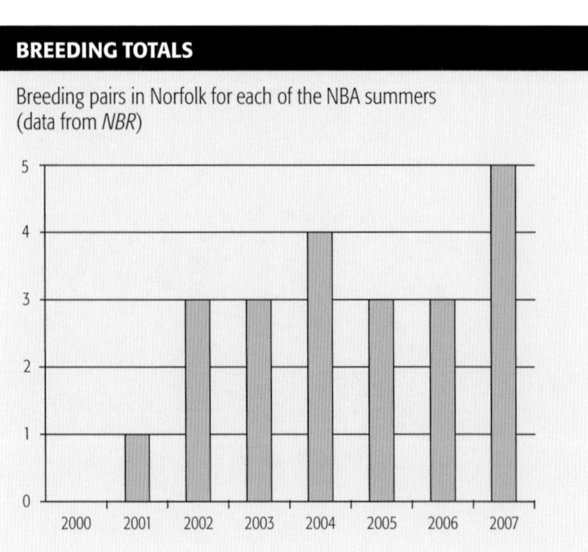

BREEDING TOTALS

Breeding pairs in Norfolk for each of the NBA summers (data from *NBR*)

lagoons and freshwater marshes. They are also feeding increasingly in arable fields just inland from the coast.

The NBA winter map shows a marked concentration in the Breydon Water/Berney area, a location where overwintering first occurred in the winter of 1992/93, involving just 44 birds (Allard 2000a). By January 2000, the count had increased to 807 (Allard 2000b) and had doubled by the next winter. The only other site in Norfolk to host over 1,000 wintering Black-tailed Godwits was Welney, with 2,156 in February 2006, from where birds regularly commute to the Wash. During the NBA winters, smaller, but still significant numbers were also reported from the north Norfolk coast. The Wash typically holds more wintering Black-tailed Godwits than any other site in Britain. Rather few were noted on the Norfolk side during NBA fieldwork, however, other than at Snettisham. While the winter distribution is primarily coastal, smaller numbers were recorded on inland grazing marshes, especially in Broadland.

As described in the 2004 *NBR*, it is now not uncommon to see three-figure flocks of birds of the *islandica* race on favoured sites at any time of year.

'Black-tailed Godwits are migratory, and birds of the nominate race winter mainly in West Africa.'

SUMMER

Small dots 1–10, medium 11–63, large 64–750 ('pairs')
Shading – breeding proved or considered likely

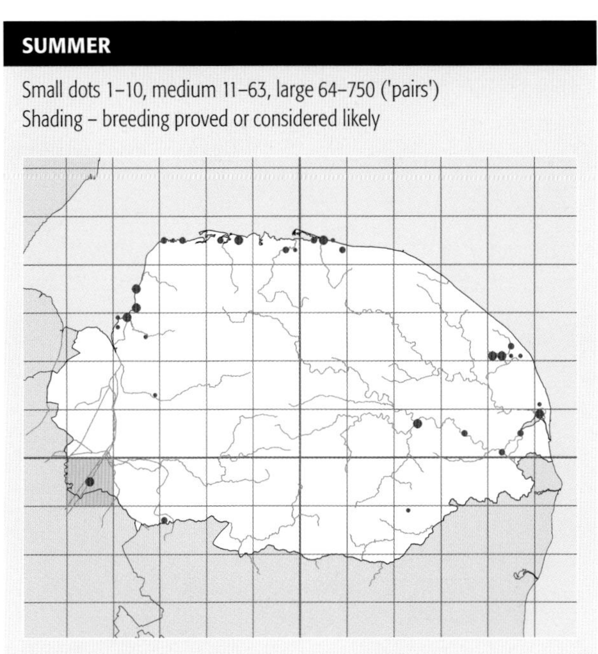

WINTER

Small dots 1–11, medium 12–151, large 152–1,700 (birds)

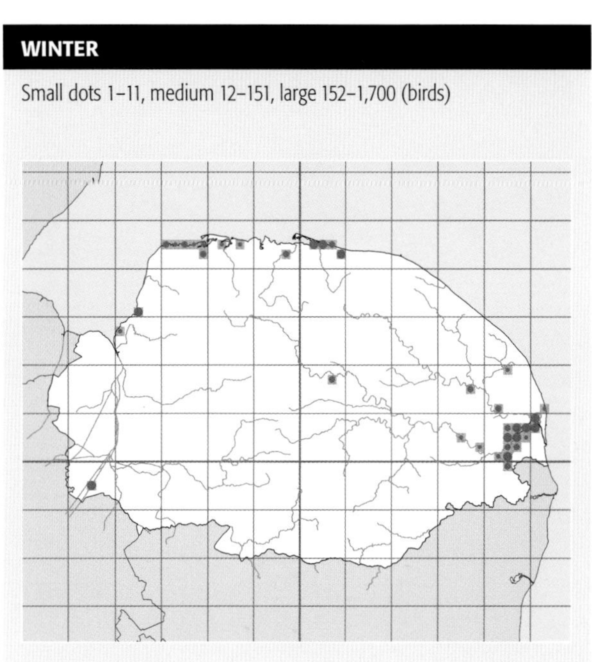

Bar-tailed Godwit
Limosa lapponica

NBA 1999–2007	SUMMER: ALL / BREEDING	WINTER
TETRADS OCCUPIED	28 (2%) / none	46 (3%)
SUMMER/WINTER ONLY	19	37
MEAN PER OCCUPIED TETRAD	35 / none	329
SUMMED MAX COUNTS	967 / none	15,126
POPULATION ESTIMATE	100–150 individuals	6,000–8,000

PREVIOUS ATLASES	SQUARES OCCUPIED	1999–2007	LOSSES	GAINS
1981–84 WINTER (10 KM)	9 (15%)	11 (18%)	0	2

THE BAR-TAILED GODWIT is one of the high-Arctic waders that make extensive use of the Wash and Norfolk's other muddy estuaries. It has always been a common shorebird in the county, arriving in large numbers in early autumn and remaining throughout the winter months. The Wash is the most important wintering area in Britain (Atkinson 1996), while the north Norfolk coast also holds internationally important numbers.

Although it is found on both muddy and sandy shores, the NBA winter map shows that the highest concentrations occur along the eastern side of the Wash and along the north Norfolk coast. Here, Bar-tailed Godwits feed along the tideline, probing for

lugworms, ragworms and bivalves with their long, slightly upcurved bills. As the tide rises, they fly to traditional, safe roosting areas, such as shingle spits, sandbars or saltings, which may lie some distance from the feeding grounds (*1981–84 Winter Atlas*).

The locations on the NBA maps with the highest concentrations generally indicate the sites of these high-tide roosts. During the NBA winters, Snettisham was the site of the main roost, with 4,000–4,500 in most of the years, peaking at 5,700 in the winter of 2002/03. Smaller roosts, generally holding fewer than 500 birds also formed in the Holme/Thornham Harbour/Titchwell and Scolt Head/Brancaster Harbour areas. No birds were recorded along the east Norfolk coast north of Breydon Water, where they were mainly found at the eastern, seaward end of the estuary. With an average winter count of about 7,000 during the

SUMMER

Small dots 1, medium 2–10, large 11–500 ('pairs')

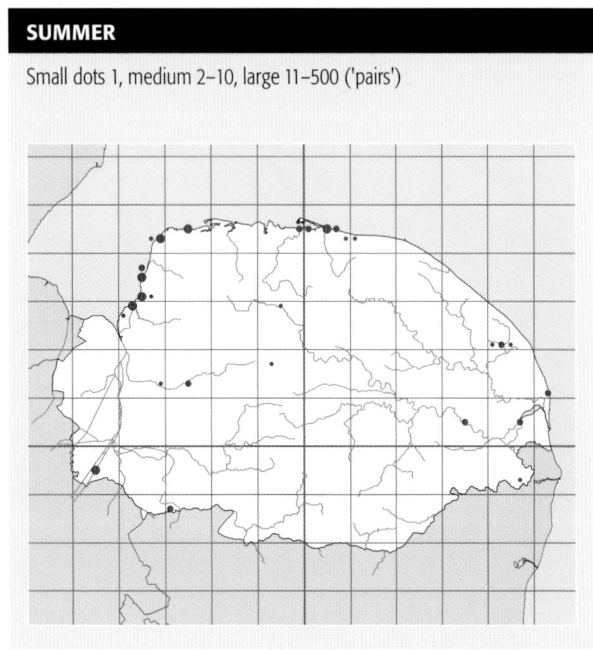

WINTER

Small dots 1–24, medium 25–170, large 171–4,150 (birds)

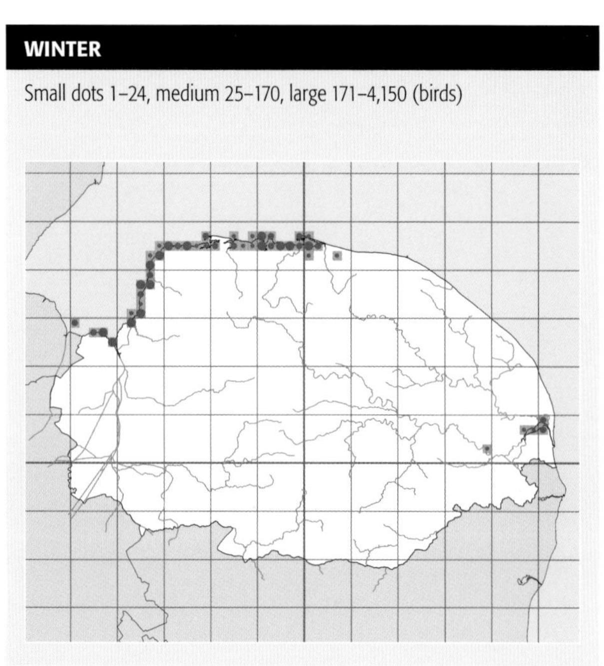

DAVID TIPLING

NBA period, it would appear that fewer Bar-tailed Godwits are currently overwintering in the county than in the 1980s and 1990s. Low counts during the NBA period may owe much to the consistently mild winter weather, however.

'Bar-tailed Godwits are unusual inland during the winter, even just inland of the seawall.'

Bar-tailed Godwits are unusual inland during the winter, even just inland of the seawall; there was only a single inland record during the NBA, of one at Cantley BF on 11th January 2002. However, they are quite frequent inland during spring passage in April and May, with high counts of 32 at Welney and 11 at Buckenham in May 2000, and up to ten daily at Hickling Broad in May 2002, where 17 were also present on 7th June 2003. Spring passage birds were also noted within the winter range, and small numbers of non-breeding, mainly first-year birds also summered on the Wash.

Curlew
Numenius arquata

NBA 1999–2007	SUMMER: ALL / BREEDING	WINTER
TETRADS OCCUPIED	176 (12%) / 37 (3%)	246 (17%)
SUMMER/WINTER ONLY	87	157
MEAN PER OCCUPIED TETRAD	5 / 3	58
SUMMED MAX COUNTS	960 / 95	14,181
POPULATION ESTIMATE	30–50 bp	5,000–6,000

PREVIOUS ATLASES	SQUARES OCCUPIED	1999–2007	LOSSES	GAINS
1968–72 (10 KM)	9 (15%)	10 (16%)	3	4
1980–85 (TETRAD)	71 (5%)	37 (3%)	48	14
1980–85 (10 KM)	17 (27%)	10 (16%)	11	4
1981–84 WINTER (10 KM)	28 (45%)	41 (66%)	5	18
1988–91 (10 KM)	18 (29%)	10 (16%)	11	3

THE CURLEW IS THE largest wader in the western Palaearctic and, with its long, decurved bill and far-carrying, bubbling song, is also one of the most distinctive.

Formerly a breeding species in Britain that was confined to the uplands, it spread during the 20th century and became widespread, if localised, in many parts of lowland Britain. However, numbers have been falling in recent years, in line with those of most other inland-breeding waders. Curlews first bred in Norfolk at Sandringham in 1889 and 1890, then at Roydon Common in 1910, a site still occupied annually by up to three territorial pairs. Breckland was first colonised in 1949, when one pair bred at Weeting, and the Brecks remain the county stronghold for this species, the relatively undisturbed Stanford TA being especially favoured.

Curlews are monogamous, with pairs using the same breeding sites in successive years. They return to their breeding areas in early February and during the nesting season defend large exclusive territories. The territorial display of the males, accompanied by the evocative, bubbling calls, ensures that potential breeding pairs are easily located during the spring, although they become far more secretive during incubation. They favour open grassland areas with good visibility, in order to detect the approach of any potential predators, constructing nests amongst grassy tussocks, or even in fields of growing crops.

The NBA summer map shows two main areas in which Curlews were located during the breeding season: on the open, mainly arable land, of northwest Norfolk and in Breckland. Indeed, these were the only two parts of the county where definite territorial pairs were noted during the NBA fieldwork. However, the vast majority of sightings in northwest Norfolk, as well as around the coast and in east Norfolk, concerned late-returning winter visitors or spring passage migrants. During the NBA years, 30–40 territorial pairs of Curlews were recorded annually in Norfolk, mainly in the Brecks, of which about two-thirds each year were in the Stanford TA.

In July, after breeding, Curlews leave their inland sites and move to the coast, where most remain throughout the winter to feed on the estuarine mudflats and muddy foreshores, roosting on the saltmarshes at high tide. During the winter months, visitors from the Continent join the more local birds. Ringing has demonstrated that the majority of Norfolk's winter visitors are from Fenno-Scandia (*Migration Atlas*). Although they tend to feed alone, Curlews do flock, especially when roosting.

The NBA winter map demonstrates the large numbers that gather around the Wash and north Norfolk coast westwards from Blakeney. Smaller numbers also occur widely inland in northwest Norfolk. Virtually none were recorded along the coastline of east Norfolk. A further area highly favoured by Curlews in winter is on and around Breydon Water, the only site in the county where over 1,000 Curlews are regularly noted each winter. Breydon Water hosted the highest number recorded during the NBA winters, with a maximum of 1,593 in January 2005, while, on the Wash, 1,461 were at Terrington in February 2000. Counts above 1,000 were also made at Snettisham and in the Scolt Head/Brancaster Harbour area.

Curlews were also recorded in many of the inland tetrads in northwest Norfolk in the winter months, where they feed on fields of winter cereal and sugar beet, as well as on stubble fields. Many of these birds roosted on the Wash and flighted inland early on winter mornings. Similarly, it is likely that daily forays from Breydon Water were responsible for winter sightings in Broadland. The birds vacate their Breckland breeding sites completely in winter, but

DAVID TIPLING

SUMMER

Small dots 1, medium 2–3, large 4–200 ('pairs')
Shading – breeding proved or considered likely

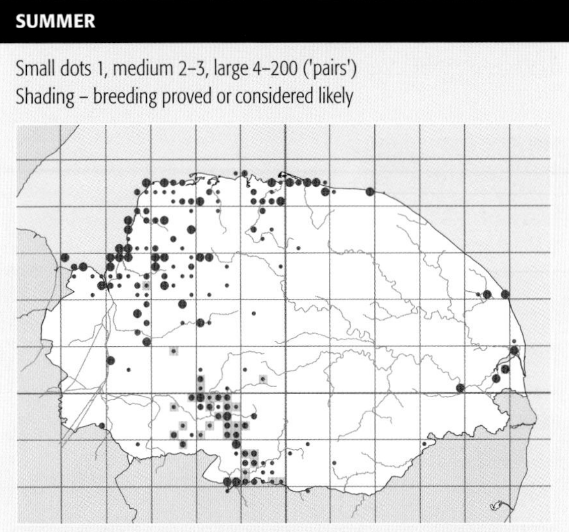

WINTER

Small dots 1–6, medium 7–31, large 32–1,060 (birds)

CHANGE SINCE 1980–85

+ Gain ✖ Loss ■ No change

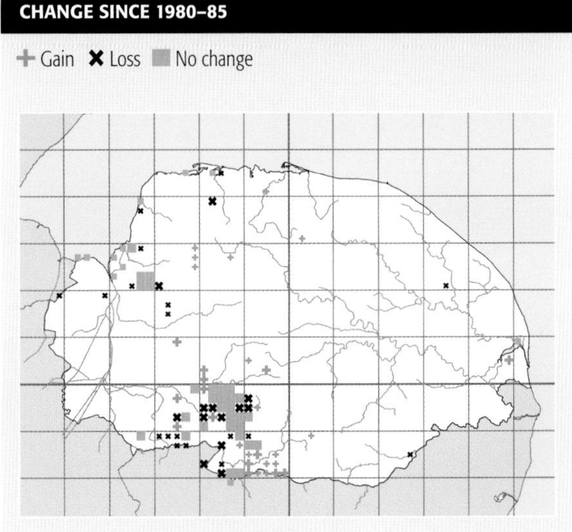

'Curlews are monogamous, with pairs using the same breeding sites in successive years.'

the first ones return to their breeding territories in February, and some records therefore appear on the winter map.

There has probably been little change in the breeding range in Norfolk since the 1960s. The change map indicates that there has been a small range extension since 1980–85 to the east of Thetford, and a mixture of gains and losses elsewhere in Breckland. Breeding of Curlews by Breydon Water would not be expected, and remains unconfirmed.

Common Sandpiper
Actitis hypoleucos

NBA 1999–2007	SUMMER: ALL/BREEDING	WINTER
TETRADS OCCUPIED	69 (5%) / none	12 (<1%)
SUMMER/WINTER ONLY	64	7
MEAN PER OCCUPIED TETRAD	2 / none	1
SUMMED MAX COUNTS	108 / none	12
POPULATION ESTIMATE	0–5 individuals	0–4

PREVIOUS ATLASES	SQUARES OCCUPIED	1999–2007	LOSSES	GAINS
1968–72 (10 KM)	1 (2%)	none	1	0
1980–85 (TETRAD)	9 (<1%)	none	9	0
1980–85 (10 KM)	9 (15%)	none	9	0
1981–84 WINTER (10 KM)	3 (5%)	8 (13%)	2	7
1988–91 (10 KM)	4 (6%)	none	4	0

THE COMMON SANDPIPER occurs in Norfolk at every season, but is most abundant on spring and autumn passage. Although the species nests primarily by upland rivers, streams and lakes, favouring those with rocky margins, there had been seven records of nesting in Norfolk prior to the NBA survey, mostly recently at Pentney GP and at Blickling in 1980 (*BoN*). Numbers have been in decline in Britain and across Europe in recent decades (*Birdtrends*).

The NBA summer map is a reflection of the distribution and abundance of spring passage migrants. It clearly shows the preponderance of inland sites that are used, with very few recorded around the coast, except on the lagoons at Titchwell and Cley. While on passage, Common Sandpipers will utilise any area of standing or flowing fresh water, no matter how small, and migrants are just as likely to be found by the side of small ponds and in ditches as around the edges of gravel pits or parkland lakes. Although there were no records of breeding during the NBA period, birds probably oversummered at Titchwell in 2004 and 2005.

Common Sandpipers are mainly summer visitors to Europe and the majority winter in tropical Africa,

SUMMER

Small dots 1, medium 2, large 3–12 ('pairs')

WINTER

Small dots 1 (bird)

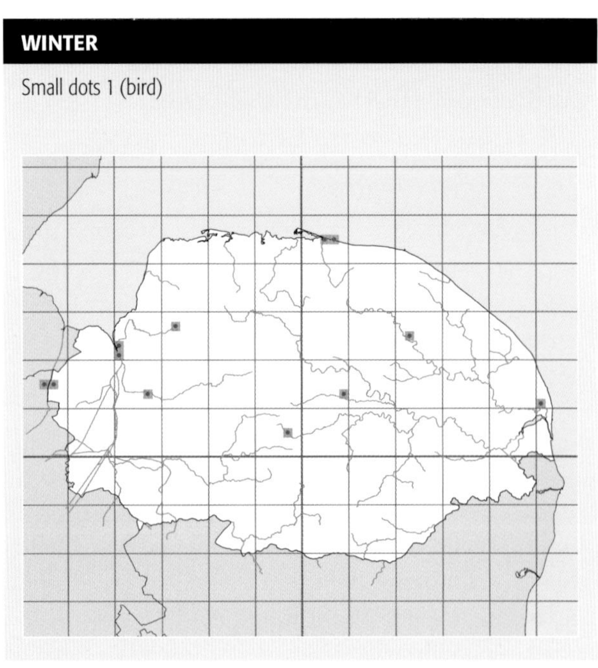

DAVID TIPLING

but small numbers have been overwintering in Britain since the 1950s. The *1981–84 Winter Atlas* clearly demonstrated a coastal bias to such records, with the main concentrations in the south and west. Over half of Norfolk's wintering records up to 1998 came from Cley or Breydon Water. Therefore, it is of interest that the NBA winter map shows that, perhaps through chance, most wintering Common Sandpipers during the recent period were located at inland sites.

At least one Common Sandpiper was recorded in most of the NBA winters, with three or four in the opening months of 2001. Some birds returned to the same site in subsequent years, including one at West Walton for four consecutive winters between 2001 and 2003. King's Lynn Fisher Fleet also held a Common Sandpiper in several of the winters. The unexpected discovery of a wintering Common Sandpiper can be a bonus for winter atlas fieldworkers: as one observer commented on finding one by a small pool at Letton Hall, Cranworth, on 27th February 2006, "I could not believe my eyes!"

'At least one Common Sandpiper was recorded in most of the NBA winters, with three or four in the opening months of 2001.'

Green Sandpiper
Tringa ochropus

NBA 1999–2007	SUMMER: ALL/BREEDING	WINTER
TETRADS OCCUPIED	55 (4%) / none	108 (7%)
SUMMER/WINTER ONLY	34	87
MEAN PER OCCUPIED TETRAD	1 / none	1
SUMMED MAX COUNTS	77 / none	159
POPULATION ESTIMATE	0–2 individuals	25–30

PREVIOUS ATLASES	SQUARES OCCUPIED	1999–2007	LOSSES	GAINS
1980–85 (TETRAD)	2 (<1%)	none	2	0
1980–85 (10 KM)	2 (3%)	none	2	0
1981–84 WINTER (10 KM)	28 (45%)	42 (68%)	10	24
1988–91 (10 KM)	1 (2%)	none	1	0

GREEN SANDPIPERS FEED unobtrusively along the muddy fringes of fresh water and often first reveal themselves as they fly noisily away, towering like a Snipe. The species breeds across northern Eurasia from Norway to the Sea of Okhotsk, wintering mainly around the Mediterranean, in tropical Africa and in India and southeast Asia. There have been a very few isolated cases of breeding in Scotland and northern England.

Although during the *1980–85 NBBS* there were three sites where observers considered that breeding was possible, it is highly unlikely that the species has ever nested in the county. Passage migrants, however, are widespread across Norfolk, with singles or small groups

DAVID TIPLING

regular by open water, at streamsides and even at farm slurry pits. Spring passage is mainly in April and early May; in autumn, much larger numbers pass through, beginning with adults returning to moult in mid June. There is little active migration after early October, but small numbers of birds remain to overwinter.

The NBA's summer recording period overlaps with both spring and autumn passage. As not all passage birds detected have found their way into the NBA database, the summer map is incomplete. Nevertheless, it indicates the broad pattern of records in spring and early autumn, with birds seen at coastal marshes as well as inland. Many of the tetrads concerned are along the courses of Norfolk's rivers, as is particularly apparent in the Yare valley.

'There is little active migration after early October, but small numbers of birds remain to overwinter.'

The winter map is more complete. It shows a wide but sparse distribution, amplifying the summer map but with very few records at this season from coastal sites. Until the mid 1980s, an average of just seven Green Sandpipers was recorded annually in Norfolk in winter, increasing to just over 20 by the late 1990s. During the NBA period, however, 25–30 have been reported each winter. It is very difficult to estimate the true wintering population, however, as some birds may have been missed altogether and others recorded at more than one site, either between winters or during the course of a single winter. Because there are many sites with similar patterns of records between winters, it is likely that some individual birds return to localities they occupied in previous winters.

SUMMER

Small dots 1, medium 2, large 3–15 ('pairs')

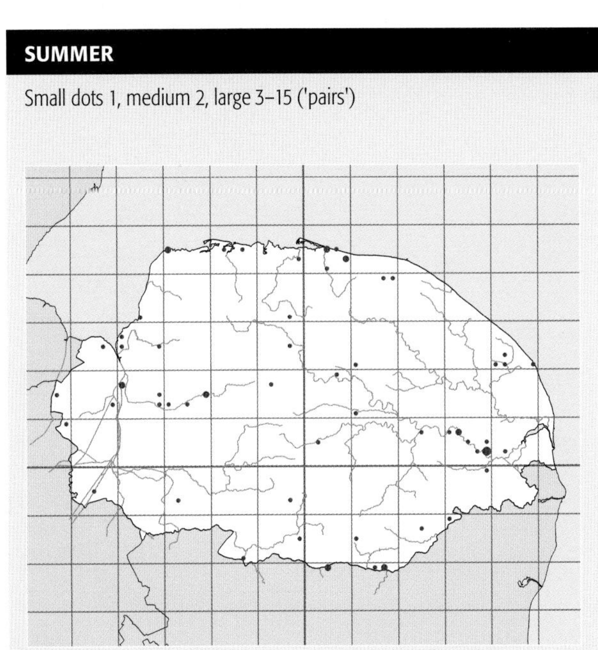

WINTER

Small dots 1, medium 2, large 3–7 (birds)

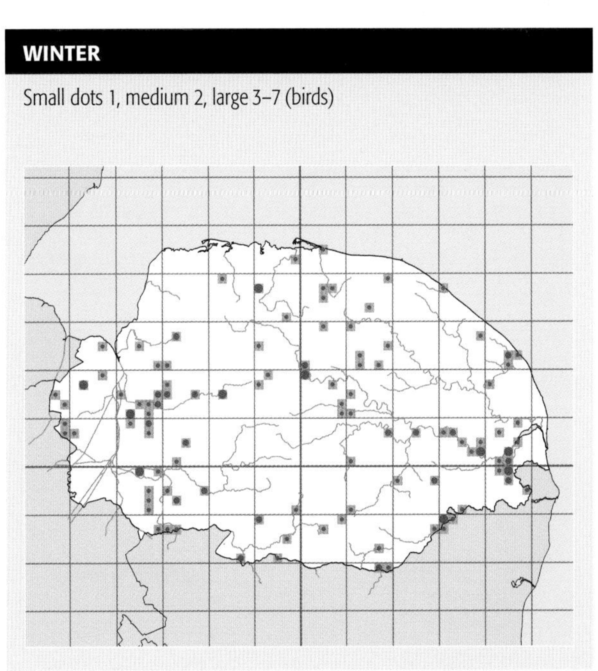

Spotted Redshank
Tringa erythropus

NBA 1999–2007	SUMMER: ALL / BREEDING	WINTER
TETRADS OCCUPIED	13 (<1%) / none	26 (2%)
SUMMER/WINTER ONLY	5	18
MEAN PER OCCUPIED TETRAD	4 / none	3
SUMMED MAX COUNTS	48 / none	80
POPULATION ESTIMATE	0–1 individuals	15–25

PREVIOUS ATLASES	SQUARES OCCUPIED	1999–2007	LOSSES	GAINS
1981–84 WINTER (10 KM)	6 (10%)	11 (18%)	1	6

DAVID TIPLING

THE SPOTTED REDSHANK is a tall and elegant wader, always a joy to watch, whether in its blackish breeding plumage or pale grey winter attire.

The species breeds in the far north of Fenno-Scandia and Russia, wintering in western Europe and in Africa. It is relatively scarce during the winter months in Britain but has become rather more widespread and numerous in recent years.

Up to 1930, only four Spotted Redshanks had been recorded in Norfolk in winter, all in the Cley/Blakeney area. From 1975, at least one has occurred in the county each winter and, by the start of the NBA fieldwork, double-figure counts had become annual. Initially, only Breydon Water and Titchwell held regular overwintering Spotted Redshanks. As can be seen from the NBA winter map, however, the species has since become rather more widespread, and no longer entirely coastal in distribution.

By the winter of 2006/07, Spotted Redshanks were using three main areas regularly in winter: Holme to Brancaster Harbour, Cley to Salthouse and Breydon Water/Berney. Each of them provides either a muddy estuarine habitat with saltmarshes or shallow, brackish lagoons. The highest counts during the NBA winters were 20 at Titchwell in December 2006 and 17 between Holme and Scolt Head in January 2007, although single-figure counts at these sites are more usual. Other maximum site counts include seven at Breydon Water/Berney and six at Cley/Salthouse.

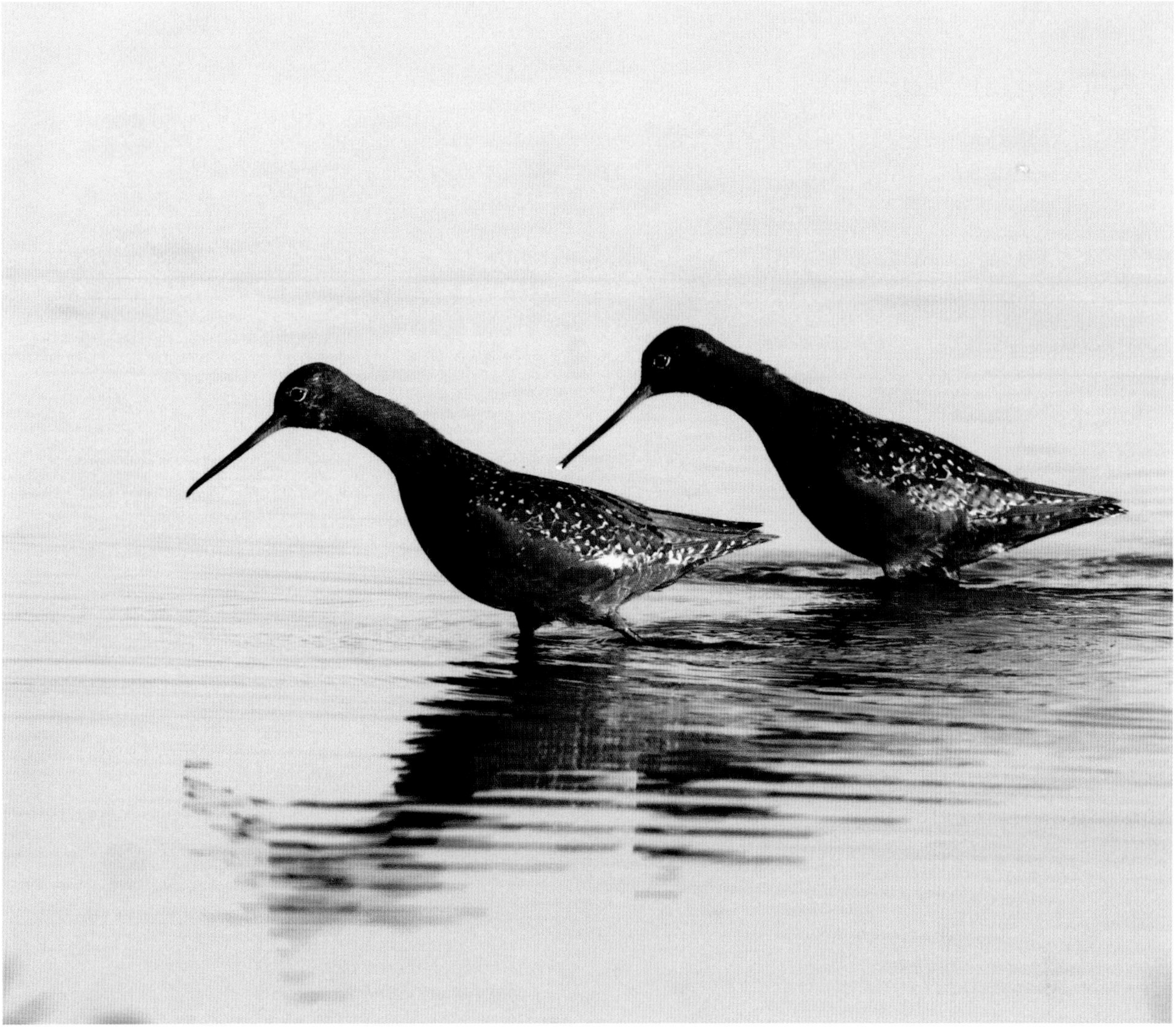

DAVID TIPLING

WINTER

Small dots 1, medium 2–3, large 4–20 (birds)

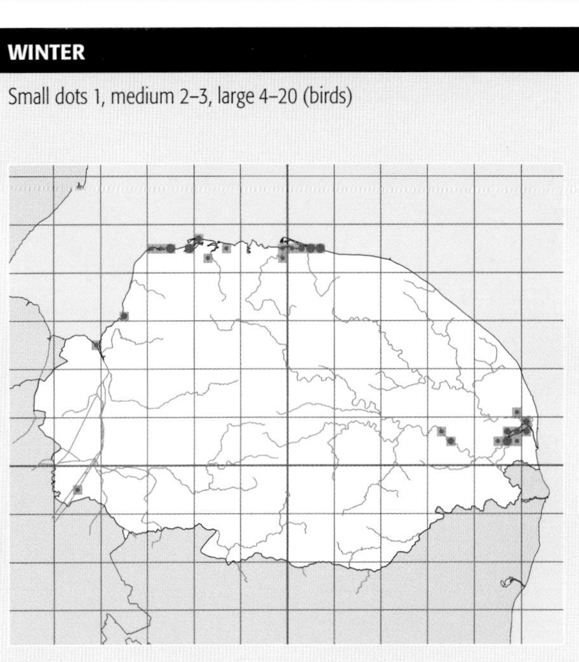

'Spotted Redshank is relatively scarce during the winter months in Britain but has become rather more widespread and numerous in recent years.'

Spotted Redshank remain rare inland in winter (excluding Berney Marshes), but singles were recorded at Welney, Mautby and Strumpshaw, with up to three at Buckenham Marshes in January 2002.

Migrant Spotted Redshanks fed or rested at many, mainly coastal passage sites during the NBA summer recording periods. It is rare for this species to oversummer in the county.

Greenshank
Tringa nebularia

NBA 1999–2007	SUMMER: ALL/BREEDING	WINTER
TETRADS OCCUPIED	42 (3%) / none	13 (1%)
SUMMER/WINTER ONLY	35	6
MEAN PER OCCUPIED TETRAD	2 / none	2
SUMMED MAX COUNTS	66 / none	23
POPULATION ESTIMATE	0–2 individuals	1–4

PREVIOUS ATLASES	SQUARES OCCUPIED	1999–2007	LOSSES	GAINS
1981–84 WINTER (10 KM)	4 (6%)	6 (10%)	2	4

THE GREENSHANK IS A large and elegant wader that nests in parts of Scotland as well as in northern continental Europe. Most populations migrate long distances south to winter, but the Gulf Stream creates conditions that allow Greenshanks to winter in Britain and Ireland at exceptionally northerly latitudes. Although it remains mainly a passage migrant in Norfolk, small numbers have begun overwintering annually in recent years.

The majority of the breeding population nests in Fenno-Scandia and northern Russia with around 1,000 pairs breeding in Scotland. Although the vast majority of Greenshanks winter in Africa south of the Sahara, around 600 remain in Britain during the winter months, predominantly along western coasts. From the departure dates of birds wintering in Britain or Ireland, almost all appear to be of Scottish stock (*1981–84 Winter Atlas*).

While occasional Greenshanks have wintered in Norfolk since the 1950s, it was not until the mid 1970s

DAVID TIPLING

that winter records became more regular, and nowadays up to four birds winter annually. The tidal saltmarshes, muddy creeks and shallow freshwater pools around Holme, Thornham, Titchwell and Brancaster have always been favoured and remain some of the most reliable places to find the species at this season. Since the early 1980s, the coastal strip between Stiffkey and Cley has also hosted one or two Greenshanks in most winters. During the NBA winters, the species was also reported from Lynn Point and inland at Welney. Perhaps surprisingly, none wintered at Breydon Water.

'It is unusual for Greenshanks to linger in Norfolk into midsummer.'

The distribution of Greenshanks during the NBA summer recording periods has not been fully mapped. Records of spring migrants were regular from coastal wetlands and came also from scattered inland sites. It is unusual for Greenshanks to linger in Norfolk into midsummer.

SUMMER

Small dots 1, medium 2–3, large 4–5 ('pairs')

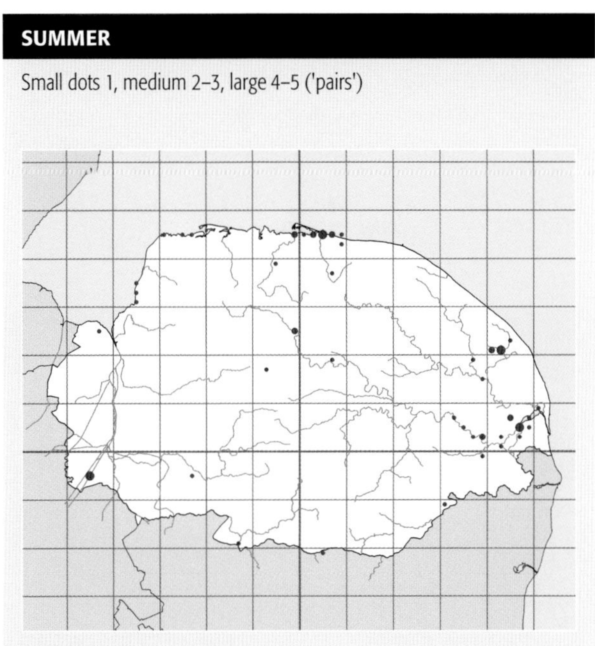

WINTER

Small dots 1, medium 2, large 3–4 (birds)

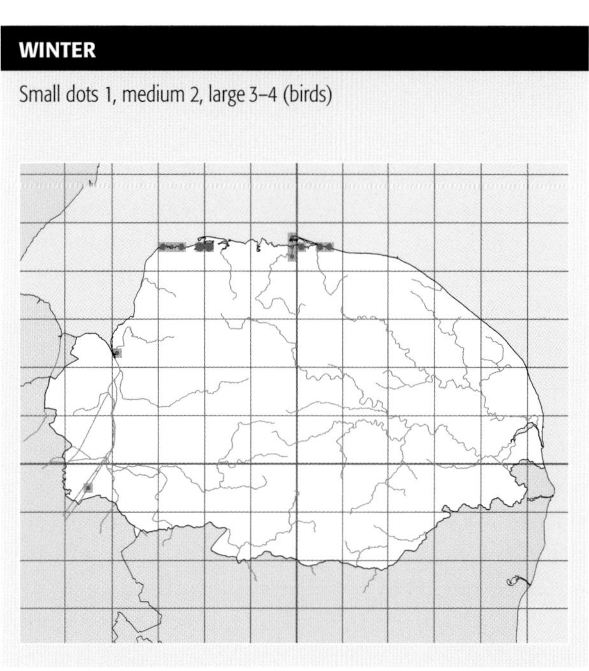

Redshank

Tringa totanus

NBA 1999–2007	SUMMER: ALL/BREEDING	WINTER
TETRADS OCCUPIED	137 (9%) / 97 (7%)	194 (13%)
SUMMER/WINTER ONLY	38	95
MEAN PER OCCUPIED TETRAD	9 / 12	55
SUMMED MAX COUNTS	1,237 / 1,150	10,600
POPULATION ESTIMATE	600–700 bp	3,000–5,000

PREVIOUS ATLASES	SQUARES OCCUPIED	1999–2007	LOSSES	GAINS
1968–72 (10 KM)	40 (65%)	23 (37%)	20	3
1980–85 (TETRAD)	167 (11%)	97 (7%)	94	24
1980–85 (10 KM)	38 (61%)	23 (37%)	19	4
1981–84 WINTER (10 KM)	31 (50%)	38 (61%)	3	10
1988–91 (10 KM)	34 (55%)	23 (37%)	15	4

THE SENTINEL OF THE marshes, as the Redshank has been described, is one of the most familiar waders on our coastal saltings, usually betraying its presence by its bold behaviour and insistent calls. As well as on saltmarshes, Redshanks breed in inland meadows, favouring areas of damp or wet grassland where a high water table has led to local saturation of the soil.

Redshanks breeding in Britain have fluctuated both in range and in abundance during the last 200 years. A marked decline took place in the early 19th century due to extensive wetland drainage, and although numbers increased between about 1865 and 1940, the population in Britain once again fell as a result of further land drainage and agricultural intensification leading to fragmentation of suitable breeding habitat (*1988–91 Atlas*). Census results show a moderate or rapid decline across Britain since the 1970s (*Birdtrends*), which has chiefly manifested itself as a withdrawal from many inland wetlands.

The NBA summer map shows an exceptionally well-defined breeding distribution. Saltmarshes were occupied around the inner Wash and a mixture of saltmarsh and meadow nesting occurred along the north coast, east to Kelling, and around Breydon Water. The Ouse Washes and a few wet meadows in Broadland held breeding birds regularly. Most of the occupied tetrads in Broadland follow the courses of the Rivers Yare and Bure. In addition, scattered sites in mid Norfolk apparently hosted occasional nesting

attempts, and a few inland migrants were recorded. Redshanks are noisy birds and it is unlikely that observers overlooked many tetrads occupied by breeding birds.

Various factors can also affect the breeding success from year to year. Unseasonable flooding at Welney in late May 2000 resulted in low fledging rates while, on the positive side, more young fledged at Berney in 2004 once the control of foxes had been reinstated.

Most populations of Redshanks are migratory, but many British birds winter around the coastal areas on which they breed, where immigrants join them, mainly from Iceland (*Migration Atlas*). At this time of year, they favour muddy estuaries and saltmarsh creeks, as shown by the marked concentrations on the NBA winter map around the Wash, along the north Norfolk coast and on Breydon Water and the adjoining marshes. The importance of the wetlands alongside the Great Ouse and its relief channels and tributaries in west Norfolk is also evident.

During the winter, Redshanks often feed alone but

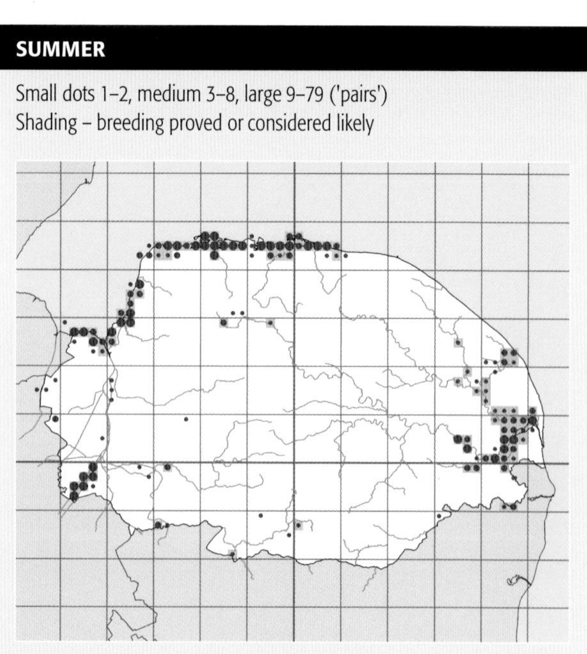

DAVID TIPLING

may form small, loose flocks, with larger numbers usually only being found at high-tide roosts. Maximum winter counts at Breydon Water exceeded 1,000 in most years and 1,096 were also recorded at Ousemouth in January 2006. The species is particularly susceptible to the effects of cold weather and large numbers may perish during spells of severe cold. In such conditions, when the ground freezes, Redshanks inland are likely to move to the coast.

Comparison of results from NBA with the previous breeding atlases shows clear evidence of loss of breeding range. At tetrad level, the change map shows that many previous breeding sites have been lost, especially in the west of the county and on the fringes of the Broadland distribution. These changes have concentrated the breeding population into smaller and more vulnerable pockets of remnant distribution.

WINTER

Small dots 1–3, medium 4–16, large 17–1,096 (birds)

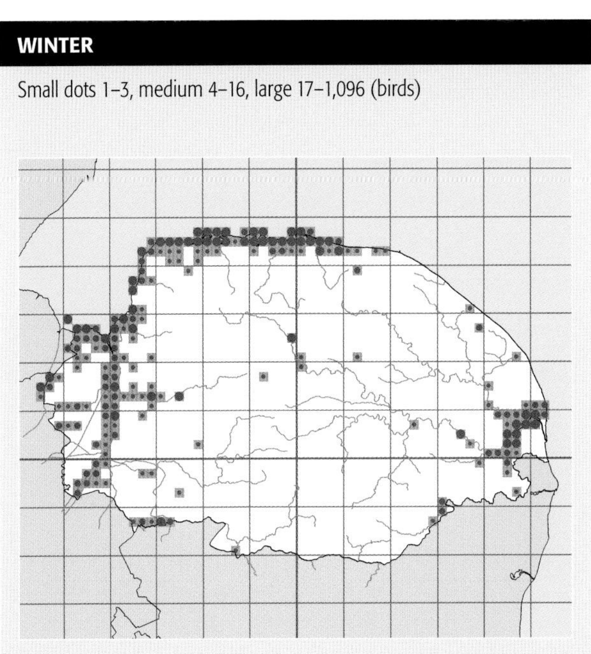

CHANGE SINCE 1980–85

+ Gain ✖ Loss ■ No change

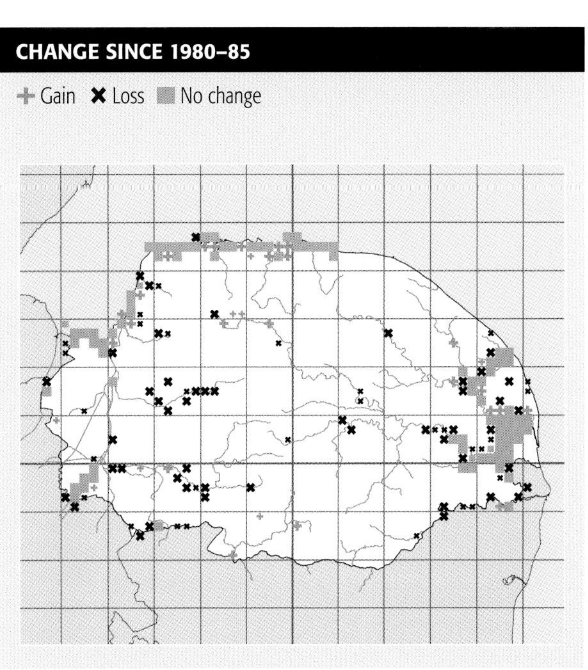

Turnstone

Arenaria interpres

NBA 1999–2007	SUMMER: ALL/BREEDING	WINTER
TETRADS OCCUPIED	33 (2%) / none	86 (6%)
SUMMER/WINTER ONLY	9	62
MEAN PER OCCUPIED TETRAD	5 / none	52
SUMMED MAX COUNTS	168 / none	4,477
POPULATION ESTIMATE	100–150 individuals	1,000–1,500

PREVIOUS ATLASES	SQUARES OCCUPIED	1999–2007	LOSSES	GAINS
1980–85 (TETRAD)	1 (<1%)	none	1	0
1980–85 (10 KM)	1 (2%)	none	1	0
1981–84 WINTER (10 KM)	15 (24%)	21 (34%)	1	7
1988–91 (10 KM)	1 (2%)	none	1	0

IN WINTER, THE Turnstone occurs around almost the entire coastline of Britain. Its confiding nature and distinctive habit of searching for food under stones and seaweed make it a familiar species also to many non-birdwatchers.

The Turnstones wintering around Britain belong mainly to the breeding populations of Ellesmere Island, in northeast Canada, and of Greenland (*Migration Atlas*). Birds on passage from Fenno-Scandia augment autumn numbers, and it is at passage times that the highest numbers visit Norfolk.

Turnstones are coastal birds throughout the year, and in winter favour rocky or stony shores, although they also occur in muddy estuaries and on sandy beaches. They also frequent manmade structures such as seawalls, groynes, harbours and jetties. They feed on small crustaceans and molluscs, which they locate by flipping over small pebbles or searching beneath piles of seaweed. As with many of the waders that winter in Norfolk, the NBA winter map shows a concentration around the Wash and along the north Norfolk coast. Birds were recorded in a variety of habitat types, such as the muddy foreshore of the Wash, the docks at King's Lynn, the harbours at Brancaster and Blakeney, the groynes and promenade at Sheringham, the beach at Walcott and the jetty at Great Yarmouth's harbour mouth.

They are gregarious birds, often feeding in small parties, although on occasion 30 or more may be found together. At high tide, large numbers gather to roost together on shingle beaches or saltings, while others may fly a short distance inland to continue feeding on coastal fields. In general, the highest

SUMMER

Small dots 1, medium 2–4, large 5–35 ('pairs')

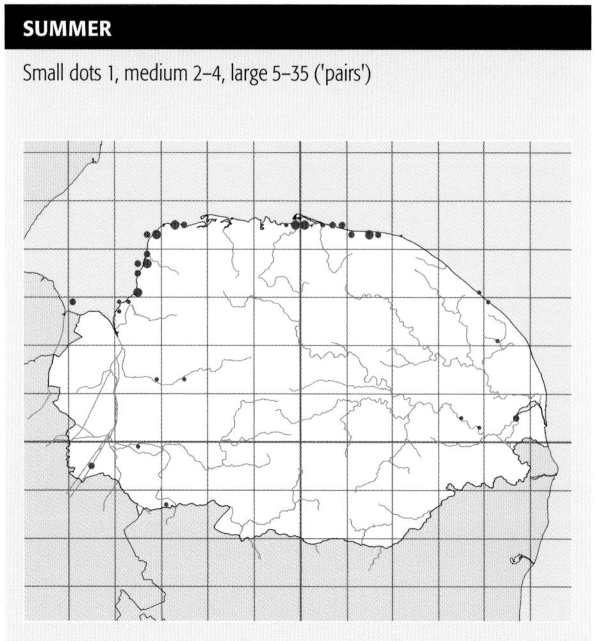

WINTER

Small dots 1–6, medium 7–36, large 37–451 (birds)

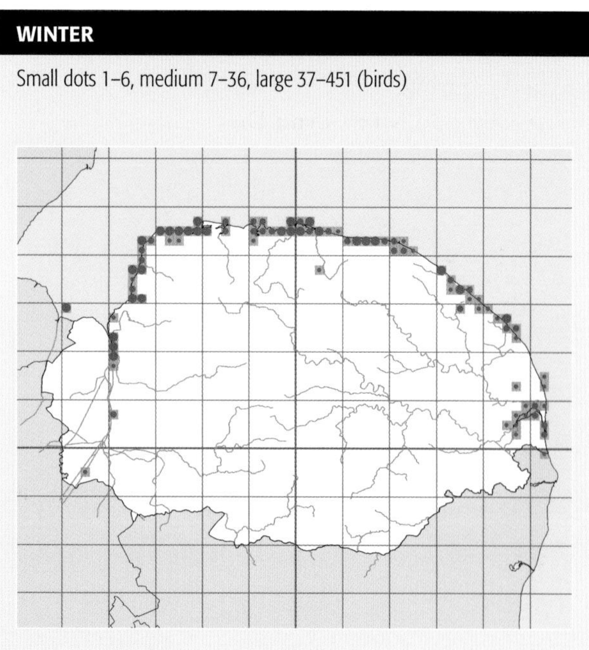

DAVID TIPLING

counts made during the NBA winters related to these high-tide roosts and included 450 at Titchwell in February 2003 and up to 150 at various times at Stiffkey, Blakeney and Sheringham. In the last few years, unusual numbers were also recorded at Fisher Fleet and King's Lynn Docks, peaking at 350 in February 2005. Through the course of a winter, Turnstones generally feed in almost the same locations from day to day; they also show winter site fidelity between years.

Turnstones are among the most adaptable of waders, scavenging whenever the opportunity arises. As well as feeding among shoreline debris, they have begun to perch and feed regularly on rooftops at Hunstanton and regularly feed on the cliff-top grassland both there and at Cromer, and on arable and pig fields at Waxham. A few were recorded at inland locations during the NBA period, including 12 on intertidal mud at Stowbridge, one at Welney on New Year's Day in 2001 and 2005, four at Saddlebow and Thornage, and one feeding along a farm track at West Walton.

'Through the course of a winter, Turnstones generally feed in almost the same locations from day to day.'

However, it is while on migration, particularly during May, that most records are made inland. During the NBA summers, small numbers of Turnstones were noted inland in May at eight well-scattered localities, including disused gravel pits and beet-factory settling ponds. Welney hosted Turnstones in several of the springs, including up to seven birds in April and May 2000.

Apart from annual fluctuations, there has been little change in winter numbers since the late 1960s. There appears, however, to have been an expansion of the winter range since the *1981–84 Winter Atlas*, when only 15 of Norfolk's 10-km squares were occupied, compared to the 21 squares occupied during the NBA winters.

Black-headed Gull
Chroicocephalus ridibundus

NBA 1999–2007	SUMMER: ALL/BREEDING	WINTER
TETRADS OCCUPIED	620 (42%) / 57 (4%)	1,322 (91%)
SUMMER/WINTER ONLY	30	732
MEAN PER OCCUPIED TETRAD	30 / 181	261
SUMMED MAX COUNTS	18,793 / 10,332	345,085
POPULATION ESTIMATE	6,000–7,000 bp	70,000–90,000

PREVIOUS ATLASES	SQUARES OCCUPIED	1999–2007	LOSSES	GAINS
1968–72 (10 KM)	20 (32%)	22 (35%)	6	8
1980–85 (TETRAD)	107 (7%)	57 (4%)	86	36
1980–85 (10 KM)	36 (58%)	22 (35%)	18	4
1981–84 WINTER (10 KM)	62 (all)	62 (all)		
1988–91 (10 KM)	15 (24%)	22 (35%)	2	9

DAVID TIPLING

THE FAMILIAR Black-headed Gull has the widest inland breeding distribution of any gull in Britain, and in Norfolk is certainly the most abundant and widespread gull species.

It greatly expanded its range during the 20th century, having come back from the verge of extinction as a British breeding bird. Indeed, it was only during the early years of the 20th century that it became a regular winter visitor to inland areas, rather than a storm-driven waif.

During the breeding season, Black-headed Gulls frequent areas of shallow, calm water, which may be fresh, brackish or saline. Being gregarious throughout the year, they nest in dense colonies amongst sand dunes, on saltmarshes and by shallow freshwater lagoons around the coast, and inland at old gravel workings, beet-factory settling ponds and areas of open water, such as the Broads.

The NBA summer map shows that the main breeding colonies are in coastal north and northwest Norfolk, between Snettisham on the Wash and Cley on the north coast. Here the colonies occupy sand dunes, slightly raised shingle banks and islands on the scrapes of the coastal reserves. Breeding success varies from year to year, the nests and young being at the mercy of the weather and especially vulnerable to raised water levels during spring tides, onshore summer gales and heavy rain. In recent years, predation by foxes, stoats and the larger gulls has also taken its toll. The previous year's success or failure can affect the location of Black-headed Gull colonies but sites that hosted at least 1,000 pairs during at least one of the NBA summers were Snettisham, Scolt Head, Holkham, Stiffkey Binks and Blakeney Point.

Away from the coast, Black-headed Gulls bred at several sites in Broadland, notably the Yare valley, where a maximum of 274 pairs nested at Strumpshaw and 200 at Cantley BF during the NBA summers. Other inland colonies exist in the west of the county, those having held over 50 breeding pairs being at Welney, Nar Valley Fisheries, Middleton GP and Wissington BF. No breeding colonies are now located in the Norfolk part of Breckland. In recent years, 6,000–7,000 breeding pairs of Black-headed Gulls have been present annually within the county compared with 1,300 in 1970, 4,700 in the mid 1980s and 9,000 in 1996–97. The NBA summer map also shows that the species was recorded in many parts of the county well away from the breeding colonies, particularly in northwest Norfolk. Some of these records would have been of coastal breeders that were feeding inland, as well as non-breeding first-summer birds and failed breeders. Conversely, there are many areas of inland Norfolk where a sighting of a Black-headed Gull would be very unusual between spring passage in April and the first returns in late June.

During the autumn and winter, Black-headed Gulls become widespread, as they forage increasingly inland to take advantage of the natural food supplies available on grassy fields, arable and grazed land, as well as the additional food at rubbish tips and even in gardens. Fields being ploughed are particularly attractive, as also have outdoor pig units proved to be in recent years. The NBA winter map shows a remarkably complete distribution at this time of year, the only areas devoid of Black-headed Gulls during the NBA winters being isolated pockets around Massingham Heath, in the Brecks to the west of Swaffham and in Thetford Forest, and in the Walpole area of the Fens. Estuaries and coastal marshes also host Black-headed Gulls throughout the winter.

The largest concentrations of Black-headed Gulls are found at their nocturnal roosts on areas of open water. From late afternoon, streams of gulls pour into the roost sites from all directions and by dusk many thousands may have gathered. The locations of some roosts show up on the NBA winter map and the maximum counts during the years of NBA fieldwork at some of these sites have included 6,600 at Welney, 10,000+ at Lynn Point and Heacham, over 17,000 at Hickling Broad and Breydon Water, and 40,000 at Wroxham Broad (the second highest count ever in Norfolk). In calmer weather, many birds roost on the sea off north Norfolk and northeast Suffolk, perhaps having travelled 30 km or more from feeding sites in inland Norfolk.

The BTO Winter Gull Roost Survey carried out in the winter of 2003/04 arrived at a total of 63,000 Black-headed Gulls in Norfolk, in addition to 32,000 other small gulls that were not specifically identified, of which about 70% were probably this species. Therefore, a total of about 85,000 Black-headed Gulls were present at the county's roosts. Most of the Black-headed Gulls from British colonies simply disperse after the breeding season rather than migrating, and our wintering population is augmented by immigrants from Fenno-Scandia, the Baltic countries and Poland. Visible westerly movements throughout the county from late June onwards indicate both immigrant arrivals and dispersal from coastal breeding colonies. Colour-ring sightings have revealed that some Baltic visitors are faithful to wintering sites over a number of years (*NBR*).

The change map suggests that there has been some breeding expansion since the *1980–85 NBBS*, although not all the apparent gains represent tetrads in which breeding definitely occurred during the NBA period.

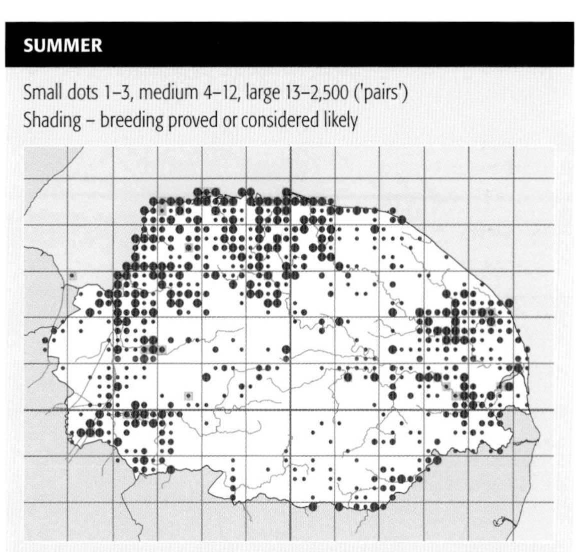

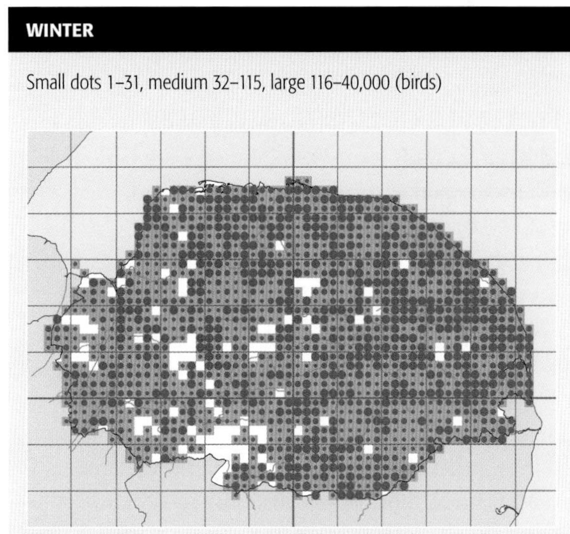

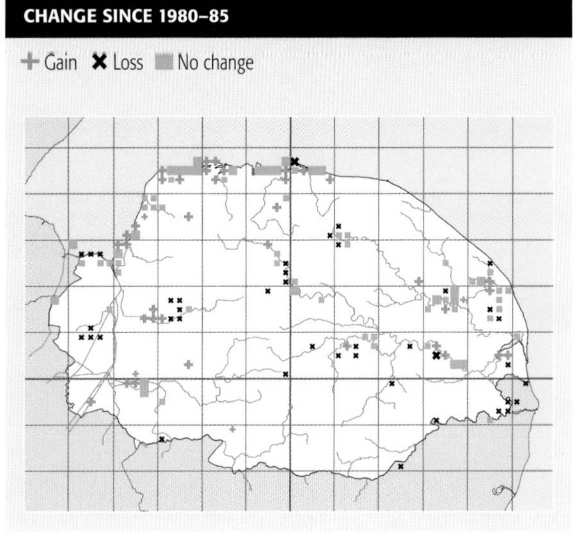

Little Gull
Hydrocoloeus minutus

NBA 1999–2007	SUMMER: ALL/BREEDING	WINTER
TETRADS OCCUPIED	40 (3%) / 1 (<1%)	34 (2%)
SUMMER/WINTER ONLY	27	21
MEAN PER OCCUPIED TETRAD	4 / 1	5
SUMMED MAX COUNTS	176 / 1	184
POPULATION ESTIMATE	0–1 bp	5–10

PREVIOUS ATLASES	SQUARES OCCUPIED	1999–2007	LOSSES	GAINS
1968–72 (10 KM)	none	1 (2%)	0	1
1980–85 (TETRAD)	none	1 (<1%)	0	1
1980–85 (10 KM)	none	1 (2%)	0	1
1981–84 WINTER (10 KM)	10 (16%)	18 (29%)	3	11
1988–91 (10 KM)	none	1 (2%)	0	1

THE LITTLE GULL is the smallest of the world's gulls and has a buoyant, tern-like flight, dipping periodically to the water surface to pick up items of food.

It breeds over a wide area of northern central Europe eastwards from Denmark, nesting in small colonies in lowland freshwater wetlands. The species nested unsuccessfully on four occasions in England between 1975 and 1987, including one attempt at Hickling Broad in 1978 when the clutch of three eggs failed to hatch (Carson *et al* 1977). In 2007, a fifth attempt was made, again in Norfolk but this time at Titchwell Marsh; on this occasion, however, the eggs were predated (Eele 2008). The previous year, an adult had been observed in display flight for one late May day only at a Norfolk Black-headed Gull colony.

Little Gulls pass through Norfolk in spring in small groups, while variable numbers of first-summer birds often remain for much of the summer at favoured coastal freshwater sites, such as Titchwell, Cley, Kelling WM and Hickling Broad. The NBA summer map represents a combination of passage and summering birds. While the majority of spring migrants noted in the county are recorded at coastal localities, some make brief stopovers at inland sites, especially in the Broads. Since the mid 1990s, Little Gulls have become more regular during the summer and often numbers build up at Titchwell, where a peak of 33 was recorded in June 2006.

Little Gulls winter offshore from the Irish and North Seas south to the Mediterranean and the Atlantic Ocean off North Africa. The numbers reported in Britain during the winter months vary from year to year and within a winter, depending on weather conditions, as they are driven close inshore during strong onshore winds, but flocks in excess of 50 are very unusual. As first-winter birds move further south, adults and second-years predominate during the winter (*1981–84 Winter Atlas*). The NBA winter map shows that the majority of sightings were made at coastal sites, and some would have been birds simply moving offshore and not lingering in the tetrad. Little Gulls were recorded infrequently inland in winter and very few birds were involved.

DAVID TIPLING

SUMMER

Small dots 1, medium 2–4, large 5–28 ('pairs')
Shading – breeding proved or considered likely

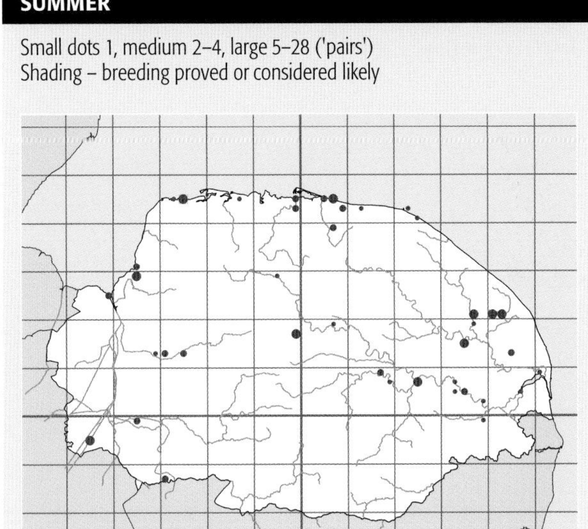

WINTER

Small dots 1, medium 2–5, large 6–100 (birds)

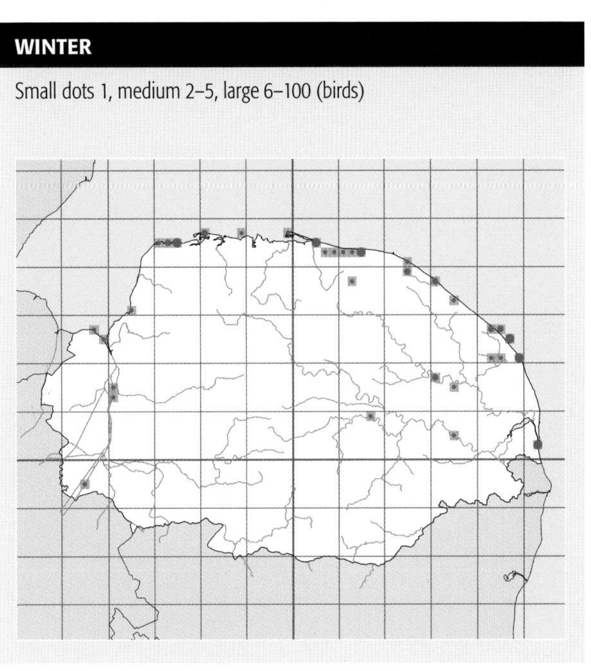

Mediterranean Gull

Larus melanocephalus

NBA 1999–2007	SUMMER: ALL/BREEDING	WINTER
TETRADS OCCUPIED	43 (3%) / 3 (<1%)	66 (5%)
SUMMER/WINTER ONLY	20	43
MEAN PER OCCUPIED TETRAD	1 / 2	4
SUMMED MAX COUNTS	53 / 5	286
POPULATION ESTIMATE	3–14 bp	80–120

PREVIOUS ATLASES	SQUARES OCCUPIED	1999–2007	LOSSES	GAINS
1968–72 (10 KM)	none	3 (5%)	0	3
1980–85 (TETRAD)	none	3 (<1%)	0	3
1980–85 (10 KM)	none	3 (5%)	0	3
1981–84 WINTER (10 KM)	6 (10%)	34 (55%)	0	28
1988–91 (10 KM)	none	3 (5%)	0	3

AN ADULT Mediterranean Gull in breeding plumage is one of our most strikingly attractive gulls. As a result of a marked expansion of its main breeding range and rapid increase in population, this species is now present in Norfolk throughout the year.

As a breeding species, it is confined to the western Palaearctic, with the bulk of the population around the Black Sea (*BWP3*). During the last 50 years or so, it has spread to many parts of northwest Europe and first bred in Britain in 1968 at a Black-headed Gull colony in Hampshire. Breeding has been annual in Britain since 1979, and the species first nested in Norfolk at both Blakeney Point and Titchwell in 1992, but not successfully until 1994.

In England, pairs invariably nest within colonies of Black-headed Gulls, occasionally interbreeding with them. Although Mediterranean Gulls had been breeding in Norfolk for 15 years by 2006, no more than six pairs were recorded in any one year. In 2007, however, 14 pairs nested at up to four sites. Breeding success has varied widely between years: for example, all five pairs failed to fledge any young in 2003, while at the same two sites in the following year all five pairs were successful.

Mediterranean Gulls were recorded in summer at widespread coastal localities, particularly in north Norfolk, which is where all the breeding sites were located. The species is recorded inland only occasionally during the spring and summer.

SUMMER

Small dots 1, medium 2, large 3–4 ('pairs')
Shading – breeding proved or considered likely

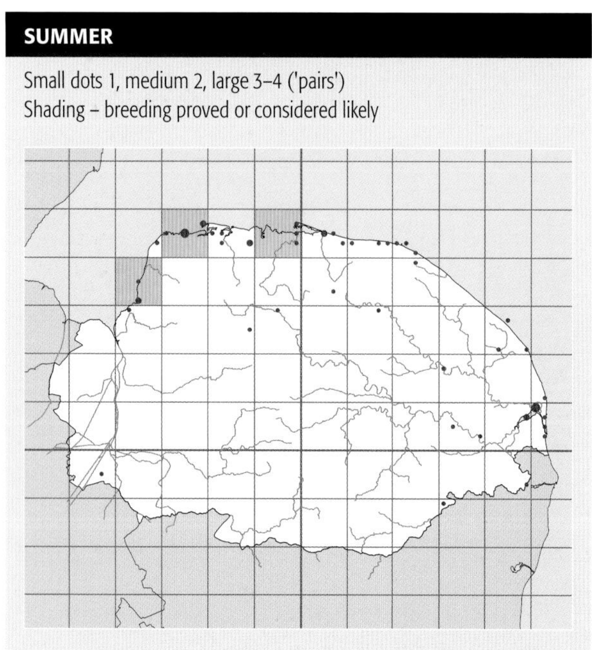

WINTER

Small dots 1, medium 2, large 3–73 (birds)

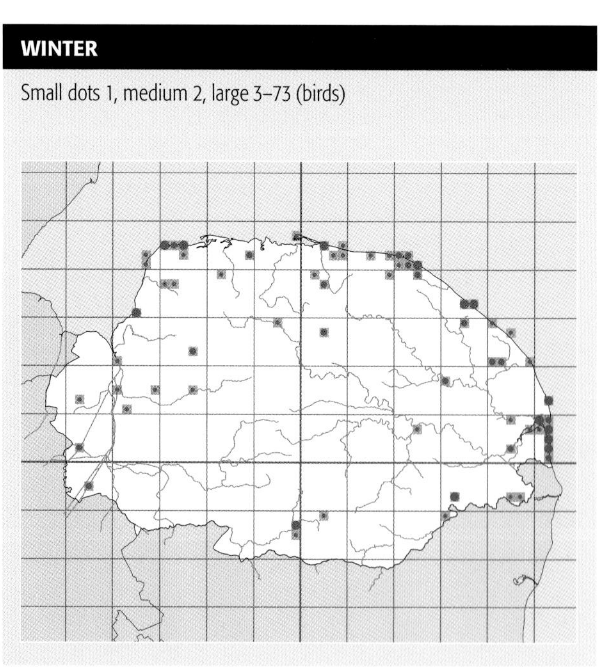

DAVID TIPLING

While most gulls of this species winter around the Mediterranean, increasing numbers have been moving to the coasts of western and northwestern Europe at this time of year. The *1981–84 Winter Atlas* showed that, in the early 1980s, birds were well scattered around the coast of England and Wales but were most numerous along the south coast between Kent and Cornwall. In Norfolk, Great Yarmouth has proved itself the pre-eminent place to see Mediterranean Gulls at almost any time of the year, but in particular the area hosts large, and steadily increasing, numbers during the winter months. In December 2006, of an estimated 91 Mediterranean Gulls in the county, around 80% were noted at Great Yarmouth. Here they frequent the sandy beach and seafront throughout the day, readily taking bread and any other food on offer from the public. During the NBA period, the Great Yarmouth wintering population of Mediterranean Gulls increased from a maximum of 19 in February 2000 to 73 in 2006/07, the birds typically crossing the town to roost at Breydon Water. Sightings of colour-ringed birds during the NBA period showed that these wintering birds originated from Belgium, France, Germany, Denmark, Poland and Hungary (Allard 2003).

While the winter map shows a notable concentration in the Great Yarmouth/Breydon Water area, it also demonstrates a scattering of sightings around the remainder of the Norfolk coastline. For a number of years, certain coastal localities have regularly hosted small numbers of Mediterranean Gulls, such as Overstrand and Titchwell, often with the same birds returning in several successive winters. Maximum site counts in winter have included eight at Titchwell, six at Holme and three at Overstrand. As was demonstrated by the *1981–84 Winter Atlas*, Mediterranean Gulls are also found inland in winter, albeit less frequently than on the coast. The NBA winter map shows records from over 20 inland localities, such as disused gravel workings, refuse tips and the Broads. Many of these records related to wandering individuals, mostly seen only on one day. Those in the East Harling and Ditchingham areas were found among the huge numbers of gulls feeding on chicken waste spread on the fields. Especially in late winter, the species often associates with flocks of Common Gulls on grassland.

Whereas the *1981–84 Winter Atlas* found only 10% of Norfolk's 10-km squares to hold Mediterranean Gulls, this figure rose to 55% during the NBA period.

Common Gull

Larus canus

NBA 1999–2007	SUMMER: ALL / BREEDING	WINTER
TETRADS OCCUPIED	255 (17%) / 6 (<1%)	1,132 (78%)
SUMMER/WINTER ONLY	20	897
MEAN PER OCCUPIED TETRAD	8 / 4	106
SUMMED MAX COUNTS	1,999 / 27	120,069
POPULATION ESTIMATE	10–20 bp	15,000–25,000

PREVIOUS ATLASES	SQUARES OCCUPIED	1999–2007	LOSSES	GAINS
1968–72 (10 KM)	2 (3%)	3 (5%)	2	3
1980–85 (TETRAD)	9 (<1%)	6 (<1%)	7	4
1980–85 (10 KM)	9 (15%)	3 (5%)	6	0
1981–84 WINTER (10 KM)	62 (all)	62 (all)		
1988–91 (10 KM)	3 (5%)	3 (5%)	3	3

IN BRITAIN, THE Common Gull breeds widely in Scotland and the north Pennines. The species does nest in Norfolk but, as in most of England, it is best known in the county as a winter visitor and passage migrant.

The breeding range expanded in Scotland during the 20th century and the species first bred in England, at a site in Kent, in 1919. During the breeding season, it is generally less maritime than other gulls and in Scotland the majority of colonies are found on moorland.

Common Gulls first bred successfully in Norfolk at Blakeney Point in 1966, having failed in the previous year. Subsequently they bred annually at this site until 1979 but then only intermittently until 1997, since when it has nested in the county each year but only in small numbers and with varying success. Scolt Head and Blakeney Point were the only breeding colonies located during the *1980–85 NBBS*.

During the NBA summers, Common Gulls bred annually at Blakeney Point and in every year except 2000 at Scolt Head. During this same period, they nested at Snettisham, Stiffkey Binks, Wells and Holkham NNR, the last site now hosting the largest colony in the county, albeit of only 9–10 pairs. The highest annual county total was of 19 breeding pairs in 2004 but none of these was successful in raising young. The locations of these breeding colonies are shown on the NBA summer map, which also shows clearly how widely distributed spring passage birds are

SUMMER

Small dots 1, medium 2–5, large 6–200 ('pairs')
Shading – breeding proved or considered likely

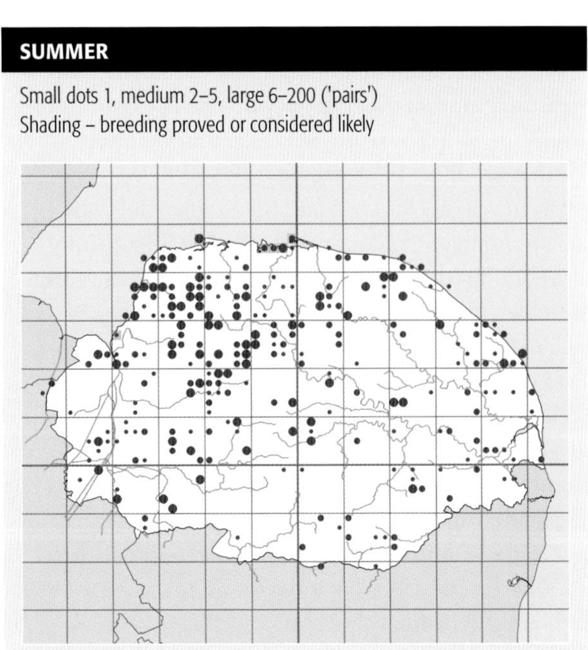

WINTER

Small dots 1–9, medium 10–35, large 36–12,000 (birds)

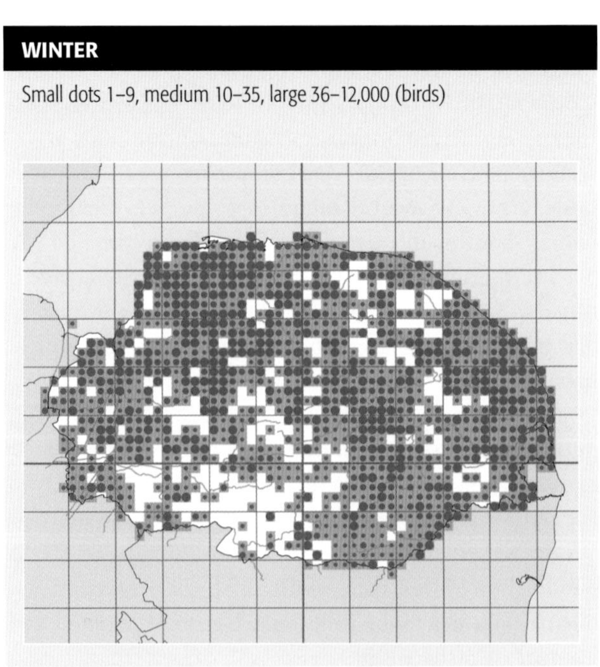

DAVID TIPLING

around the county, particularly in northwest Norfolk. Most records made during the early part of the summer recording period related to flocks of adults, on occasion of a hundred or more, which were gathering prior to returning to their breeding areas in Fenno-Scandia and other parts of northern Europe. By May, the vast majority of sightings refer to first-summer birds, some of which stay to oversummer in Norfolk.

The NBA winter map shows a very widespread inland distribution, with only a few isolated pockets of absence, for example around Thetford Forest. Common Gulls are also found at most coastal locations in winter, feeding on the intertidal zones, be they sandy beaches or muddy estuaries, and are numerous on the outer shores of the Wash. As on spring passage, Common Gulls feed inland in winter on well-grazed grassland and other expanses of short turf such as are found on school playing fields and at airfields. They also follow the plough and move onto areas of recently flooded grassland, where their main prey of earthworms are more easily located.

'Common Gulls first bred successfully in Norfolk at Blakeney Point in 1966, having failed in the previous year.'

The largest counts were made at roost sites around the Wash, on inshore waters or on the Broads. The highest count of Common Gulls ever made in Norfolk was of 12,000 birds at Heacham South Beach in December 2001. Other roosts in excess of 5,000 were recorded at Scolt Head and on the Broads at Hickling, Hoveton and Wroxham. The ten-yearly BTO Winter Gull Roost Survey that took place in the winter of 2003/04 found a county total of 19,434 Common Gulls at 12 localities in Norfolk. With fewer than 20 breeding pairs in the county, the winter population consists almost entirely of winter visitors from Fenno-Scandia and elsewhere in northern Europe.

Lesser Black-backed Gull

Larus fuscus

NBA 1999–2007	SUMMER: ALL/BREEDING	WINTER
TETRADS OCCUPIED	421 (29%) / 13 (<1%)	430 (29%)
SUMMER/WINTER ONLY	245	254
MEAN PER OCCUPIED TETRAD	14 / 195	39
SUMMED MAX COUNTS	5,801 / 2,535	16,633
POPULATION ESTIMATE	1,200–1,500 bp	8,000–12,000

PREVIOUS ATLASES	SQUARES OCCUPIED	1999–2007	LOSSES	GAINS
1968–72 (10 KM)	none	8 (13%)	0	8
1980–85 (TETRAD)	4 (<1%)	13 (<1%)	2	11
1980–85 (10 KM)	3 (5%)	8 (13%)	2	7
1981–84 WINTER (10 KM)	37 (60%)	59 (95%)	3	25
1988–91 (10 KM)	3 (5%)	8 (13%)	1	6

THE LESSER BLACK-backed Gull is an elegant gull, despite its size, and in flight is noticeably more graceful and buoyant than the Herring Gull. Both as a breeding and a wintering bird in Britain, the status of the species has changed very markedly during recent decades.

Until the 1940s, the Lesser Black-backed Gull was known as a summer migrant to Britain, with its breeding population wintering around the Atlantic coasts of Iberia and North Africa, and only the occasional birds overwintering in Britain. Even in 1953, a survey found just 165 birds wintering throughout the whole of England and Wales. Subsequently the winter population in Britain grew rapidly and had already exceeded 60,000 by 1993. Despite the growth of the British winter population, young birds from British colonies have shown little change in their tendency to move southwest in autumn (*Migration Atlas*).

There has also been a corresponding increase in the number of breeding colonies in England, particularly in the southern half of the country. Lesser Black-backed Gulls first bred successfully in Norfolk at Blakeney Point in 1978 and have done so almost annually there ever since. Both Titchwell and the saltmarshes at Wells/Warham held small nesting colonies in the 1980s. By 1991, about 100 pairs were breeding on the Wash Outer Trial Bank, increasing quickly to 860 by 1995, the year that roof nesting first occurred at Great Yarmouth. Since 2000, the species has bred at more than ten Norfolk localities, as indicated on the NBA summer map. Apart from the Outer Trial Bank, the largest colonies are currently at Holkham NNR, with 200 pairs in 2006, and the Great Yarmouth and

SUMMER

Small dots 1, medium 2–4, large 5–2,034 ('pairs')
Shading – breeding proved or considered likely

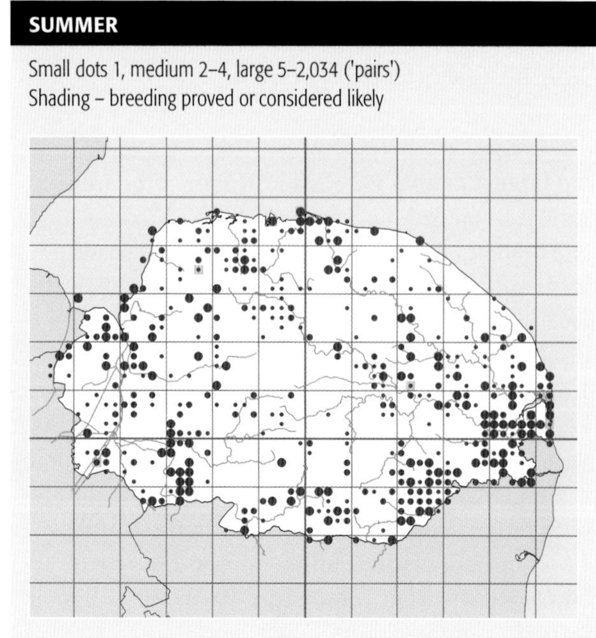

WINTER

Small dots 1–2, medium 3–8, large 9–2,500 (birds)

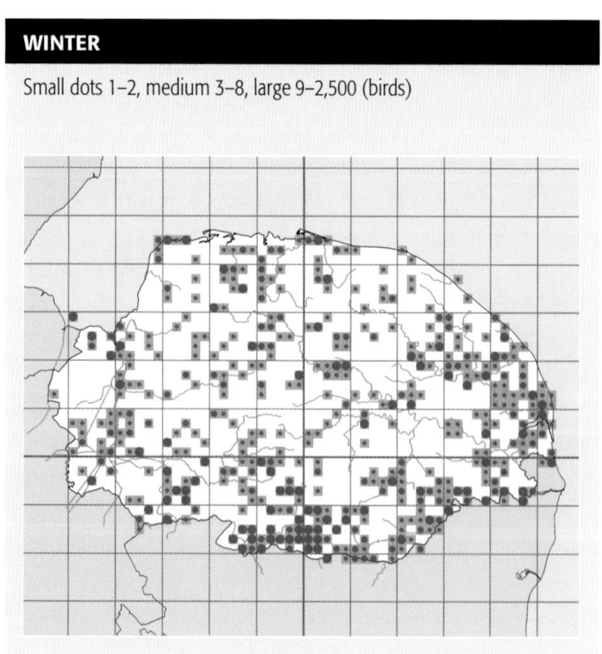

DAVID TIPLING

Gorleston area, where a survey in 2006 found 790 breeding pairs. In that year, a few pairs also nested for the first time on roofs at King's Lynn docks and well inland in the centre of Norwich. This is a far cry from the handful of nesting pairs that were recorded at just three north Norfolk sites by the *1980–85 NBBS*.

The spread of the roof-nesting birds in the Great Yarmouth area has been well documented (Allard 2007). Here, both Lesser Black-backed and Herring Gulls use factory roofs. At the start of the NBA period, only ten pairs of Lesser Black-backed Gulls were nesting there, and even at this early stage were actively being discouraged from doing so. Despite this, numbers have increased at an astonishing rate, and the habit has spread to neighbouring Southtown and Gorleston. Even after some of the buildings were demolished in the winter of 2002/03, the gulls were not deterred and began to nest on the ground in the cleared areas! Complaints from the public about the noise, mess and aggressive behaviour led to a cull being undertaken in 2005, but this in turn resulted in an outcry from the locals about the methods being used. As in many urban areas in Britain, the presence of nesting gulls is an ongoing problem, with no easy solution.

In addition to the nesting pairs, non-breeding summering Lesser Black-backed Gulls of all age classes were recorded at many inland sites and are plotted on the NBA summer map. While some were located at wetland sites, for example gravel pits and along river valleys, many more were present on arable land.

Up to the mid 1990s, comparatively few Lesser Black-backed Gulls wintered in Norfolk and yet by the winter of 2002/03 well over 10,000 were estimated to be present at roost sites and elsewhere in the county. The NBA winter map shows that it is more widely distributed than in summer and that the winter distribution is almost entirely inland. The perception of this gull as a summer visitor, long outdated on the county scale, still holds true around the main Norfolk breeding colonies of large gulls, which are dominated by Herring Gulls during the winter months, and more generally along the north coast. There were particularly large gatherings in south Norfolk, where huge gull flocks gather around outdoor pig units and especially where chicken waste is being spread on the fields, with the favoured locations changing every year or two. At East Harling up to 2,100 were attracted by chicken waste, alongside up to nine other species of gulls. Four-figure counts have also been made at Hockwold Washes (2,500) and Banham Moor (1,200). Typically, Lesser Black-backed Gulls forage on farmland (much more so than Herring Gulls), at gravel pits and landfill sites, returning to roost at night on large areas of open water.

Colour ringing has demonstrated that some of our wintering Lesser Black-backed Gulls are from local colonies and others from northern England, the near Continent, and Scandinavia (some of these being noticeably darker-mantled).

Herring Gull
Larus argentatus

NBA 1999–2007	SUMMER: ALL/BREEDING	WINTER
TETRADS OCCUPIED	262 (18%) / 14 (1%)	533 (37%)
SUMMER/WINTER ONLY	94	365
MEAN PER OCCUPIED TETRAD	18 / 103	65
SUMMED MAX COUNTS	4,587 / 1,436	34,846
POPULATION ESTIMATE	1,000–1,500 bp	8,000–12,000

PREVIOUS ATLASES	SQUARES OCCUPIED	1999–2007	LOSSES	GAINS
1968–72 (10 KM)	1 (2%)	7 (11%)	0	6
1980–85 (TETRAD)	11 (<1%)	14 (1%)	7	10
1980–85 (10 KM)	7 (11%)	7 (11%)	3	3
1981–84 WINTER (10 KM)	56 (90%)	61 (98%)	1	6
1988–91 (10 KM)	3 (5%)	7 (11%)	0	4

THE HERRING GULL, as it is currently recognised, comprises the races *argenteus* of Britain, Ireland, Iceland and northern France, and nominate *argentatus* of the Baltic, Fenno-Scandia and Svalbard. Like the other large gulls it is a very adaptable species, which partly explains the marked increase in its distribution in Britain during the first two-thirds of the 20th century. It is now a red-listed bird of UK conservation concern, however, having suffered rapid declines in both breeding and wintering population (*BoCC3*). In Norfolk, however, the picture appears to be a healthy one, especially among breeding birds.

Formerly, the Herring Gull bred only around rocky coastlines and on offshore islands, and it was not until 1972 that the species first nested successfully in Norfolk, at Blakeney Point. Since then breeding has taken place at half-a-dozen or so coastal localities and well over 1,000 pairs now breed annually in the county, including many on rooftops in urban areas.

The NBA summer map shows the colony locations that were in use during the NBA period. By far the largest breeding colony was on the Wash Outer Trial Bank, where over 1,000 pairs nested, alongside similar numbers of Lesser Black-backed Gulls. Since 2005 the Holkham NNR has hosted up to 400 pairs, while over 250 pairs have bred in the Great Yarmouth/Gorleston area, having colonised the area in 1995 (Allard 2007). Smaller colonies also occupy the Wells saltmarshes and the reserves at Titchwell, Scolt Head and Blakeney Point. A pair possibly nested on a roof in Norwich in 2005. Other locations mapped in the summer period represent spring passage of breeding birds and oversummering by non-breeding birds of all ages. In

SUMMER

Small dots 1, medium 2–5, large 6–872 ('pairs')
Shading – breeding proved or considered likely

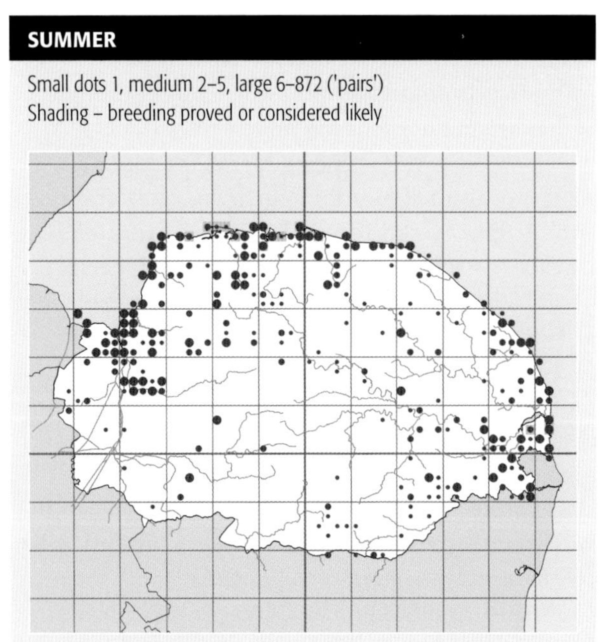

WINTER

Small dots 1–2, medium 3–10, large 11–6,000 (birds)

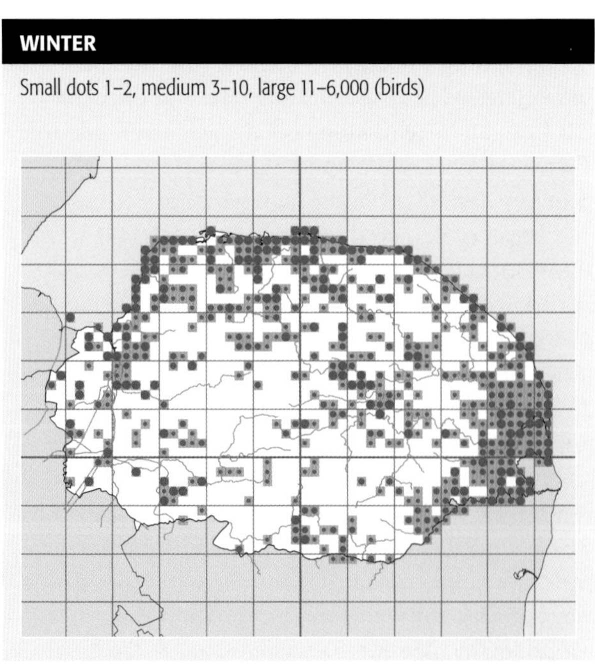

DAVID TIPLING

south Norfolk lone adult pairs are commonly observed courting in grassy fields in April, far distant from any known nesting sites. Less charmingly, birds make extensive use of landfill sites such as at Blackborough End and Aldeby throughout the summer, although typically outnumbered by Lesser Black-backed Gulls.

Exceptional numbers of Herring Gulls were present along the northwest Norfolk coast in mid April 2000, following the deposition of vast numbers of starfish on the tideline during a spell of northerly gales. It was estimated that 16,200 Herring Gulls were feeding on this food bonanza between Holme and Scolt Head, with 10,000 at the latter site alone.

Being omnivorous, Herring Gulls in winter are attracted to sources of discarded food, as well as more natural food items as are found along tidelines and on muddy estuaries. This is well demonstrated on the NBA winter map, which shows that the species was not only found in almost every coastal tetrad but was also far more widely distributed inland in winter than in summer. The largest concentrations were at rubbish tips and gravel pits (where they may rest and bathe), and although almost always greatly outnumbered by Lesser Black-backed Gulls, increasing numbers are being found on farmland.

'Norfolk's breeding population is augmented in winter by visitors from other parts of Britain and by nominate birds from northern Europe.'

The highest counts included up to 3,500 in the Holme/Thornham/Titchwell area and 6,000 at Scolt Head, and inland 2,800 at Blackborough End Tip and 2,000 at Saddlebow. At the latter site, large numbers of gulls feed on heaps of factory waste before bathing in the relief channel and then departing (Wilson 2001).

Norfolk's breeding population is augmented in winter by visitors from other parts of Britain and by nominate birds from northern Europe; NBA winter totals of Herring Gulls were regularly at least 10,000. Some counts almost certainly involved birds that were passing along the north Norfolk coast, such as 7,000 that flew west in two hours at Holme on 5th December 1999. As well as using some of the larger inland waters for night-time roosting, Herring Gulls spend the night on mudflats or inshore waters, on occasion in flocks of 1,000 or more.

Yellow-legged Gull
Larus michahellis

NBA 1999–2007	SUMMER: ALL / BREEDING	WINTER
TETRADS OCCUPIED	15 (1%) / none	42 (3%)
SUMMER/WINTER ONLY	5	32
MEAN PER OCCUPIED TETRAD	2 / none	3
SUMMED MAX COUNTS	25 / none	141
POPULATION ESTIMATE	10–20 individuals	30–50

PREVIOUS ATLASES	SQUARES OCCUPIED	1999–2007	LOSSES	GAINS
1981–84 WINTER (10 KM)	none	26 (42%)	0	26

THE YELLOW-LEGGED GULL is a mainly Mediterranean species that increased in numbers and began to spread north and west within Europe during the 1970s. Nowadays, Yellow-legged Gulls are recorded in Britain throughout the year, with peak numbers occurring in late summer and early autumn, as both adults and juveniles move north after the breeding season. The species was first reported in Norfolk in 1962 but it is only since 1983 that Yellow-legged Gulls have been recorded annually. In 2005, the BOU Records Committee formally recognised it as a distinct species, rather than as a race of Herring Gull.

The NBA winter map shows the rather limited distribution of records, with many located at the places where Lesser Black-backed Gulls tend to gather; there is almost always a strong association between the two species. Locations hosting double-figure counts have been near the relief channel at Saddlebow, where the gulls feed on factory waste (Wilson 2001), Hockwold Washes, East Harling and Banham Moor. The number of Yellow-legged Gulls reported in Norfolk during the NBA winters increased rapidly from 14 in 1999/2000 to up to 40 in the closing NBA years.

Yellow-legged Gulls return from Britain to their

SUMMER

Small dots 1, medium 2, large 3–4 ('pairs')

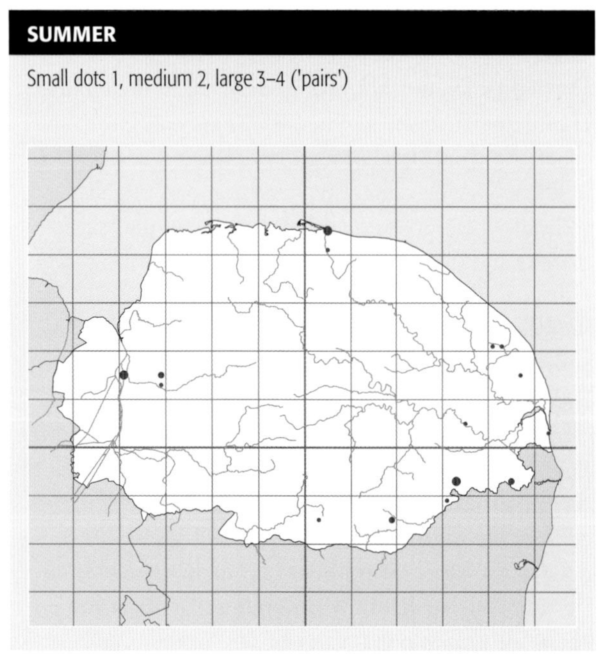

WINTER

Small dots 1, medium 2–4, large 5–15 (birds)

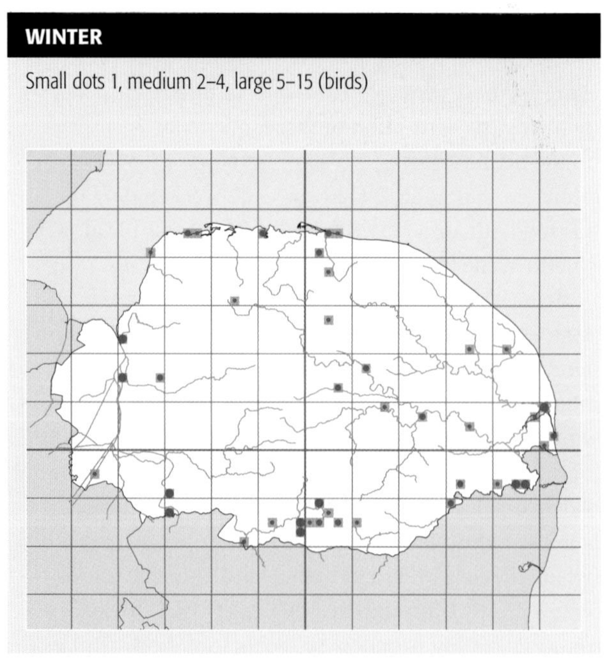

DAVID TIPLING

breeding colonies in France and Spain normally by early spring. Small numbers of birds, mainly immatures, remain in spring and summer, and some were recorded during the NBA summer fieldwork. Many were at Saddlebow and other locations also mapped by NBA in winter.

'The winter map shows the rather limited distribution of records, with many located at the places where Lesser Black-backed Gulls tend to gather.'

No reliable data are available from previous atlases, which treated Yellow-legged as a form of Herring Gull and did not record them separately. Thus, while Yellow-legged Gulls have undoubtedly increased their range in Norfolk at both seasons, the extent of this spread cannot be measured by this means. The marked increase in records in recent years is at least partly attributable to increased observer awareness and improved identification skills (Wilson & Balmer 2002).

Caspian Gull
Larus cachinnans

NBA 1999–2007	SUMMER: ALL / BREEDING	WINTER
TETRADS OCCUPIED	4 (<1%) / none	24 (2%)
SUMMER/WINTER ONLY	1	21
MEAN PER OCCUPIED TETRAD	1 / none	2
SUMMED MAX COUNTS	5 / none	42
POPULATION ESTIMATE	2–5 individuals	10–15

PREVIOUS ATLASES	SQUARES OCCUPIED	1999–2007	LOSSES	GAINS
1981–84 WINTER (10 KM)	none	17 (27%)	0	17

JIM ALMOND

THE CASPIAN GULL is known to have occurred in Britain only since 1995 and was officially regarded as a race of Herring Gull until 2007. Historically it has bred around the Caspian and Black Seas, but a westward range expansion is in progress, with some now nesting as close to Britain as Germany. After breeding, some adults and immatures move westwards across Europe, reaching southern Britain in small and apparently increasing numbers.

The first two Norfolk records were both at Cley in 1997, with a second-winter bird in November followed by an adult in December. Four more were recorded the next year, of which three were at inland rubbish tips. Since then the number of records has increased annually, in part related to increased observer awareness. During the NBA period, the annual total of individuals seen in Norfolk has risen from about 14 in 2000 to over 60 in 2006, although the majority have occurred outside the NBA summer and winter recording periods.

The NBA winter map shows that, like Yellow-legged Gull, the species was recorded in a few, well-scattered localities, most of which were inland, with rubbish tips and outdoor pig units being most favoured. Peak winter numbers were generally recorded between January and March and, in 2006, 59% at this time of year were first-winter birds. Normally only single birds have been recorded at each site in winter but up to four were present at Smoker's Hole (Saxlingham), at East Harling and at Blackborough End Tip. The last-named locality had an impressive total of 34 Caspian Gull sightings during 2005. The maximum recorded in Norfolk during the NBA winter recording period was 14 in the winter of 2002/03.

Caspian Gulls, mostly immatures, were recorded summering but generally in smaller numbers than those recorded in winter. A bird ringed as a chick in Poland in May 2005 was observed at Blackborough End in May 2006 and between May and July in 2007, thus demonstrating fidelity to a summering site. Other green-ringed birds, presumably from Poland, were also observed at several locations around the county during the winter months.

WINTER

Small dots 1, medium 2–3, large 4 (birds)

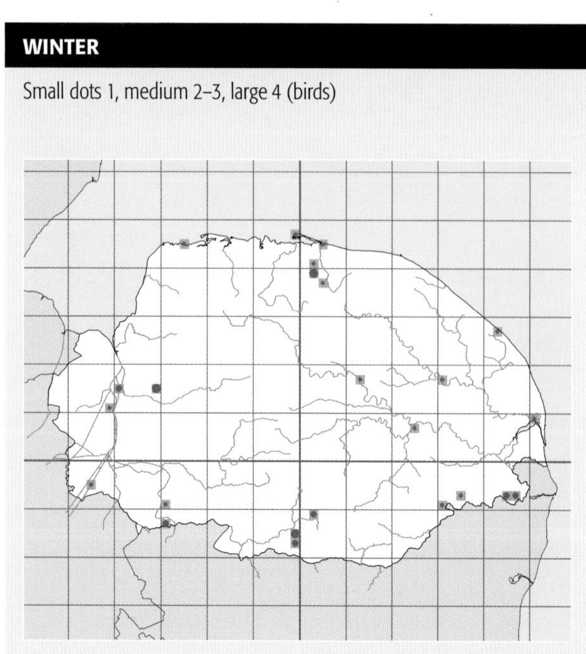

Iceland Gull
Larus glaucoides

NBA 1999–2007	SUMMER: ALL/BREEDING	WINTER
TETRADS OCCUPIED	4 (<1%) / none	24 (2%)
SUMMER/WINTER ONLY	2	22
MEAN PER OCCUPIED TETRAD	1 / none	1
SUMMED MAX COUNTS	4 / none	25
POPULATION ESTIMATE	none	0–10

PREVIOUS ATLASES	SQUARES OCCUPIED	1999–2007	LOSSES	GAINS
1981–84 WINTER (10 KM)	5 (8%)	15 (24%)	3	13

DAVID TIPLING

THE ICELAND GULL is the smaller and more delicate of the two white-winged gulls that regularly visit Norfolk from Arctic breeding areas. Most sightings in the county are made in March and April, when birds are returning towards Greenland, and, since so many of the winter sightings are of transient individuals, Iceland Gulls are perhaps more passage migrants than regular winter visitors.

It has always been a very scarce bird in the county. *Stevenson* was able to confirm only a single record, but by 1930, 16 had been recorded and it has been an annual visitor since 1969. Its winter distribution in Britain is noticeably more westerly than that of Glaucous Gull and fewer are recorded inland (*1981–84 Winter Atlas*). Up to the start of NBA recording, the majority of sightings were along the north Norfolk coast, especially between Cley and Cromer. In contrast, the map of NBA records from the December to February period shows a total absence of Iceland Gulls using the tetrads along that stretch of coastline, although some fly-by sightings may not have reached the NBA database because the birds were thought not to be using the tetrad in which they were seen.

Iceland Gulls feed on fish and waste, and it is therefore perhaps not surprising that some were recorded in northwest Norfolk and in the King's Lynn area. But what is particularly striking about the distribution during the NBA period is the number of inland records, which outnumber those made around the coast. Many of these birds were attracted to landfill sites, such as those at Aldeby and Blackborough End. The latter site hosted an Iceland Gull for three consecutive winters, while a second-year bird was present there from 14th January 2005 until mid April. Most records involved birds that were present only for a day or two, although an elusive adult was in the Holme/Titchwell area for a month from mid February 2005. Others joined the huge inland gatherings of Lesser Black-backed Gulls around pig fields or arable land fertilised with chicken waste.

During the NBA period, only a few Iceland Gulls were recorded in any one winter (all involving single birds), except for 2004/05 when ten were present in Norfolk between December and February. A few passage birds lingered into April, but the species is very rare in Norfolk in May and exceptionally so in June. There were no late spring or summer records in Norfolk during the NBA period.

WINTER

Small dots 1, medium 2 (birds)

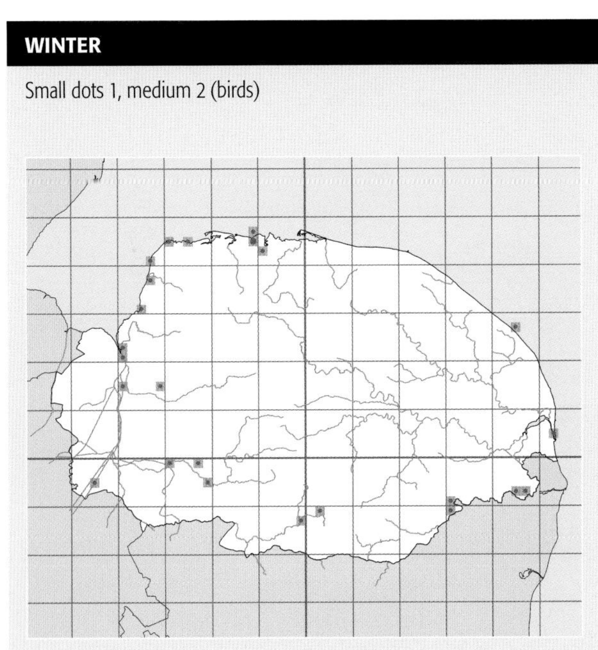

Glaucous Gull
Larus hyperboreus

NBA 1999–2007	SUMMER: ALL/BREEDING	WINTER
TETRADS OCCUPIED	11 (<1%) / none	56 (4%)
SUMMER/WINTER ONLY	3	48
MEAN PER OCCUPIED TETRAD	1 / none	1
SUMMED MAX COUNTS	11 / none	64
POPULATION ESTIMATE	none	1–15

PREVIOUS ATLASES	SQUARES OCCUPIED	1999–2007	LOSSES	GAINS
1981–84 WINTER (10 KM)	15 (24%)	24 (39%)	3	12

THE GLAUCOUS GULL has always been noted as a scarce winter visitor to Norfolk, although it is likely that adults have become more common in recent years. Variable numbers visit Britain annually, the *1981–84 Winter Atlas* demonstrating a clear northerly bias to the coastal distribution. Increased numbers of Glaucous Gulls reach Scotland, in particular, during severe winters. The stretch of coast between Blakeney Point and Weybourne has hosted two individual that each returned annually for many years – one of these was seen in 16 winters between 1963 and 1979.

DAVID TIPLING

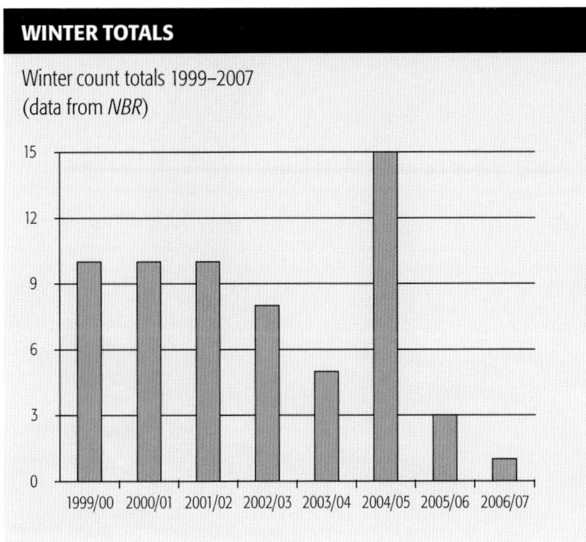

As expected from their previous history in the county, Glaucous Gulls were recorded more frequently than Iceland Gulls during the NBA period, and were more likely to occur between December and February. These factors are reflected in the winter distribution map. The species was recorded in over twice as many tetrads and at some localities two or three birds were present, including two first-winter birds in the same field during 6th–9th February 2003 at East Harling, where fields were being spread with chicken waste. On the north coast there was a clear concentration of records on the beaches and reserves between Holkham and West Runton. Glaucous Gulls are scavengers and so are drawn to household rubbish tips, where they feed in the company of the other large gulls, as well as loafing around during the day on the surrounding fields. During the last few years, Blackborough End Tip has been particularly favoured, with up to three present in the winter of 2004/05. Other sites to host wintering Glaucous Gulls have included gravel pits and the docks at King's Lynn.

While most Glaucous Gulls have left the county by early April, a wintering second-year bird remained throughout the summer in the King's Lynn area in 2000, roosting at Ousemouth. It was also reported from Blackborough End Tip and Saddlebow. It was last seen in August 2000 before returning to Fisher Fleet, King's Lynn, the following February, where it was seen intermittently until the end of the year, and its final sighting was at Blackborough End Tip in March 2002. At least four individuals were seen in the Thornham Point to Scolt Head area in early to mid April 2000.

'As expected, Glaucous Gulls were recorded more frequently than Iceland Gulls during the NBA period, and were more likely to occur between December and February.'

During the NBA winters, a handful of birds suspected of being hybrids between Glaucous and Herring Gulls were reported. Such birds have been reported as frequent in Iceland, but are generally resident there and this plumage is seldom recorded in Britain (*1981–84 Winter Atlas*).

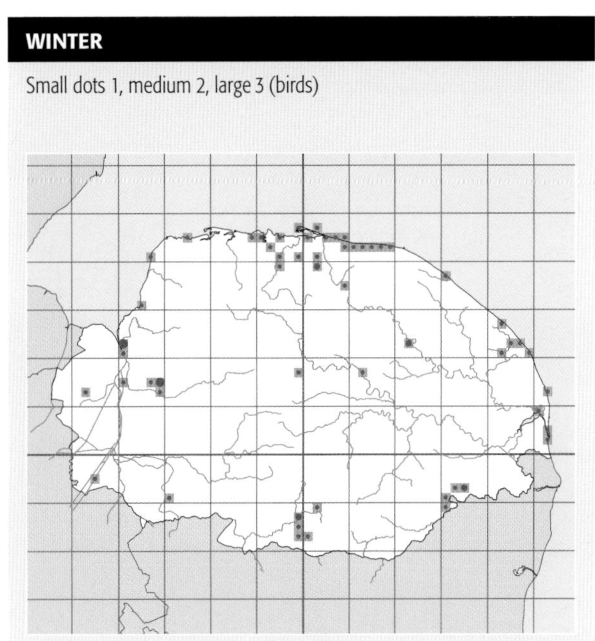

Great Black-backed Gull

Larus marinus

NBA 1999–2007	SUMMER: ALL/BREEDING	WINTER
TETRADS OCCUPIED	96 (7%) / none	347 (24%)
SUMMER/WINTER ONLY	36	287
MEAN PER OCCUPIED TETRAD	10 / none	14
SUMMED MAX COUNTS	934 / none	4,917
POPULATION ESTIMATE	100–200 individuals	700–1,000

PREVIOUS ATLASES	SQUARES OCCUPIED	1999–2007	LOSSES	GAINS
1981–84 WINTER (10 KM)	58 (94%)	58 (94%)	2	2

THE GREAT BLACK-BACKED GULL has never been proved to breed in Norfolk, despite one breeding record published in error (*1968–72 Atlas*) and a footnote in *Stevenson* that indicates that a pair may have bred in the vicinity of Blakeney Marshes between 1820 and 1835. Indeed it is entirely absent as a nesting species from the coasts of eastern and southeastern England. As it favours rocky coasts and generally avoids nesting on flat beaches or saltmarshes, breeding in the county is not expected. It has occurred in Norfolk as a non-breeding summer visitor for at least the last 200 years, however, and is a common winter visitor.

From the NBA summer map it can be seen that although it is largely a coastal bird in summer, usually solitary or in small groups only, some of the largest concentrations were recorded inland both along the upper reaches of the River Wensum in central Norfolk and in the Fens. One of the highest counts concerned 250 that were following crab boats off Overstrand on 1st May 2005, while over 200 have roosted at times in Blakeney Harbour in the early part of the NBA summer recording period.

SUMMER

Small dots 1, medium 2–7, large 8–145 ('pairs')

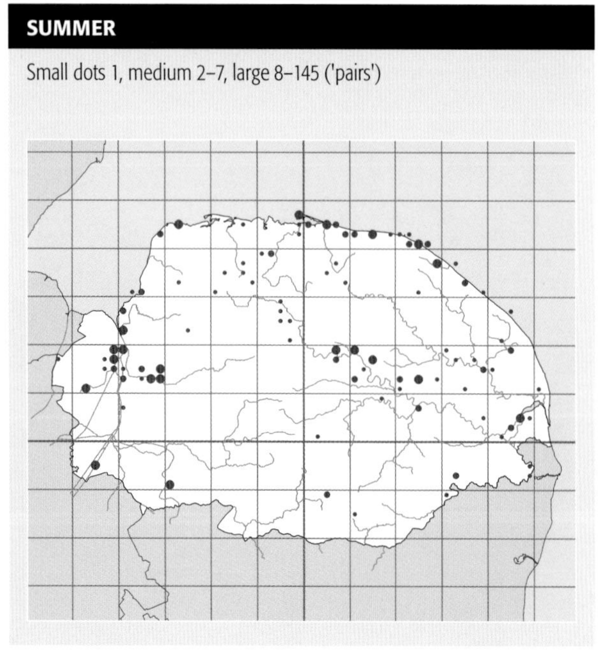

WINTER

Small dots 1, medium 2–4, large 5–505 (birds)

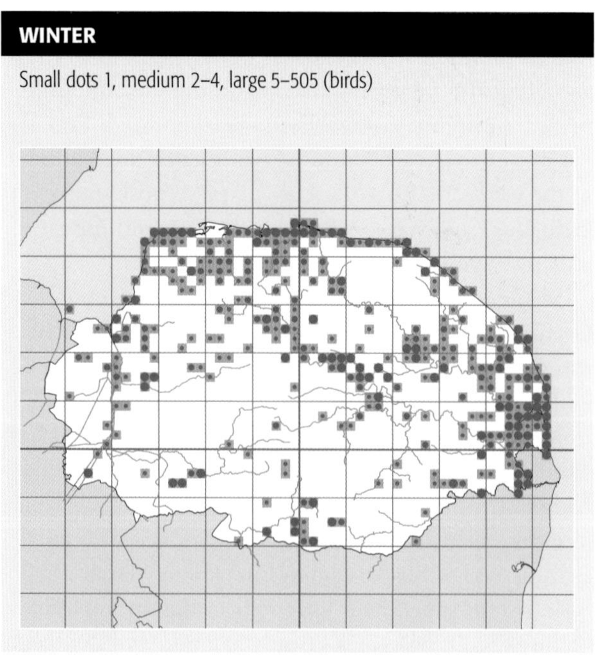

DAVID TIPLING

In winter large numbers of birds, from all around the Norwegian coast, visit England, many of the adults returning to the same areas in subsequent years (*Migration Atlas*). The NBA winter map shows how much more widespread they are then than during the summer, with small numbers being found scattered around Norfolk, particularly in the northern half of the county. Great Black-backed Gulls are habitual scavengers and many of the larger daytime gatherings were near rubbish tips, such as those at Blackborough End and Beetley, where over 200 have been recorded, while over 500 have been counted at Attlebridge. As well as coastal locations, such as Scolt Head/Brancaster Harbour, Stiffkey saltmarsh and Breydon Water, where counts of 200–300 have been made, several inland gravel pits have hosted nocturnal roosts, the largest, at Cranwich, holding a maximum of almost 300 Great Black-backed Gulls.

'As Great Black-backed Gulls favour rocky coasts and generally avoid nesting on flat beaches or saltmarshes, breeding in the county is not expected.'

Little Tern
Sternula albifrons

NBA 1999–2007	SUMMER: ALL/BREEDING	WINTER
TETRADS OCCUPIED	58 (4%) /18 (1%)	none
SUMMER/WINTER ONLY	58	none
MEAN PER OCCUPIED TETRAD	17 / 50	none
SUMMED MAX COUNTS	1,014 / 894	none
POPULATION ESTIMATE	400–600 bp	none

PREVIOUS ATLASES	SQUARES OCCUPIED	1999–2007	LOSSES	GAINS
1968–72 (10 KM)	11 (18%)	6 (10%)	6	1
1980–85 (TETRAD)	46 (3%)	18 (1%)	35	7
1980–85 (10 KM)	14 (23%)	6 (10%)	8	0
1988–91 (10 KM)	9 (15%)	6 (10%)	3	0

DAVID TIPLING

NORFOLK HAS AN important part to play in the conservation of the Little Tern, which, with its population of fewer than 2,000 pairs, is one of Britain's rarest nesting seabirds.

The species' range contracted throughout Europe during the 19th and 20th centuries. In Britain, numbers have not only declined during the last seven or so decades, but have become more concentrated: around 60–70% of the British population is now estimated to breed at the ten best sites (*BoCC3*). More than half the British colonies are around the coast between Lincolnshire and Hampshire, despite high human pressures on beaches in this region (*1988–91 Atlas*).

Little Terns nest in colonies, normally holding up to about 30 pairs, on strips of bare sand, shingle or shell, only just above the high-tide line. They avoid beaches backed by cliffs. Most feeding is in shallow waters close inshore or in creeks and lagoons, close to the breeding colonies. The main concentrations of breeding sites are along the protected beaches of north Norfolk, and the more easily accessible strands in east Norfolk. Just six areas hosted Little Tern colonies in every one of the NBA summers: these were Holme, Scolt Head, Holkham NNR, Blakeney Point, Winterton and Great Yarmouth North Beach. Between them, five of these areas held 400–450 pairs in each of the NBA summers, although there was considerable annual variation between the numbers at individual sites. Other sites held colonies in most of the eight seasons. In 2002 a new site for a colony was founded at Eccles-on-Sea, in an area newly protected by sea-defence reefs: in 2003, only its second season, 37 pairs raised 60 young.

Scolt Head held 90–95 pairs in most years, but the number of young reared to fledging varied from none to 60. While breeding numbers at Blakeney Point ranged from 17 to 116 pairs, in no year were more than 20 young fledged. At Great Yarmouth North Beach the colony grew to 261 pairs in 2001 and in that year over 100 young fledged, but generally the breeding success there was very low. The most successful NBA seasons were 2003, when following unavoidable disturbance the Great Yarmouth colony relocated to Winterton and 450–500 young were reared by 233 pairs, and 2006, when 673 young were raised by 369 pairs at Great Yarmouth North Beach. These are the largest numbers of young fledged by a single colony in Britain since monitoring began in 1969. Success was a direct result of 24-hour wardening, fencing around the colony extending to the shoreline, electric fencing around the colony to prevent access by foxes, cats and hedgehogs, and supplementary diversionary feeding of the local pair of Kestrels. Elsewhere in the county only 35 young were raised by 230 pairs due to predation, flooding, bad weather and lack of food.

In 2000, 551 pairs bred in Norfolk, which represented 28% of the British & Irish total for that year. During the subsequent NBA summers, the number of breeding pairs in Norfolk varied between 418 and 585. During the *1980–85 NBBS*, the Norfolk population varied between 330 and 470 pairs, and during the *1988–91 Atlas* three of the four colonies to hold more than 100 pairs were in Norfolk, at Holkham, Blakeney Point and Great Yarmouth. Numbers of Little Terns breeding in Norfolk have thus fluctuated, but have shown no clear trend since at least 1980; their numbers may have become more important in national

the colony, the greater the likelihood of predator activity. Even Winterton, where unprecedented success occurred in 2003, had disasters in the following two years because the adults had to fly much further to find fish.

terms over this period, however, and their productivity therefore more significant. There were no NBA nesting records in the Wash, where possible or probable breeding had been recorded during 1980–85 and where pairs nested on the Outer Trial Bank during 1989–92.

Every colony has always been vulnerable to a variety of threats to breeding success. The reasons for failure vary between years and, within a year, may differ between colonies. Gale-blown sand or high tides may overwhelm nests, which are often built near to the high-water mark. Unseasonable cold and summer storms have adversely affected the colony at Scolt Head in recent years – as did sea foam, up to waist deep, in 2001. Success here and at Burnham Overy was also limited by a lack of small fish in Brancaster Harbour. Predation of eggs and young by gulls has been a problem at Blakeney Point, while at Scolt Head similar predation was first recorded in 2003 and may become a major issue if nesting numbers of Common Gulls in the county continue to increase. Even Oystercatchers are known to have inflicted significant losses, while marauding foxes and stoats may trouble any site.

The large breeding colony at Great Yarmouth North Beach has suffered particularly severely from a variety of problems, despite intensive wardening and the erection of temporary fences to discourage pedestrian access to the nesting area. Kestrels have always been a problem there, although at Scolt Head up to five Kestrels regularly hunted near the terns in 2003 and yet no young were seen to be taken. In 2001, when the Great Yarmouth colony held 261 pairs of Little Terns, no fewer than 450 chicks fell victim to Kestrels. In 2002, vandals ripped up the fencing at night and threw it into the colony causing total desertion. In the following year, a missing child in Great Yarmouth prompted daily helicopter searches over the area, and these combined with the unwelcome attention of gulls, Kestrels and hedgehogs resulted in the colony relocating to Winterton. At the new colony at Eccles-on-Sea, following a successful season in 2003, all 80 chicks were taken the following year, probably by a single Kestrel, and in 2005 all the clutches were predated by Carrion Crows and Magpies. It appears that, the larger

Little Terns rarely nest inland in Britain, and the only NBA records of inland nesting were of two pairs at Rush Hills on Hickling Broad; the outcome was unknown. Inland passage records are similarly rare: in the NBA period, almost half were in 2005 and included sightings in Broadland and at Pentney GP, Welney and Hockwold Washes.

SUMMER

Small dots 1–2, medium 3–5, large 6–261 ('pairs')
Shading – breeding proved or considered likely

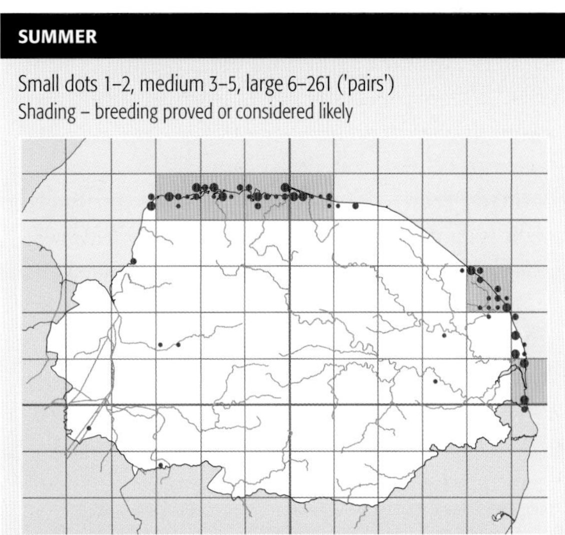

BREEDING TOTALS

Breeding pairs in Norfolk for each of the NBA summers (data from *NBR*)

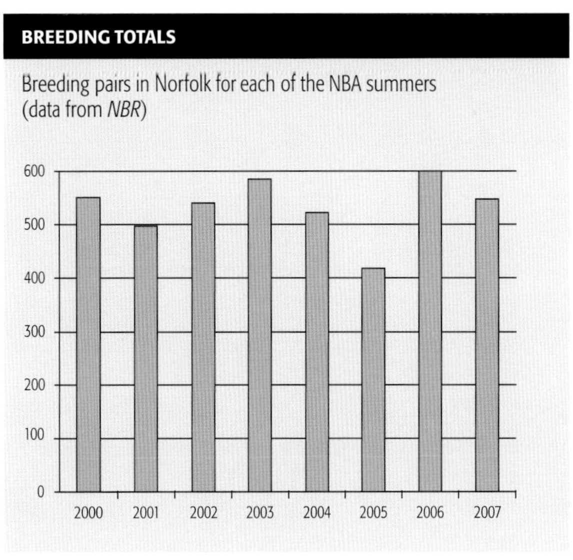

Black Tern
Chlidonias niger

NBA 1999–2007	SUMMER: ALL / BREEDING	WINTER
TETRADS OCCUPIED	41 (3%) / none	none
SUMMER/WINTER ONLY	41	none
MEAN PER OCCUPIED TETRAD	5 / none	none
SUMMED MAX COUNTS	185 / none	none
POPULATION ESTIMATE	0–10 individuals	none

PREVIOUS ATLASES	SQUARES OCCUPIED	1999–2007	LOSSES	GAINS
1968–72 (10 KM)	2 (3%)	none	2	0

THE BLACK TERN is a most attractive summer visitor that breeds in scattered colonies across the western Palaearctic, with the highest numbers nesting in Russia. In Britain, it occurs mainly as an irregular spring and autumn passage migrant.

It formerly bred in large numbers in southeast England, especially in the Fens and Broadland, but because of wetland drainage and egg collecting, it became extinct as a British breeding species in the middle of the 18th century, with the last nest in the Broads at Sutton in 1858. The next instance of successful breeding was at Welney in 1969, since when sporadic attempts were made until 1975. The *1968–72 Atlas* also mentioned a pair carrying food in Broadland in 1970, but nothing is known of this in county records.

SUMMER

Small dots 1, medium 2–4, large 5–42 ('pairs')

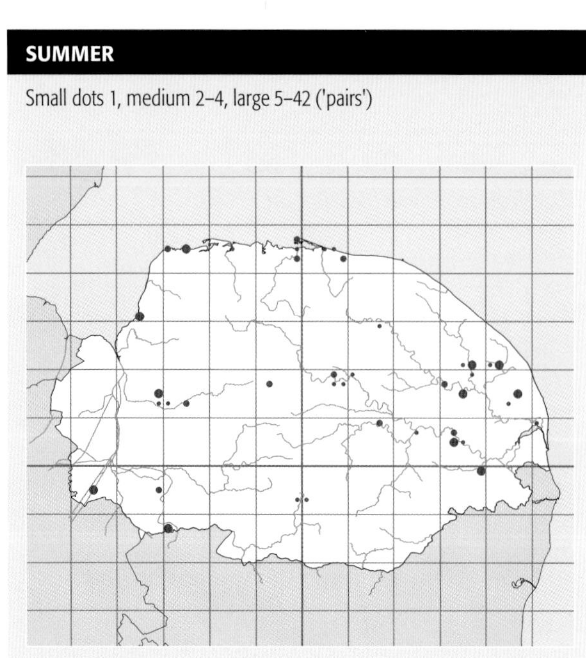

DAVID TIPLING

Variable numbers of Black Terns pass through Norfolk on passage in spring and it is records of these migrants that comprise the NBA summer map. It can be seen that this passage is noted both around the coast, where the Black Terns usually gather and feed over the lagoons of the coastal reserves before moving on, and over areas of open water inland, such as the gravel pits along the river valleys and in the Broads. The highest counts during the years of NBA fieldwork included 83 at Welney, 30 at Hardley Flood, where a pair were also seen displaying on 27th April 2002, and 25 at Barton Broad.

The first Black Terns of the spring are usually noted from mid April onwards; one at Barton Broad on 8th April 2004 was the earliest county record by just one day. Peak passage normally takes place in the first half of May but the number of birds observed each spring varied from fewer than 30 to over 550 between 1st and 15th May 2000. Only a few were recorded each year in June.

Sandwich Tern

Sterna sandvicensis

NBA 1999–2007	SUMMER: ALL/BREEDING	WINTER
TETRADS OCCUPIED	29 (2%) / 4 (<1%)	4 (<1%)
SUMMER/WINTER ONLY	26	1
MEAN PER OCCUPIED TETRAD	301 / 2,036	1
SUMMED MAX COUNTS	8,732 / 8,144	5
POPULATION ESTIMATE	3,000–4,500 bp	none

PREVIOUS ATLASES	SQUARES OCCUPIED	1999–2007	LOSSES	GAINS
1968–72 (10 KM)	4 (6%)	3 (5%)	2	1
1980–85 (TETRAD)	11 (<1%)	4 (<1%)	8	1
1980–85 (10 KM)	7 (11%)	3 (5%)	4	0
1981–84 WINTER (10 KM)	2 (3%)	3 (5%)	2	3
1988–91 (10 KM)	2 (3%)	3 (5%)	2	3

THE SANDWICH TERN was first proved to breed in Norfolk in 1920, at Blakeney Point, one of only two sites at which colonies are still regular, the other being Scolt Head. Up to the mid 1940s, Salthouse held an annual colony and, in east Norfolk, Scroby Sands off Great Yarmouth were occupied until the 1970s, by which time the sands were being inundated at most high tides.

Sandwich Terns are gregarious throughout the year and nest in large, dense colonies on sand-spits or shingle-bars close to the sea, often in association with breeding Black-headed Gulls. During the NBA period, three sites hosted Sandwich Tern colonies in Norfolk: Scolt Head and Blakeney Point in each of the eight summers, and Stiffkey Binks from 2001 to 2004, the first time this site had been used since the mid 1970s. Numbers of breeding pairs at the two main sites varied from year to year and in only one year, 2003, did those at Blakeney Point outnumber the Scolt Head ternery. In that year 2,900 pairs bred at Blakeney Point, split into four separate colonies from which 2,300 young were fledged, making it the best year since 1993. The Scolt Head colony peaked in 2000 with 4,200 pairs raising 5,000 young. During the NBA period, there was a slight decrease in the number of breeding pairs in Norfolk, but fluctuating numbers are characteristic of the species throughout its range. In 2000, the British population was estimated to be 10,536 pairs, of which 4,275 pairs (41%) were in Norfolk: the county population is thus very important in national and indeed international terms.

Many factors can have an effect on success or failure at a breeding colony. Sandwich Terns are very prone to disturbance by mammalian predators during the egg-laying stage, which is synchronised throughout the colony. If disturbed in the early part of the season, all the birds may leave and settle elsewhere. Predation of both eggs and young by Herring and Lesser Black-backed Gulls was a particular problem at Blakeney Point in 2000, while Common, Herring and Great Black-backed Gulls, and brown rats, all took their toll in 2003. Foxes used to be the main hazard at Scolt Head, but are no longer a major problem. In 2004, bad weather in June adversely affected all three Norfolk colonies, especially at Scolt Head, where it resulted in the deaths of a thousand young, some almost ready to fly.

In addition to the breeding colonies, Sandwich Terns were recorded at many other sites in north Norfolk, as shown on the map. Sandwich Terns arrive in the spring already paired and prior to reaching the breeding colonies gather at pre-breeding roosts to continue their courtship and displays (*BWP4*). One such site is Arnold's Marsh at Cley, where up to 800 Sandwich Terns were recorded in spring. Other sightings around the coast, including comparatively few off east Norfolk, relate to feeding terns.

Sandwich Terns are rare inland and there were only a handful of such records during the NBA period. Midwinter records were even rarer and perhaps involved just two birds: there were two in Blakeney Harbour on 3rd December 2000, one between Blakeney Point and Sheringham on 15th, one at Winterton on 26th, and one at Holme on 5th and 11th January 2001, the first January record ever for the county.

SUMMER

Small dots 1, medium 2–10, large 11–4,200 ('pairs')
Shading – breeding proved or considered likely

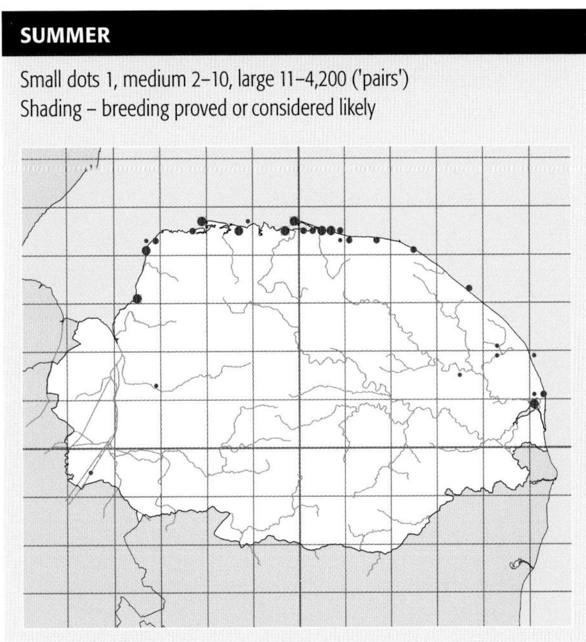

Common Tern
Sterna hirundo

NBA 1999–2007	SUMMER: ALL / BREEDING	WINTER
TETRADS OCCUPIED	192 (13%) / 39 (3%)	none
SUMMER/WINTER ONLY	192	none
MEAN PER OCCUPIED TETRAD	8 / 32	none
SUMMED MAX COUNTS	1,553 / 1,242	none
POPULATION ESTIMATE	800–1,000 bp	none

PREVIOUS ATLASES	SQUARES OCCUPIED	1999–2007	LOSSES	GAINS
1968–72 (10 KM)	19 (31%)	21 (34%)	6	8
1980–85 (TETRAD)	76 (5%)	39 (3%)	60	23
1980–85 (10 KM)	25 (40%)	21 (34%)	12	8
1988–91 (10 KM)	16 (26%)	21 (34%)	3	8

THE COMMON TERN IS the most widely distributed tern breeding in Britain, with colonies scattered across much of lowland England, but is outnumbered by both the Arctic and Sandwich Terns.

The number of pairs of Common Terns breeding fell substantially during the 19th century as a result of egg gathering, shooting and the Victorian millinery trade, but following the passing of the Sea Birds Preservation Act in 1869, a colony of 400–500 had built up at Wells by 1890. The Norfolk breeding population peaked in 1938 with 4,400 nesting pairs but had fallen to 1,500 by 1980. Since then the number of breeding pairs has never exceeded a thousand.

The Common Terns that breed in Britain winter along the coast of West Africa. Up to the late 1990s, the first birds returning to Norfolk were generally not seen until the first half of April, whereas during the NBA period the first Common Tern was normally recorded in the last week of March, with the earliest on 21st March and the latest on 1st April.

Common Terns nest in colonies both around the Norfolk coast and at a few scattered inland sites, the majority in Broadland or at flooded gravel pits along the river valleys. Coastal colonies are virtually confined to protected reserves. The largest coastal colonies, as indicated on the NBA summer map, are at Scolt Head, Blakeney Point and Snettisham, but breeding success is highly variable. At Scolt Head up to 300 pairs have bred in recent years; the 2003 season was particularly successful there, assisted by factors including a plentiful supply of food locally, aggressive control of predators, the lack of any spring flooding, and generally fine weather. At Blakeney Point high tides and predation by Herring Gulls can have disastrous effects, and the

SUMMER

Small dots 1, medium 2–3, large 4–285 ('pairs')
Shading – breeding proved or considered likely

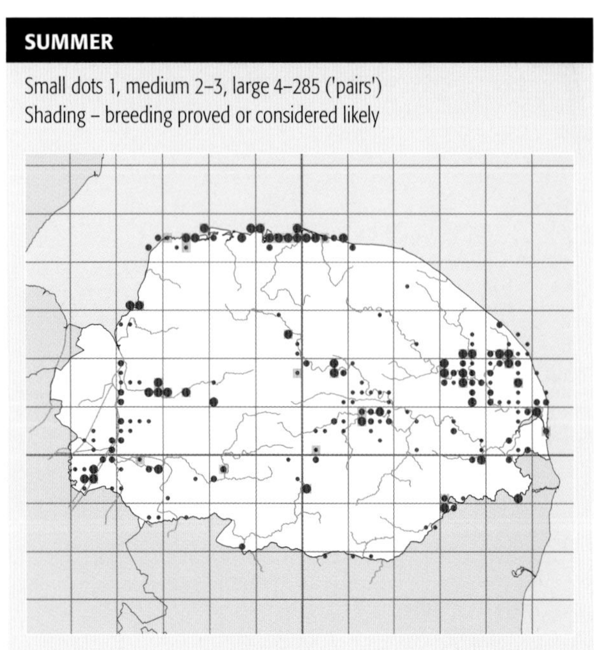

CHANGE SINCE 1980–85

+ Gain ✖ Loss ■ No change

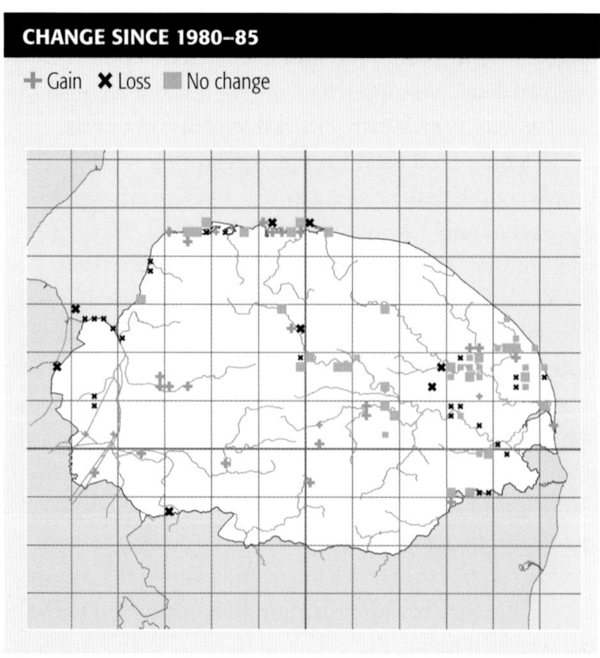

DAVID TIPLING

selective culling of just four Herring Gulls in 2006 proved very beneficial to breeding success. In five of the years between 2000 and 2006, the colony of up to 115 pairs at Snettisham Pits failed almost completely, for no apparent reason, to produce young, while other ground-nesting species enjoyed better success.

In Broadland, and indeed in the county as a whole, the most consistently successful colony has been at Breydon Water. Nesting first took place there in 1977 on a small raft that was converted to a floating breeding platform and tethered near the eastern end. Nowadays the colony occupies several fixed platforms, which have raised sides and are divided into sections by partitions. From 17 pairs in the first year, about 200 pairs now nest annually on these platforms with an average of over one young per pair being fledged in most years. Elsewhere in Broadland, smaller colonies of 20–30 pairs were recorded at Barton, Martham and Ranworth Broads, again on wooden platforms.

The summer of 2006 saw the first record of roof nesting by Common Terns in Norfolk, with two pairs on the corrugated, sloping roof of a disused building at Great Yarmouth South Denes (Dye 2007).

The map includes many tetrads in which the birds that were observed were not breeding; such sightings include passage migrants and summering non-breeders, and breeding birds also forage and even indulge in courtship at long distances from their breeding sites.

While the number of breeding pairs in the county has fallen since 1980, far more inland sites were occupied during the NBA summers than during the *1980–85 NBBS*, as is apparent on the change map. The Wash Outer Trial Bank was first colonised in 1985, peaking at 150 pairs in 1990, but terns subsequently disappeared due to the growth of the Herring and Lesser Black-backed Gull colony there.

Arctic Tern

Sterna paradisaea

NBA 1999–2007	SUMMER: ALL/BREEDING	WINTER
TETRADS OCCUPIED	34 (2%) / 4 (<1%)	1 (<1%)
SUMMER/WINTER ONLY	34	1
MEAN PER OCCUPIED TETRAD	4 / 6	1
SUMMED MAX COUNTS	126 / 23	1
POPULATION ESTIMATE	10–20 bp	none

PREVIOUS ATLASES	SQUARES OCCUPIED	1999–2007	LOSSES	GAINS
1968–72 (10 KM)	6 (10%)	2 (3%)	4	0
1980–85 (TETRAD)	3 (<1%)	4 (<1%)	1	2
1980–85 (10 KM)	3 (5%)	2 (3%)	1	0
1981–84 WINTER (10 KM)	none	1 (2%)	0	1
1988–91 (10 KM)	3 (5%)	2 (3%)	2	1

DAVID TIPLING

THE ARCTIC TERN IS the most numerous tern in Britain, with a population more than double that of all the other species put together. It is mainly a bird of high latitudes and in Norfolk it is mainly a migrant, though small numbers also breed. After breeding, they depart for another high summer in the southern hemisphere, sometimes reaching Antarctica.

Although there has been little recent change in the species' breeding range in Britain, the Orkney and Shetland populations, in particular, have endured low breeding success in recent decades due to a crash in the sand eel population on which they feed their young.

Away from the north and west of Scotland, with the notable exceptions of Anglesey and the Farne Islands, most Arctic Terns nest in mixed colonies with coastal Common Terns, and this is the case in Norfolk. Very few Arctic Terns breed in the county, however, and the NBA summer map shows that nesting occurred at only four localities during the years of NBA fieldwork. The species has bred almost annually at Blakeney Point since 1922 with a maximum of 16 pairs in 2001 and 18 pairs in 2003, but in most years fewer than ten pairs were recorded. Up to two pairs also nested annually on Scolt Head, while Stiffkey Binks held

DAVID TIPLING

three pairs in 2001 and one or two pairs nested on Wells New Ridge in 2005 and 2006. Unfortunately, very few young fledged, if any, due to predation by large gulls and stoats, high tides and inclement weather.

During the NBA period, the first Arctic Terns were generally recorded in Norfolk during the second week of April, either in Broadland or at Welney. Spring passage usually involved fewer than 100 birds, but in some years 200–300 were reported. In Britain, more Arctic Terns are recorded inland in spring than in other parts of their migratory range and it was passage migrants that accounted for the scattering of inland records on the NBA summer map.

'Very few breed in the county and the summer map shows that nesting occurred at only four localities...'

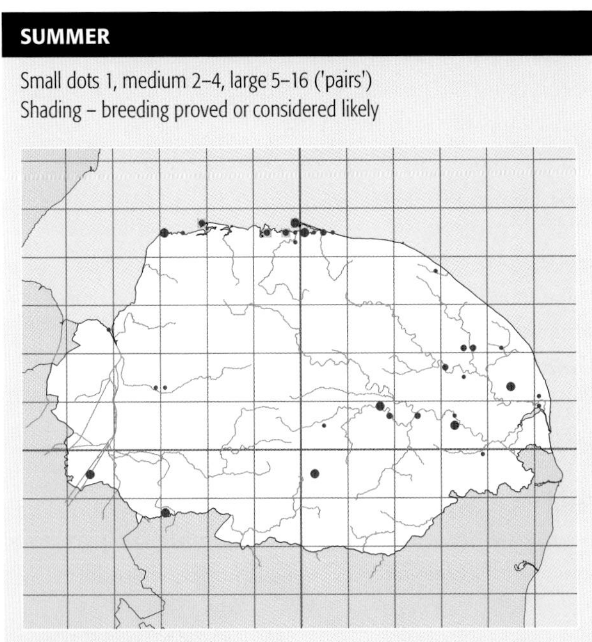

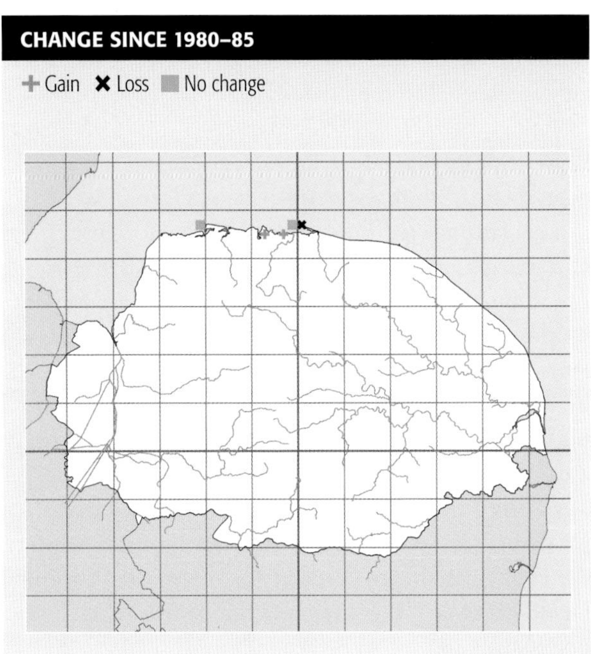

Feral Pigeon
Columba livia

NBA 1999–2007	SUMMER: ALL / BREEDING	WINTER
TETRADS OCCUPIED	542 (37%) / 386 (26%)	571 (39%)
SUMMER/WINTER ONLY	192	221
MEAN PER OCCUPIED TETRAD	7 / 9	20
SUMMED MAX COUNTS	3,979 / 3,337	11,620
POPULATION ESTIMATE	4,000–6,000 bp	10,000–15,000

PREVIOUS ATLASES	SQUARES OCCUPIED	1999–2007	LOSSES	GAINS
1968–72 (10 KM)	32 (52%)	62 (all)	0	30
1980–85 (TETRAD)	228 (16%)	386 (26%)	141	299
1980–85 (10 KM)	56 (90%)	62 (all)	0	6
1981–84 WINTER (10 KM)	59 (95%)	62 (all)	0	3
1988–91 (10 KM)	54 (87%)	62 (all)	0	8

THE FEW POPULATIONS of pure-bred native Rock Doves that remain in Britain are confined to the north and west coasts of Scotland. After thousands of years of selective breeding for appearance or homing ability, the Feral Pigeons that have descended from them have the most variable plumage of any British bird, ranging from all black, through blue-greys and red-browns, to all white. What constitutes a 'Feral Pigeon', as opposed to a semicaptive, dovecote bird, or a homing pigeon released for a race, is often impossible to determine in field conditions, and observers are likely to take differing views of such birds. It is likely that birds from all of these categories are represented in the NBA data.

Wild Rock Doves nest in crevices and cavities on coastal cliffs, while the nests of Feral Pigeons are usually constructed in or on buildings. However, cliff nesting by Feral Pigeons has been occurring at Hunstanton since the late 1980s and birds are present on the cliffs at Beeston Bump throughout the year. Pairs usually breed in loose groups, in urban areas mainly utilising church towers, steeples or other tall buildings, especially if they are old or derelict; in rural areas, Feral Pigeons commonly nest in open barns. They breed throughout the year, each nesting pair producing an average of five clutches annually, while the young are able to breed at six to seven months old (*1988–91 Atlas*). It is therefore not surprising that the population appears to be expanding.

The NBA summer map shows that Feral Pigeons are widely scattered throughout the county but with distinct concentrations in Norwich and other major towns, such as King's Lynn and Great Yarmouth, where there are always plentiful supplies of waste food. The species was also present in most of the smaller towns and larger villages in Norfolk (especially those with granaries), as well as in many more-rural areas. During the NBA summers, the two tetrads that hosted the highest numbers were King's Lynn Docks, where the birds are attracted to spilt grain, and the centre of Norwich. Not all birds present during the summer are necessarily breeding pairs, however: some birds counted may have been young of the year, for example, which are generally indistinguishable from adults.

Feral Pigeons ate largely sedentary and the NBA winter map shows a very similar distribution to that in the summer. They are gregarious throughout the year and often join Stock Doves and Woodpigeons to feed on arable fields, being especially attracted to outdoor pig units. As in the summer, the largest tetrad counts were from King's Lynn Docks and the centre of Norwich with 450 and 368 respectively, and more than 200 Feral Pigeons were recorded also at Hunstanton (284) and at Burgh Castle (269).

Feral Pigeons in Britain have a poorly documented population history (*Birdtrends*). The number of 10-km squares in Norfolk recorded as occupied increased from 52% to 87% between the *1968–72* and *1988–91* Atlases, and range increase is evident in all atlas comparisons. The

'Wild Rock Doves nest in crevices and cavities on coastal cliffs, while the nests of Feral Pigeons are constructed in or on buildings.'

change map shows an apparent rapid spread since the *1980–85 NBBS*, especially into rural areas of southwest and southeast Norfolk, although with a small cluster of losses in the Fens. Some of this increase will be the result of greater observer awareness, however: it has been common for birdwatchers and writers on birds to disregard Feral Pigeons, even after the species was belatedly admitted to the BOU Records Committee's category C in 1993.

SUMMER

Small dots 1–2, medium 3–6, large 7–126 ('pairs')
Shading – breeding proved or considered likely

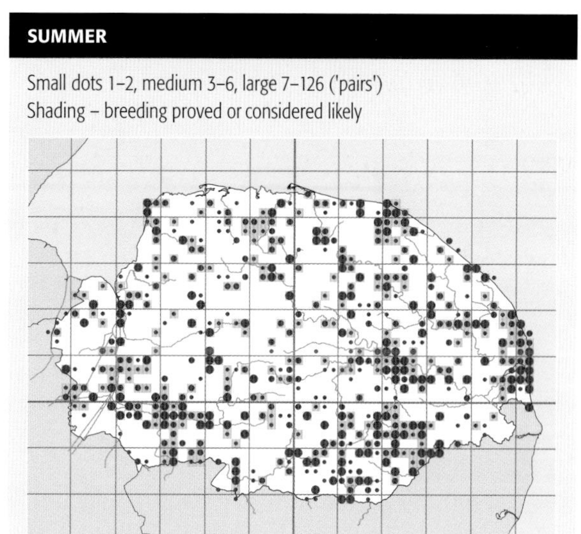

WINTER

Small dots 1–6, medium 7–16, large 17–450 (birds)

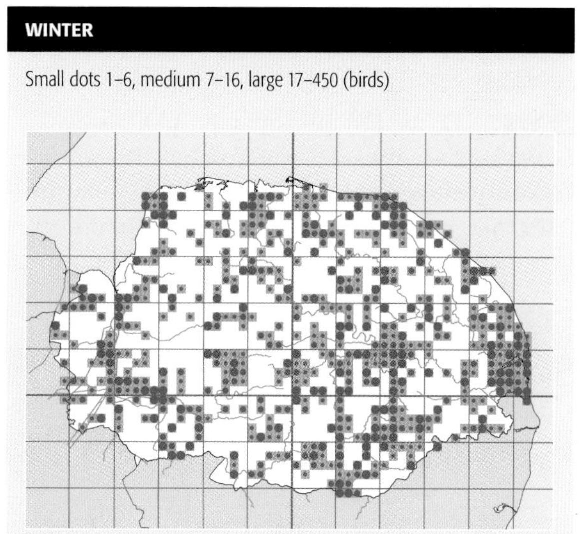

CHANGE SINCE 1980–85

+ Gain ✖ Loss ■ No change

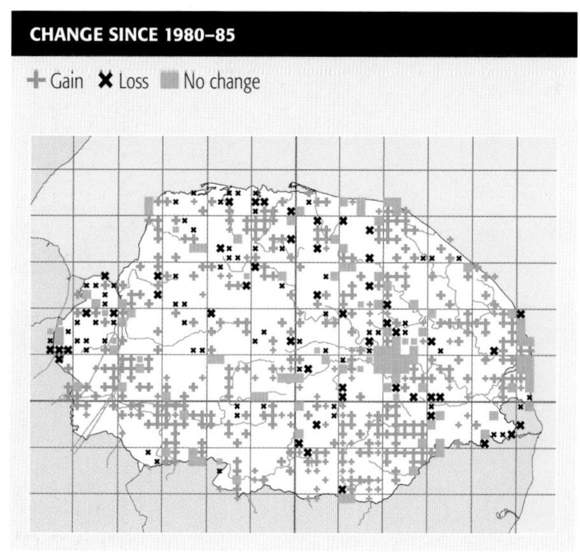

Stock Dove
Columba oenas

NBA 1999–2007	SUMMER: ALL / BREEDING	WINTER
TETRADS OCCUPIED	1,169 (80%) / 1,068 (73%)	1,061 (73%)
SUMMER/WINTER ONLY	208	100
MEAN PER OCCUPIED TETRAD	5 / 5	16
SUMMED MAX COUNTS	5,457 / 5,276	16,666
POPULATION ESTIMATE	6,000–8,000 bp	15,000–20,000

PREVIOUS ATLASES	SQUARES OCCUPIED	1999–2007	LOSSES	GAINS
1968–72 (10 KM)	62 (all)	62 (all)		
1980–85 (TETRAD)	718 (49%)	1,068 (73%)	181	531
1980–85 (10 KM)	62 (all)	62 (all)		
1981–84 WINTER (10 KM)	61 (98%)	62 (all)	0	1
1988–91 (10 KM)	60 (97%)	62 (all)	0	2

AS A DIRECT RESULT of the spread of arable farming during the second half of the 19th century, the range of the Stock Dove expanded considerably in Britain, but its fortunes were reversed in the 1950s due to poisoning by organochlorine seed-dressings, and it became extinct in parts of eastern England. After these chemicals were banned in the early 1960s, the species recovered and the Stock Dove has returned to being a widespread and common bird in Norfolk's farms and woods.

During the breeding season, Stock Doves favour forest edges and parkland, where mature trees provide holes for nesting and open fields or meadows are rich in suitable food-plants. The species will also nest in uninhabited buildings and wartime pillboxes or even underground in rabbit burrows.

The NBA summer map shows that Stock Doves were widespread during the breeding season, with particular concentrations just inland from the north Norfolk coastal strip and in the Fens. For many years, the Brecks have been a stronghold for the Stock Dove, and in particular the Stanford TA, where there is an abundance of mature deciduous trees, uninhabited

EDMUND FELLOWES

buildings and rabbit warrens, all of which provide nest sites. It is therefore not surprising that a tetrad in this area, near Bodney, held the highest count with 40 breeding pairs, while three others with 28 pairs each were well scattered around the county at Emneth, South Creake and Wilby. One of the more unusual nest sites was in the roof of the old lifeboat house on Blakeney Point, a location that was first used in 1994. The young from first broods gather into flocks after fledging and, as they are almost indistinguishable in the field from adults, may have resulted in some falsely high counts during the second of the summer set visits.

Stock Doves remain gregarious throughout the winter, although they are generally found in far smaller flocks than Woodpigeons, with groups of more than 50 being unusual in most parts of the county. Whereas they often feed in the same fields as Woodpigeons, they tend to remain apart from their larger relatives and form single-species flocks on taking flight, thus making it easier to obtain a reasonably accurate count.

The NBA winter map shows a very similar distribution to that in the summer, as one would expect from a largely sedentary species. A withdrawal in winter from parts of north Norfolk has been suggested (Bloomfield & McCallum 1999). If anything, however, this was an area of high numbers during the NBA winters, along with concentrations in the Fens and to a lesser extent in Broadland. Most of the highest tetrad counts were made in northwest Norfolk: 440 at Holme, 260 at Langham and 200 each at Thornham, Ringstead and North Wootton.

The change map shows a massive range increase in Norfolk since the *1980–85 NBBS*. Nationally the recovery in population had almost stabilised by then (*Birdtrends*), indicating that recovery in Norfolk may have taken longer than in other parts of the country. That 20% of tetrads still remained unoccupied may suggest that there is scope for further expansion of the Norfolk population.

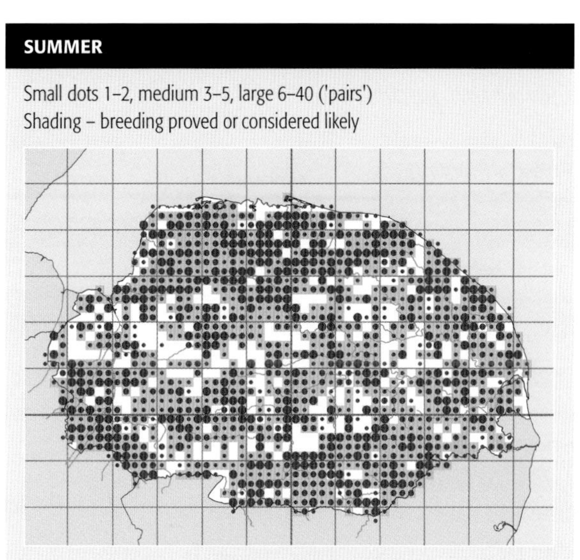

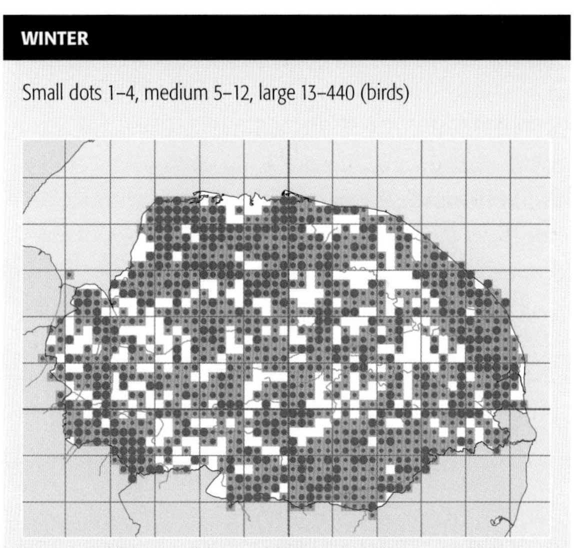

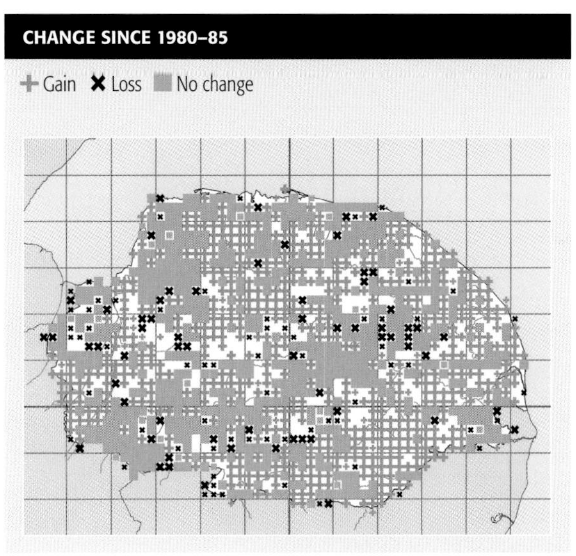

Woodpigeon
Columba palumbus

NBA 1999–2007	SUMMER: ALL / BREEDING	WINTER
TETRADS OCCUPIED	1,427 (98%) / 1,405 (96%)	1,419 (97%)
SUMMER/WINTER ONLY	20	12
MEAN PER OCCUPIED TETRAD	62 / 63	378
SUMMED MAX COUNTS	88,079 / 87,859	536,501
POPULATION ESTIMATE	100,000–120,000 bp	300,000–350,000

PREVIOUS ATLASES	SQUARES OCCUPIED	1999–2007	LOSSES	GAINS
1968–72 (10 KM)	62 (all)	62 (all)		
1980–85 (TETRAD)	1,388 (95%)	1,405 (96%)	30	47
1980–85 (10 KM)	62 (all)	62 (all)		
1981–84 WINTER (10 KM)	62 (all)	62 (all)		
1988–91 (10 KM)	62 (all)	62 (all)		

WOODPIGEONS, THROUGH THEIR large size and abundance, constitute the biggest biomass of any bird in Britain (Dolton & Brooke 1999), with the possible exception of Pheasant as poults are released in the autumn. Following decline in the 1960s, the species has shown rapid increase consistently since the 1970s (*Birdtrends*), their outstanding ability to adapt to alterations in land use having enabled them to take advantage of recent changes in farming practices. It is one of the most widespread and abundant birds in the county, throughout the year.

The peak of nesting is from July to September, to coincide with ripening crops, and thus outside the NBA summer recording period. Throughout most of the spring and early summer, Woodpigeons remain in flocks feeding on arable land, and in woodlands and hedgerows taking fresh leaves and developing buds. The breeding map is thus largely a reflection of these summer feeding flocks. For example, counts of 800–1,100 birds were made in three different tetrads in April. As with other flocking species, the count of pairs was estimated by halving the number of Woodpigeons in a flock.

The highest density of nests occurs around the periphery of woods, both coniferous and deciduous, in copses and along hedgerows, although most foraging is on farmland. Although colonisation of built-up areas began in the early 19th century, it is only in the last 20–30 years that Woodpigeons have become a common sight in the gardens and open grassy spaces in Norwich and most of Norfolk's towns. In recent years up to five pairs have bred on Scolt

SUMMER

Small dots 1–33, medium 34–65, large 66–700 ('pairs')
Shading – breeding proved or considered likely

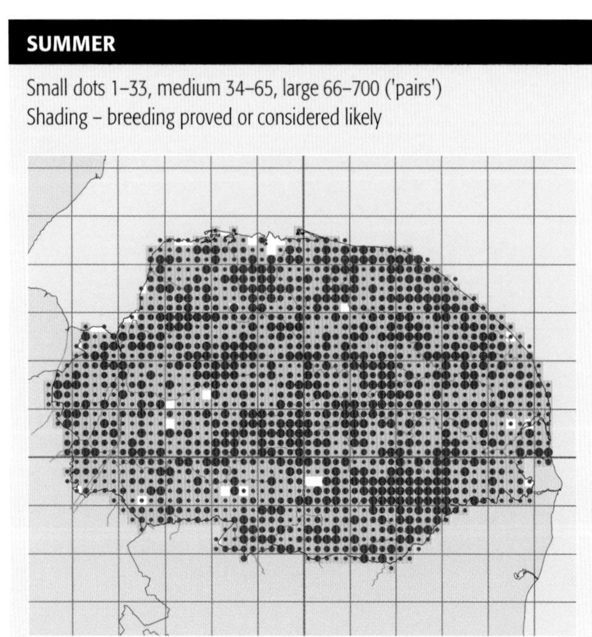

WINTER

Small dots 1–172, medium 173–421, large 422–5,000 (birds)

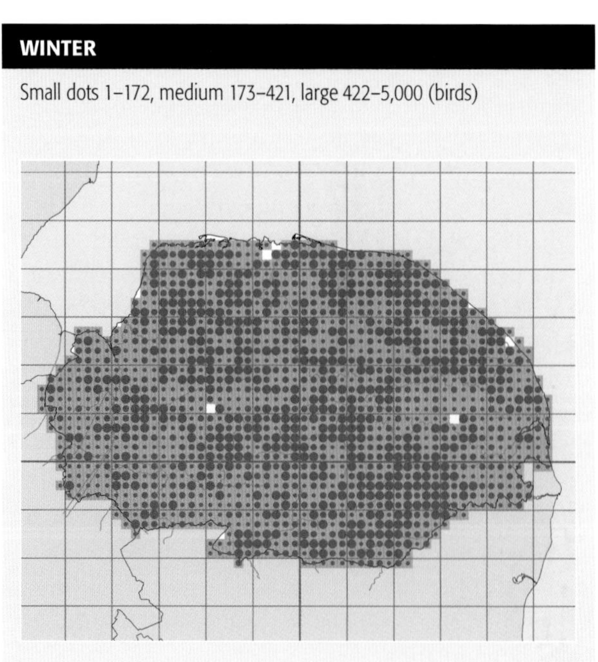

DAVID TIPLING

Head and one pair at Blakeney Point. Woodpigeons were absent only from the saltmarsh at Wells and from a handful of tetrads across the county.

Visible migration around the coast is considerable, but ringing has provided little evidence that winter visitors are continental immigrants (*Migration Atlas*). It is likely, therefore, that the large winter flocks consist almost entirely of local birds that have gathered to take advantage of the available winter food in arable areas. Formerly this was mainly winter stubble and clover leys, but in recent years, with the change to autumn-sown cereal and the planting of oilseed rape, the latter has become one of the most important sources of sustenance. It is available throughout the winter period and has greatly improved the Woodpigeon's ability to survive a hard winter. However, as around a third of a million Woodpigeons are present in Norfolk in winter, it is not surprising that this bird can be a serious pest to oilseed rape growers. The highest counts during the NBA winters were of 5,000 at Horsey and of a similar number leaving a woodland roost near Brancaster.

'The peak of nesting is from July to September, to coincide with ripening crops, and thus outside the NBA summer recording period.'

CHANGE SINCE 1980–85

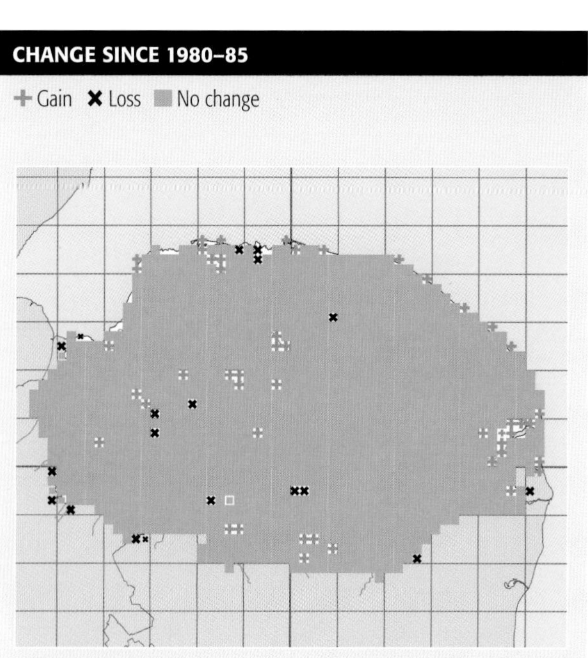

Atlasing, even at tetrad level, has had very limited scope for showing range increase in the county. The change map does indicate minor infilling, however, since the *1980–85 NBBS* distribution, when the species already occupied 95% of the county's tetrads.

Collared Dove
Streptopelia decaocto

NBA 1999–2007	SUMMER: ALL/BREEDING	WINTER
TETRADS OCCUPIED	1,265 (87%) / 1,224 (84%)	1,226 (84%)
SUMMER/WINTER ONLY	100	61
MEAN PER OCCUPIED TETRAD	11 / 11	22
SUMMED MAX COUNTS	13,356 / 13,264	26,636
POPULATION ESTIMATE	13,000–16,000 bp	30,000–40,000

PREVIOUS ATLASES	SQUARES OCCUPIED	1999–2007	LOSSES	GAINS
1968–72 (10 KM)	53 (85%)	62 (all)	0	9
1980–85 (TETRAD)	672 (46%)	1,224 (84%)	47	599
1980–85 (10 KM)	61 (98%)	62 (all)	0	1
1981–84 WINTER (10 KM)	61 (98%)	62 (all)	0	1
1988–91 (10 KM)	61 (98%)	62 (all)	0	1

OWING TO THE astonishing spread of the Collared Dove across Europe during the 20th century, it is now one of the most familiar birds in Britain, drawing attention to itself with its monotonous song and being a regular visitor to many gardens.

Prior to 1930, it was confined in Europe to Turkey and the Balkans, but over the course of the next 50–60 years it spread westwards and is now found in all the countries of Europe. Norfolk provided the species' first breeding record in Britain, at Cromer, in 1955 (Richardson *et al* 1957).

Throughout the year, Collared Doves are closely associated with human habitation and are found in towns and villages, especially in parks and large gardens with ornamental evergreens, in churchyards and around farmyards. They feed almost exclusively on grain and so are often found concentrated in areas where there is a ready supply of spilt grain, such as silos, maltings and docks, as well as near poultry runs and other places where grain is fed to livestock.

The NBA summer map shows how widespread the species has become in the county. They were still absent, however, from much of Thetford Forest and from scattered tetrads elsewhere. Although Collared Doves tend to be absent from the more open countryside, the presence of farm buildings will often attract them. Towns and villages

SUMMER

Small dots 1–5, medium 6–12, large 13–77 ('pairs')
Shading – breeding proved or considered likely

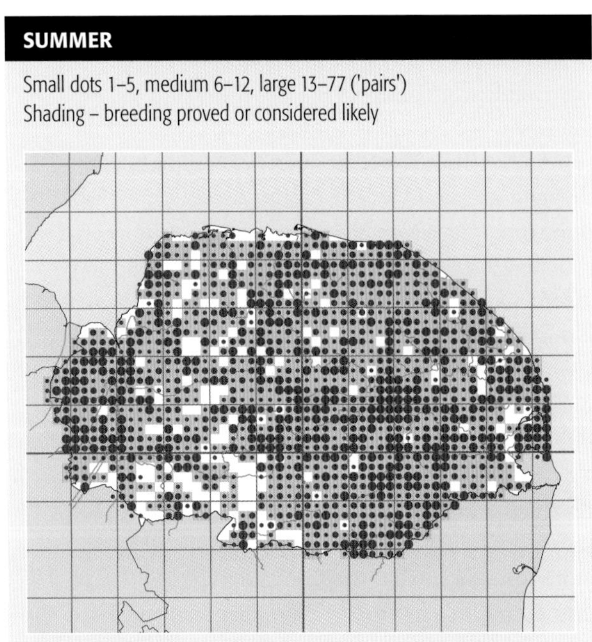

WINTER

Small dots 1–7, medium 8–22, large 23–547 (birds)

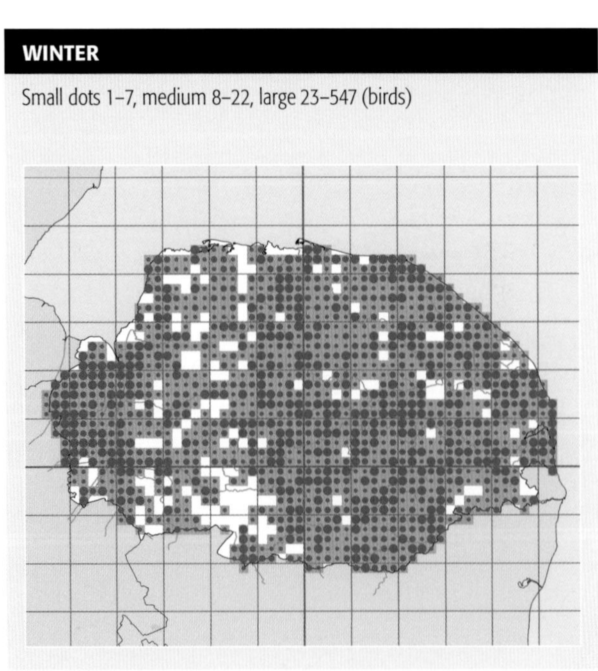

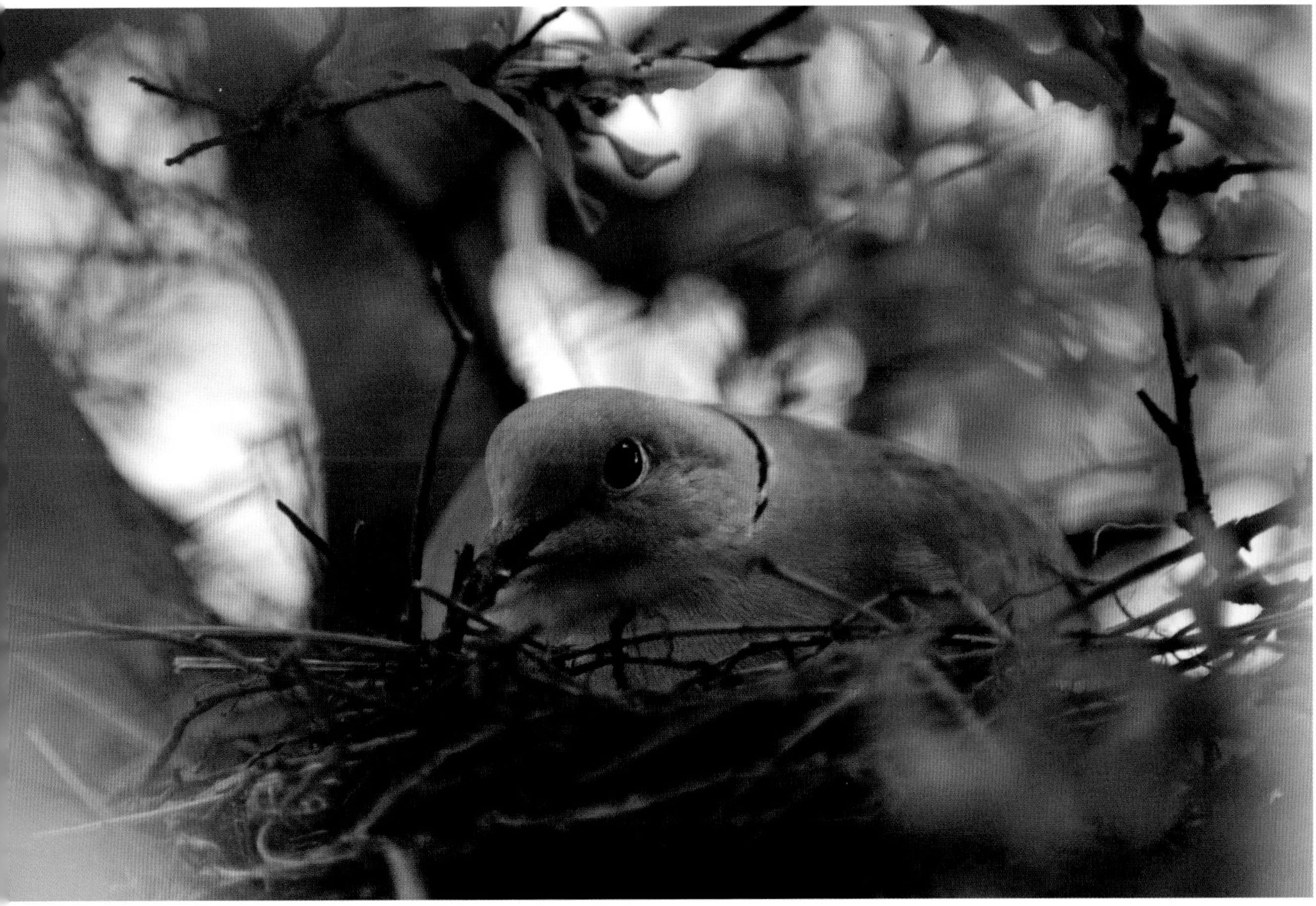

DAVID TIPLING

remain the favoured habitat and the highest number of breeding pairs in a single tetrad during the NBA summers included 77 at Cromer, 70 at King's Lynn, 68 at Mattishall and 67 at Wighton.

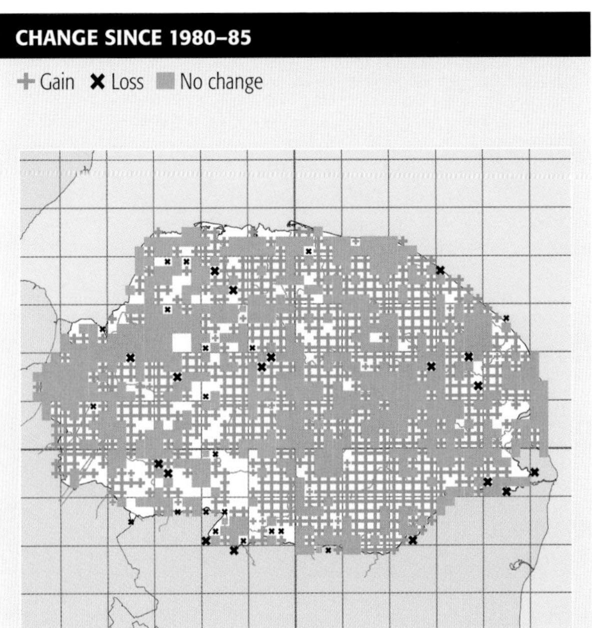

'Throughout the year, Collared Doves are closely associated with human habitation and are found in towns and villages...'

CHANGE SINCE 1980–85

+ Gain ✖ Loss ■ No change

For a species that is now largely resident, and has a breeding season that can be almost year-round, it is not surprising that the NBA winter and summer maps are almost identical. In winter, however, much larger numbers often gather where there is a plentiful supply of grain. The highest tetrad counts included 547 at Docking, 300 at King's Lynn Docks and 280 at West Walton Highway. Some gardens where seed is regularly put out also attract flocks of Collared Doves, and up to 61 were counted in just such a garden in Langham. Although they roost communally in winter in conifers, holly and thick ivy, sometimes in concentrations of several hundred, no such roosts were reported during the NBA winters.

Compared with the *1980–85 NBBS*, occupied tetrads rose by 82%. The change map shows that Collared Doves were recorded in many of the more rural areas of the county from which they had been absent in the early 1980s.

Turtle Dove
Streptopelia turtur

NBA 1999–2007	SUMMER: ALL / BREEDING	WINTER
TETRADS OCCUPIED	781 (54%) / 704 (48%)	1 (<1%)
SUMMER/WINTER ONLY	781	1
MEAN PER OCCUPIED TETRAD	2 / 2	1
SUMMED MAX COUNTS	1,787 / 1,688	1
POPULATION ESTIMATE	1,200-1,800 bp	0–1

PREVIOUS ATLASES	SQUARES OCCUPIED	1999–2007	LOSSES	GAINS
1968–72 (10 KM)	62 (all)	61 (98%)	1	0
1980–85 (TETRAD)	1,161 (80%)	704 (48%)	555	98
1980–85 (10 KM)	62 (all)	61 (98%)	1	0
1981–84 WINTER (10 KM)	1 (2%)	1 (2%)	1	1
1988–91 (10 KM)	61 (98%)	61 (98%)	1	1

THE TURTLE DOVE is the smallest dove that breeds in Britain and the only one that is a summer visitor, spending the winter in Africa south of the Sahara.

Both its British range and breeding population have fluctuated widely during the last two centuries, related in part to changes in agricultural practices. In recent years, a widespread decline has taken place across Europe, due to factors that have also included drought in the winter quarters and heavy shooting of migrants around the Mediterranean. It has been estimated, for example, that around 100,000 Turtle Doves are shot annually in Malta. In England, a massive 84% decline was charted in the 25 years leading up to 2007 (*Birdtrends*).

The range has never extended to northern or western Britain and is now withdrawing towards the southeast, thus heightening the national importance of the Norfolk population. As Turtle Doves feed almost exclusively on weed seeds, most are found in the more varied, arable parts of the county.

The NBA summer map clearly shows that Turtle Doves are now very patchily distributed across the county. Of particular interest is the clear concentration around Harleston, part of a wider area of continuous occupation across southeast Norfolk. Of the ten tetrads in Norfolk that held ten or more breeding pairs of Turtle Doves, six were in the 10-km square TM28. The most favoured were near Denton (17 pairs) and at Alburgh (13 pairs).

Turtle Doves are birds of arable farmland with overgrown hedgerows, thickets and scrub, and to a lesser extent open woodland and large gardens. Breeding pairs

SUMMER

Small dots 1, medium 2–3, large 4–17 ('pairs')
Shading – breeding proved or considered likely

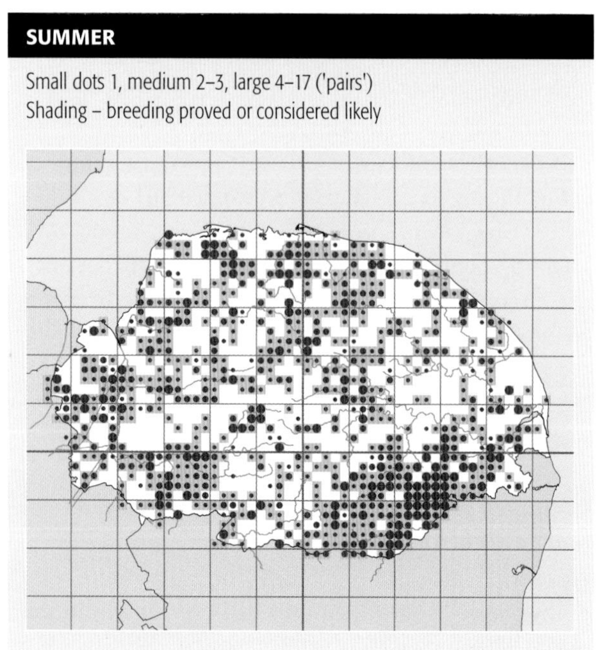

CHANGE SINCE 1980–85

+ Gain ✖ Loss ■ No change

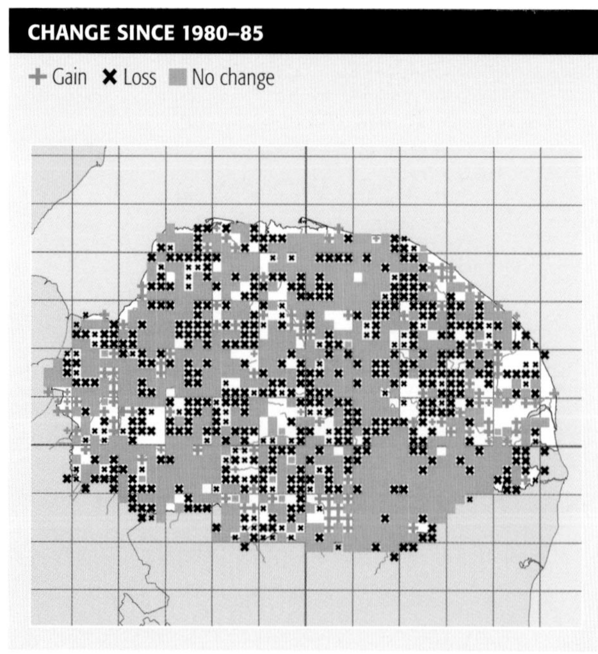

DAVID TIPLING

were also recorded in young conifer plantations while, in the Fens, young deciduous plantations also proved attractive. They tend to avoid breeding in or near towns or villages, and this is apparent from the lack of occupied tetrads in the Norwich, King's Lynn, Great Yarmouth and Thetford areas.

Turtle Doves are easily located by their distinctive purring song, so characteristic of a warm summer's day, and it is unlikely that many breeding pairs were missed during the NBA survey. Observers in several parts of the county commented on the noticeable decline in numbers as the NBA survey progressed, particularly in Broadland and the northern half of the county. Despite this, some impressive counts of breeding pairs were made including 30–40 pairs along the Methwold Cut-off Channel, up to 15 pairs in the Great Ryburgh area, 12 pairs at Welney, 11 pairs at Sandringham and ten pairs within a five-mile radius of Docking.

'As Turtle Doves feed almost exclusively on weed seeds, most are found in the more varied, arable parts of the county.'

Most Turtle Doves have left Norfolk by early October, but a first-winter bird was present at Ormesby in December 2001, the seventh midwinter record for the county.

Little change in range is evident by comparing the distributions since 1968–72 at the 10-km level. The change map, however, shows how gaps in the tetrad distribution have appeared almost everywhere except southeast Norfolk since the *1980–85 NBBS*, with a net loss of 40% of the tetrads then occupied by the species.

Cuckoo
Cuculus canorus

NBA 1999–2007	SUMMER: ALL / BREEDING	WINTER
TETRADS OCCUPIED	780 (53%) / 650 (45%)	none
SUMMER/WINTER ONLY	780	none
MEAN PER OCCUPIED TETRAD	1 / 2	none
SUMMED MAX COUNTS	1,118 / 981	none
POPULATION ESTIMATE	300–400 singing males	none

PREVIOUS ATLASES	SQUARES OCCUPIED	1999–2007	LOSSES	GAINS
1968–72 (10 KM)	62 (all)	62 (all)		
1980–85 (TETRAD)	1,081 (74%)	650 (45%)	552	121
1980–85 (10 KM)	62 (all)	62 (all)		
1988–91 (10 KM)	62 (all)	62 (all)		

CUCKOOS ARE POPULAR birds, widely welcomed as harbingers of spring, despite their breeding habits, perhaps off-putting to more delicate sensibilities, of nest parasitism on small songbirds, They occupy a wide range of habitats including farmland, forest, heathland, wetlands and coastal dunes, avoiding only the more built-up areas. In Britain, the three main host species are Meadow Pipit, Dunnock and Reed Warbler, and these are the species that are most often parasitised in Norfolk.

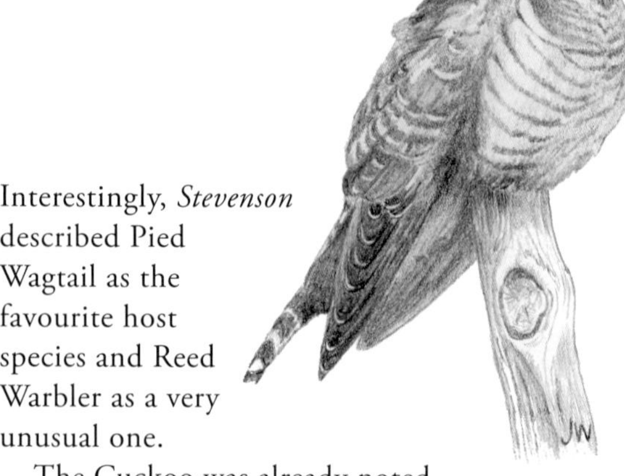

Interestingly, *Stevenson* described Pied Wagtail as the favourite host species and Reed Warbler as a very unusual one.

The Cuckoo was already noted as being in decline in Norfolk in the 1960s but, during 1982–2007, roughly equating to the period between the *1980–85 NBBS* and the close of NBA, a further 62% decline had been recorded across England as a whole (*Birdtrends*) and the species had been added to the UK red list of birds of conservation concern *(BoCC3)*.

The NBA summer map shows that the Cuckoo remained widely distributed through the county, although with substantial gaps where the Cuckoo's familiar call was not noted during any of the eight summers. The highest tetrad counts concerned seven singing males near Denton, and six at two sites in the Brecks and one in Broadland. Breckland appeared to be the most widely and densely occupied region of the county.

SUMMER

Small dots 1, medium 2, large 3–7 ('pairs')
Shading – breeding proved or considered likely

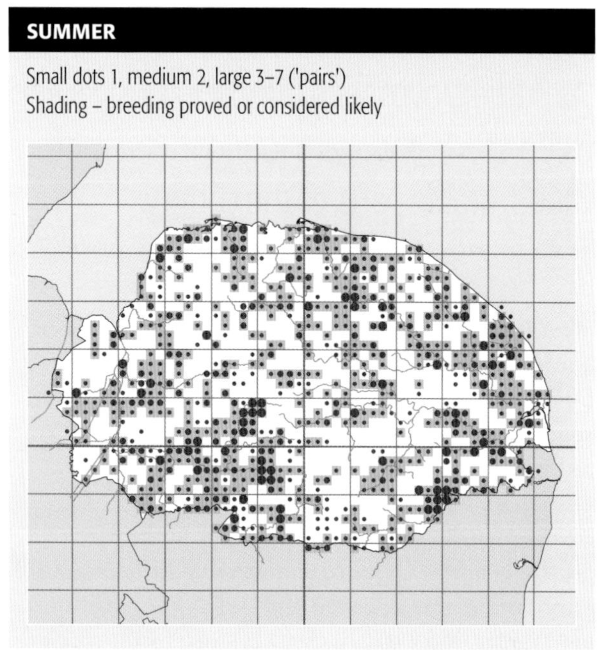

CHANGE SINCE 1980–85

+ Gain ✖ Loss ■ No change

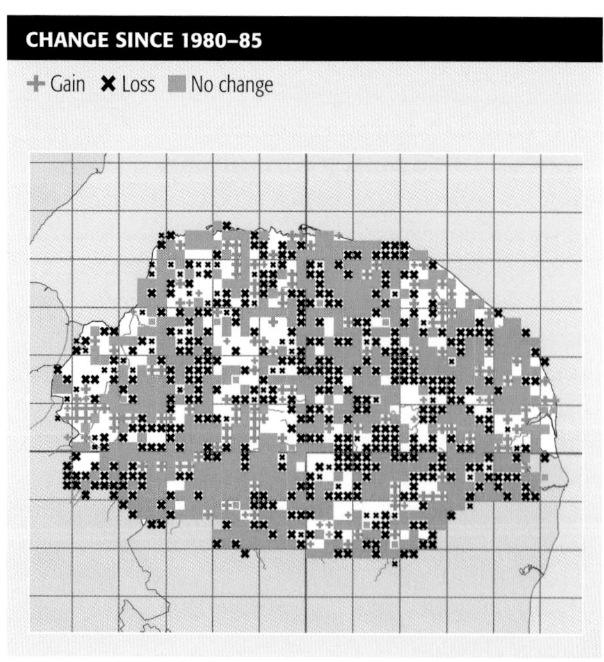

CHRIS KNIGHTS

For such a vocal and well-known species, it is unlikely that many occupied tetrads were missed. However, some of the NBA records may well have referred to migrating Cuckoos rather than to breeding birds: ten different migrants were recorded at Winterton, for example, during spring 2006. Much duplication of individual birds is likely between tetrads, especially as the territories occupied by breeding males can be very large, and females may well visit more than one tetrad in the hunt for potential hosts. It seems that the Norfolk population may have fallen to as low as 300 territorial males by the end of the NBA period. The species seemed especially scarce on farmland, while maintaining its numbers rather better in wetland areas, where Reed Warblers were available as a host, and in forest.

The rufous or hepatic morph of the female Cuckoo is rare but three were reported during the NBA summers, one of which remained in the North Wootton area for most of the 2005 summer.

'It seems that the Norfolk population may have fallen to as low as 300 territorial males by the end of the NBA period.'

The change map highlights the gaps in distribution that have opened up in the tetrad distribution since the *1980–85 NBBS*. These may tend to be areas of more open farmland, where potential host species are scarce. A few areas have apparently been colonised, including a substantial one in the Fens. Reed Warblers are available as hosts in these Fenland tetrads, but this is not an area to which Reed Warblers have spread since 1980–85.

Barn Owl
Tyto alba

NBA 1999–2007	SUMMER: ALL/BREEDING	WINTER
TETRADS OCCUPIED	716 (49%) / 568 (39%)	649 (44%)
SUMMER/WINTER ONLY	262	195
MEAN PER OCCUPIED TETRAD	1 / 1	1
SUMMED MAX COUNTS	896 / 746	927
POPULATION ESTIMATE	400–600 bp	1,000–1,500

PREVIOUS ATLASES	SQUARES OCCUPIED	1999–2007	LOSSES	GAINS
1968–72 (10 KM)	61 (98%)	60 (97%)	2	1
1980–85 (TETRAD)	340 (23%)	568 (39%)	194	422
1980–85 (10 KM)	58 (94%)	60 (97%)	2	4
1981–84 WINTER (10 KM)	54 (87%)	62 (all)	0	8
1988–91 (10 KM)	50 (81%)	60 (97%)	1	11

NORFOLK HAS PROBABLY long had one of the highest breeding populations of Barn Owls in Britain but, nevertheless, the county population appears to have increased strongly in recent years. The Barn Owl is currently a familiar bird almost throughout the county, often seen hunting at dawn and dusk along roadside verges or over farmland meadows.

Both the range and numbers of breeding Barn Owls have been in a long-term decline since the 19th century as a result of more intensive farming methods, loss of habitat and during the 1950s and 1960s the use of toxic organochlorine chemicals. In the last few decades, however, there are indications that there has been an upturn in the species' fortunes, aided by nestbox schemes and by more sympathetic farmland management, and Barn Owls are now reappearing in many areas where they had formerly been common.

DAVID TIPLING

The Barn Owl is primarily a species of open farmland, where meadows, rough grassland, hedges, banks and ditches provide cover for the small mammals, such as mice, small voles and shrews, on which they mainly feed. They nest in old barns, derelict buildings, haystacks and in hollows in trees, and in recent years in the many nest boxes that are now provided for them. Traditionally the highest natural densities have been found on country estates with lightly grazed parkland and plenty of mature trees with suitable cavities for nesting. Although Barn Owls mostly avoid towns and larger villages, a pair did nest in a church in the centre of Great Yarmouth in 2002.

The NBA summer map reveals a clear-cut pattern of distribution, with an abundance of occupied tetrads in the northern and central parts of the county, in the southwest, in Broadland and in the far southeast. There appear to be few pairs in and around the outskirts of Norwich, and in the more wooded areas to the northwest of the city around Attlebridge and Felthorpe. Barn Owls were also unrecorded from the upper Waveney and Little Ouse valleys, including Thetford Forest, an area north of Attleborough, and the King's Lynn area.

Barn Owls are not easy to survey during the summer months, unless specific dawn or dusk visits are undertaken to look for them. However, many breeding records were received from the Northwest Norfolk Ringing Group, who have advanced an intensive programme of ringing Barn Owl nestlings, and may be responsible, at least in part, for the wider distribution of records across the northern half of the county. Also, landowners and farmers are usually very proud to host nesting pairs on their land, and are happy to pass on this information, while the discovery of fresh Barn Owl pellets at a roost site in a barn or below a hollow tree will also confirm their presence.

Barn Owls are sedentary birds, pairs often remaining together throughout the year, although young birds tend to disperse a short distance from their natal areas. The NBA winter map shows a very similar distribution to that in the summer, suggesting that the possible observer bias has rather little effect on the summer map. Similar areas of absence are apparent on both maps, but there may be a tendency in winter for more tetrads to be occupied at the coast and along the river valleys.

In winter, the north Norfolk coastal marshes prove particularly attractive to hunting Barn Owls, where they may be seen at any time of the day. Up to seven or eight were recorded on occasion at Holme and Holkham GM, while a maximum of 13 was recorded on one day at Choseley. Roadside verges are especially favoured during the winter months and up to nine were counted along the A148 between Holt and King's Lynn early one morning and a similar number by the Fakenham to Themelthorpe road. Unfortunately, many Barn Owls are killed by traffic, and this cause of death accounts for a high proportion of the one- to two-thirds of fledged young that die during their first winter. Barn Owls are also very susceptible to severe winter weather, when snow cover, high winds and heavy rain can curtail hunting. It is often during periods of colder weather that the greatest numbers of Barn Owls are seen over the unfrozen coastal marshes.

Atlas comparisons give an indication of the extent of population recovery since the 1980s, but suggest little change between the *1968–72 Atlas* and NBA. In the *1980–85 NBBS* only 23% of the county's tetrads were occupied, compared with 39% where breeding was at least considered likely during NBA summer fieldwork, and Barn Owls were absent from 12 of the 10-km squares in the *1988–91 Atlas* but from only two during the NBA summers, a remarkable recovery over 10–15 years. Part of this may well have been due to the provision of nest boxes in barns and on trees and poles, especially in the Fens, Broadland and in many other farmland areas. This project, promoted by the Hawk and Owl Trust, has helped to offset the loss of potential nesting sites through barn conversions, and the demolition of old buildings and of disused windpumps, which were frequently utilised by breeding pairs in wetland areas.

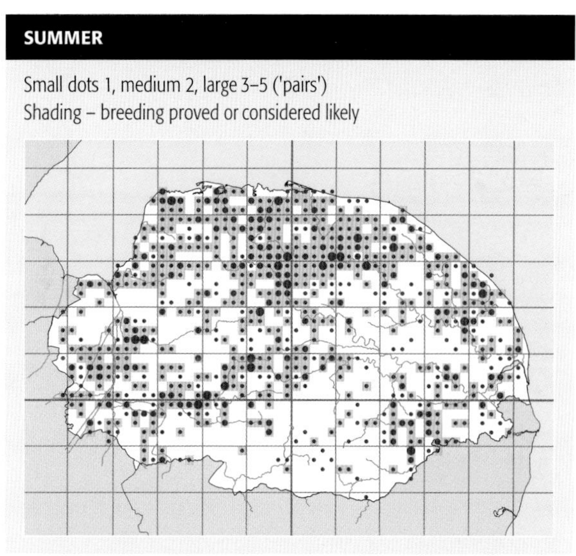

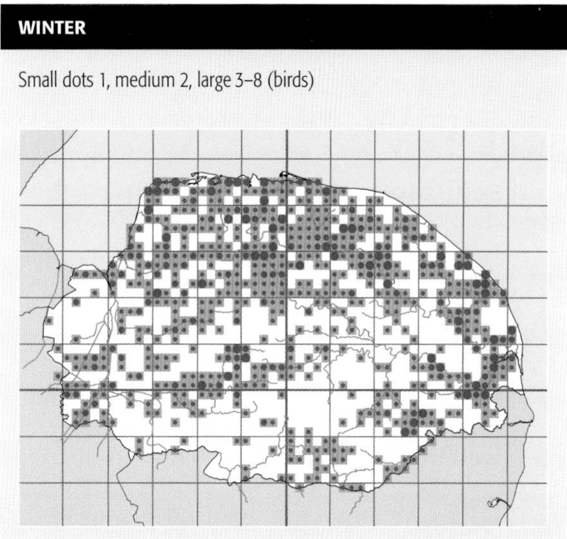

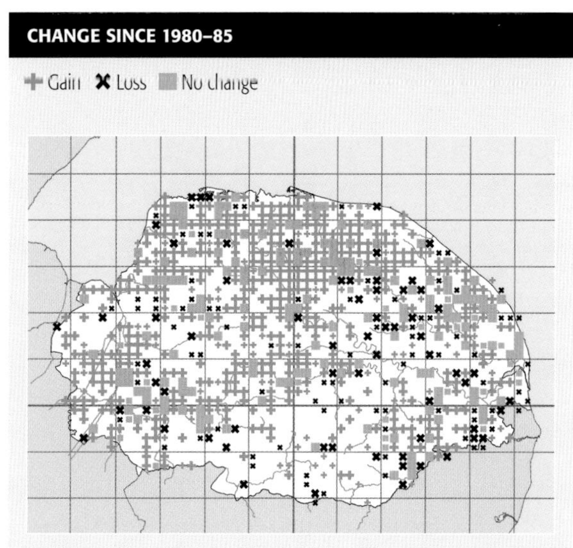

Little Owl
Athene noctua

NBA 1999–2007	SUMMER: ALL/BREEDING	WINTER
TETRADS OCCUPIED	387 (27%) / 324 (22%)	224 (15%)
SUMMER/WINTER ONLY	265	102
MEAN PER OCCUPIED TETRAD	1 / 1	1
SUMMED MAX COUNTS	476 / 413	305
POPULATION ESTIMATE	400–500 bp	900–1,200

PREVIOUS ATLASES	SQUARES OCCUPIED	1999–2007	LOSSES	GAINS
1968–72 (10 KM)	60 (97%)	56 (90%)	6	2
1980–85 (TETRAD)	227 (16%)	324 (22%)	156	253
1980–85 (10 KM)	54 (87%)	56 (90%)	4	6
1981–84 WINTER (10 KM)	38 (61%)	56 (90%)	1	19
1988–91 (10 KM)	45 (73%)	56 (90%)	1	12

THE LITTLE OWL IS the smallest owl that breeds in Britain but, as a result of its loud calls and habit of perching in the open during the day and especially at dusk, is perhaps the easiest to survey. The presence of Little Owls, even if not detected by NBA fieldworkers, was often known to farmers or gamekeepers.

Little Owls are characteristic birds of the agricultural countryside, particularly where hedges and mature trees are a feature, as well as of old orchards and parkland. They generally nest in hollow, deciduous trees or old farm buildings, but where these are not present will utilise old rabbit holes.

The species was brought to Britain in the late 19th century through a series of introductions in various counties. The British population probably peaked in the early 1950s. Many large insects on which they feed have since declined, and this, combined with the loss of nest sites as hedgerows and their associated mature trees were removed, and an increase in road mortality as traffic became heavier, may have brought about the Little Owl's current shallow decline.

The NBA summer map shows a rather sparse but well-scattered distribution with a distinct clustering of occupied tetrads in southeast Norfolk, where much of the old wood–pasture landscape is retained. In the Fens, Little Owls nest in pollarded willows and probably thrive in this area due to the scarcity of Tawny Owls,

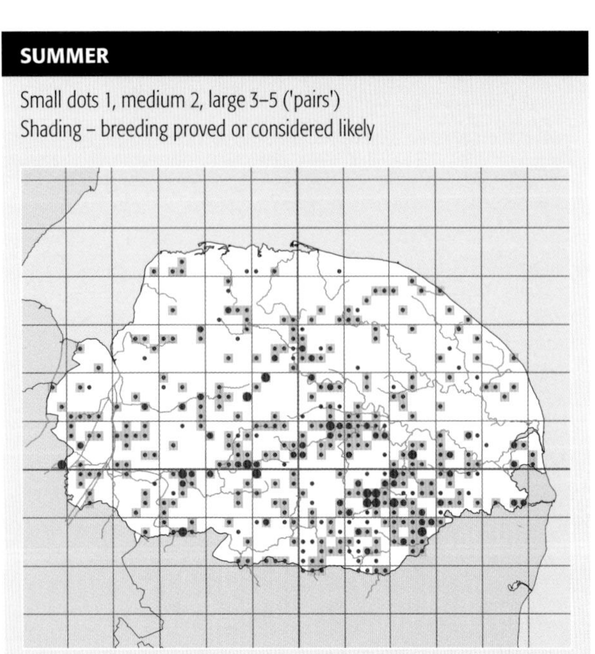

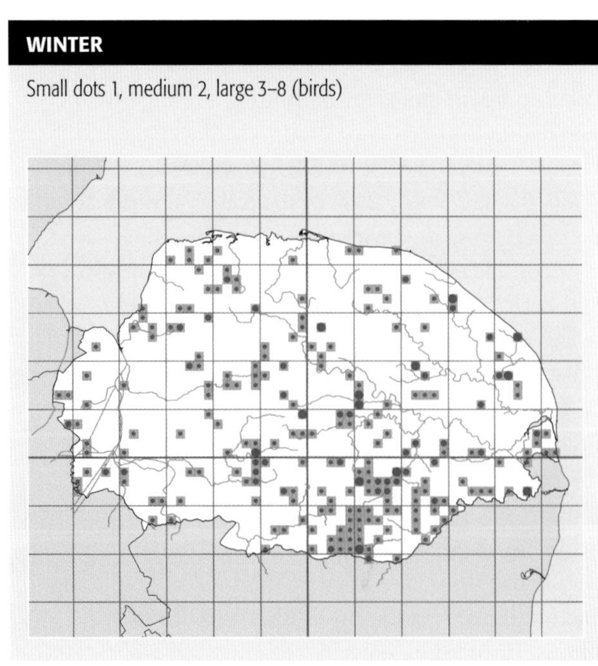

DAVID TIPLING

which might otherwise take them as prey. The species remains absent from much apparently suitable habitat in the north and east of the county. Three Norfolk tetrads held five breeding pairs each, although on average only a single pair was detected in each occupied tetrad.

'The species remains absent from much apparently suitable habitat in the north and east of the county.'

CHANGE SINCE 1980–85

+ Gain ✖ Loss ■ No change

As Little Owls are sedentary and many remain as pairs within their territories throughout the year, it is not surprising that the NBA winter map shows a similar, if less widespread, distribution as that in the summer, again with a concentration of occupied tetrads in southeast Norfolk. It appears that, despite the lack of foliage on hedgerow trees, Little Owls are less easily located in winter, perhaps because they call less or or active less often during daylight. A maximum of eight Little Owls was found in two tetrads in winter, at Hainford and near Foulsham.

Just two Norfolk 10-km squares were unoccupied during the *1968–72 Atlas*, but this figure had risen to 17 by 1988–91. Since the *1980–85 NBBS*, however, a clear range expansion has been noted in Norfolk at tetrad level, despite the decline of 39% that took place in England as a whole during 1982–2007 (*Birdtrends*). The change map indicates that gains have been concentrated in central and particularly in southeastern areas of the county.

Tawny Owl
Strix aluco

NBA 1999–2007	SUMMER: ALL/BREEDING	WINTER
TETRADS OCCUPIED	552 (38%) / 526 (36%)	379 (26%)
SUMMER/WINTER ONLY	317	144
MEAN PER OCCUPIED TETRAD	1 / 1	2
SUMMED MAX COUNTS	769 / 743	619
POPULATION ESTIMATE	900–1,200 bp	2,000–2,500

PREVIOUS ATLASES	SQUARES OCCUPIED	1999–2007	LOSSES	GAINS
1968–72 (10 KM)	62 (all)	60 (97%)	2	0
1980–85 (TETRAD)	578 (40%)	526 (36%)	320	268
1980–85 (10 KM)	59 (95%)	60 (97%)	1	2
1981–84 WINTER (10 KM)	51 (82%)	60 (97%)	1	10
1988–91 (10 KM)	58 (94%)	60 (97%)	1	3

THE TAWNY OWL, with its well-known wavering hoot, is by far the most common breeding owl in Britain, and retains this status in Norfolk despite the rise of the Barn Owl, which NBA data indicate is the most widespread of the county's owls.

During the 19th century, Tawny Owls were heavily persecuted and as a result numbers declined markedly, to such an extent in Norfolk that *Stevenson*, writing in the 1860s, described it as

'extremely scarce'. From the start of the 20th century to about 1930, the British population recovered, since when it has remained fairly stable.

Tawny Owls typically inhabit deciduous or mixed woodland, nesting mainly in holes in mature trees. They are also found in mature coniferous woods, a habitat generally lacking in holes large enough for nesting and so they occasionally nest on the ground in such situations. Pairs will also breed in farmland trees, in churchyards, parks and large gardens, even in urban environments, and take well to specially designed nest boxes.

The NBA summer map shows a widespread distribution throughout the county, not confined solely to those parts with extensive woodlands. Birds were absent, however, from the more open, treeless parts of such area as the Fens and Halvergate Marshes, and apparently also from other areas throughout the county where the habitat was seemed suitable. Tawny Owls are not easily located by day unless attention is drawn to the presence

SUMMER

Small dots 1, medium 2, large 3–6 ('pairs')
Shading – breeding proved or considered likely

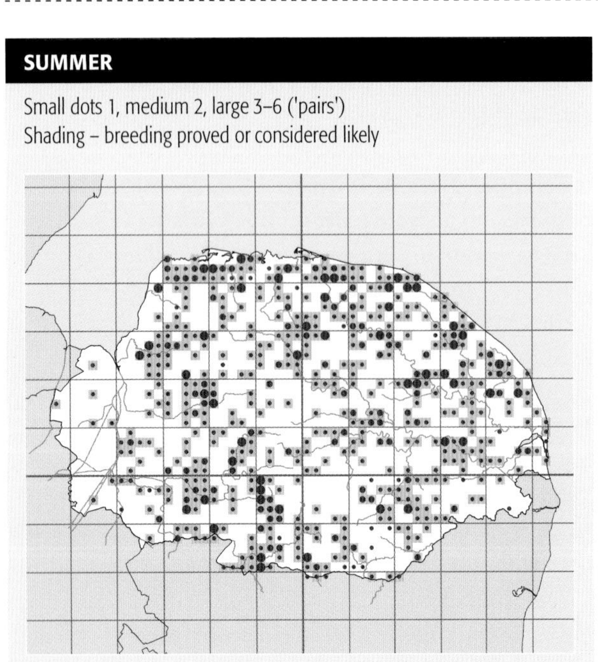

WINTER

Small dots 1, medium 2, large 3–7 (birds)

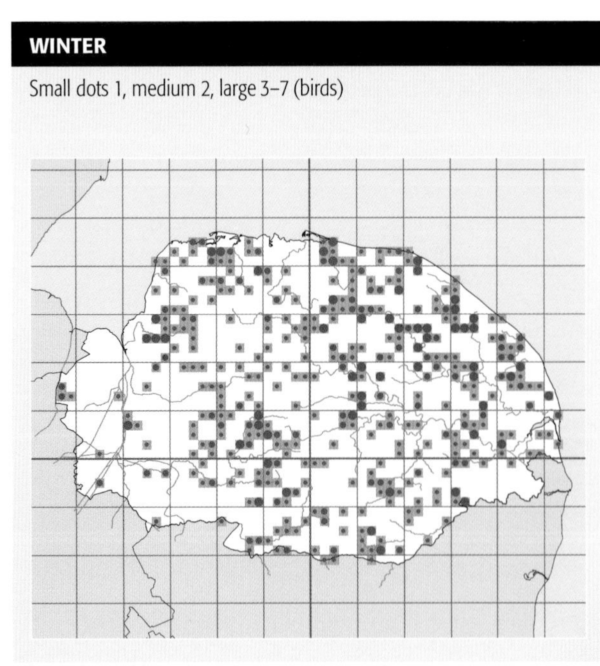

DAVID TIPLING

of a roosting bird by the mobbing calls of other smaller birds, often led by Blackbirds or Jays, or by the husky begging calls of young fledglings. Tawny Owls are most vocal in October and November, when pairs are formed and the young of the year are seeking new territory, but this falls outside both the winter and summer recording periods for the NBA. Only a small proportion of tetrads received specific extra visits at night. Thus, for this species, many occupied tetrads could easily have been missed.

CHANGE SINCE 1980–85

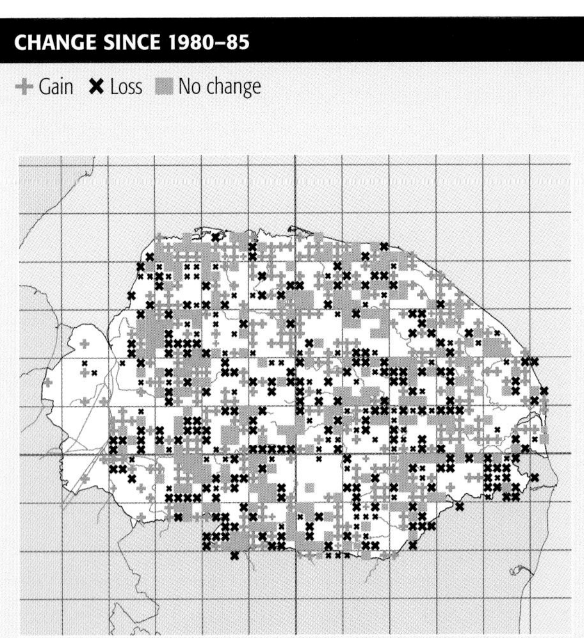

The highest tetrad counts during the years of NBA fieldwork were six pairs at Houghton and five each at Swanton Novers, Thornage and Glandford, while a maximum of eight calling males was located on the Brancaster Thompson Farms, all five localities being in the northern part of the county. Estimating the breeding population in Norfolk is not easy but, given that almost 750 pairs were located, according to the tetrad totals, about 1,000 pairs seems probable.

Tawny Owls are sedentary birds, remaining in pairs throughout the year and staying within their territories at all seasons. The NBA winter survey suffered from the same problems, of the species' low detectability, as in the summer. The distribution on the winter map is very similar to that in summer, however, as would be expected, although many fewer occupied tetrads were identified in the winter season. The highest tetrad counts in winter were of seven at Buckenham and six each at Foulsham, Honing and Forncett St Peter.

The change map suggests a very substantial turnover of occupied tetrads between the *1980–85 NBBS* and NBA, involving more than half of the total tetrads found to be occupied in one or other survey. Both surveys show a broadly similar overall pattern, however. It is entirely possible that no real change occurred between the surveys and that most of the tetrads that were found to be occupied in one or other survey were in fact occupied in both.

Long-eared Owl
Asio otus

NBA 1999–2007	SUMMER: ALL / BREEDING	WINTER
TETRADS OCCUPIED	68 (5%) / 23 (2%)	37 (3%)
SUMMER/WINTER ONLY	52	21
MEAN PER OCCUPIED TETRAD	1 / 1	1
SUMMED MAX COUNTS	69 / 24	48
POPULATION ESTIMATE	30–50 bp	80–150

PREVIOUS ATLASES	SQUARES OCCUPIED	1999–2007	LOSSES	GAINS
1968–72 (10 KM)	22 (35%)	14 (23%)	16	8
1980–85 (TETRAD)	76 (5%)	23 (2%)	63	10
1980–85 (10 KM)	30 (48%)	14 (23%)	18	2
1981–84 WINTER (10 KM)	8 (13%)	22 (35%)	3	17
1988–91 (10 KM)	15 (24%)	14 (23%)	8	7

THE LONG-EARED OWL is one of the county's most elusive breeding birds, being very easily overlooked, despite occasionally hunting by day. Winter visitors to Britain from northern and eastern Europe appear to be in strong decline.

The British breeding population increased during the 19th century as more conifer plantations became established, and may also have benefited from the persecution of Tawny Owls. However, Long-eared Owl began to decline during the 20th century as the Tawny Owl population recovered. It is of interest that in Ireland, where Tawny Owls are absent, Long-eared Owls appear to take their place, especially in deciduous woodland.

In Norfolk, Long-eared Owls are birds of coniferous woodland, often isolated, mature plantations near to open areas of grassland or farmland, where the adults can hunt small mammals at night (Kemp 1981). Their nests, which are usually the old stick nests of Carrion Crows, are also found in tall, overgrown hedges and hawthorn or elder scrub. They avoid nesting near human habitation or by busy roads or railways. An incubating female will sit tightly and her mate will often roost against the trunk of a nearby tree, but both rely on concealment and neither is easily flushed. Adults are also far less vocal than Tawny Owls, although the species' triple hoot and wing-clapping are very distinctive, while young birds draw attention to themselves by their penetrating, 'rusty hinge' calls. It remains exceptionally difficult to locate pairs of breeding Long-eared Owls,

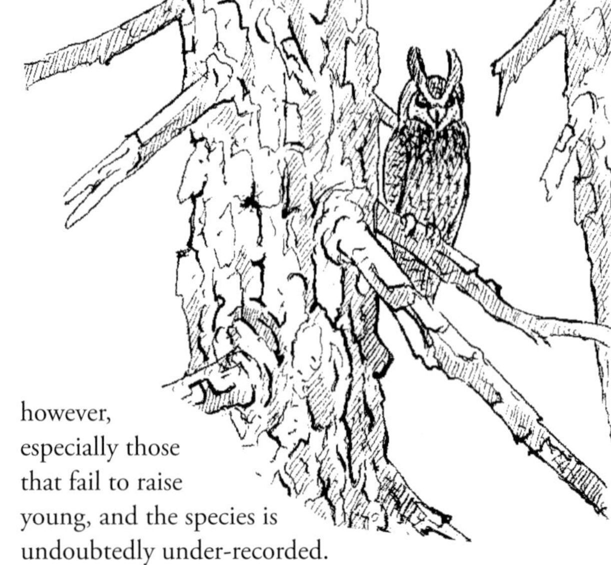

however, especially those that fail to raise young, and the species is undoubtedly under-recorded.

The summer map shows a very sparse and scattered distribution with a definite westerly bias to the records. Breckland, with its numerous mature conifer plantations, has always been the stronghold of the species in the county. NBA shows this, as did the *1980–85 NBBS*, although then the records from west Norfolk were enhanced by a breeding Long-eared Owl survey that was carried out over a three-year period (Kemp 1981, 1982). There can be little doubt that Long-eared Owls are more numerous and widespread than is suggested by the NBA summer map, as comparatively few observers visited their tetrads specifically to search for crepuscular and nocturnal species. Many of the coastal records, however, referred to migrants in April.

Although Tawny Owls are abundant in Breckland, where Long-eareds are most often detected, there may be a tendency for Long-eared Owls to avoid the presence of this more powerful and aggressive species by choosing sites with good access to open habitat suitable for hunting on the wing.

Long-eared Owls in Britain are resident, the adults often remaining within their breeding territories throughout the year and starting to call and wing-clap in February. Autumn migrants from Fenno-Scandia enhance the wintering population. The majority of records shown on the NBA winter map refer to birds that were discovered roosting, and even fewer were reported than during the summer survey. Through the entire NBA period, only six Long-eared Owls were found during winter set visits, the vast majority of occupied tetrads being detected through supplementary records.

DAVID TIPLING

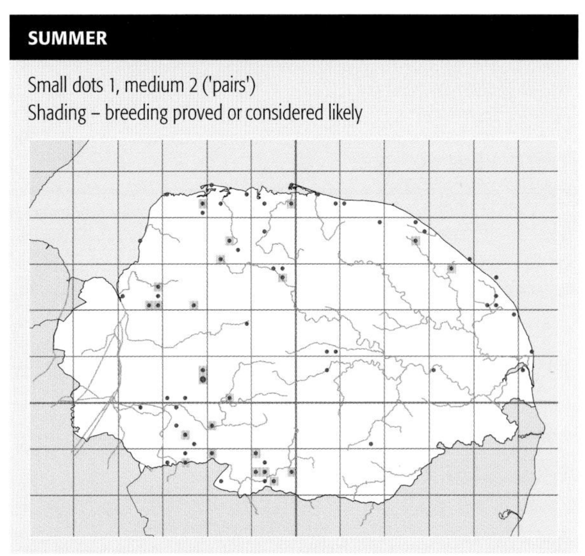

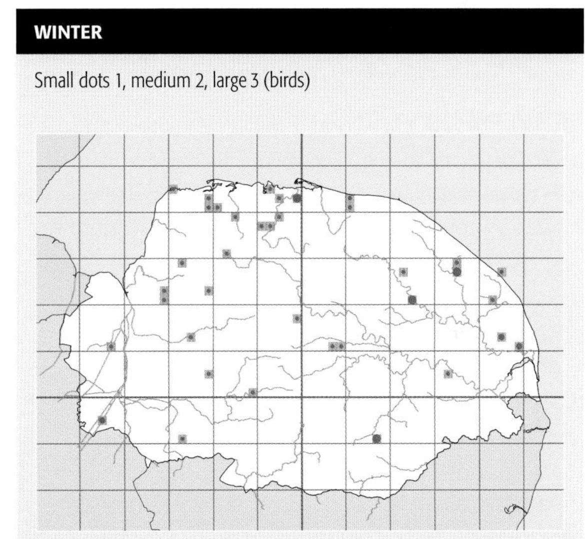

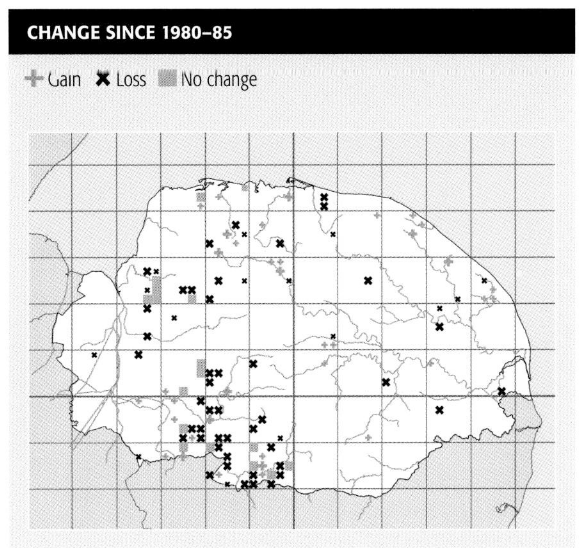

'Through the entire NBA period, only six Long-eared Owls were found during winter set visits...'

In winter, Long-eared Owls roost, sometimes communally, in thick hedgerows, in dense scrub or on ivy-covered trees, often overhanging water, and often at sites used each winter over a number of years. Nationally, many fewer such winter roosts are being located, and the trend appears to relate to a decline among winter visitors from the Continent. Nevertheless, the county's wintering population must be considerably higher than is suggested by the NBA map. A maximum of three Long-eared Owls roosting together was recorded at four sites during the NBA winters. This number may be significant as Kemp (1982) suggested that winter roosts might consist of family parties.

Comparison with the *1980–85 NBBS* suggests a reduction in tetrad occupancy. This may in part be a real trend, despite the difficulty of surveying this species and the shortage of reliable data.

Short-eared Owl

Asio flammeus

NBA 1999–2007	SUMMER: ALL / BREEDING	WINTER
TETRADS OCCUPIED	73 (5%) / 2 (<1%)	95 (7%)
SUMMER/WINTER ONLY	36	58
MEAN PER OCCUPIED TETRAD	1 / 1	2
SUMMED MAX COUNTS	76 / 2	185
POPULATION ESTIMATE	0–2 bp	20–40

PREVIOUS ATLASES	SQUARES OCCUPIED	1999–2007	LOSSES	GAINS
1968–72 (10 KM)	16 (26%)	2 (3%)	14	0
1980–85 (TETRAD)	33 (2%)	2 (<1%)	32	1
1980–85 (10 KM)	15 (24%)	2 (3%)	13	0
1981–84 WINTER (10 KM)	36 (58%)	30 (48%)	12	6
1988–91 (10 KM)	12 (19%)	2 (3%)	10	0

DESPITE FREQUENTLY BEING crepuscular in their habits, Short-eared Owls can be seen hunting at any time of day, especially during the winter months.

The species' main breeding range is in northern and eastern Europe, and in Britain it is a regular breeder only in upland areas. Both its range and population fluctuate in accordance with the abundance of the small mammals on which it mainly feeds.

Short-eared Owls bred regularly in north Norfolk and the Brecks from the 1930s and around the Wash from the 1960s, while an unprecedented 18 pairs were located at Hickling and Horsey in the summer of 1933 during a plague of short-tailed field voles *Microtus agrestis*.

Short-eared Owls are birds of open country, well populated with rodents and remote from human disturbance, where they both nest and roost on the ground. Extensive tracts of heathland and saltmarsh, and young forestry plantations, all provide suitable conditions for nesting.

During the NBA summers, breeding was proved only in 2005, when one pair bred at a site in northwest Norfolk and a second pair probably did so near the Wash. In 2002, single pairs were seen displaying at two other sites but each only on a single date. The NBA summer map shows that a large majority of the records made were of birds around the coast, with most of the inland sightings being in Broadland, including the Yare valley. Many of these reports would have involved lingering wintering birds or those on return passage to their northern European breeding areas.

SUMMER

Small dots 1, medium 2 ('pairs')
Shading – breeding proved or considered likely

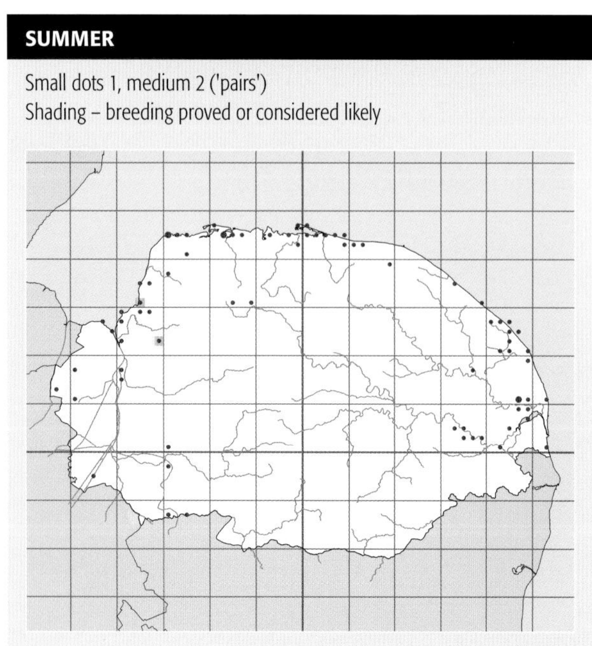

WINTER

Small dots 1, medium 2–3, large 4–6 (birds)

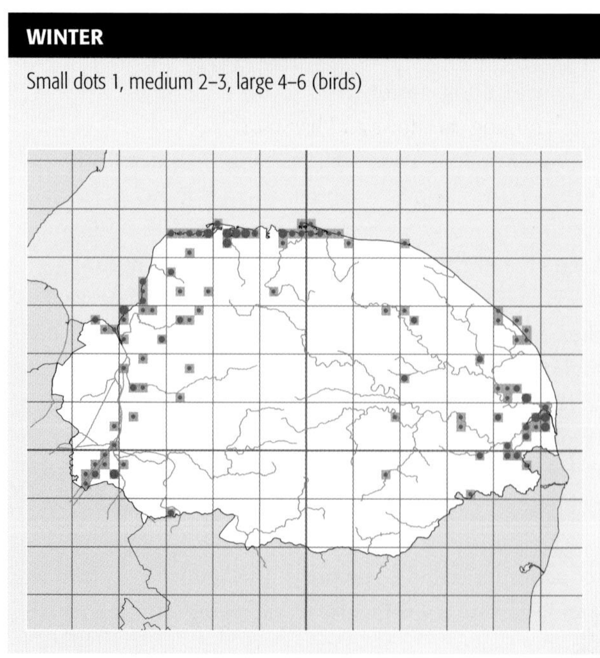

DAVID TIPLING

In winter, Short-eared Owls inhabit coastal saltmarshes, rough grazing meadows and harvested fields, where they hunt for small mammals. The NBA winter map shows that they are sparsely distributed but with more being recorded inland, particularly in the west of the county, than during the summer months. They are mainly solitary outside the breeding season, and the small concentrations in north Norfolk and around Breydon Water are related to small communal roosts, on salt and freshwater marshes. The Short-eared Owls that winter in Norfolk almost certainly include birds from both the British and Fenno-Scandian breeding populations.

Clearly the species has undergone a marked decline as a Norfolk breeding bird over the last 30–40 years. During the *1968–72 Atlas*, breeding was confirmed in nine 10-km squares, this figure falling to four during the *1980–85 NBBS*, only three in the *1988–91 Atlas*, and a maximum of two for NBA.

'During the NBA summers, breeding was proved only in 2005, when one pair bred at a site in northwest Norfolk and a second pair probably did so near the Wash.'

A winter decline has also occurred. No more than five or six birds were noted at any one site, which is a far cry from the numbers wintering in the Halvergate area in earlier years. For example, in the winter of 1964/65, two roosts contained a total of 80 Short-eared Owls, while on Christmas Eve 1972 no fewer than 116 were roosting alongside the Fleet Wall there, of which 80 were visible in the air together!

Nightjar

Caprimulgus europaeus

NBA 1999–2007	SUMMER: ALL / BREEDING	WINTER
TETRADS OCCUPIED	99 (7%) / 45 (3%)	none
SUMMER/WINTER ONLY	99	none
MEAN PER OCCUPIED TETRAD	2 / 3	none
SUMMED MAX COUNTS	198 / 144	none
POPULATION ESTIMATE	300–350 bp	none

PREVIOUS ATLASES	SQUARES OCCUPIED	1999–2007	LOSSES	GAINS
1968–72 (10 KM)	27 (44%)	21 (34%)	12	6
1980–85 (TETRAD)	59 (4%)	45 (3%)	38	24
1980–85 (10 KM)	20 (32%)	21 (34%)	5	6
1988–91 (10 KM)	15 (24%)	21 (34%)	3	9

BEING A CREPUSCULAR and nocturnal bird, the Nightjar has always been one of Britain's most enigmatic breeding species. Its peculiar churring song is evocative of warm, summer nights on open heathland.

Since about 1950, both the range and population of Nightjars in northwest Europe have declined, due to a combination of habitat loss, disturbance related to various leisure activities and the increasing use of pesticides that has resulted in a reduction in the large moths on which they primarily feed. In Britain, however, the population more than doubled between surveys in 1981 and 2004 (*Birdtrends*).

Nightjars favour dry, open habitats, such as heathland, commons, open coniferous and mixed woodland, and young forestry plantations. Such conditions are met on the Sandringham estate, along the Cromer to Holt ridge and in Breckland, the last area having been the county's stronghold for the species for at least the last 200 years. It is in these three areas that the main concentrations occurred during the NBA summers. In Breckland, in particular, the species has benefited from the spread of new clearings as the conifer plantations have reached the age for harvesting, and birds continue to utilise such areas for the first few years after replanting. The continuing importance of the Brecks for Nightjars was clearly demonstrated by the BTO survey in 2004, which found a total of 314 males in Norfolk, of which 190 were in Breckland. Most of the remainder were in northwest Norfolk, with smaller numbers along the Cromer to Holt ridge, and in central and east Norfolk. In the most favoured areas, up to 19 churring males were located in a single tetrad.

Nightjars winter in Africa south of the Sahara and the first returning birds are normally recorded during the first two weeks of May. There were two early records during the NBA period: at Cley on 30th April 2001 and Weybourne on 29th April 2003, only the second and third April records in recent years. Migration is at

DAVID TIPLING

SUMMER

Small dots 1, medium 2–3, large 4–19 ('pairs')
Shading – breeding proved or considered likely

'Nightjars favour dry, open habitats, such as heathland, commons, open coniferous and mixed woodland, and young forestry plantations.'

night and Nightjars are not often seen while migrating. Occasional birds were recorded at coastal sites, however, where breeding was clearly unlikely.

Comparison with previous atlas data indicates a more extensive distribution in 1968–72, followed by a retraction of range by 1988–91 and a subsequent partial recovery. The high degree of turnover in occupied tetrads between the *1980–85 NBBS* and the NBA is presumably related to forestry rotations, which can affect habitat suitability for Nightjars over substantial areas.

Common Swift
Apus apus

NBA 1999–2007	SUMMER: ALL/BREEDING	WINTER
TETRADS OCCUPIED	1,182 (81%) / 819 (56%)	2 (<1%)
SUMMER/WINTER ONLY	1,182	none
MEAN PER OCCUPIED TETRAD	11 / 13	1
SUMMED MAX COUNTS	13,199 / 10,448	2
POPULATION ESTIMATE	3,000–6,000 bp	none

PREVIOUS ATLASES	SQUARES OCCUPIED	1999–2007	LOSSES	GAINS
1968–72 (10 KM)	62 (all)	62 (all)		
1980–85 (TETRAD)	1,089 (75%)	819 (56%)	397	127
1980–85 (10 KM)	62 (all)	62 (all)		
1981–84 WINTER (10 KM)	none	2 (3%)	0	2
1988–91 (10 KM)	61 (98%)	62 (all)	0	1

THE COMMON SWIFT is the most widespread and most numerous member of its family in the western Palaearctic, and is the only one that breeds in northern Europe. Throughout its breeding range, all populations are migratory, European birds wintering in tropical Africa. Alerts have been raised over recent population decline in the UK, and the species has newly been amber listed as a species of conservation concern (*BoCC3*).

Swifts breed in colonies, usually containing no more than 30–40 pairs (*BWP4*), and the individual nest sites are normally under the tiles or eaves of older houses. The construction of modern housing often allows no access to nesting Swifts, while traditional sites may become inaccessible as older properties are re-roofed.

DAVID TIPLING

The NBA map shows a very wide distribution of Swifts in summer and of likely breeding. Breeding birds of this supremely aerial species range very widely, however, and may feed or even mate many miles from the nest. It is possible that some observers were overenthusiastic in recording breeding as 'likely', and did so even where the birds were unlikely to be nesting in the tetrads in which they were observed, thus making the pattern more difficult to interpret at tetrad level. Although the largest breeding colonies in Norfolk are in Norwich and in the towns and larger villages, few of these places stand out on the map. The highest counts were made mostly at places where Swifts were gathering to feed on flying insects or airborne spiders over the open countryside, or over areas of open water, such as gravel pits, flooded marshes, lakes, meres or Broads; large gatherings over water occurred especially during adverse weather conditions or when aquatic rather than terrestrial insects were emerging. Although breeding Swifts often feed fairly close to their colonies, they are frequently joined by non-breeding, prospecting birds two or three years old, which may inflate estimates of breeding pairs.

'Although breeding Swifts often feed fairly close to their colonies, they are frequently joined by non-breeding, prospecting birds two or three years old, which may inflate estimates of breeding pairs.'

SUMMER

Small dots 1–4, medium 5–10, large 11–250 ('pairs')
Shading – breeding proved or considered likely

During the NBA summers, few estimates were made of the actual number of breeding pairs of Swifts in specific towns or villages, but up to 30 pairs bred at Cley and Wighton, and a single house in Martham hosted 25 pairs in 2004. The earliest annual arrival date for a Swift in Norfolk was 6th April with the latest on 24th April, the average over the eight years being 17th April. In 2000, a Swift was present in the Brancaster Staithe/ Burnham Deepdale area between 1st and 4th December, only the second Norfolk December record.

Comparison with the *1980–85 NBBS* does not give any clear indication of whether any change in breeding range has occurred in Norfolk. Observers then may have been generous in assigning tetrads to the 'possible breeding' category. In view of its amber listing, however, this species would be a good candidate for future, carefully designed monitoring surveys at local or county level.

Kingfisher

Alcedo atthis

NBA 1999–2007	SUMMER: ALL/BREEDING	WINTER
TETRADS OCCUPIED	240 (16%) / 117 (8%)	272 (19%)
SUMMER/WINTER ONLY	115	147
MEAN PER OCCUPIED TETRAD	1 / 1	1
SUMMED MAX COUNTS	257 / 133	323
POPULATION ESTIMATE	100–150 bp	200–400

PREVIOUS ATLASES	SQUARES OCCUPIED	1999–2007	LOSSES	GAINS
1968–72 (10 KM)	52 (84%)	43 (69%)	14	5
1980–85 (TETRAD)	157 (11%)	117 (8%)	118	78
1980–85 (10 KM)	42 (68%)	43 (69%)	11	12
1981–84 WINTER (10 KM)	40 (65%)	57 (92%)	2	19
1988–91 (10 KM)	43 (69%)	43 (69%)	12	12

THE KINGFISHER'S DAZZLING electric-blue back and rump make it one of the most attractively plumaged of Britain's birds.

Marked fluctuations in its numbers occur due to its susceptibility to harsh winter weather and to its high breeding potential; it can also be adversely affected by water pollution caused by agricultural run-off or industrial contamination. Straightening the meandering courses of rivers and the grading of river banks are also detrimental to Kingfisher populations, since they remove safe breeding sites.

In the breeding season, Kingfishers favour relatively shallow, still or slow-moving fresh water, providing a plentiful supply of small fish, suitable lookout perches and banks in which they can excavate their nesting cavities. Such conditions are found along streams and small rivers, and at lakes, flooded gravel pits, Breckland meres and around the edges of the Broads. Kingfishers sometimes nest several hundred metres away from water, thus needing to fly over fields and even through woodland to reach suitable feeding areas. As well as freshwater habitats, they also utilise brackish and salt water in winter, particularly if severe weather results in freezing conditions inland.

SUMMER

Small dots 1, medium 2, large 3 ('pairs')
Shading – breeding proved or considered likely

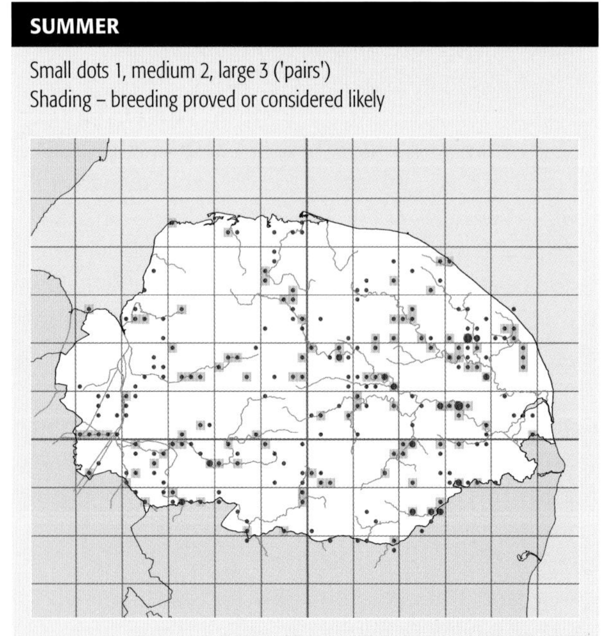

WINTER

Small dots 1, medium 2, large 3–4 (birds)

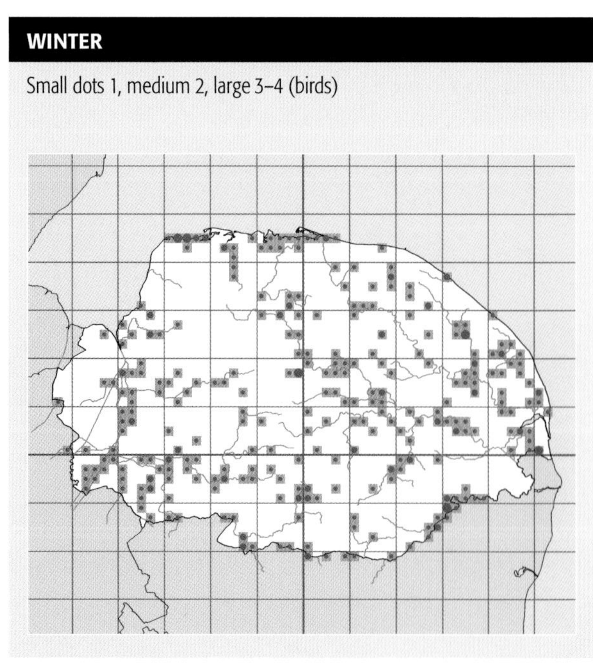

DAVID TIPLING

The NBA summer map shows a mainly linear distribution of occupied tetrads, with concentrations of records in Broadland and along the courses of many of the county's rivers, in particular the Rivers Bure, Yare and Waveney in the east, and the Little Ouse, Great Ouse, Nar and Wissey in the west. They were absent from the dry arable, forested and heathland areas of the county, including large sections of northwest Norfolk.

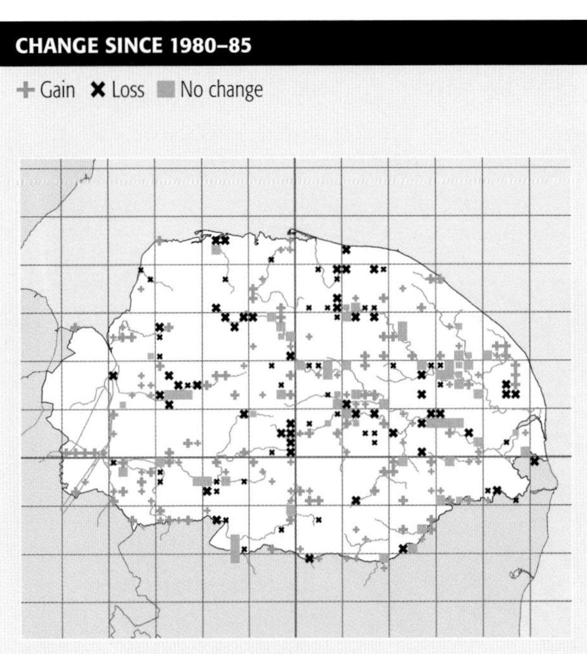

Although so bright, the plumage can be surprisingly cryptic in shade, and Kingfishers are not always easy to locate. Some breeding pairs may have been entirely missed during the NBA summer surveys but, conversely, others may have been observed in more than one tetrad. In two tetrads, at Strumpshaw and Neatishead, three pairs of Kingfishers were recorded, with two pairs in 13 tetrads and just one in the remaining occupied tetrads, some of which would have involved birds that were actually breeding in adjacent squares. Some non-breeding adults or young of the year may also have been encountered.

Whereas adult Kingfishers may remain in the general area of their breeding territories during the winter, unless a freeze sends them to larger waters or to the coast, the young birds disperse more widely. Only a few more tetrads than in summer were occupied during the winter periods, but there were certainly more coastal tetrads occupied, particularly in northwest Norfolk. The highest winter tetrad count during the NBA winters was four at Titchwell, with counts of three at five other localities.

Comparison with earlier atlas data suggests that some range contraction may have occurred since 1968–72, when 84% of the county's 10-km squares were occupied. Compared with the findings during the *1980–85 NBBS*, Kingfishers are now more widespread in the southern half of the Fens and more generally in south Norfolk and in the Broads, but less so in parts of mid and north Norfolk.

Green Woodpecker

Picus viridis

NBA 1999–2007	SUMMER: ALL/BREEDING	WINTER
TETRADS OCCUPIED	988 (68%) / 835 (57%)	870 (60%)
SUMMER/WINTER ONLY	266	148
MEAN PER OCCUPIED TETRAD	2 / 2	2
SUMMED MAX COUNTS	1,978 / 1,803	1,525
POPULATION ESTIMATE	1,500–2,000 bp	3,000–4,000

PREVIOUS ATLASES	SQUARES OCCUPIED	1999–2007	LOSSES	GAINS
1968–72 (10 KM)	59 (95%)	62 (all)	0	3
1980–85 (TETRAD)	326 (22%)	835 (57%)	72	581
1980–85 (10 KM)	54 (87%)	62 (all)	0	8
1981–84 WINTER (10 KM)	46 (74%)	62 (all)	0	16
1988–91 (10 KM)	54 (87%)	62 (all)	0	8

THE GREEN WOODPECKER is a large, conspicuous bird with a far-carrying, distinctive call, whose presence is hard to miss. From being a scarce species outside Breckland in the 1980s, it has become familiar in many parts of Norfolk, with a county population approaching 2,000 pairs.

Green Woodpeckers are birds of lowland deciduous and mixed woodland with nearby areas of short grassland, as well as of farmland with scattered trees, parkland, heathland and commons. They feed largely on adult and pupal ants, which they obtain from their underground nests, which are most numerous on short, grazed turf. Garden lawns are a favourite feeding site, although the birds tend to be timid and to flee at the first sign of human presence.

The NBA summer map clearly demonstrates that the species is currently very widespread almost throughout the county, having been recorded in every single 10-km square and more than two-thirds of tetrads. As in the *1980–85 NBBS*, the species' stronghold remains in Breckland, and it was in this area that all five tetrads were located in which the count of breeding pairs reached double figures. High counts were also made along the Waveney valley between Diss and Bungay, and in other parts of southeast Norfolk. The map confirms observers' impressions that the species is less numerous in the northern third of the county. Absences were also noted from most parts of Fenland and from Halvergate Marshes.

Although Green Woodpeckers are easily located, especially during the breeding season, proof of breeding is not easy to obtain and in less densely populated areas an individual pair can occupy an extensive feeding territory. Therefore the presence of a pair does not necessarily mean that breeding is taking place in that particular tetrad. As 1,803 pairs of likely breeders were counted in 835 tetrads during the NBA summers, however, the current breeding population is likely to be in the range 1,500–2,000 pairs.

The NBA winter map shows a very similar distribution to that in the summer, again with concentrations in the Brecks and parts of southeast Norfolk. Green Woodpeckers tend to be more solitary in winter but some impressive counts were made in individual tetrads during the years of NBA fieldwork, with 12 at Tasburgh and in the Brecks 11 near both Croxton and Thompson Water. Green Woodpeckers are resident but, because of their reliance on soil invertebrates, they are very susceptible to severe winter weather, especially to protracted periods of frost and heavy snow.

The data from previous atlases suggests some range contraction between the *1968–72* and *1988–91 Atlases*, from 95% to 87% of 10-km squares occupied. Since the 1980s, however, there has clearly been a very substantial range gain in both the breeding season and the

'Green Woodpeckers are resident but, because of their reliance on soil invertebrates, they are very susceptible to severe winter weather, especially to protracted periods of frost and heavy snow.'

winter. The change map shows vividly how much the range has expanded since the *1980–85 NBBS*, especially along the Suffolk and Cambridgeshire boundaries and in central south Norfolk.

BTO surveys indicate a rise of 114% in the English breeding population during the 25-year period 1982–2007, although numbers in Wales are stable or perhaps decreasing (*Birdtrends*).

SUMMER

Small dots 1, medium 2, large 3–13 ('pairs')
Shading – breeding proved or considered likely

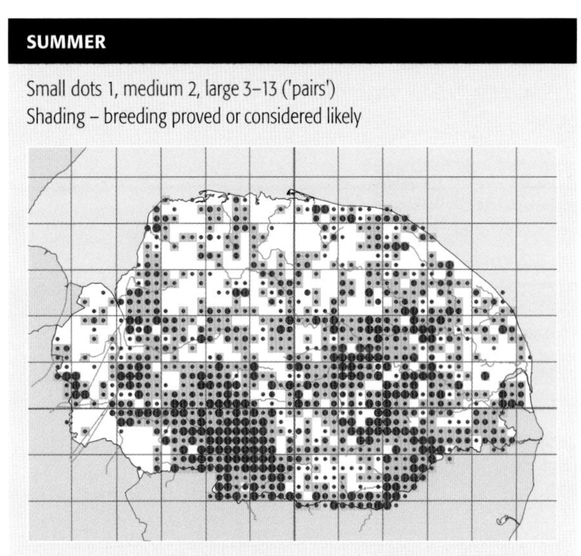

WINTER

Small dots 1, medium 2, large 3–12 (birds)

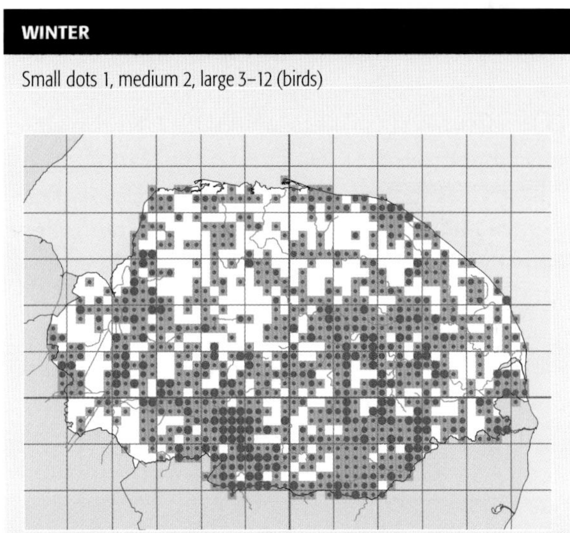

CHANGE SINCE 1980–85

+ Gain ✖ Loss ■ No change

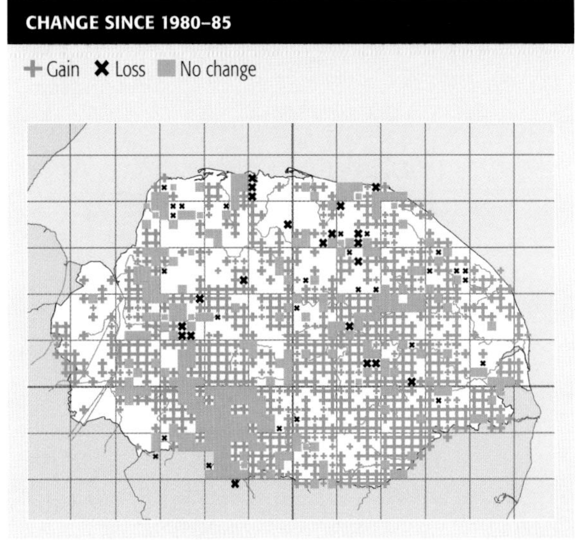

Great Spotted Woodpecker

Dendrocopos major

NBA 1999–2007	SUMMER: ALL / BREEDING	WINTER
TETRADS OCCUPIED	1,111 (76%) / 1,027 (70%)	1,077 (74%)
SUMMER/WINTER ONLY	171	137
MEAN PER OCCUPIED TETRAD	2 / 2	2
SUMMED MAX COUNTS	2,464 / 2,364	2,646
POPULATION ESTIMATE	2,000–2,500 bp	4,000–5,000

PREVIOUS ATLASES	SQUARES OCCUPIED	1999–2007	LOSSES	GAINS
1968–72 (10 KM)	60 (97%)	62 (all)	0	2
1980–85 (TETRAD)	538 (37%)	1,027 (70%)	80	569
1980–85 (10 KM)	59 (95%)	62 (all)	0	3
1981–84 WINTER (10 KM)	60 (97%)	62 (all)	0	2
1988–91 (10 KM)	58 (94%)	62 (all)	0	4

THE GREAT SPOTTED WOODPECKER is the most abundant of the woodpeckers in Norfolk. Like the Green Woodpecker, it has shown a very marked increase and spread, which has brought it out of its former woodland haunts to become also a bird of farmland and gardens.

The Great Spotted Woodpecker population was at a low ebb during the 19th century, having become almost extinct in northern England and Scotland. Numbers began to recover towards the end of that century and in the 1950s it began to appear in suburban and even urban areas. There was rapid increase during the 1970s, apparently associated with Dutch elm disease, which provided much standing dead timber, and the species has taken readily to food provided in garden feeders.

Great Spotted Woodpeckers occur wherever trees are found, be they isolated or scattered as in parks, along hedgerows, in orchards or gardens, as well as in dense woodland. Mature deciduous and mixed woodland is preferred; the species will nest in coniferous woods, but at least 30 years' growth is needed to provide trunks of sufficient diameter for excavating a nest cavity.

SUMMER

Small dots 1, medium 2–3, large 4–11 ('pairs')
Shading – breeding proved or considered likely

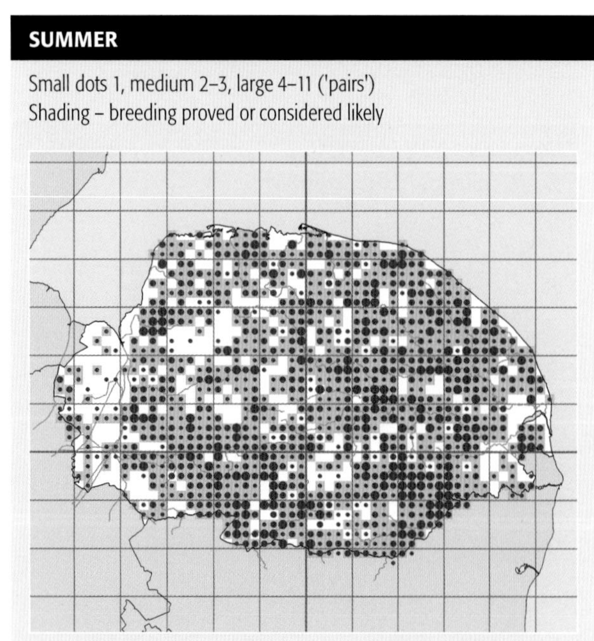

WINTER

Small dots 1, medium 2–3, large 4–15 (birds)

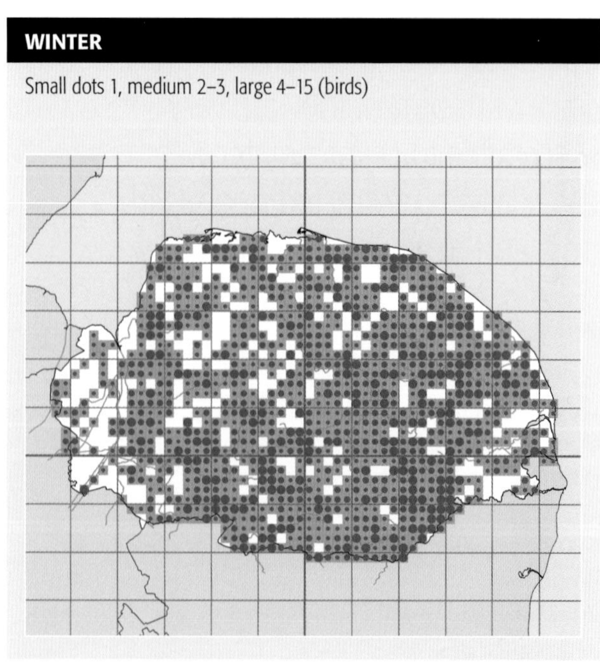

CHRIS KNIGHTS

The NBA summer map shows that the species is very widely distributed, having been recorded in 12% more tetrads than the Green Woodpecker. Like the Green, the Great Spotted Woodpecker was scarce in the Fens, and missing from the treeless grazing marshes in the Breydon Water area. Perhaps surprisingly, many of the higher tetrad counts were made in southeast Norfolk, rather than in the more wooded regions in the north and west of the county. The highest tetrad counts, however, all of 11 pairs, were made in two areas of the Sandringham estate and at Fritton.

Great Spotted Woodpeckers are vocal throughout the year, and drumming can be heard in breeding territories from midwinter through to June. Breeding pairs are therefore easy to locate, as are the nesting holes from which the growing young call incessantly for food. The birds are also fairly easy to find during the winter months, when the trees are bare and when they are more likely to visit garden feeding stations.

Not surprisingly, the NBA winter map shows a very similar distribution to that in summer, with records from most of the county, again with a concentration of higher counts in southeast Norfolk, while the species also appears rather more numerous overall in the eastern half of the county. There is no indication that any continental birds overwinter in Norfolk. While Great Spotted Woodpeckers are mostly solitary outside the breeding season, several may gather where feeding conditions are particularly favourable. Seeds form an important part of their diet in winter and no doubt good supplies of these accounted for some of the higher counts made during that season. The highest tetrad counts were of 15 at Starston, 12 at Bridgham and 11 each at Brettenham, Felbrigg and Hedenham.

CHANGE SINCE 1980–85

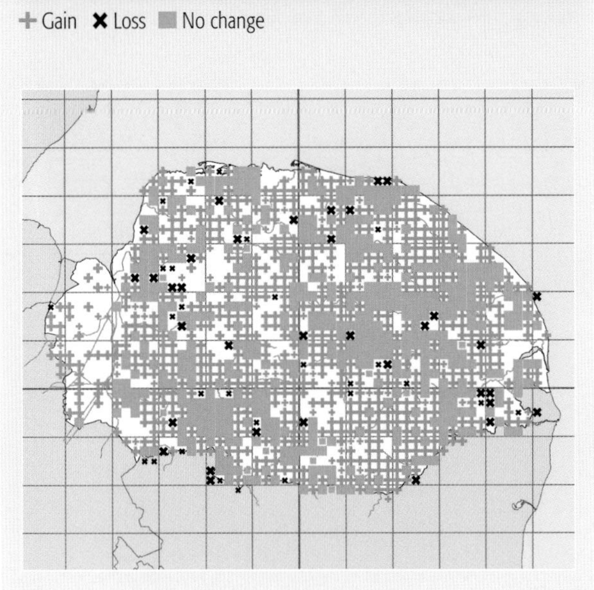

+ Gain ✖ Loss ■ No change

Comparison with previous atlases provides little evidence of range change at the 10-km scale. The species has almost doubled its occupation of Norfolk tetrads, however, since the *1980–85 NBBS*, when it was recorded in 37% of Norfolk's tetrads compared to 70% during the NBA summers. The change map indicates that nearly all of the previous gaps in tetrad distribution had been filled. Like Green Woodpecker, it has been able to colonise Fenland along the Cambridgeshire border, perhaps as trees there have matured. During a similar period, the 25 years 1982–2007, the English population rose by an estimated 123% (*Birdtrends*).

Lesser Spotted Woodpecker

Dendrocopos minor

NBA 1999–2007	SUMMER: ALL / BREEDING	WINTER
TETRADS OCCUPIED	80 (5%) / 59 (4%)	93 (6%)
SUMMER/WINTER ONLY	52	65
MEAN PER OCCUPIED TETRAD	1 / 1	1
SUMMED MAX COUNTS	89 / 68	122
POPULATION ESTIMATE	25–50 bp	60–120

PREVIOUS ATLASES	SQUARES OCCUPIED	1999–2007	LOSSES	GAINS
1968–72 (10 KM)	50 (81%)	30 (48%)	23	3
1980–85 (TETRAD)	265 (18%)	59 (4%)	241	35
1980–85 (10 KM)	53 (85%)	30 (48%)	23	0
1981–84 WINTER (10 KM)	47 (76%)	40 (65%)	14	7
1988–91 (10 KM)	39 (63%)	30 (48%)	19	10

THE LESSER SPOTTED WOODPECKER is the smallest of the western Palaearctic woodpeckers and is notoriously elusive and unobtrusive. In complete contrast to Norfolk's other woodpeckers, the population appears to be in free fall and the species may be in danger of extinction in the county within a few decades unless the trend reverses.

In Britain, the range has formerly extended throughout England and Wales, with a few records also from the central belt of Scotland. Recent numbers peaked around 1980, perhaps having benefited from Dutch elm disease during the 1970s, which provided an abundance of beetles and their larvae beneath the bark of dying and dead trees (*1988–91 Atlas*). Since then, the CBC index had fallen by around 80% by 2000, when the species had become too scarce for national monitoring to continue (*Birdtrends*).

Lesser Spotted Woodpeckers favour open, broadleaved woodland, copses, parkland and orchards, as well as lines of poplars and alders along river valleys, and in Norfolk, Broadland carrs. However, their distribution as shown on the NBA summer map is so sparse that it is difficult to relate it to any specific habitat features. The highest counts of breeding pairs were all made in the early years of the NBA and concerned four pairs in the Stanford TA and three pairs

SUMMER

Small dots 1, medium 2, large 3 ('pairs')
Shading – breeding proved or considered likely

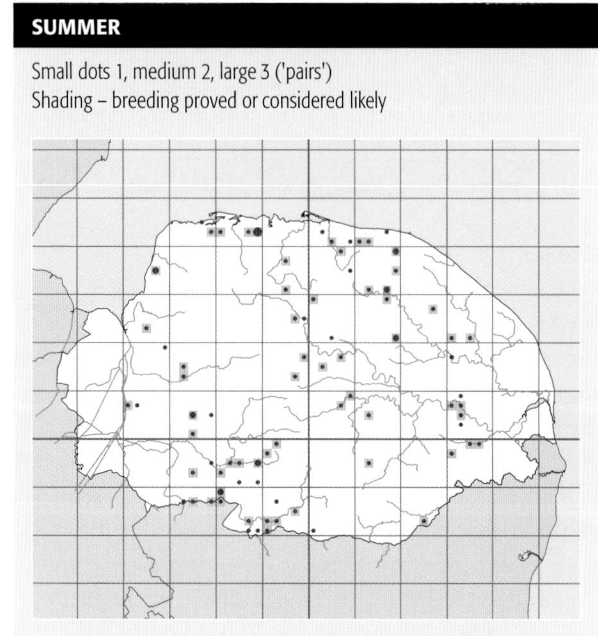

WINTER

Small dots 1, medium 2, large 3–4 (birds)

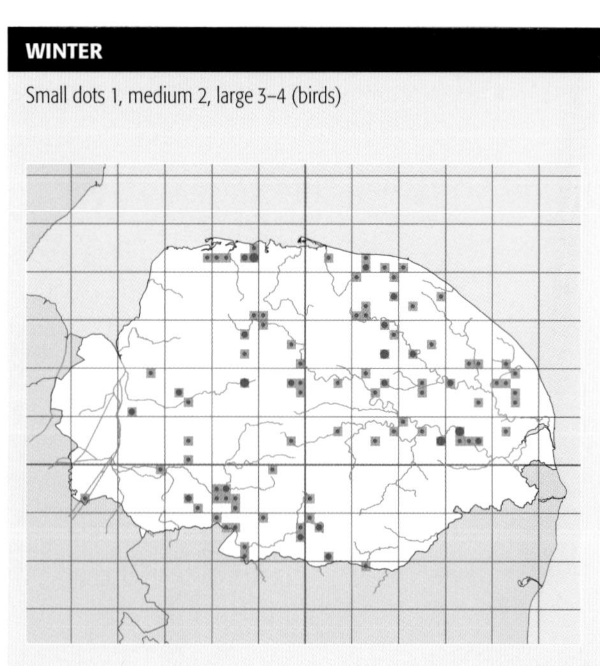

DAVID TIPLING

at Holkham Park. At the latter site nine pairs bred in 1995 and 1996, but only four in 1997. The Little Ouse valley, along the Suffolk border, also held several breeding territories throughout the NBA period.

Difficulty in locating breeding pairs of Lesser Spotted Woodpeckers is compounded by several factors, in addition to their small size and shy, inconspicuous behaviour. Where numbers are very low, as is now the case, drumming and calling may be restricted to just a few days in early spring and home ranges may become very large. The nest hole tends to be higher up than that of other woodpeckers, making the calling young more difficult to hear from the ground.

Finding Lesser Spotted Woodpeckers is no easier during the winter months, although they do become more conspicuous in February when they form pairs and begin to call and drum. Unlike its larger congener, the Lesser Spotted Woodpecker rarely visits garden feeding stations, as they feed almost exclusively on insects throughout the year. As in summer, the NBA winter map shows a well-scattered, sparse distribution, with no clear pattern. The maximum winter counts during the years of NBA fieldwork were of four at Strumpshaw and three each at Cawston and Holkham Park. It is perhaps encouraging that 65 of the winter tetrads are additional to those found to be occupied in summer; some of these may indicate undetected breeding territories, though most are presumably the result of birds being more mobile in the winter season.

Lesser Spotted Woodpeckers were absent year-round from large areas of the county, however, including much of northwest Norfolk, the Fens and the Waveney valley. The more isolated tetrads that remain occupied are probably most in danger of being lost, and some undoubtedly were lost even before NBA fieldwork concluded in 2007.

CHANGE SINCE 1980–85

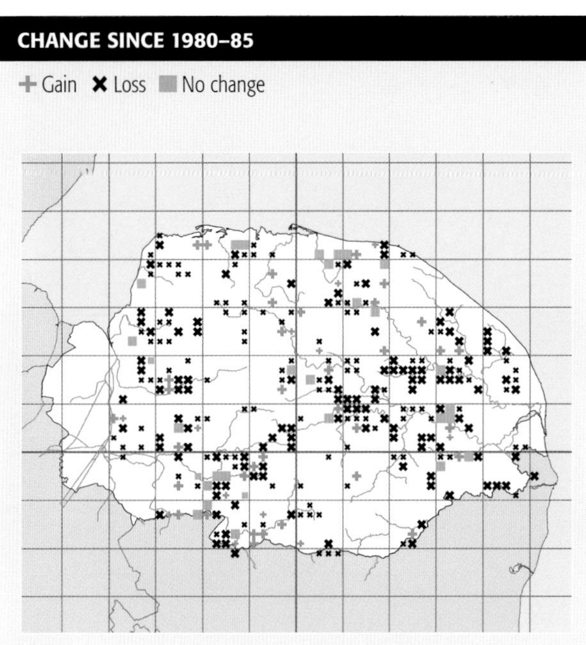

The numbers of Norfolk's 10-km squares that were occupied increased from 50 in 1968–72 to 53 in the *1980–85 NBBS*, which may have coincided well with the population peak, then fell to 39 in 1988–91 and to 30 during the NBA period. At tetrad scale, the change map since 1980–85 shows alarming losses in all parts of the former range.

Golden Oriole

Oriolus oriolus

NBA 1999–2007	SUMMER: ALL / BREEDING	WINTER
TETRADS OCCUPIED	36 (2%) / 2 (<1%)	none
SUMMER/WINTER ONLY	36	none
MEAN PER OCCUPIED TETRAD	1 / 2	none
SUMMED MAX COUNTS	39 / 3	none
POPULATION ESTIMATE	0–3 bp	none

PREVIOUS ATLASES	SQUARES OCCUPIED	1999–2007	LOSSES	GAINS
1968–72 (10 KM)	2 (3%)	2 (3%)	1	1
1980–85 (TETRAD)	21 (1%)	2 (<1%)	20	1
1980–85 (10 KM)	9 (15%)	2 (3%)	8	1
1988–91 (10 KM)	5 (8%)	2 (3%)	4	1

DESPITE ITS DAZZLING yellow and black plumage, even a male Golden Oriole can be remarkably difficult to see as it sits or moves around in the light and shade of a high, leafy canopy. Their summer presence has added tropical glamour to a few of Norfolk's woodlands.

The species has bred in East Anglia, including Norfolk, since about 1966 and nests have been built almost exclusively in maturing plantations of hybrid black poplars (Dagley 1994). The most famous site, at Lakenheath, lies just into Suffolk. In Norfolk, the species is found mainly in the Fenland basin but occurs elsewhere in small numbers on spring migration, especially near north Norfolk coasts. Birds can turn up on passage in almost any type of deciduous, coniferous or mixed woodland.

The earliest arrival date during the NBA period was 22nd April 2006. The main spring arrival takes place in May, with birds back at the breeding sites by the middle of the month. The vast majority of migrants are recorded on a single date only, but away from the known breeding sites occasional birds have remained for over a week. Isolated breeding pairs may be easy

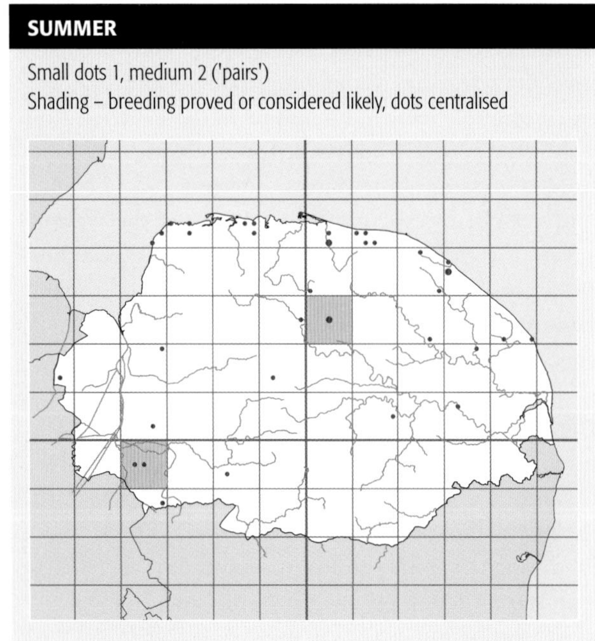

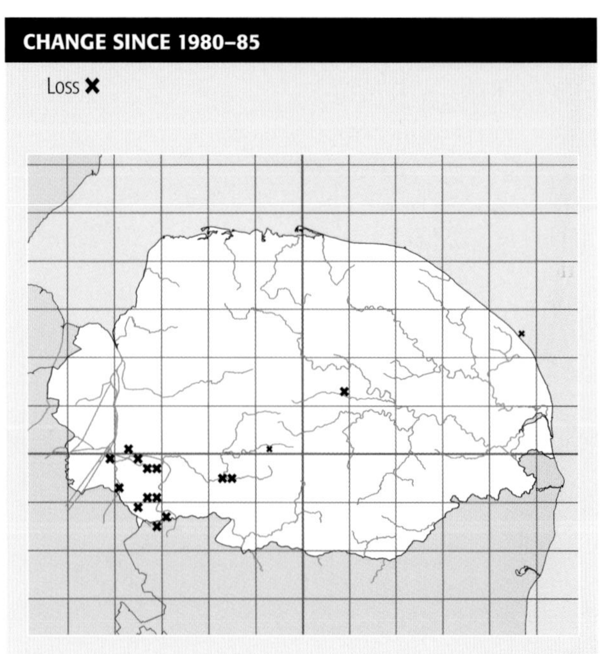

CHRIS KNIGHTS

to overlook, as singing often ceases once a breeding territory has been established.

The NBA summer map shows mainly the distribution of migrants recorded in spring, which shows a strong coastal bias. During the NBA springs, certain sites have tended to be favoured by Golden Orioles on passage, including Holme, Holkham, Swanton Novers and the Cromer to Holt ridge. Although the species has bred in Norfolk almost annually since the mid 1980s, only once has it been proved to nest away from the Fens, in central Norfolk in 1994.

Although several sites have been occupied in the Fens, no more than two or three pairs were proved to have nested in any of the NBA summers, despite an earlier peak of 12 breeding pairs in 1987. In 2006–07, no breeding attempts were made in Norfolk, for the first time in over 20 years.

'The NBA summer map shows mainly the distribution of migrants recorded in spring, which shows a strong coastal bias.'

The change map documents the loss of breeding range in the county since the *1980–85 NBBS*. Several of the previously occupied sites have been felled or are in poor condition and unlikely to be recolonised.

The steady decline in Golden Oriole numbers is intimately linked to the demise of poplar as a commercial crop (Dagley 1994). Breeding success is highly dependent on the weather, being adversely affected by high winds, rain and low temperatures. The continuing presence of breeding birds in Fenland now rests heavily on sympathetic management at the Lakenheath reserve.

Great Grey Shrike
Lanius excubitor

NBA 1999–2007	SUMMER: ALL/BREEDING	WINTER
TETRADS OCCUPIED	7 (<1%) / none	25 (2%)
SUMMER/WINTER ONLY	6	24
MEAN PER OCCUPIED TETRAD	1 / none	1
SUMMED MAX COUNTS	7 / none	25
POPULATION ESTIMATE	none	0–3

PREVIOUS ATLASES	SQUARES OCCUPIED	1999–2007	LOSSES	GAINS
1981–84 WINTER (10 KM)	14 (23%)	12 (19%)	8	6

THE GREAT GREY SHRIKE is the largest European shrike and has by far the most northerly distribution. A handful of individuals, probably from Fenno-Scandian nesting areas, occupy regular winter ranges in Norfolk.

There has always been a marked fluctuation in numbers visiting Britain from Fenno-Scandia, perhaps related to variations in breeding success. Visitors have almost certainly become less numerous since the 19th century (*Stevenson*). They are much scarcer in winter now than during the period from the mid 1960s to the early 1990s, when forestry changes in Scandinavia produced extensive clear-fell areas and resulted in a population boom; since then habitat degradation has occurred and increased use of pesticides has reduced available insect prey (*BWP7*).

DAVID TIPLING

In winter, Great Grey Shrikes favour fairly open country with scattered bushes and small trees, such as is found on heaths and commons. Here they are able to sit sentinel-like on a high perch scouring the surrounding area for the insects, particularly beetles, and small birds and mammals on which they prey. Like other shrikes, they store any excess food by spiking it on thorns or barbed wire. Great Grey Shrikes are known to return to the same general area in consecutive winters, in which they set up large hunting territories. Even when known to be present, they can often be remarkably elusive.

The map shows the few, well-scattered clusters of records that were made during the NBA winters. The largest number of reports was from the Brecks, where most probably referred to a single wide-ranging

WINTER

Small dots 1 (bird)

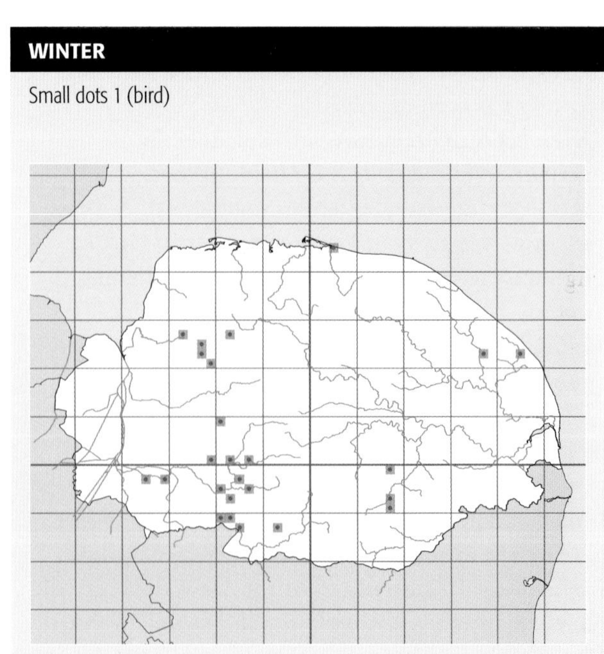

DAVID TIPLING

individual that was present in the Grimes Graves area over several winters. Another Great Grey Shrike remained in the Massingham/Grimston Heath area for a prolonged winter stay. It too occupied a very large territory and was probably the same bird that reappeared the following winter. One lucky observer at Hilborough encountered a Great Grey Shrike briefly visiting their garden.

Occupancy of 10-km squares was higher in the *1981–84 Winter Atlas* than in the NBA winters. In earlier decades, Salthouse Heath hosted a Great Grey Shrike almost every winter and yet not one was recorded there during the NBA period. Similarly, Roydon Common, another site that had been favoured in the past, failed to attract any wintering birds, although one was seen there in March 2002. A maximum of three Great Grey Shrikes was recorded during the 2004/05 winter but, in two of the NBA winters, no birds at all were found.

'In winter, Great Grey Shrikes favour fairly open country with scattered bushes and small trees, such as is found on heaths and commons.'

Many more Great Grey Shrikes are currently recorded on spring and autumn passage than overwinter in the county. During the NBA summer recording periods, eight were noted in April and one in May, at both inland and coastal sites.

Magpie
Pica pica

NBA 1999–2007	SUMMER: ALL/BREEDING	WINTER
TETRADS OCCUPIED	1,214 (83%) / 1,101 (75%)	1,284 (88%)
SUMMER/WINTER ONLY	67	137
MEAN PER OCCUPIED TETRAD	4 / 4	8
SUMMED MAX COUNTS	4,692 / 4,542	9,730
POPULATION ESTIMATE	8,000–10,000 bp	20,000–25,000

PREVIOUS ATLASES	SQUARES OCCUPIED	1999–2007	LOSSES	GAINS
1968–72 (10 KM)	60 (97%)	62 (all)	0	2
1980–85 (TETRAD)	618 (42%)	1,101 (75%)	104	587
1980–85 (10 KM)	60 (97%)	62 (all)	0	2
1981–84 WINTER (10 KM)	61 (98%)	62 (all)	0	1
1988–91 (10 KM)	62 (all)	62 (all)		

MAGPIES, WITH THEIR distinctive pied plumage, long tail and harsh, chattering calls are familiar birds to most people. Their presence is unwelcome on shooting estates, however, and persecution in such places has had a substantial effect on their past and present distribution.

In previous centuries, the Magpie was essentially a bird of farmland, but a steep rise in population was measured across the UK between the late 1960s and late 1980s, associated with a colonisation of suburban and even urban sites, such as parks, cemeteries and even gardens (*Birdtrends*). Nowadays, Magpies can be more abundant in urban and suburban areas, where they are safer from persecution, than they are on farmland.

In their more natural surroundings, Magpies are birds of fairly open country, where they are able to forage on the ground, but with the presence of scattered trees and bushes, to which they can retreat if danger threatens. They also inhabit both deciduous and coniferous woodland, provided it is not too dense, and glades and other open areas are present. Their large, domed nests in trees, thickets and tall hedgerows are familiar sights in winter once the leaves have fallen.

The NBA summer map shows that the species was very widespread throughout much of the county, although it was largely absent from the heavily keepered estates of north and northwest Norfolk, where a Magpie is rarely seen.

SUMMER

Small dots 1–2, medium 3–5, large 6–31 ('pairs')
Shading – breeding proved or considered likely

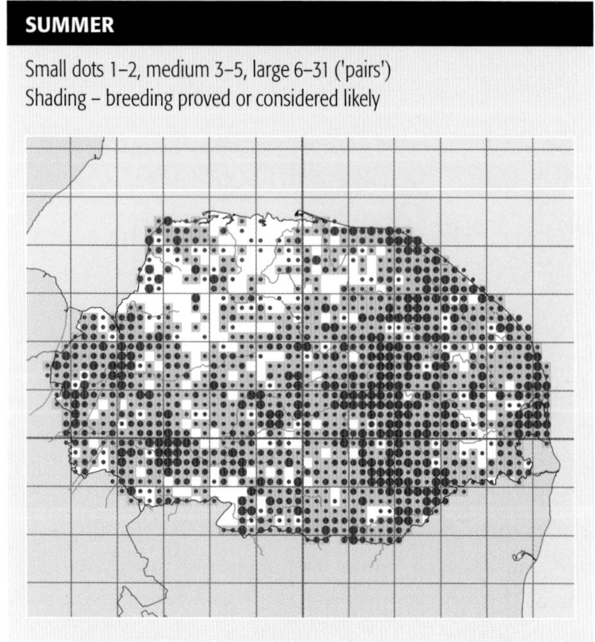

WINTER

Small dots 1–3, medium 4–8, large 9–144 (birds)

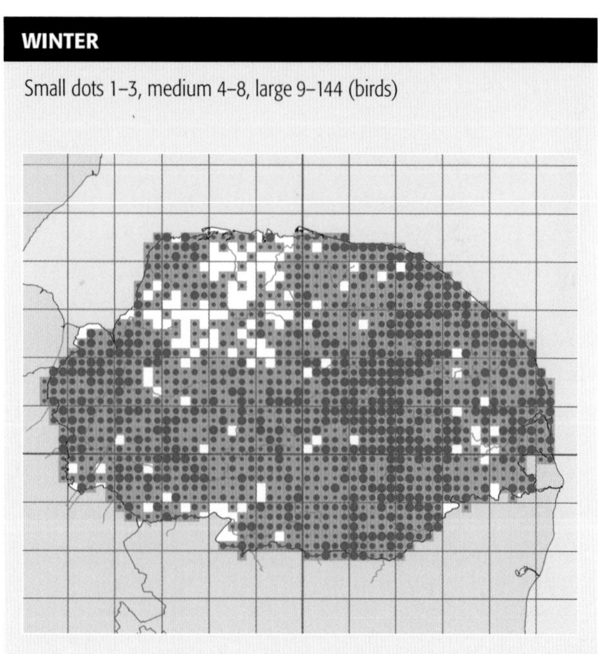

DAVID TIPLING

Habitat may be unsuitable, perhaps, in some gaps in the distribution, as in Thetford Forest and the Sandringham estate. Urban concentrations are apparent in and around Norwich, Great Yarmouth and King's Lynn. The two tetrads with the highest number of pairs during the summer counts were both in the Norwich area, with 29 at Costessey and 23 at Earlham Park. No fewer than seven tetrads in the 10-km square TG10, which lies just southwest of Norwich, contributed double-figure counts. During the summer months, however, non-breeding Magpies are present in many areas and the counts do not differentiate these non-breeders from territory-holding pairs.

CHANGE SINCE 1980–85

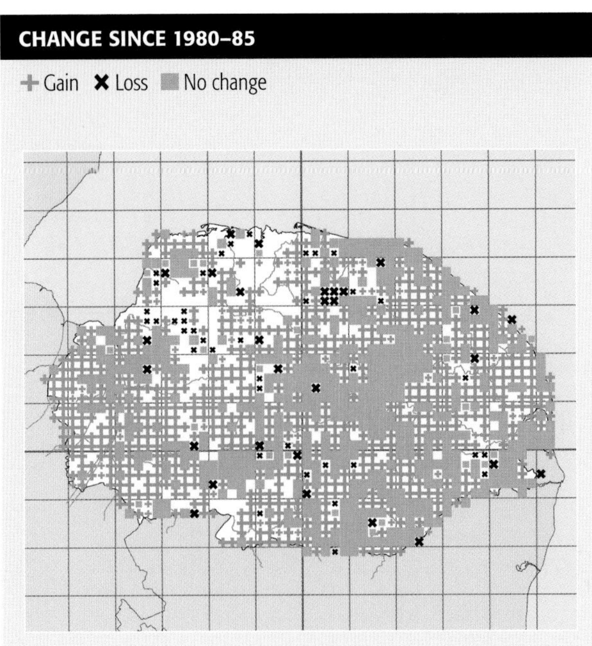

Many Magpies remain paired and within their territories throughout the winter, particularly if they are occupying optimal habitat (*1981–84 Winter Atlas*). Others, and in particular first-year birds, gather into small roving parties, feeding on pastures and areas of open, rough country. In towns, Magpies are frequent visitors to lawns and in many areas now regularly feed on bird tables. The NBA winter distribution map is virtually identical to the summer one, however, and very few additional tetrads were occupied. There is clearly some dispersal though; 60 Magpies were culled during 1999/2000 at Knapton, whereas the maximum NBA count there during that winter was only 21.

In winter, parties of Magpies gather into noisy, pre-roost assemblies before flying to safe traditional roost sites, usually in dense, thorny thickets. These pre-roost gatherings accounted for the highest winter tetrad counts and included 91 at Harling, 90 at Whitlingham Lane CP, 76 at Earlham Park and 65 at Sweet Briar in Norwich. However, for a number of years, the Roydon Common roost has been the largest in the county and regularly holds over 100 Magpies. The peak counts there during the NBA winters were 128 in January 2003 and 144 in December 2004.

The population size across England increased by only 26% between 1982 and 2007, the steep increase having levelled off in the mid 1980s (*Birdtrends*). There was a 78% rise, though, in tetrad occupancy across Norfolk between the *1980–85 NBBS* and the NBA summers, suggesting that population increase might have continued later in Norfolk than elsewhere in England. Large sections of the range that were empty during 1980–85 have since been filled. A relaxation of persecution in some areas of the county is likely to have contributed to this pattern.

Jay
Garrulus glandarius

NBA 1999–2007	SUMMER: ALL/BREEDING	WINTER
TETRADS OCCUPIED	1,018 (70%) / 870 (60%)	1,120 (77%)
SUMMER/WINTER ONLY	105	207
MEAN PER OCCUPIED TETRAD	2 / 2	4
SUMMED MAX COUNTS	2,354 / 2,160	4,379
POPULATION ESTIMATE	4,000–5,000 bp	9,000–12,000

PREVIOUS ATLASES	SQUARES OCCUPIED	1999–2007	LOSSES	GAINS
1968–72 (10 KM)	61 (98%)	61 (98%)		
1980–85 (TETRAD)	720 (49%)	870 (60%)	175	325
1980–85 (10 KM)	59 (95%)	61 (98%)	0	2
1981–84 WINTER (10 KM)	59 (95%)	62 (all)	0	3
1988–91 (10 KM)	59 (95%)	61 (98%)	1	3

THE COLOURFUL JAY is generally wary of humans, for good reason, and often all that is seen of its bright plumage is the bird's white rump as it flies noisily away. It has always been a common and widespread bird in Britain, although it was particularly heavily persecuted during the 19th century.

Jays are essentially woodland birds, favouring those woods, both deciduous and coniferous, with a fairly thick cover of trees and scrub and a dense shrub layer. They tend to avoid the more open areas, such as glades and woodland rides, and oak woods are particularly favoured. In autumn especially, however, Jays may make long excursions onto farmland in search of acorns. Many acorns are buried, to be retrieved when food is in short supply during the winter months.

The NBA summer map demonstrates a widespread breeding distribution across the county, with clusters of more heavily occupied tetrads in the wooded areas around Norwich, along the Cromer to Holt ridge and to a lesser extent in the Sandringham area, as well as in the coniferous and mixed woodland in the Brecks. The species is largely absent from the Fens and the extensive grazing marshes in east Norfolk. Its absence in other, more suitable habitats around the county is likely to be due to persecution by gamekeepers. The highest numbers of pairs in a single tetrad were 17 at Mundford in the Brecks and 16 at Fritton in east Norfolk, though it is not clear that all of these would have nested within those tetrads. In spring, Jays gather into

SUMMER

Small dots 1, medium 2–3, large 4–17 ('pairs')
Shading – breeding proved or considered likely

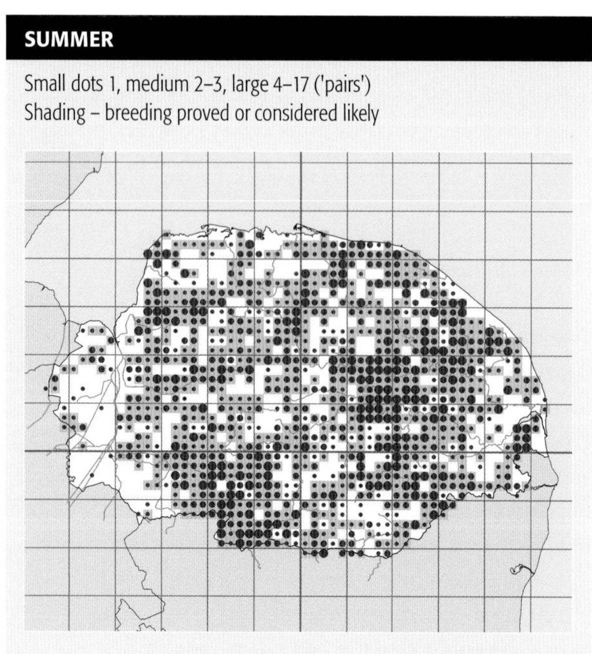

WINTER

Small dots 1–2, medium 3–5, large 6–52 (birds)

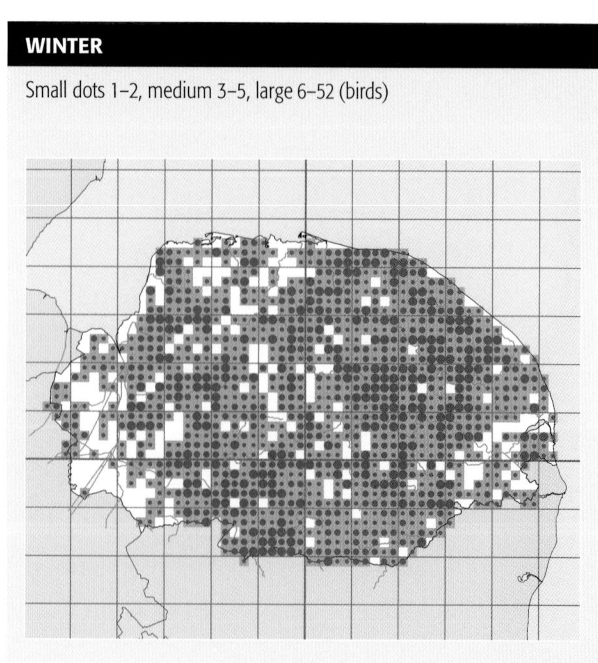

DAVID TIPLING

groups, involving a dozen birds or more, for display and pair formation. A loose gathering of 20 at Holkham Park in April 2005 may well have been one such party.

The NBA winter map shows a very similar distribution but with slightly more tetrads occupied than in summer. In winter, Jays wander more widely in pairs or small groups, and make greater use of hedgerows and scrub that is relatively open. At this time of year, they are also more likely to be recorded in parkland and orchards, and occur more frequently in gardens, even visiting bird tables. The highest tetrad counts recorded during the winter were of 52 at Horsford and 28 at Taverham, both places being northwest of Norwich.

British Jays are mostly sedentary but some from northeast Europe undertake eruptive movements in years when the acorn crops fails. The last major invasion into Britain took place in 1983 and in none of the NBA winters was there any evidence of significant immigration from the Continent.

CHANGE SINCE 1980–85

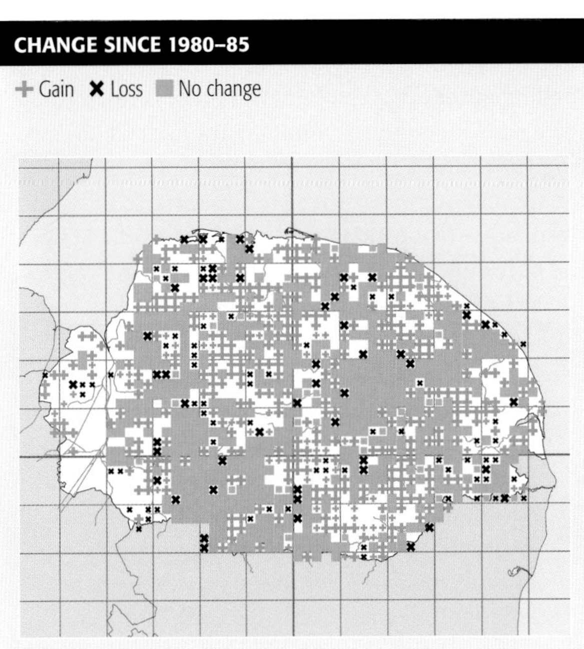

The number of 10-km squares occupied in the *1968–72 Atlas* was the same as in the NBA period, but occupancy was slightly lower during the 1980s. There has also been a substantial range increase at tetrad level since the *1980–85 NBBS*, as shown by the change map. The population level in England has changed little over the period 1982–2007 (*Birdtrends*). A relaxation of persecution in some parts of Norfolk may therefore have contributed to this pattern.

It is possible that the species is following Magpie in colonising more urban sites, such as Great Yarmouth cemetery, where a pair nested for the first time in 2002.

Jackdaw

Corvus monedula

NBA 1999–2007	SUMMER: ALL / BREEDING	WINTER
TETRADS OCCUPIED	1,265 (87%) / 1,153 (79%)	1,244 (85%)
SUMMER/WINTER ONLY	107	86
MEAN PER OCCUPIED TETRAD	12 / 13	84
SUMMED MAX COUNTS	15,748 / 15,175	103,972
POPULATION ESTIMATE	15,000–20,000 bp	40,000–60,000

PREVIOUS ATLASES	SQUARES OCCUPIED	1999–2007	LOSSES	GAINS
1968–72 (10 KM)	62 (all)	62 (all)		
1980–85 (TETRAD)	525 (36%)	1,153 (79%)	67	695
1980–85 (10 KM)	61 (98%)	62 (all)	0	1
1981–84 WINTER (10 KM)	62 (all)	62 (all)		
1988–91 (10 KM)	61 (98%)	62 (all)	0	1

WITH THEIR SMALL size and unique hole-nesting behaviour, Jackdaws are among the more distinctive members of the crow family. They join with Rooks in forming spectacular night-time roosts at traditional sites across the county.

Stevenson, writing in the 19th century, implied that the abundance of the species in Norfolk was related to the county's famously large number of churches, since these often provide suitable nesting sites. A temporary fall in numbers in East Anglia in the 1960s was attributed to a reduction in grass leys, but the Norfolk population is probably higher now than it has ever been in the past.

Jackdaws are one of the characteristic birds of traditional parkland, where the scattered trees provide nesting sites and the pasture is ideal for foraging. The species is gregarious throughout the year and semi-colonial in its nesting habits. Pair formation takes place in the birds' first autumn and pair bonds are maintained for life, even if breeding is unsuccessful. Typically, Jackdaws nest in holes in trees but they also use cavities in manmade structures such as church towers and chimneys.

The NBA summer map shows that the species is very well distributed throughout the county, with rather few unoccupied tetrads, these mostly in the arable, less wooded parts of central Norfolk and in the clear-fell and coniferous plantations of Thetford Forest. Most parts of the Fens held breeding birds, as did most of Broadland, where pairs often nest in disused drainage mills. Despite its presence in many suburban and urban areas, Great Yarmouth appears to be the only major conurbation in the county to host high numbers of Jackdaws, a finding also in the *1980–85 NBBS*.

Although Jackdaws pair up during their first autumn, they do not generally breed until they are two years old and so many of the pairs recorded would have been non-breeders. Felbrigg and Holkham Parks have always hosted large numbers of breeding Jackdaws; at the latter site up to 100 pairs were recorded during the NBA summers. Other notable counts of pairs included 150 at Thurlton and 114 at Matlaske, but these may well have included birds gathering in suitable feeding areas.

During the winter months, Jackdaws frequently associate with Rooks and large, mixed feeding flocks are a common sight in many livestock, arable and grassland areas of the county. As British Jackdaws are largely sedentary, it is not surprising that the summer and winter NBA maps show few differences in distribution. Once again, the species is scarcer in the central, relatively treeless part of the county.

Feeding gatherings can be substantial, such as 1,000 at Edgefield landfill site and 800 at Quidenham. Large flocks feed at outdoor pig farms, alongside other corvids and Starlings. They are also attracted to areas where other livestock are being fed on vegetable waste and beet tops. The largest parkland gathering was of 700 at Felbrigg in January 2001.

Tetrad counts of under a hundred were more usual, except in those areas where pre-roost gatherings occurred. During the winter months, Jackdaws use traditional roost sites, alongside Rooks. Estimating the relative proportions of Jackdaws and Rooks flying into the roost site is never easy, let alone counting the numbers of birds involved! For many years, the county's largest corvid roost has been at Buckenham Carr, where in January/February 2005 an estimated 40,000

DAVID TIPLING

'Most parts of the Fens held breeding birds, as did most of Broadland, where pairs often nest in disused drainage mills.'

corvids were roosting, of which 15,000 were Jackdaws. Other large Jackdaw roosts noted during the NBA winters included 8,000 at Cranwich GP and at Bressingham Fen, 4,000 at Shouldham Warren and 3,000 at Roydon Common and at East Harling.

Small numbers of continental Jackdaws arrive for the winter months. These include the occasional 'Nordic' Jackdaw, showing the whitish neck-patch indicative of an origin in northern or eastern Europe.

The CBC/BBS index for England has shown consistent increase since the mid 1960s, including a 51% rise between 1982 and 2007 (*Birdtrends*). Comparison with the *1980–85 NBBS* shows that Jackdaws are now far more widely distributed in Norfolk than in the 1980s. The number of occupied tetrads has risen from 36% in the *1980–85 NBBS* to 79% in which breeding was at least likely during the NBA summers. According to the change map, gains are evident throughout the county, with only a tiny number of tetrads recorded as losses.

SUMMER

Small dots 1–5, medium 6–13, large 14–180 ('pairs')
Shading – breeding proved or considered likely

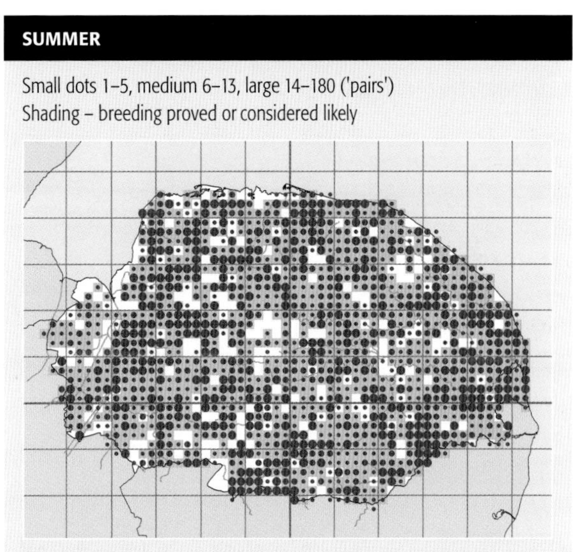

WINTER

Small dots 1–16, medium 17–50, large 51–8,000 (birds)

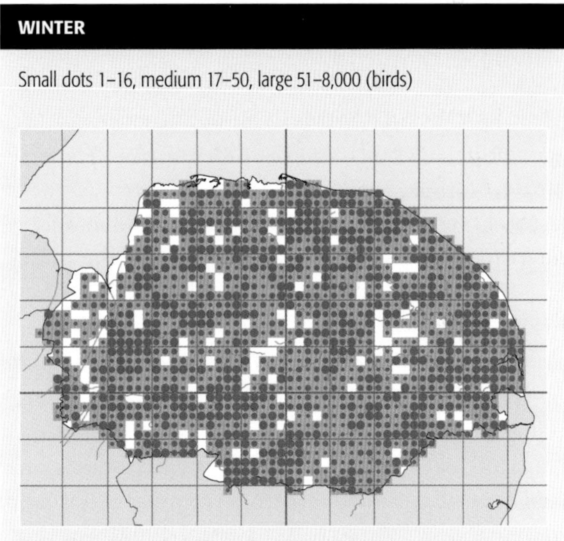

CHANGE SINCE 1980–85

+ Gain ✖ Loss ■ No change

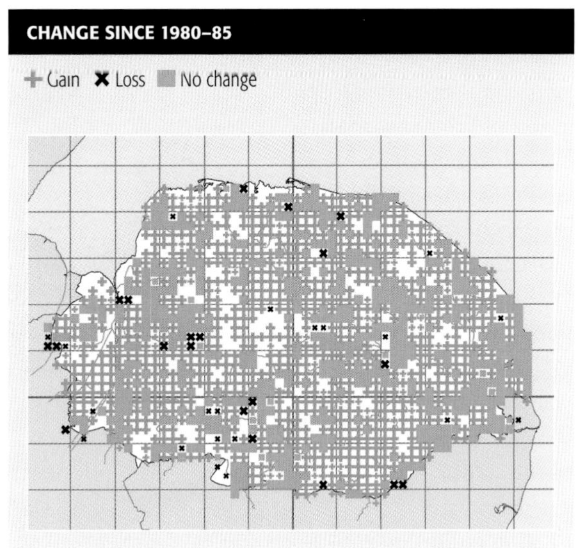

Rook

Corvus frugilegus

NBA 1999–2007	SUMMER: ALL/BREEDING	WINTER
TETRADS OCCUPIED	1,000 (69%) / 423 (29%)	1,125 (77%)
SUMMER/WINTER ONLY	113	238
MEAN PER OCCUPIED TETRAD	40 / 63	208
SUMMED MAX COUNTS	39,584 / 26,635	234,427
POPULATION ESTIMATE	25,000–30,000 bp	75,000–150,000

PREVIOUS ATLASES	SQUARES OCCUPIED	1999–2007	LOSSES	GAINS
1968–72 (10 KM)	62 (all)	58 (94%)	4	0
1980–85 (TETRAD)	481 (33%)	423 (29%)	268	210
1980–85 (10 KM)	59 (95%)	58 (94%)	3	2
1981–84 WINTER (10 KM)	62 (all)	61 (98%)	1	0
1988–91 (10 KM)	60 (97%)	58 (94%)	3	1

THE ROOK IS COMMON in well-wooded agricultural lowlands, and is a widespread and familiar bird in Norfolk.

Rooks return to their colonies in late winter and their strategy of early breeding ensures that the young have fledged while the ground is still soft and soil invertebrates easy to find. Nests are generally built in tall deciduous trees, fewer than 10% being in conifers, and most rookeries are located in small woods and spinneys, or in hedgerow trees. The vast majority are close to both grassland and arable fields, as the breeding adults rarely feed more than a kilometre from the rookery during the nesting season (Mason & Macdonald 2004). For this reason rookeries are not evenly distributed, the pattern depending on the land use of the surrounding countryside. It is still the case that Rooks are persecuted in some areas, and this also affects their distribution.

The NBA summer map includes records of feeding and post-breeding flocks, which may have been well away from the location of the actual rookeries, with shading indicating tetrads where rookeries were reported. One of the most important areas in Norfolk for Rooks is the Yare valley, which held 3,752 nests in 2006 (an increase of 6% compared with 2003; Cocker 2004). They make use of the extensive grazing marshes on Haddiscoe Island and arable land adjacent to the many rookeries, where adults and fledged young can forage for beetles and earthworms. Southeast Norfolk, however, was the area where rookeries were most frequent; in TM18, only five of the 25 tetrads did not hold a rookery. In northwest Norfolk, 650 nests were counted in the Docking area in 2006, a part of the county where Rooks were absent from many tetrads. A similar lack of Rooks is apparent on the map in some more open parts of the Fens, in the extensive conifers of Thetford Forest and around the city of Norwich. In an Essex study area, the highest densities were found in areas where there was a combination of 55% grassland and 45% tillage (Mason & Macdonald 2004).

The highest individual tetrad counts, each relating to several rookeries in each square, included 888 at Reedham, 840 at Larling and 709 at Haddiscoe. Very occasionally, sites other than trees were used for nesting, for example at Flordon where 17 nests were constructed on electricity pylons.

After the breeding season, Rooks remain in their large flocks feeding mainly on grassland, especially where livestock are grazing, and later in the summer on harvested and ploughed land. By autumn, they have already started to use their traditional communal night-time roosts, which they leave each morning to feed wherever the ground is suitable. Throughout winter, flocks are highly mobile and during NBA counting there will inevitably have been much duplication. Nevertheless, the winter map shows a very similar distribution to that in the summer, with northwest Norfolk again largely devoid of Rooks, except in the Docking area. This

DAVID TIPLING

may be related to the extensive areas of autumn-sown winter cereals, which are unsuitable for foraging Rooks during the winter months, and the consequent lack of winter stubbles. This is also the area, however, where Norfolk's corvids appear most exposed to persecution.

The emphasis of NBA counts was on where birds spent the day, but high winter tetrad counts were made at some roost sites or pre-roost gatherings; these included 7,000 at Didlington, 6,300 at Bressingham and 6,000 at Weston Longville. At the well-known Buckenham Carr roost, a maximum of 40,000 Rooks were present in the winter of 2004/05. Surveys of flight lines have indicated that the Buckenham roost gathers Rooks from as far as 20 km away (Cocker 2007). The distribution of night-time roosts of Rooks in Norfolk and the use made of them through the year are poorly documented. Immigrants from the Netherlands and Germany are known to increase the Norfolk population in winter, but without obvious effect on the pattern of distribution.

Rook populations across much of Britain have risen since 1975 (*Birdtrends*), and the Norfolk population appears to be increasing steadily. Since 1980–85, the change map shows there has been marked expansion of nesting birds, for example into the fringes of the Fens and Thetford Forest, as well as around the edges of the previous distribution.

SUMMER

Small dots 1–10, medium 11–37, large 38–888 ('pairs')
Shading – breeding proved or considered likely

WINTER

Small dots 1–45, medium 46–160, large 161–7,000 (birds)

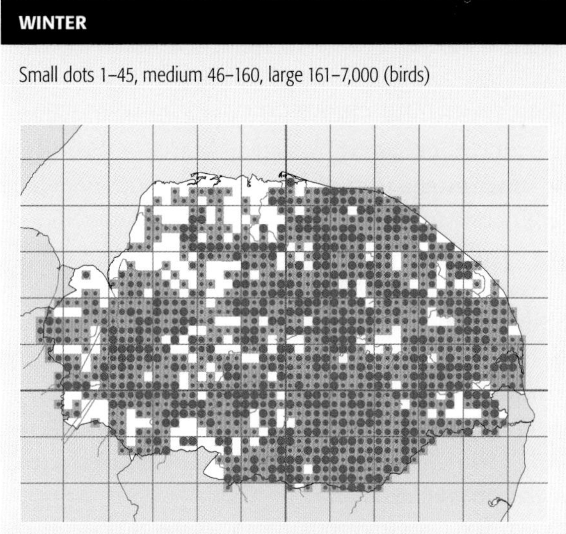

CHANGE SINCE 1980–85

+ Gain ✖ Loss ■ No change

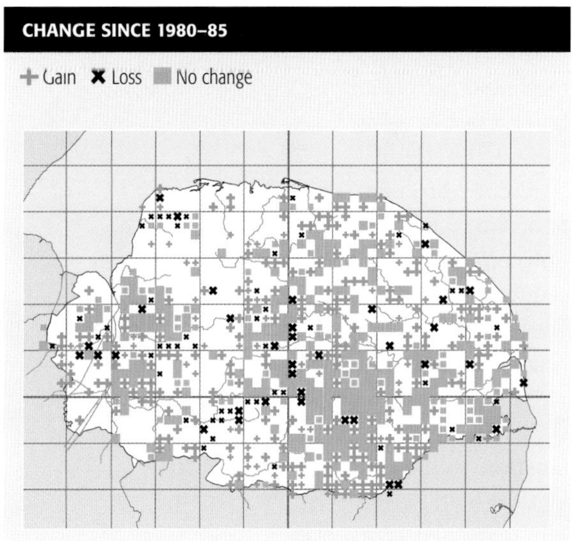

Carrion Crow

Corvus corone

NBA 1999–2007	SUMMER: ALL/BREEDING	WINTER
TETRADS OCCUPIED	1,338 (92%) / 1,209 (83%)	1,356 (93%)
WINTER/SUMMER ONLY	53	71
MEAN PER OCCUPIED TETRAD	6 / 6	15
SUMMED MAX COUNTS	8,128 / 7,550	20,264
POPULATION ESTIMATE	9,000–12,000 bp	20,000–25,000

PREVIOUS ATLASES	SQUARES OCCUPIED	1999-2007	LOSSES	GAINS
1968–72 (10 KM)	62 (all)	62 (all)		
1980–85 (TETRAD)	574 (39%)	1,209 (83%)	88	723
1980–85 (10 KM)	61 (98%)	62 (all)	0	1
1981–84 WINTER (10 KM)	62 (all)	62 (all)		
1988–91 (10 KM)	60 (97%)	62 (all)	0	2

THE CARRION CROW used to be distinguishable from the Rook simply by its tendency to be seen in pairs or family groups, rather than in flocks. With population levels now very high, however, it is not unusual in some places for several hundred Crows to gather.

Carrion Crows were so heavily persecuted during the 19th century that *Riviere* described them as very scarce in Norfolk. Between the two World Wars, the lack of gamekeeping provided some respite. There has been a sustained population increase across England since the early 1960s, however, and numbers in Norfolk have increased very markedly.

Carrion Crows inhabit open country with scattered trees, spinneys or woods, building their nests high in an isolated tree or along a woodland edge. In recent years, they have also spread into towns and even the centre of Norwich, where they have become regular garden visitors. They are highly vocal and often draw attention to themselves by their loud territorial calls. Pairs remain together for several years and many remain within their breeding territory for much of the year. Crows take a very wide range of foods including invertebrates, cereal grain, birds' eggs and nestlings, and carrion. During the spring and summer, they feed mainly on rough grassland and pastures, moving onto arable land in autumn and winter.

The NBA summer map shows that the species is very widespread throughout Norfolk, the few pockets of absence almost certainly being due to the depredations of the local gamekeepers. The map also suggests that during the summer they are more abundant in the central and southern parts of the county. However, not all Carrion Crows recorded during the summer counts would have been breeding pairs. Many non-breeding, territorial pairs are present, as they first nest at three years of age, and others, mainly first-year birds, gather into flocks at favoured sites in summer and winter. For example, in April 2004 229 non-breeding birds were recorded in two feeding flocks at Fersfield Airfield. Similarly, 177 'pairs' were noted at West Harling Heath and 80 'pairs' on Burgh Marshes, where no breeding birds were located.

While many breeding pairs remain within their territories for much of the winter, leaving only during feeding forays or to join roosts, parties of non-breeding birds may occur more widely during the winter. The NBA winter map shows a distribution that is very evenly distributed, and only a fraction wider than that in summer. Additional squares hosting the species in the winter are mostly in coastal areas. Many Carrion Crows form communal winter roosts, normally in dense woodland and used over a period of many years but separate from the sites used by Rooks and Jackdaws. The one at Roydon Common has been used annually since at least 1971, peaking at 700 Carrion Crows in January 1986. During the NBA

DAVID TIPLING

SUMMER

Small dots 1–3, medium 4–7, large 8–177 ('pairs')
Shading – breeding proved or considered likely

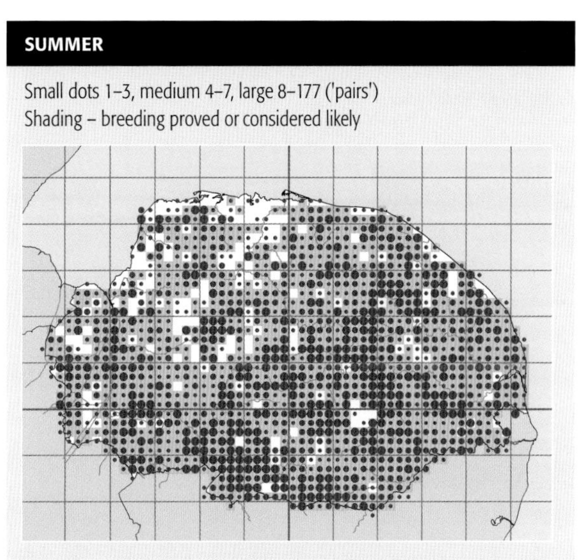

WINTER

Small dots 1–6, medium 7–13, large 14–320 (birds)

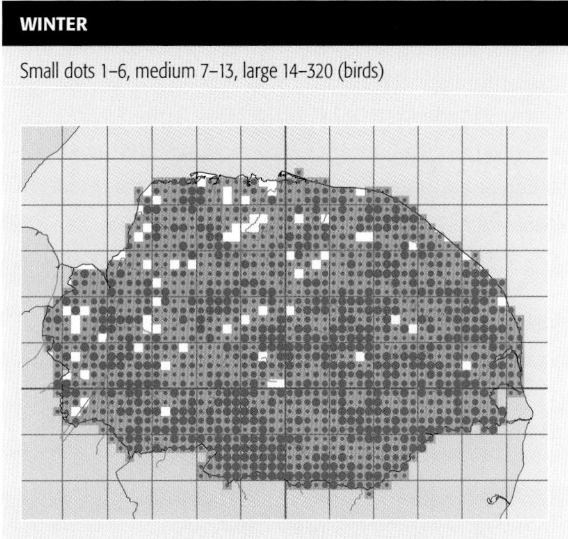

CHANGE SINCE 1980–85

+ Gain ✖ Loss ■ No change

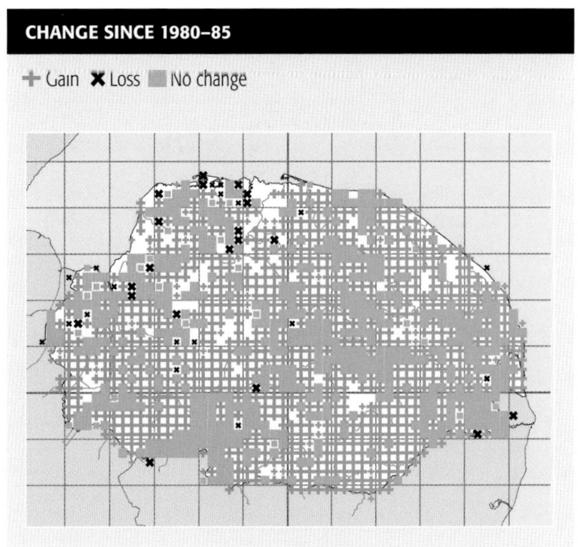

'Carrion Crows were so heavily persecuted during the 19th century that *Riviere* described them as very scarce in Norfolk.'

winters, a maximum count of 285 was made there in December 1999. Other notable gatherings included 320 at Attlebridge and 300 in two adjacent tetrads at West Harling Heath and at Sunderland Farm, northeast of Docking.

A huge expansion in tetrad occupancy has occurred in Norfolk since the *1980–85 NBBS*, when the species was recorded in just 39% of tetrads: during the NBA summers, breeding was considered at least likely in 83%. The change map shows that large areas of the range now occupied have been colonised since 1980–85, and that only a few tetrads, mainly in the northwest, lost their Crows over this period. Over a similar period, 1982–2007, the population index for England rose by 49%.

Hampshire (2005), looking at the causes of the marked increase in east Norfolk, and particularly around Hickling, gave the following possible reasons: less persecution, more areas of woodland for nesting, milder winters as a result of climate change, low rates of natural predation, greater abundance of mammalian and avian carcasses, and provision of beet and other vegetable fodder for livestock.

Hooded Crow

Corvus cornix

NBA 1999–2007	SUMMER: ALL/BREEDING	WINTER
TETRADS OCCUPIED	5 (<1%) / none	33 (2%)
SUMMER/WINTER ONLY	2	30
MEAN PER OCCUPIED TETRAD	1 / none	1
SUMMED MAX COUNTS	5 / none	45
POPULATION ESTIMATE	none	0–12

PREVIOUS ATLASES	SQUARES OCCUPIED	1999–2007	LOSSES	GAINS
1981–84 WINTER (10 KM)	20 (32%)	17 (27%)	11	8

GONE ARE THE DAYS when hundreds of handsome Hooded Crows descended on Norfolk in winter from Fenno-Scandia. Now it is a very scarce visitor and only tiny numbers are recorded in the winter months.

The Hooded Crow has often been treated as conspecific with Carrion Crow, with which it readily interbreeds where the ranges of the two forms meet. In 2002, however, the BOU Records Committee concluded that it should be treated as a full species.

During Victorian times, the Hooded Crow was a winter visitor to Norfolk in large numbers, and even up to the 1930s many hundreds were wintering in the Holkham and Broadland areas (*Riviere*). It was still fairly common during the 1950s but, as Carrion Crows became more widespread inland, pressure from territory-holding pairs caused the Hooded Crows to become more concentrated in coastal areas. Numbers arriving in the autumn subsequently fell and by the mid 1980s very few were overwintering in the county. This decline is believed to be due to more of the Fenno-Scandian population remaining in their breeding areas throughout the year (*Migration Atlas*).

WINTER

Small dots 1, medium 2 (birds)

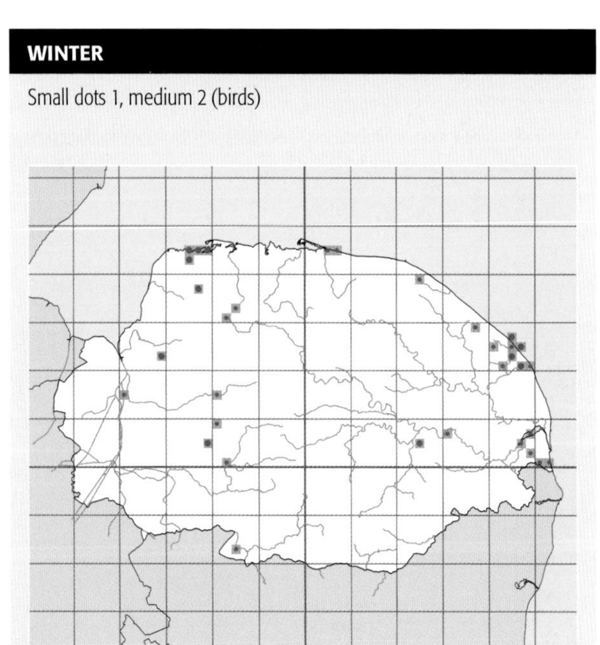

The NBA map shows a strong cluster in the Waxham/Horsey/Winterton region, which, for many years, has been one of the most reliable areas of Norfolk in which to find Hooded Crows. Although a number of tetrads in that part of the county hosted the species, only one to three birds were involved, wandering fairly widely throughout the winter months. Similarly the small cluster of records in northwest Norfolk relates to two Hooded Crows that wintered in the Docking/Brancaster/Titchwell area in the winter of 1999/2000. Other Hooded Crows during the NBA winters included several inland, especially in the west of the county.

Most sightings referred to single birds but up to three were recorded in the Horsey area in January/February 2000, among 12 present in Norfolk that winter. This was by far the highest number recorded in any of the NBA winters.

Where Hooded Crows interbreed with Carrion Crows, some of the resulting young can easily be mistaken for pure-bred Hoodies. The last mixed pair to breed in Norfolk did so at Winterton in

DAVID TIPLING

1998, and one of their presumed descendants was still resident in the Horsey/Somerton area, creating an identification pitfall for the unwary. Two other hybrids were also present in the Burgh Castle area of east Norfolk for a number of years. It is not known whether any hybrids have attempted to breed.

A few Hooded Crows were also recorded in April, during the NBA summer period; these were either overwintering birds yet to depart for their breeding areas or individuals on spring passage at the coast.

'During Victorian times, the Hooded Crow was a winter visitor to Norfolk in large numbers, and even up to the 1930s many hundreds were wintering in the Holkham and Broadland areas.'

Goldcrest
Regulus regulus

NBA 1999–2007	SUMMER: ALL/BREEDING	WINTER
TETRADS OCCUPIED	935 (64%) / 895 (61%)	1,044 (72%)
SUMMER/WINTER ONLY	135	244
MEAN PER OCCUPIED TETRAD	4 / 4	6
SUMMED MAX COUNTS	3,757 / 3,700	5,840
POPULATION ESTIMATE	6,000–8,000 bp	15,000–25,000

PREVIOUS ATLASES	SQUARES OCCUPIED	1999–2007	LOSSES	GAINS
1968–72 (10 KM)	60 (97%)	62 (all)	0	2
1980–85 (TETRAD)	587 (40%)	895 (61%)	143	451
1980–85 (10 KM)	59 (95%)	62 (all)	0	3
1981–84 WINTER (10 KM)	59 (95%)	62 (all)	0	3
1988–91 (10 KM)	57 (92%)	62 (all)	0	5

THE GOLDCREST is the smallest bird in the western Palaearctic but despite this, and the fact that it is insectivorous throughout the year, it is able to occupy many British breeding sites year-round.

The Goldcrest's thin bill is ideally suited to picking food from between the needles of coniferous trees. It is a characteristic bird of coniferous woodland but also breeds where conifers grow among broad-leaved trees. It is likely that the Norfolk population became more plentiful following the extensive planting of spruce, larch and other firs from the mid 19th century onwards, and especially with the planting of Thetford Forest in the 1920s.

British Goldcrests spend most of the year within their breeding territories in coniferous and mixed woodland, and in parks, cemeteries and large gardens containing native conifers, yews and ornamental evergreens, such as cypresses. Pairs are monogamous and generally rear two overlapping broods, the second clutch often being laid in a new nest before the first brood is fledged. This is only possible by a strict division of labour between the sexes (*BWP6*).

The summer map shows that Goldcrests are widely distributed throughout the county, with the highest concentrations in those parts of Norfolk with extensive tracts of coniferous woodland, such as Sandringham, the Cromer to Holt ridge and in particular, Thetford Forest. Not surprisingly the species is virtually absent from the open marshes in the Halvergate area and from much of the Fens, although Goldcrests did breed at Welney for the first time in 2002. Goldcrests can hold small territories in dense conifer stands and it is likely that many breeding pairs were missed in prime habitat. In addition, the high-pitched songs and calls may not have been fully audible to some observers. Despite these potential problems, eight tetrads recorded over 20 pairs of Goldcrests, the highest counts being 28 in coniferous woodland at Fulmodeston and 25 at Holkham Meals.

Immigrants from Fenno-Scandia, the Baltic and western Russia arrive on the east coast of Britain in the autumn and overwinter in Britain before returning the following spring. Undoubtedly, continental Goldcrests swell Norfolk's wintering population appreciably, although greatly outnumbered by birds of more local origin.

Many Norfolk-breeding Goldcrests remain for most of the winter within a fairly restricted area, temporarily joining up with tit flocks as they pass through. Others wander more widely, foraging amongst the twigs and crowns of deciduous trees and shrubs, and visiting gardens and heathland, where they may be closely observed amongst the gorse. Lone birds may be unobtrusive and hard to detect.

The NBA winter map shows a similar distribution to that in the summer, but with records from 12% more tetrads than during the breeding season. Counts of 30 or more birds were made in 11 tetrads, with over 50 in three, including 55 at Coxford Wood. Interestingly, none of the tetrads with the highest

'...a characteristic bird of coniferous woodland but also breeds where conifers grow among broad-leaved trees.'

winter counts were among those with the highest numbers of breeding pairs.

Although Goldcrests are highly vulnerable to severe winter weather and show large fluctuations in population, numbers in England changed relatively little over the 25 years to 2007 (*Birdtrends*). Comparisons with the previous atlases suggest that range gain has occurred in Norfolk, however, even at the 10-km scale.

During the NBA summers, the species was recorded in 52% more tetrads than during the *1980–85 NBBS*. The change map shows far more occupied tetrads throughout the range, and especially in southeast Norfolk. As for Blackcap, however, and perhaps other warblers, there is a possibility that the *1980–85 NBBS* may have under-recorded birds in the Diss–Wymondham–Harleston triangle.

Comparison with the *1981–84 Winter Atlas* shows that three 10-km squares in Norfolk were unoccupied then by wintering birds, but the distribution during the NBA winters was complete.

SUMMER

Small dots 1–2, medium 3–5, large 6–31 ('pairs')
Shading – breeding proved or considered likely

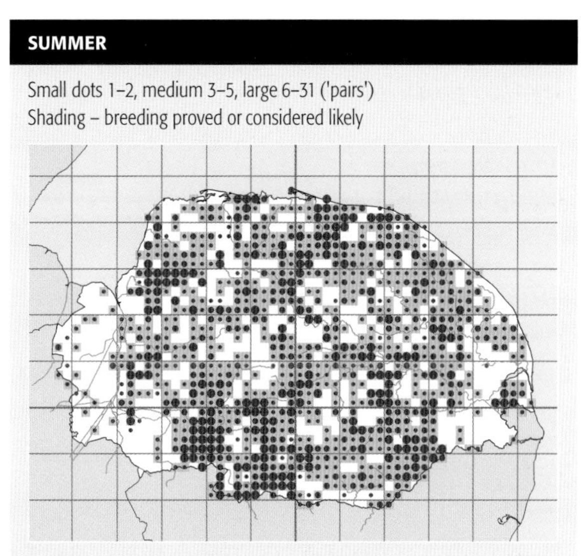

WINTER

Small dots 1–2, medium 3–6, large 7–62 (birds)

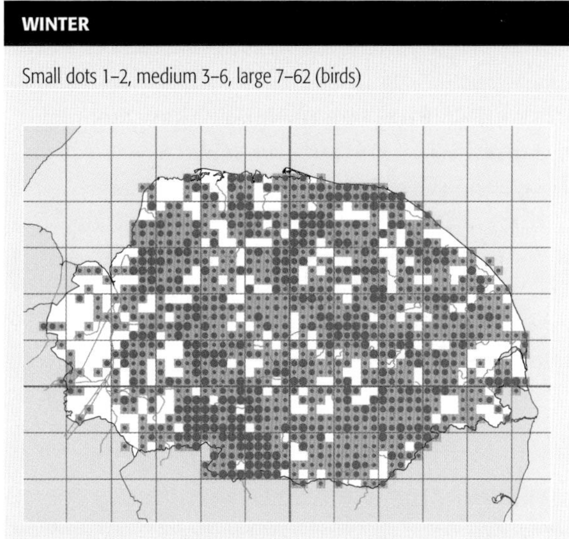

CHANGE SINCE 1980–85

+ Gain ✖ Loss ■ No change

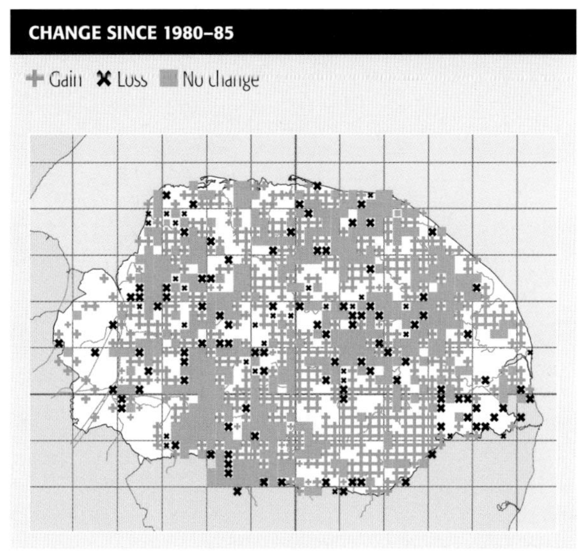

Firecrest
Regulus ignicapilla

NBA 1999–2007	SUMMER: ALL / BREEDING	WINTER
TETRADS OCCUPIED	84 (5%) / 14 (1%)	41 (3%)
SUMMER/WINTER ONLY	63	20
MEAN PER OCCUPIED TETRAD	1 / 2	2
SUMMED MAX COUNTS	105 / 34	62
POPULATION ESTIMATE	15–60 singing males	20–30

PREVIOUS ATLASES	SQUARES OCCUPIED	1999–2007	LOSSES	GAINS
1968–72 (10 KM)	1 (2%)	9 (15%)	1	9
1980–85 (TETRAD)	7 (<1%)	14 (1%)	6	13
1980–85 (10 KM)	5 (8%)	9 (15%)	4	8
1981–84 WINTER (10 KM)	5 (8%)	25 (40%)	2	22
1988–91 (10 KM)	3 (5%)	9 (15%)	3	9

THE FIRECREST, one of Norfolk's most stunningly beautiful birds, is currently consolidating and expanding its status in the county.

The world breeding range of the species is confined to the southwestern quarter of Europe, from Poland and Greece west to England and Portugal. A marked expansion in range took place during the first half of the 20th century, and records concurrently became more frequent in Norfolk. By 1913, it had been recorded in the county on only seven occasions. The first British breeding record was in Hampshire in 1962, but by 1975 Wendover Woods in Buckinghamshire held 46 singing males and 80–250 pairs were estimated to be present in Britain during 1988–91, the majority in the southern counties. Breeding in Norfolk was first proved in 1984.

Firecrests are less dependent on conifers than Goldcrests are. Most birds in Norfolk occur among soft, feathery, bushy conifers such as Douglas fir, Norway spruce, western red cedar and yew, or among deciduous trees with thickly ivy-covered trunks (Morrison 2006).

The summer map shows clear clusters of records in fairly discrete areas, a feature that was also noted nationally in 1988–91. The largest concentration of records was along the Cromer to Holt ridge, where three main groups of breeding and singing Firecrests were located, occupying a plantation of mature Douglas firs,

SUMMER

Small dots 1, medium 2–3, large 4–5 ('pairs')
Shading – breeding proved or considered likely

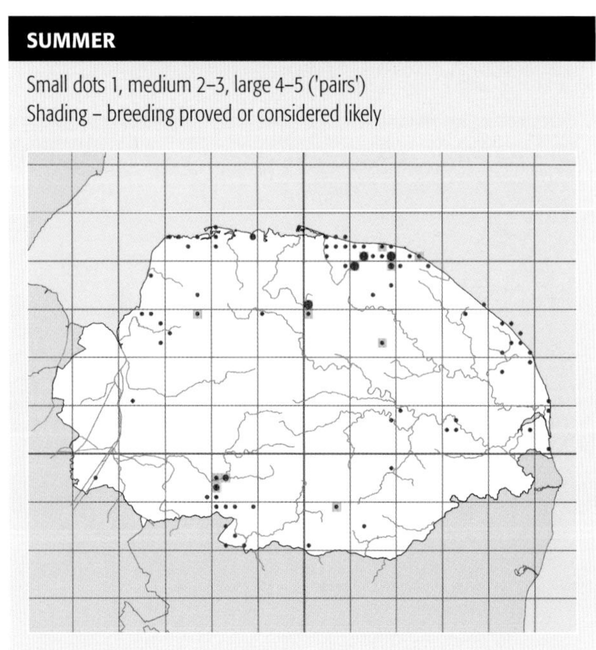

WINTER

Small dots 1, medium 2, large 3–4 (birds)

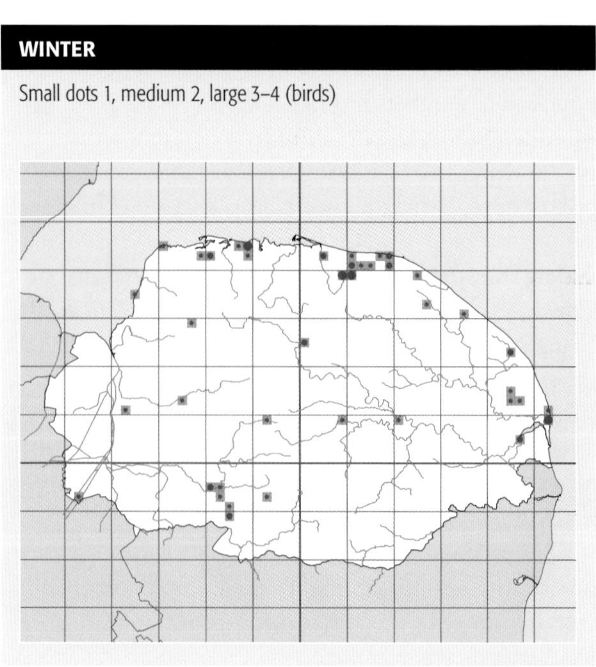

CHRIS KNIGHTS

a mixture of deciduous trees with ivy, rhododendrons and exotic conifers, and a patch of mature western red cedars (Morrison 2006). During the NBA summers, a maximum of 23 singing males was located along the Cromer to Holt ridge in 2006, with 16 in 2004 and 14 in 2005, and breeding was proved at several sites. Male Firecrests usually sing while foraging, the song period extending to mid June, but it is likely that many males remain unpaired (*1988–91 Atlas*).

Another large cluster of records is shown in Thetford Forest, where 17 singing males were present in 2006. Nesting occurs there in Douglas firs with box understorey, and exotic deciduous and coniferous trees (Morrison 2006). Several Firecrests were also in song during the breeding season at Swanton Novers. Elsewhere, singing males or single pairs were present during the NBA summers at a number of well-scattered localities, at one of which breeding was proved. The map also shows records from many places where breeding was not thought likely, mainly around the coast, that probably refer to spring migrants. These were perhaps a mixture of birds arriving from and returning to the near Continent.

In Norfolk, winter habitat requirements appear to be similar to those during the breeding season. Firecrests appear to favour areas of sheltered coniferous or mixed woodland with a dense understorey, often feeding in deciduous trees and at a lower level than Goldcrests, where they are often more easily observed. Other sites with evergreens, such as cemeteries, also host wintering Firecrests. In other parts of Britain, wintering birds appear to favour waterside habitats (*1988–91 Atlas*).

The NBA winter map shows the same main concentrations of records as in the summer, along the Cromer to Holt ridge and in Thetford Forest, and a thin scattering of birds elsewhere in the county. Some birds are likely to be winter visitors from the near Continent but, in Thetford Forest at least, some birds appear to be resident year-round. The highest winter counts have been of four birds at three different sites, including Holkham Meals and Great Yarmouth cemetery. The highest county total was of 19 birds reported during the winter of 2003/04. Higher wintering numbers appear to follow high autumn passage numbers, suggesting that continental birds are involved (Morrison 2006).

During the NBA period, the number of singing male Firecrests reported from suitable breeding habitat increased to 20 in 2004 and 22 in 2005, compared with a total of just seven during the *1980–85 NBBS*. Firecrests are also becoming commoner in Norfolk during the winter, with five times as many 10-km squares holding the species during the NBA winters as during the *1981–84 Winter Atlas*.

Blue Tit

Cyanistes caeruleus

NBA 1999–2007	SUMMER: ALL / BREEDING	WINTER
TETRADS OCCUPIED	1,387 (95%) / 1,379 (95%)	1,397 (96%)
SUMMER/WINTER ONLY	13	23
MEAN PER OCCUPIED TETRAD	13 / 13	25
SUMMED MAX COUNTS	17,573 / 17,565	35,573
POPULATION ESTIMATE	60,000–70,000 bp	140,000–180,000

PREVIOUS ATLASES	SQUARES OCCUPIED	1999–2007	LOSSES	GAINS
1968–72 (10 KM)	62 (all)	62 (all)		
1980–85 (TETRAD)	1,340 (92%)	1,379 (95%)	26	65
1980–85 (10 KM)	62 (all)	62 (all)		
1981–84 WINTER (10 KM)	62 (all)	62 (all)		
1988–91 (10 KM)	62 (all)	62 (all)		

THE FAMILIAR BLUE Tit has an extensive breeding range throughout much of the western Palaearctic and is the most widely distributed and most numerous tit in Britain.

Originally a bird of broad-leaved woodland, it is a very versatile species that may be found wherever trees or bushes are located. As well as deciduous and mixed woodland, where it nests in holes in trees, it also breeds in mature trees along hedgerows and roads, in parkland, orchards and gardens. Sometimes holes in walls are used as nest sites, and the species takes readily to nest boxes. Blue Tits are highly vocal, both sexes giving the rather tremulous song and the distinctive scolding calls, so that breeding pairs are easily located. On the second summer visits, song would have largely ceased and most pairs reported would have been noted as family parties.

The NBA summer map confirms that Blue Tit is one of the most widely distributed birds in the county, even occurring in the relatively treeless areas of the Fens and the Halvergate Levels. The map also suggests that it is more numerous in the eastern half of the county, and especially in the southeast. In over a dozen tetrads, 45 or more breeding pairs were located, with 86 pairs in the woodland, parkland and gardens around the University of East Anglia campus and Earlham Park.

After breeding Blue Tits remain within their family parties for a few weeks before dispersing. Later in the

SUMMER

Small dots 1–8, medium 9–15, large 16–86 ('pairs')
Shading – breeding proved or considered likely

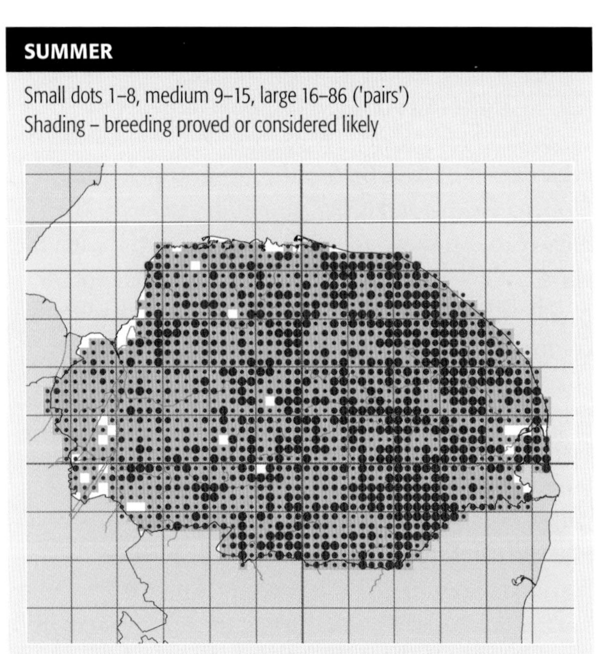

WINTER

Small dots 1–14, medium 15–29, large 30–223 (birds)

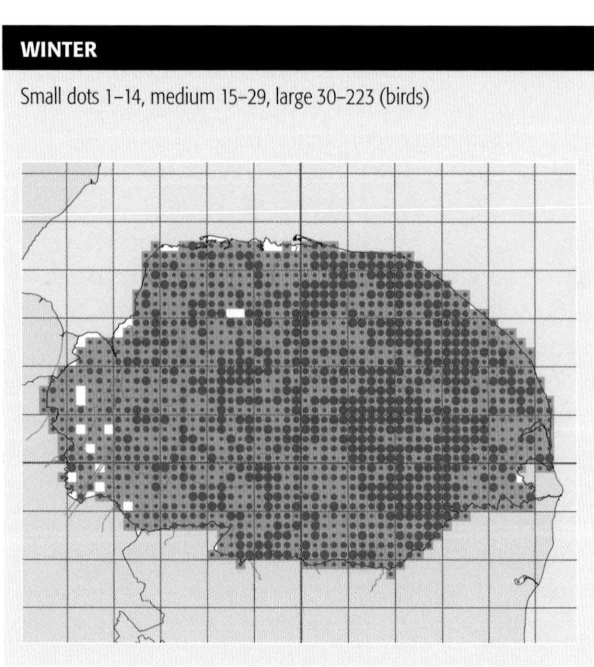

DAVID TIPLING

autumn and throughout the winter, birds gather into roving flocks, often mixing with other species of tits, as well as Goldcrests and Treecreepers. Many of these flocks remain within woodland, only leaving in periods of severe weather or in those years with a poor beechmast crop (*1981–84 Winter Atlas*). Others pass through gardens in their constant search for food and are more likely to be recorded in higher numbers in urban areas at this time of year, when many householders put out food for birds.

'The NBA summer map confirms that Blue Tit is one of the most widely distributed birds in the county...'

CHANGE SINCE 1980–85

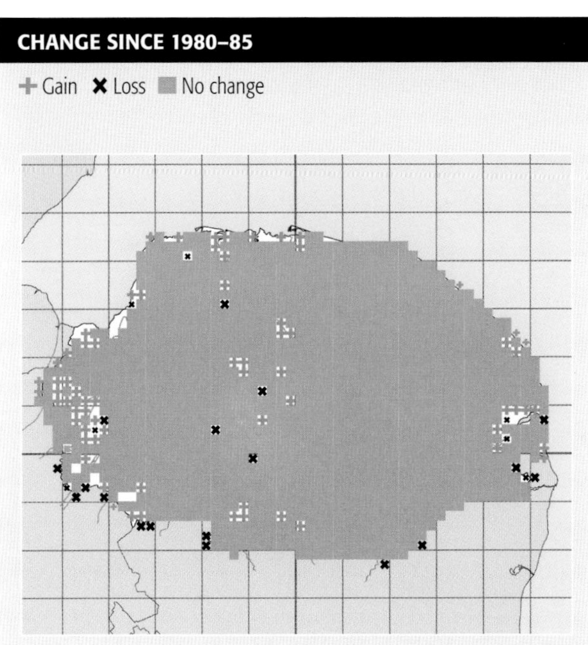

The NBA winter map is almost identical to the summer one, with Blue Tits missing from very few tetrads and, as in summer, the eastern half of the county appears to be favoured. While it was unusual to see more than about 20 Blue Tits in a winter flock, 50 were counted at Stanford Water in January 2001, and 80 tetrads returned counts of 60 or more. In ten of these tetrads, three-figure counts of Blue Tits were recorded, including 223 in the same Earlham tetrad that held the highest count of breeding pairs, 129 at Holt and 125 at Flordon.

There is very little evidence from the previous atlas surveys of any range change in the county, although the change map shows that, of the few tetrads gained since the *1980–85 NBBS*, most represented extensions into the Fens or the Halvergate Levels, where the distribution is still not quite complete.

Great Tit

Parus major

NBA 1999–2007	SUMMER: ALL / BREEDING	WINTER
TETRADS OCCUPIED	1,364 (93%) / 1,357 (93%)	1,367 (94%)
SUMMER/WINTER ONLY	28	31
MEAN PER OCCUPIED TETRAD	10 / 10	19
SUMMED MAX COUNTS	14,109 / 14,102	25,813
POPULATION ESTIMATE	40,000–50,000 bp	100,000–130,000

PREVIOUS ATLASES	SQUARES OCCUPIED	1999–2007	LOSSES	GAINS
1968–72 (10 KM)	62 (all)	62 (all)		
1980–85 (TETRAD)	1,292 (89%)	1,357 (93%)	38	103
1980–85 (10 KM)	62 (all)	62 (all)		
1981–84 WINTER (10 KM)	62 (all)	62 (all)		
1988–91 (10 KM)	62 (all)	62 (all)		

LIKE ITS SMALLER cousin the Blue Tit, the Great Tit is common throughout most of Norfolk, occurring wherever there are trees and bushes.

During the summer it inhabits woodland, including conifer plantations, hedgerows, orchards, parkland and gardens, where it nests in holes in trees and will readily use nest boxes. It is more likely than Blue Tits to occupy cavities in manmade structures, such as walls and pipes.

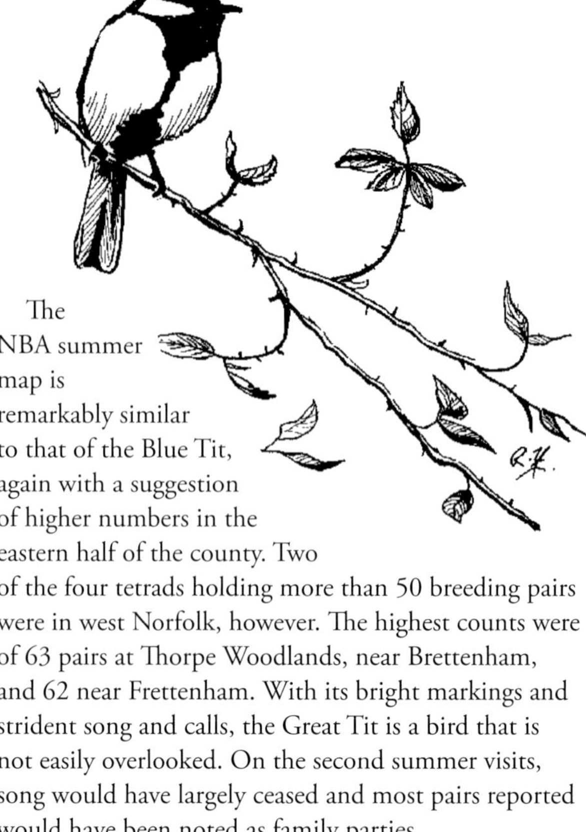

The NBA summer map is remarkably similar to that of the Blue Tit, again with a suggestion of higher numbers in the eastern half of the county. Two of the four tetrads holding more than 50 breeding pairs were in west Norfolk, however. The highest counts were of 63 pairs at Thorpe Woodlands, near Brettenham, and 62 near Frettenham. With its bright markings and strident song and calls, the Great Tit is a bird that is not easily overlooked. On the second summer visits, song would have largely ceased and most pairs reported would have been noted as family parties.

In winter, Great Tits are often found in mixed foraging parties in association with other species of tits. Some, however, remain in single-species flocks, usually comprising fewer than ten birds, although a party of 45 was recorded at Buckenham Tofts in January 2000 and another of 25 at Blickling Park in December 2004.

SUMMER

Small dots 1–6, medium 7–12, large 13–63 ('pairs')
Shading – breeding proved or considered likely

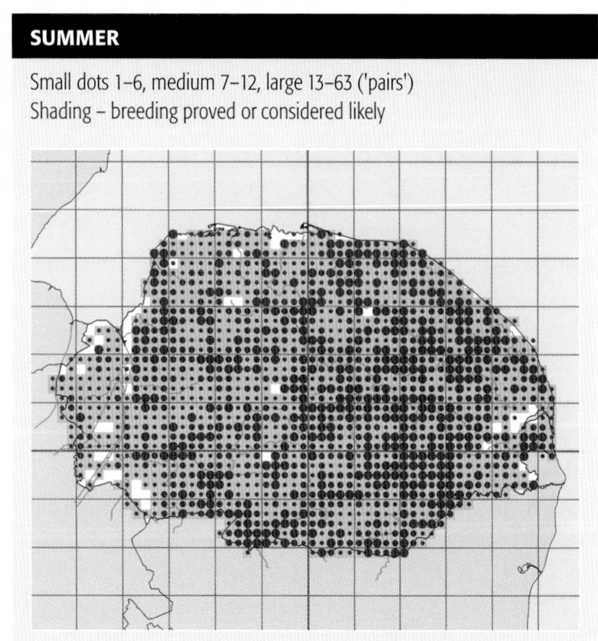

WINTER

Small dots 1–11, medium 12–21, large 22–141 (birds)

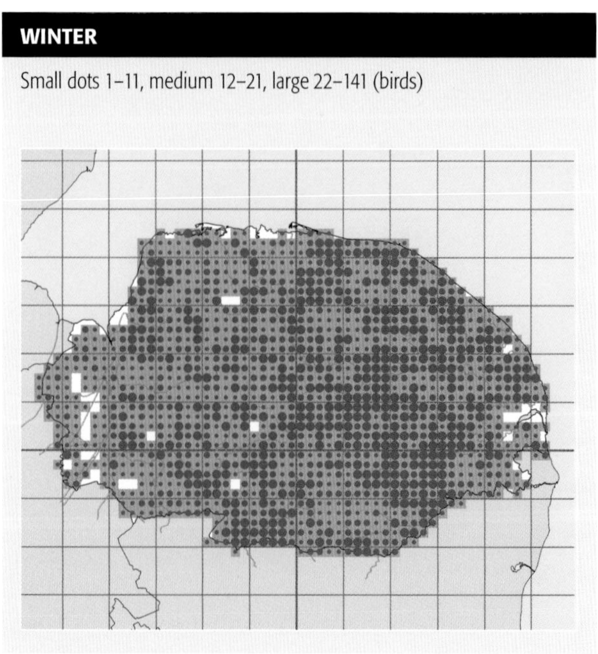

DAVID TIPLING

Concentrations of Great Tits in winter are usually found in beech woods, in years with a heavy crop of beechmast, where they forage for the seed on the ground. In years with a poor crop and during severe winter weather they are more frequent visitors to garden bird tables.

'Concentrations of Great Tits in winter are usually found in beech woods, in years with heavy crop of beechmast, where they forage for the seed on the ground.'

CHANGE SINCE 1980–85

+ Gain ✖ Loss ■ No change

The winter map shows a very similar distribution to that in the summer, again with rather more in the eastern half of Norfolk. As would be expected, concentrations were found in tetrads containing areas of woodland, especially in the hinterland of Norwich. Five tetrads contributed three-figure counts: these were at Earlham, where a maximum of 141 was recorded, Holt, Frettenham, Honing and West Mere, Tottington.

There has been little scope for increase in the county distribution since the previous atlases. Since the *1980–85 NBBS*, however, the number of occupied tetrads has increased slightly. As for Blue Tit, the tetrad gains are concentrated on the edges of the previous range, in Fenland and on the levels around Breydon, but the gains for Great Tit have been a little more extensive. The county population may well have increased over the same period, as the CBC/BBS index for England rose by 45% between 1982 and 2007 (*Birdtrends*).

Coal Tit

Periparus ater

NBA 1999–2007	SUMMER: ALL/BREEDING	WINTER
TETRADS OCCUPIED	794 (54%) / 752 (52%)	868 (59%)
SUMMER/WINTER ONLY	139	213
MEAN PER OCCUPIED TETRAD	4 / 4	6
SUMMED MAX COUNTS	3,153 / 3,107	4,874
POPULATION ESTIMATE	5,000–7,000 bp	12,000–18,000

PREVIOUS ATLASES	SQUARES OCCUPIED	1999–2007	LOSSES	GAINS
1968–72 (10 KM)	62 (all)	60 (97%)	2	0
1980–85 (TETRAD)	523 (36%)	752 (52%)	138	367
1980–85 (10 KM)	60 (97%)	60 (97%)	2	2
1981–84 WINTER (10 KM)	56 (90%)	62 (all)	0	6
1988–91 (10 KM)	56 (90%)	60 (97%)	1	5

LIKE THE GOLDCREST, the Coal Tit is a characteristic bird of coniferous woodland and a frequent visitor to gardens, especially in winter.

Its long toes and fine bill make it admirably suited to foraging in conifers for the insects and spiders on which it feeds in spring and summer. Coal Tits inhabit both native and introduced conifers and, although reaching highest densities in pure conifer stands, they are also found in broad-leaved as well as mixed woodland.

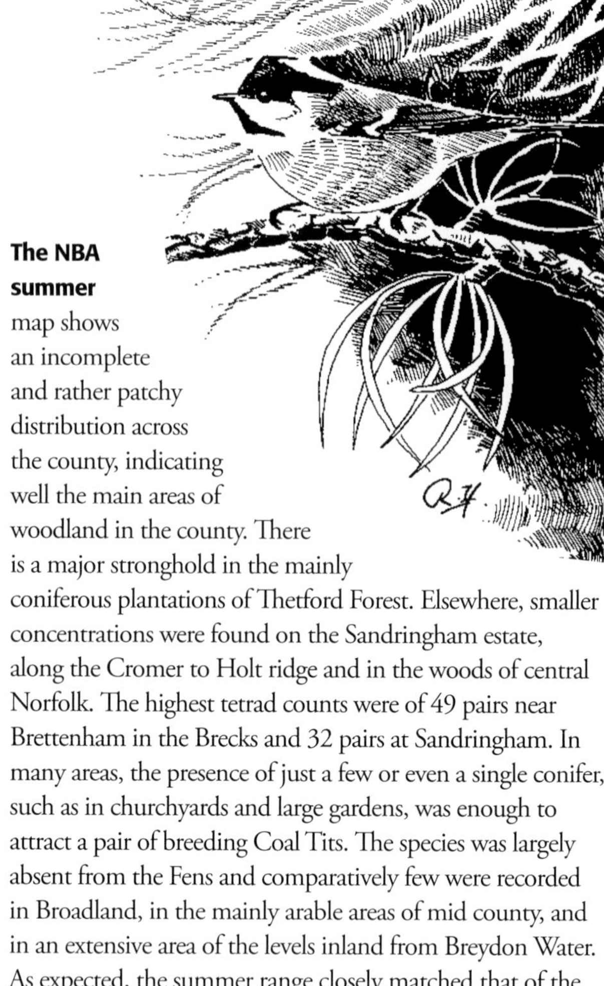

The NBA summer map shows an incomplete and rather patchy distribution across the county, indicating well the main areas of woodland in the county. There is a major stronghold in the mainly coniferous plantations of Thetford Forest. Elsewhere, smaller concentrations were found on the Sandringham estate, along the Cromer to Holt ridge and in the woods of central Norfolk. The highest tetrad counts were of 49 pairs near Brettenham in the Brecks and 32 pairs at Sandringham. In many areas, the presence of just a few or even a single conifer, such as in churchyards and large gardens, was enough to attract a pair of breeding Coal Tits. The species was largely absent from the Fens and comparatively few were recorded in Broadland, in the mainly arable areas of mid county, and in an extensive area of the levels inland from Breydon Water. As expected, the summer range closely matched that of the Goldcrest, as was noted during the *1980–85 NBBS*.

Coal Tits are both gregarious and vocal during the winter months and, as in the summer, are easily located. They

SUMMER

Small dots 1, medium 2–4, large 5–49 ('pairs')
Shading – breeding proved or considered likely

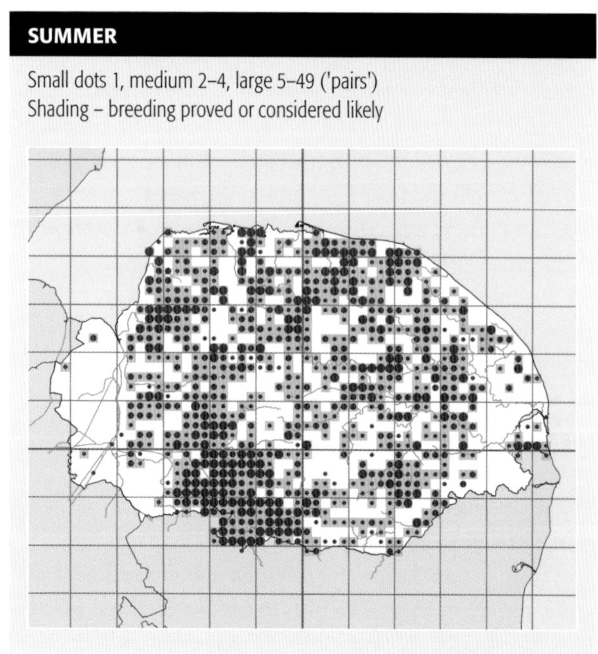

WINTER

Small dots 1–2, medium 3–5, large 6–87 (birds)

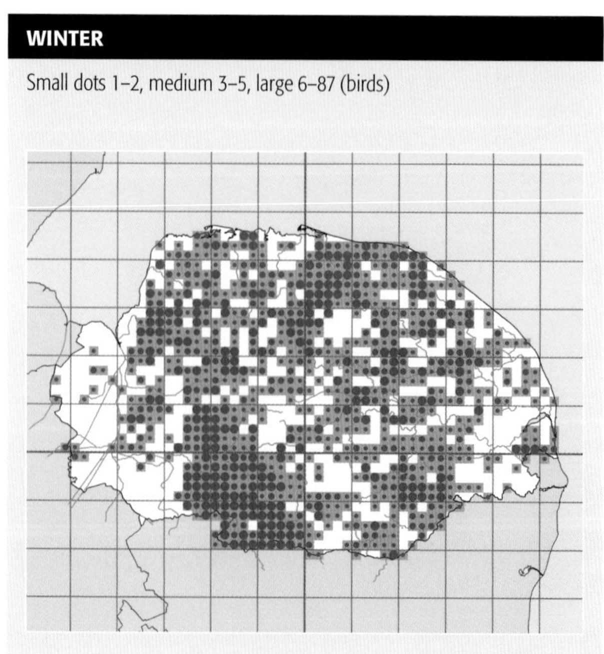

DAVID TIPLING

continue to feed on any available insects and spiders, but also add seeds, especially those of spruce, to their diet. Their small body size means that they are unable to store large fat reserves during the winter and so hoard food for later consumption.

CHANGE SINCE 1980–85

+ Gain ✖ Loss ■ No change

'Coal Tits are both gregarious and vocal during the winter months and, as in the summer, are easily located.'

The winter map shows a very similar but rather wider distribution to that in the summer. Two of the highest winter tetrad counts were made in adjacent squares in Thetford Forest between Cranwich and Weeting, with 87 and 70 birds recorded, and 75 were recorded nearby at West Tofts Heath. Some birds joined roving tit flocks or sought food at garden feeding stations, although relatively few birds were recorded in the larger conurbations.

The proportion of 10-km squares occupied during the NBA summers was not complete, as it had been in the *1968–72 Atlas*. There has been a substantial increase since the *1980–85 NBBS*, however, in the number of occupied tetrads. The change map indicates that gains and losses were scattered widely across the range, but that gains predominated in some areas, for example in Thetford Forest and further east in south Norfolk.

Willow Tit

Poecile montana

NBA 1999–2007	SUMMER: ALL/BREEDING	WINTER
TETRADS OCCUPIED	107 (7%) / 67 (5%)	147 (10%)
SUMMER/WINTER ONLY	51	91
MEAN PER OCCUPIED TETRAD	1 / 1	2
SUMMED MAX COUNTS	134 / 91	250
POPULATION ESTIMATE	40–90 bp	100–250

PREVIOUS ATLASES	SQUARES OCCUPIED	1999–2007	LOSSES	GAINS
1968–72 (10 KM)	56 (90%)	35 (56%)	23	2
1980–85 (TETRAD)	224 (15%)	67 (5%)	209	52
1980–85 (10 KM)	50 (81%)	35 (56%)	19	4
1981–84 WINTER (10 KM)	52 (84%)	45 (73%)	10	3
1988–91 (10 KM)	44 (71%)	35 (56%)	15	6

WILLOW TIT WAS first proved to breed in Norfolk in 1934, the species then having been recognised as distinct from Marsh Tit for just a few decades. The early history of the species in Norfolk is therefore unknown.

After a peak in population in the early 1970s, the species entered a steep phase of decline, which is still continuing. During the 25 years to 2007, numbers in England are estimated to have fallen by 83% (*Birdtrends*), leaving the species everywhere scarce and highly vulnerable to further local extinction. Predation, for example by Great Spotted Woodpeckers and grey squirrels, and loss of habitat quality are believed to be partly responsible for the decline. Competition with other tit species may also be a factor. In areas where Marsh Tits also occur, they tend to be dominant, on occasion even taking over the nest cavities that Willow Tits have excavated in rotten stumps (*1988–91 Atlas*).

Throughout the NBA period, observers have commented on the declining numbers in Norfolk. In recent decades, Willow Tits have been found throughout the year in damp stands of alders, birches and willows, often along rivers or around the edges of deciduous woodland or overgrown, flooded gravel pits. Its habitat requirements within the county have not always been so specialised, however. Drier woods and even well-wooded farmland have been occupied in the recent past.

SUMMER

Small dots 1, medium 2, large 3–6 ('pairs')
Shading – breeding proved or considered likely

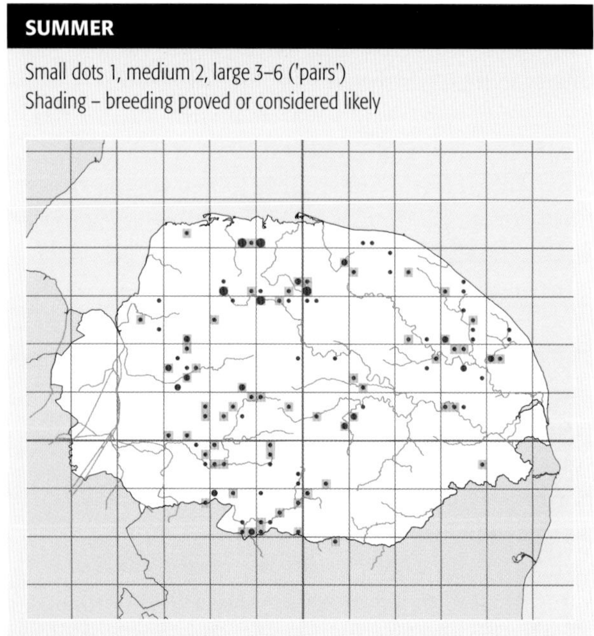

WINTER

Small dots 1, medium 2, large 3–11 (birds)

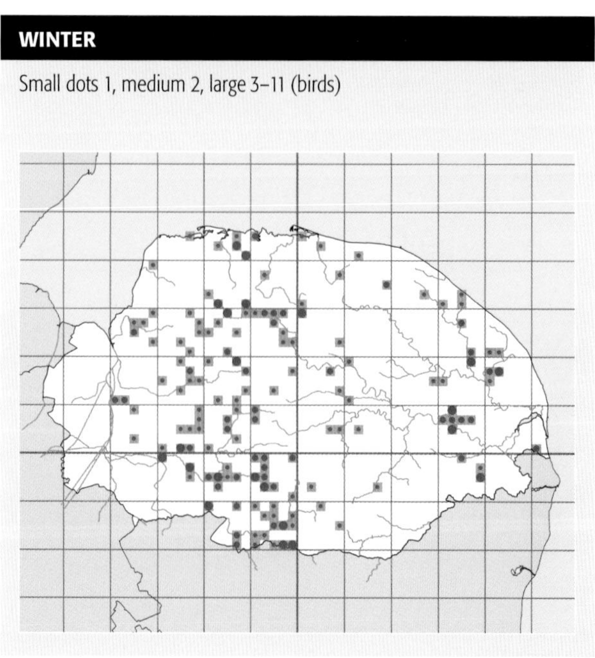

JIM ALMOND

The NBA summer map shows a very patchy and fragmented remnant distribution, with the majority of locations close to the county's rivers. During the 1990s, the species was being reported from up to 80 Norfolk localities in a single year, whereas during the eight NBA summers breeding was thought to be likely in only 67 tetrads. A marked fall was noted in Broadland in 2001 and more recently at one of the county's strongholds in the extensive woodlands at Swanton Novers. Very few sites currently hold more than one or two pairs.

CHANGE SINCE 1980–85

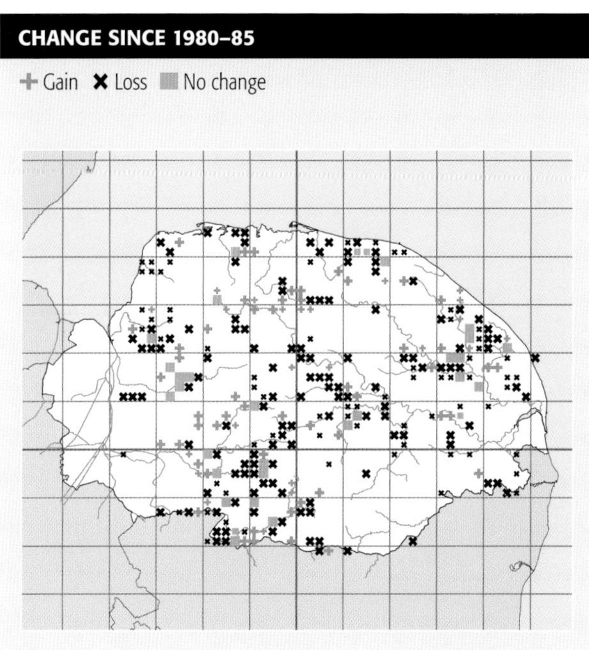

'Throughout the NBA period, observers have commented on the declining numbers in Norfolk.'

The winter map shows that they have a slightly wider distribution at that season than in the summer, especially in the west of the county. Pairs may remain on territory throughout the year, feeding in the winter on seeds, especially beechmast, and like Coal Tits they also store food. Some birds, however, perhaps mainly young of the year, wander a little more widely within suitable habitat in the winter season. Many records were of two birds together, but there were few sightings of more than just a pair, although up to six were present at Wheatfen in 2002.

The number of 10-km squares occupied by breeding birds has fallen sequentially from 56 in the *1968–72 Atlas* to just 35 in the NBA summers. Many of the remaining 10-km squares were represented by just one or two tetrads and are clearly vulnerable to further loss. Comparing the two county tetrad surveys, breeding was considered at least likely in only 67 tetrads in NBA summers compared with 224 in the *1980–85 NBBS*. The change map confirms that range loss has occurred in all parts of the former range within the county.

With perhaps as few as 40 pairs remaining, it appears that Willow Tit is one of the species currently most at risk of extinction in the county.

Marsh Tit

Poecile palustris

NBA 1999–2007	SUMMER: ALL / BREEDING	WINTER
TETRADS OCCUPIED	441 (30%) / 411 (28%)	607 (42%)
SUMMER/WINTER ONLY	83	249
MEAN PER OCCUPIED TETRAD	2 / 2	3
SUMMED MAX COUNTS	865 / 835	1,827
POPULATION ESTIMATE	1,200–1,600 bp	3,000–5,000

PREVIOUS ATLASES	SQUARES OCCUPIED	1999–2007	LOSSES	GAINS
1968–72 (10 KM)	59 (95%)	54 (87%)	6	1
1980–85 (TETRAD)	307 (21%)	411 (28%)	158	262
1980–85 (10 KM)	50 (81%)	54 (87%)	3	7
1981–84 WINTER (10 KM)	56 (90%)	57 (92%)	2	3
1988–91 (10 KM)	49 (79%)	54 (87%)	3	8

MARSH TITS ARE very close to Willow Tits in appearance but differ in voice and nowadays are much more abundant. Their habits are more similar to the other woodland tits, with which they sometimes associate.

Writing in 1930, *Riviere* described them as occurring in Norfolk in similar numbers to Coal Tits, but in the late 1960s numbers began to decline throughout Britain and they became much more localised in the county. A long-term decline had also been noted in several European countries, and the CBC/BBS index for England fell by 43% during 1982–2007 (*Birdtrends*). Like Willow Tits, Marsh Tits are red-listed birds of conservation concern on the strength of their population decline (*BoCC3*).

Marsh Tits usually remain within their woodland territories throughout the year, favouring mixed deciduous woods, where oaks provide caterpillars for their nestlings and the mast from beech trees is available during the winter months.

The NBA summer map shows a fairly sparse distribution, with breeding likely in only 28% of tetrads. There are clear concentrations in the more wooded parts of the county, especially the Brecks

SUMMER

Small dots 1, medium 2, large 3–17 ('pairs')
Shading – breeding proved or considered likely

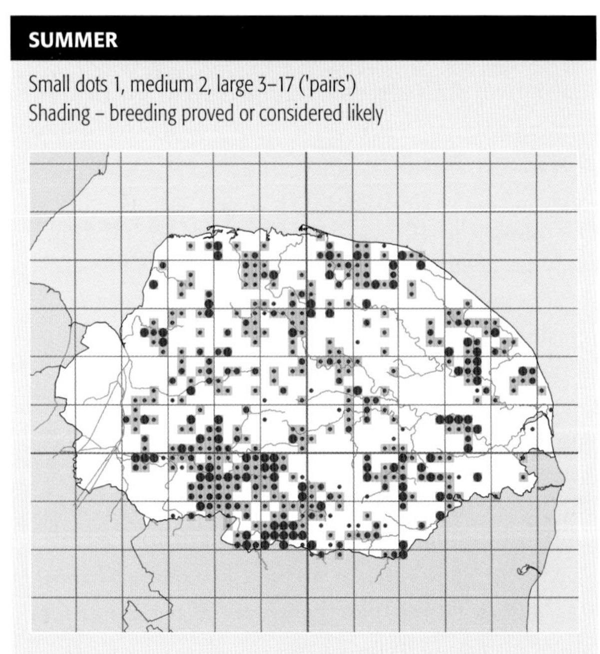

WINTER

Small dots 1–2, medium 3–4, large 5–24 (birds)

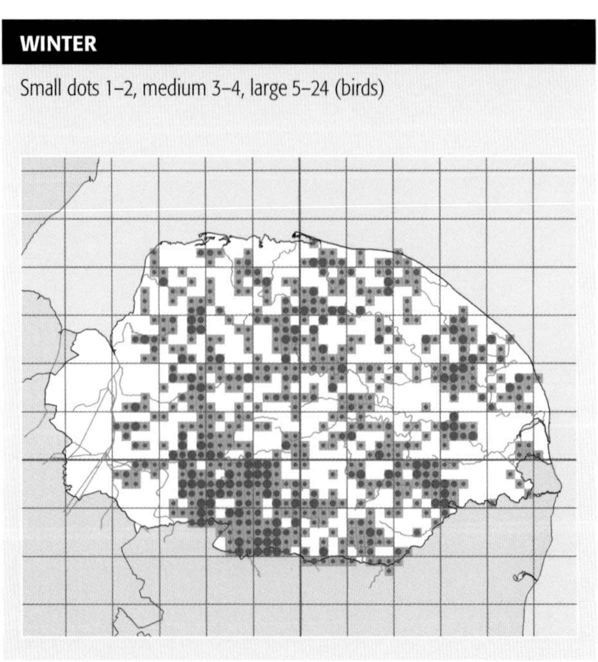

CHRIS KNIGHTS

and Thetford Forest, although the species is not usually seen in pure coniferous stands. Their absence during the breeding season from the major urban conurbations, such as Norwich, King's Lynn and Great Yarmouth, is notable, while suitable woodland habitat is completely lacking from the Fens. The species breeds at low density in some agricultural areas of the county, however, where it is able to make use of quite small woodland patches. The two sites that held the highest number of Marsh Tits during the NBA summers were Strumpshaw, with nine pairs in 2003, and Swanton Novers, with 15 singing males in 2005. It is likely that breeding took place, or at least was attempted, in almost all the tetrads shown on the summer map.

Although many pairs remain on territory through the winter, some movement and dispersal occurs, with some birds joining foraging tit flocks. They also visit gardens more frequently at this time of year. The species' distribution is therefore substantially wider in winter, often including wetter habitats such as around disused gravel pits that were formerly more usually associated with Willow Tits. As Marsh Tit song peaks in February and March, the species was possibly more conspicuous during the winter season. As in the summer, the highest winter tetrad count was at Swanton Novers, with 18 birds in December 2003.

Comparison with previous 10-km atlases indicates that occupancy fell between the *1968–72* and *1988–91 Atlases*, but has subsequently shown a partial recovery. An increase has also been recorded at tetrad level since 1980–85, when 21% of tetrads were occupied by birds possibly breeding, compared to 28% during the NBA summers.

CHANGE SINCE 1980–85

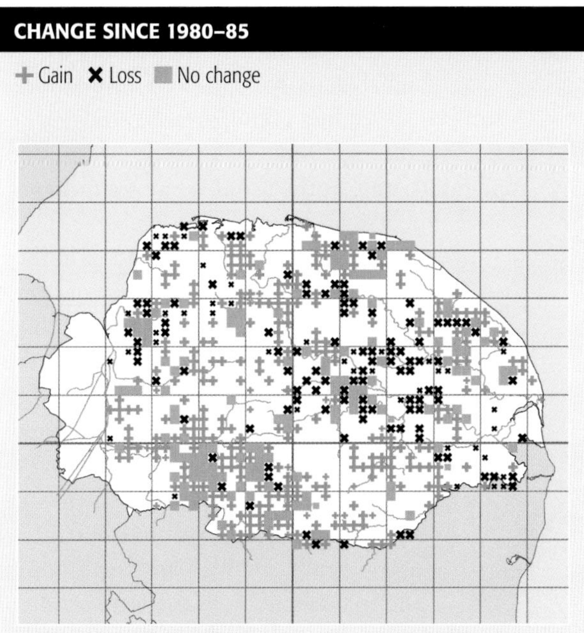

The change map shows that there is now a relative paucity of records in the hinterland of Norwich, particularly to the west. There are far more records in southeast Norfolk, however, centred around Long Stratton. Kelly, in the *1980–85 NBBS*, commented on the absence of records from ostensibly suitable woodland on the claylands of south Norfolk. It may well be that the species was largely overlooked in that area during the earlier survey. There have also been many tetrad gains in Breckland and in central parts of inland north Norfolk.

Bearded Tit

Panurus biarmicus

NBA 1999–2007	SUMMER: ALL/BREEDING	WINTER
TETRADS OCCUPIED	53 (4%) / 48 (3%)	55 (4%)
SUMMER/WINTER ONLY	13	15
MEAN PER OCCUPIED TETRAD	5 / 5	9
SUMMED MAX COUNTS	241 / 236	492
POPULATION ESTIMATE	200–250 bp	500–600

PREVIOUS ATLASES	SQUARES OCCUPIED	1999–2007	LOSSES	GAINS
1968–72 (10 KM)	14 (23%)	11 (18%)	5	2
1980–85 (TETRAD)	39 (3%)	48 (3%)	15	24
1980–85 (10 KM)	12 (19%)	11 (18%)	2	1
1981–84 WINTER (10 KM)	17 (27%)	15 (24%)	6	4
1988–91 (10 KM)	12 (19%)	11 (18%)	2	1

THE EXTRAORDINARY Bearded Tit and its strange calls are now familiar in many of the larger reedbeds across Britain, including those in Norfolk, which were once its last British refuge.

For at least the last 200 years, the population of Bearded Tits in Norfolk has fluctuated widely, being particularly susceptible to severe winter weather and to habitat changes, such as wetland drainage and water pollution. Broadland has always been the main stronghold within the county.

Bearded Tits are totally dependent on *Phragmites*, whether growing in large stands as at many of the county's wetland reserves or more thinly along the edges of the Broads, rivers and dykes. They breed in loose colonies, often raising three or more broods during the course of the summer.

The NBA summer map shows two clusters of occupied tetrads in the Broads and three more in the reedbeds along the north Norfolk coast. In Broadland, the occupied tetrads follow the Rivers Yare and Bure from Breydon Water, including Haddiscoe Island, the River Ant marshlands and the upper reaches of the River Thurne. It is in this last area that the largest concentration of Bearded Tits breed, based around Hickling Broad. Numbers increased there during the NBA period, largely due to the run of mild winters, and 84 pairs were found in 2005. In north Norfolk, up to 21 pairs bred at Titchwell during the NBA summers with smaller numbers at the other coastal sites.

Lopham Fen marks an unusually isolated inland outpost of the breeding range. Reedbeds here had become dry and overgrown but were restored to good condition in the 1990s; wintering birds returned to the site in 1998/99 and breeding was first suspected in 2002. The rapid colonisation of newly created reedbeds at Lakenheath, just beyond Norfolk's boundary, also shows the enormous potential of habitat creation for expanding the range of this species. Bearded Tits were also recorded during the summer recording period at Welney and at Colney GP.

Although Bearded Tits draw attention to themselves by their distinctive pinging calls, they wander widely through the reedbeds during the breeding season and no particularly reliable method has been devised for surveying breeding populations. A study at Hickling during 1980–2004 was, however, able to identify some of the possible environmental influences on Bearded Tit numbers (Cadbury 2005). In addition to the well-established effect of severe winter weather, especially prolonged snow cover, the Bearded Tit population there was also adversely affected by increased salinity and by increased levels of nitrates and phosphates, from sewage effluent and excretions from roosting gulls. Dieback and regression of the reed fringe, from the wave action of passing boat traffic and from grazing by

DAVID TIPLING

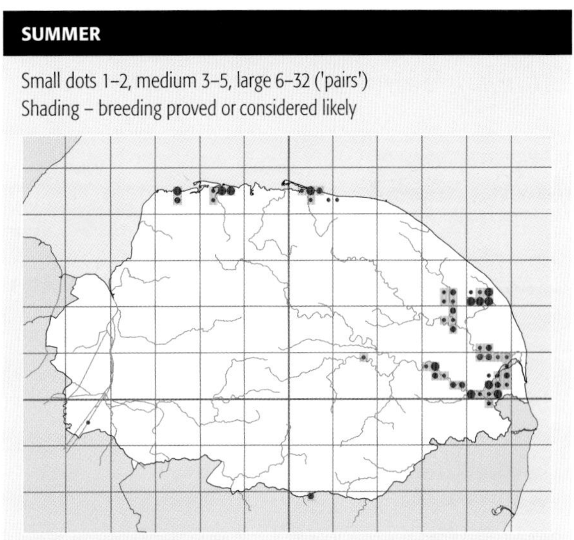

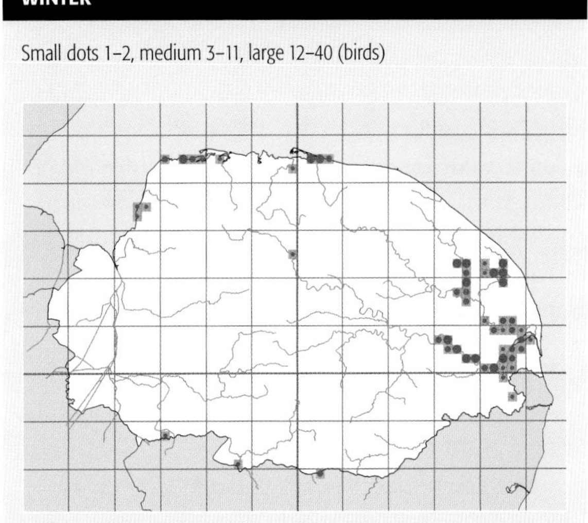

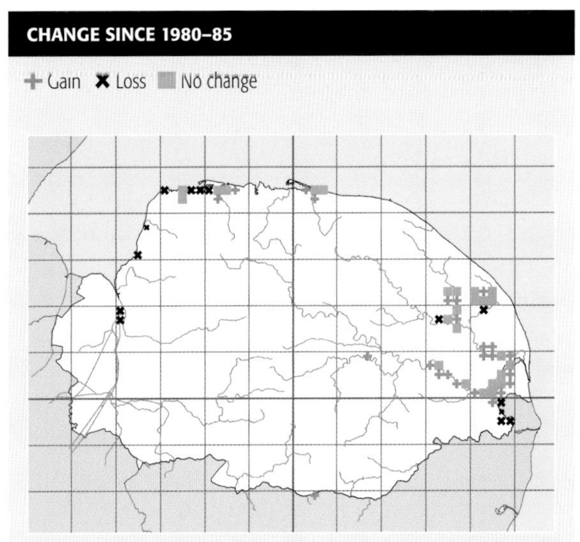

Greylag Geese, also had a negative effect.

The species is highly gregarious outside the breeding season and, although some move away from the natal reedbeds, the NBA winter map shows that Bearded Tits occupy the same general areas as in the summer. In addition, a few winter visitors were recorded at a few scattered localities where smaller reedbeds are present. Double-figure counts in winter were made at very few sites but included up to 40 at Titchwell, 25 at Cley, 48 at Hickling Broad and 26 at Strumpshaw.

Whereas between the 1960s and 1980s Bearded Tits were arriving from the Continent as winter visitors and East Anglian birds were wintering at distant localities across England, the species has become much less migratory and movement in and out of Norfolk is probably now very limited.

Comparisons with previous atlases suggest that the population has become more concentrated into its core areas. The number of occupied 10-km squares fell from 14 in 1968–72 to 11 in the NBA summers. More tetrads were occupied during NBA than in the *1980–85 NBBS*, however, with gains within the Broads, and colonisation at Lopham Fen and Colney GP, but losses in west Norfolk.

Woodlark
Lullula arborea

NBA 1999–2007	SUMMER: ALL / BREEDING	WINTER
TETRADS OCCUPIED	142 (10%) / 111 (8%)	70 (5%)
SUMMER/WINTER ONLY	86	14
MEAN PER OCCUPIED TETRAD	2 / 2	5
SUMMED MAX COUNTS	272 / 237	328
POPULATION ESTIMATE	180–300 bp	100–250

PREVIOUS ATLASES	SQUARES OCCUPIED	1999–2007	LOSSES	GAINS
1968–72 (10 KM)	10 (16%)	21 (34%)	2	13
1980–85 (TETRAD)	10 (<1%)	111 (8%)	2	103
1980–85 (10 KM)	4 (6%)	21 (34%)	0	17
1981–84 WINTER (10 KM)	2 (3%)	20 (32%)	2	20
1988–91 (10 KM)	3 (5%)	21 (34%)	0	18

THE WOODLARK is justly famous for its wonderful lilting song, which is delivered in flight high above a common or clearing, on the ground, or even from a tree. It formerly bred across almost all of England and Wales but in recent times has had a very patchy distribution, of which Breckland has long been an important part.

Woodlarks favour well-drained sites with areas of bare ground and short vegetation, such as heather. Farmland is occupied in some regions, but the birds usually avoid intensive agriculture. Such conditions are provided on Norfolk's heathland and commons, and in Thetford Forest. At most sites, patches of bare, broken ground appear to be one of the major attractions.

For at least the last 200 years, the species, which is endemic to the western Palaearctic, has shown marked fluctuations across its range in both distribution and population (*BWP5*). Prior to the early 1920s, Woodlarks had become very rare in the county but subsequently they spread once more throughout the Brecks. As the conifers that had been planted in the 1920s and 1930s matured and began to be felled during the 1980s, the replanted parts of Thetford Forest produced suitable habitats for breeding Woodlarks and the Breckland population increased thirteen-fold between 1984 and 1998. However, the young conifer plantations remain suitable for nesting Woodlarks for only six years (Hoblyn *et al* 2004). To overcome this problem, the ground can be ploughed between the rows of young trees so that the vegetation remains low.

The NBA summer map clearly shows the main stronghold of the species to be in Breckland, especially Thetford Forest, with smaller foci in the Sandringham/Roydon Common area and on the north Norfolk heaths. Away from Breckland, where 100–250 pairs of Woodlarks were present during the NBA summers, an additional 20–30 pairs occupied sites in west, central and north Norfolk, with Roydon Common being particularly favoured. Other records indicate spring migration and, in addition to those mapped, several were recorded singly as flyovers at coastal sites. One bird spent the whole of a May day in the ternery at Scolt Head!

Male Woodlarks sing mainly while looking for a mate and in the immediate period after pairing; consequently the location of pairs may be far more difficult later on in the breeding season. Although not colonial, several pairs are often found in fairly close proximity. It is a characteristic of the species that breeding sites occupied in one year may well remain vacant in the next year, despite successful nesting.

Woodlarks in the north and east of their breeding range are migratory, whereas those further south and west are resident. In East Anglia, the breeding sites are deserted in winter, whereas the Woodlarks that nest in southern England, particularly in the southwest, are largely resident. In Norfolk, the birds gather into flocks in the autumn before moving away for the winter; some remain on local farmland, however, for example 18 on barley stubble at Feltwell in December 1993 and up to 37 in 1995.

Although there appear to be differing habitat requirements between winter and summer, the NBA winter map is remarkably similar to that in the summer, with a distinct concentration in Breckland, as well as scattered records from the breeding areas in west and north Norfolk. This is largely due to Woodlarks' habit of returning to their breeding sites in late winter; many were back on territory

CHRIS KNIGHTS

and in song by late January or early February, and were thus present during the winter recording period. Unprecedented winter numbers were recorded in the county during 2004/05 and 2005/06, however. In January 2005, counts on a stubble field at Beachamwell peaked at 95, while a further 58 birds were present on barley stubbles, at Croxton, Feltwell, Ickburgh and Weeting. The NBA population estimates for the two seasons allow for at least part of the Norfolk breeding population leaving the county in winter.

The varying fortunes of the species in Norfolk are well demonstrated by the numbers of occupied 10-km squares recorded during the *1968–72 Atlas* (10), the *1980–85 NBBS* (4), the *1988–91 Atlas* (3), and NBA (21). These figures are influenced though by the withholding of records from the *1980–85 NBBS* by some observers, which has precluded the presentation of a change map, and by the relatively long period of NBA fieldwork. An annual survey of breeding Woodlark pairs in Thetford Forest has been carried out since 1984; the histogram shows changes in the Norfolk section of the Forest during the NBA period, missing 2001 when data were incomplete. Although numbers fell in Thetford Forest between 2000 and 2007, the Sandringham/Roydon Common population increased over the NBA period.

SUMMER

Small dots 1, medium 2–3, large 4–11 ('pairs')
Shading – breeding proved or likely, dots centralised away from Breckland

WINTER

Small dots 1, medium 2–3, large 4–95 (birds)

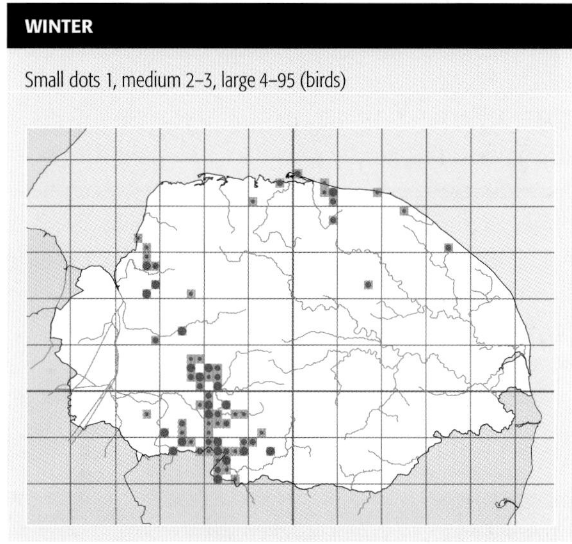

BREEDING TOTALS

Breeding pairs in Norfolk for each of the NBA summers (data from *NBR*)

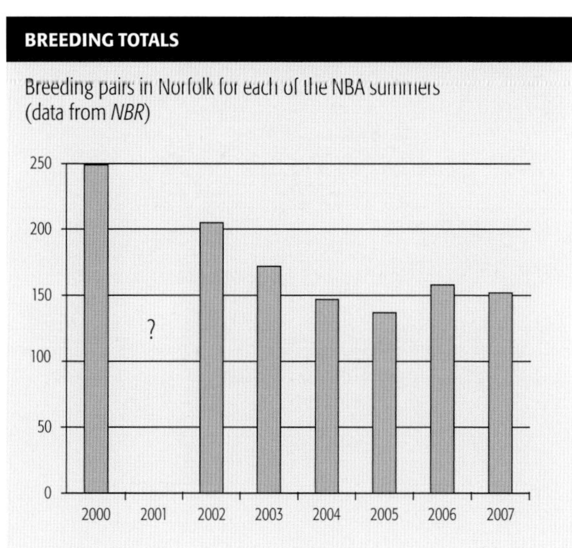

Skylark
Alauda arvensis

NBA 1999–2007	SUMMER: ALL / BREEDING	WINTER
TETRADS OCCUPIED	1,374 (94%) / 1,358 (93%)	1,252 (86%)
SUMMER/WINTER ONLY	150	28
MEAN PER OCCUPIED TETRAD	12 / 12	34
SUMMED MAX COUNTS	16,542 / 16,492	42,785
POPULATION ESTIMATE	25,000–30,000 bp	60,000–80,000

PREVIOUS ATLASES	SQUARES OCCUPIED	1999–2007	LOSSES	GAINS
1968–72 (10 KM)	62 (all)	62 (all)		
1980–85 (TETRAD)	1,379 (95%)	1,358 (93%)	80	59
1980–85 (10 KM)	62 (all)	62 (all)		
1981–84 WINTER (10 KM)	62 (all)	62 (all)		
1988–91 (10 KM)	62 (all)	62 (all)		

THE SKYLARK IS the commonest and most widespread lark in the western Palaearctic. In rural Norfolk, the joyous song for which the species is celebrated can be heard almost countywide.

In Britain and most other northern and western European countries, the numbers of breeding Skylarks have fallen strongly since 1980 as a result of a reduction in crop diversity, the increasing use of pesticides and herbicides, and the change to autumn-sown cereals. The planting of winter wheat and winter barley has meant that fewer winter stubble fields are available to Skylarks, as well as the finches and buntings, and by the spring the crop is too tall for the Skylarks to nest in. In England, the decrease has been estimated at 41% between 1982 and 2007 (*Birdtrends*).

Skylarks are birds of open country, especially arable farmland but also heathland, grazing marshes, sand dunes and saltmarshes. The NBA summer map shows that they are one of the most widespread species in the county, having been recorded in 94% of tetrads. Their absence from the built-up areas of central Norwich and King's Lynn are understandable, but the lack of records from the Tilney area of the Fens is less easily explained, as their song flight makes them easy to locate and Skylarks sing throughout the spring and early summer. It is of interest to note that in many tetrads the count of singing Skylarks was higher in the second summer set visit than in the first.

SUMMER

Small dots 1–7, medium 8–14, large 15–63 ('pairs')
Shading – breeding proved or considered likely

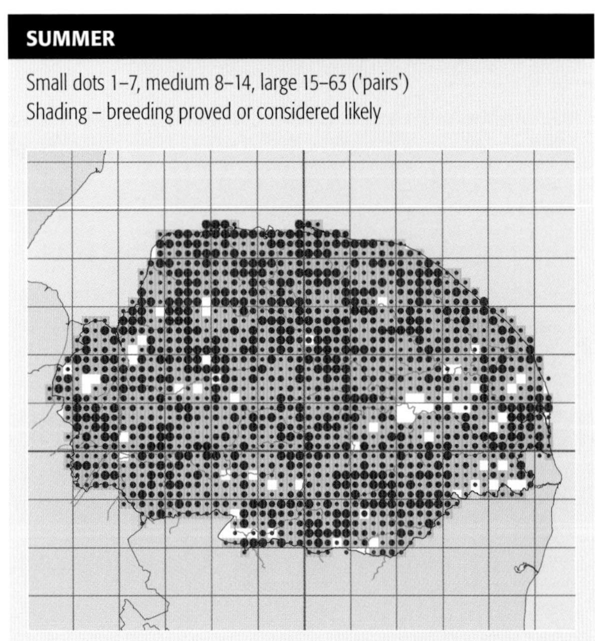

WINTER

Small dots 1–8, medium 9–30, large 31–700 (birds)

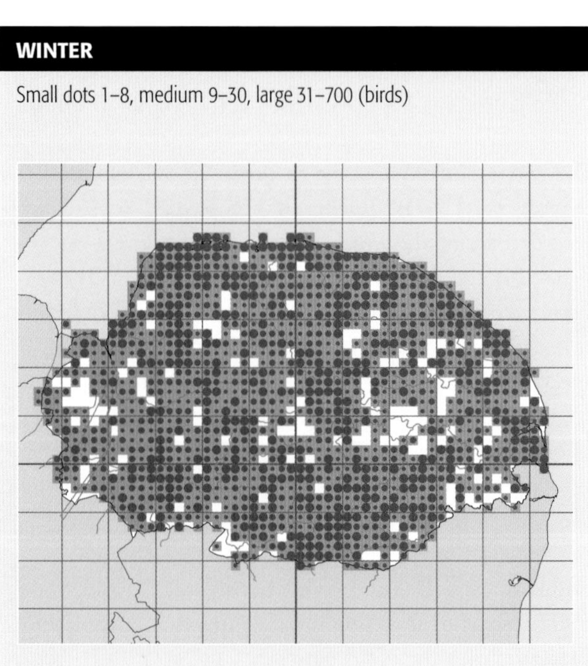

DAVID TIPLING

In general, the higher densities of breeding pairs were found in those parts of the county where cereals and root crops, particularly sugar beet, were grown. At a more local level, bulb fields proved particularly attractive, as did the presence of set-aside and uncropped field margins. The importance of coastal grazing marshes and arable land was well demonstrated by the two tetrads covering the Burnham Overy Marshes, which held 63 and 57 breeding pairs respectively, two of the highest tetrad counts in the county. Nearby, the saltmarshes and sand dunes at Scolt Head held 80–90 pairs during the NBA summers, peaking at 97 in 2006.

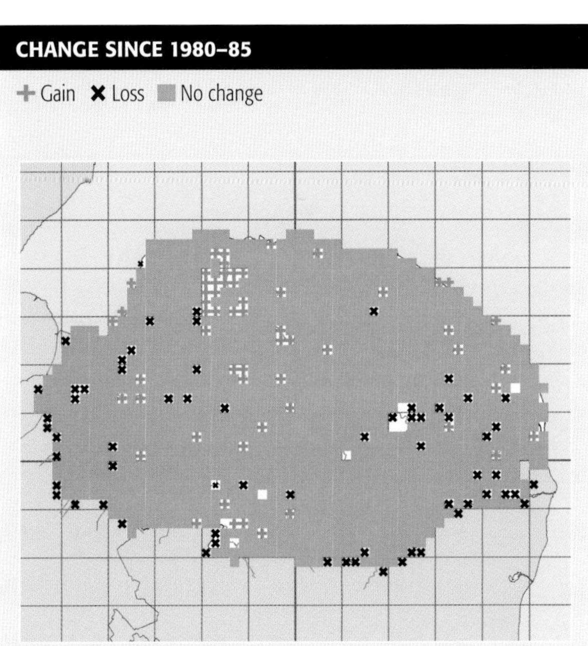

Skylarks gather into flocks outside the breeding season and spend the winter in similar habitats to those in which they summer. Stubble fields are particularly favoured, as are fields where sugar beet is being lifted. They are also found around the coast along shingle beaches, sand dunes and saltmarshes, especially during periods of hard weather. The NBA winter map also shows the species to be very widely distributed, although again it is absent from urban Norwich and from isolated pockets in central Norfolk, as well as the fenland around Tilney and Wiggenhall. The coastal strip between Holme and Cromer is clearly an important area for wintering Skylarks, as is the Diss area of central south Norfolk.

Norfolk's Skylarks are generally resident, moving only short distances except during periods of severe weather; however, many birds from northern Europe move through the county in autumn and spring, and influxes from the Continent prompted by cold weather can occur at any time through the winter. Some of the largest flocks recorded during the NBA winters were in December 2001 and January 2002, with 845 at Scolt Head and 700 at Kelling WM, while 800 were present in a sixty-acre field at Gooderstone in December 2003, and flocks of 500 were recorded at Waxham, Paston and Langham in other winters. A flock of 500 was also noted roosting in a field of oilseed rape at Aylmerton in late February 2004, the birds possibly held up on their return to the Continent.

Despite the extent of national decline in numbers, any such trend within Norfolk has had no effect on range as measured at the 10-km or tetrad level. The only change of interest since the *1980–85 NBBS* has been an increase of four tetrads in the area of Norwich that is unoccupied by the species.

Shore Lark

Eremophila alpestris

NBA 1999–2007	SUMMER: ALL/BREEDING	WINTER
TETRADS OCCUPIED	17 (1%) / none	19 (1%)
SUMMER/WINTER ONLY	9	11
MEAN PER OCCUPIED TETRAD	3 / none	15
SUMMED MAX COUNTS	58 / none	276
POPULATION ESTIMATE	none	10–150

PREVIOUS ATLASES	SQUARES OCCUPIED	1999–2007	LOSSES	GAINS
1981–84 WINTER (10 KM)	9 (15%)	9 (15%)	2	2

WITH ITS STRIKING yellow and black head pattern, the Shore Lark is our most attractively plumaged lark. It is a scarce winter visitor to Norfolk from its breeding grounds in the mountains of Scandinavia and the Russian tundra.

The first British record was of one killed at Sheringham in March 1830. Regular wintering in Britain, mainly along the east coast between Grampian and Kent, dates only from the 1870s (Brown & Grice 2005).

During the NBA winters, the population has been confined largely to the saltmarshes and beaches of northwest Norfolk, with very few records from elsewhere. Shore Larks have been recorded during migration, however, from many other coastal and even inland sites. Despite their bright head markings their presence can easily be missed, as they often crouch or run rather than fly. Snow Buntings or the other buntings or finches with which they often associate may draw attention to them. Their favoured feeding areas are the beaches below coastal sand dunes, shingle banks and exposed saltmarshes, where they feed mainly on the seeds of *Salicornia* (*1981–84 Winter Atlas*). The combination of these three habitats in the Holkham Bay and Blakeney areas attracts the largest groups.

Numbers fluctuate widely between winters. During the *1981–84 Winter Atlas* there were estimated to be a maximum of 300 birds in Britain. In Norfolk there were just one or two birds in 1988/89, but a coordinated count in December 1998 found an extraordinary total of 591, more than double the previous peaks in the 1970s (Lawton 1999). In the NBA winters, there were as few as 10 in the 2000/01 winter and a peak of 143 in 2002/03. During the latter winter, up to 100 were present daily on the constantly exposed saltmarsh at Holkham Bay. Over recent years this has always been one of the species' favourite feeding sites, along with the shingle bank between Blakeney Point and Salthouse, where birds feed on the seeds of yellow horned poppy.

In earlier decades, when Shore Larks were more abundant, inland observations on farmland were far commoner. During the NBA period, there were only three such records: 17 on a field of winter wheat between Morston and Stiffkey on 28th December 2002, six on arable land near Wells on 31st January 2004 and four at Hempstead on 3rd April 2005. This last locality is well away from the coast and the birds concerned would have been on spring passage.

WINTER

Small dots 2–4, medium 5–12, large 13–100 (birds)

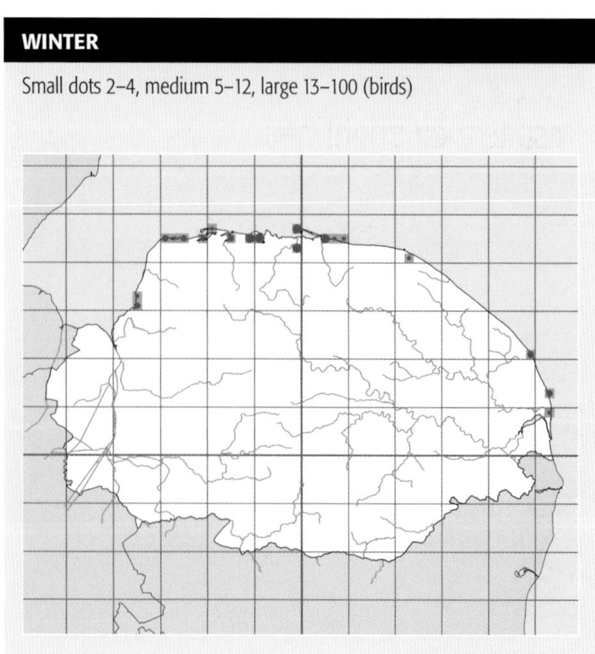

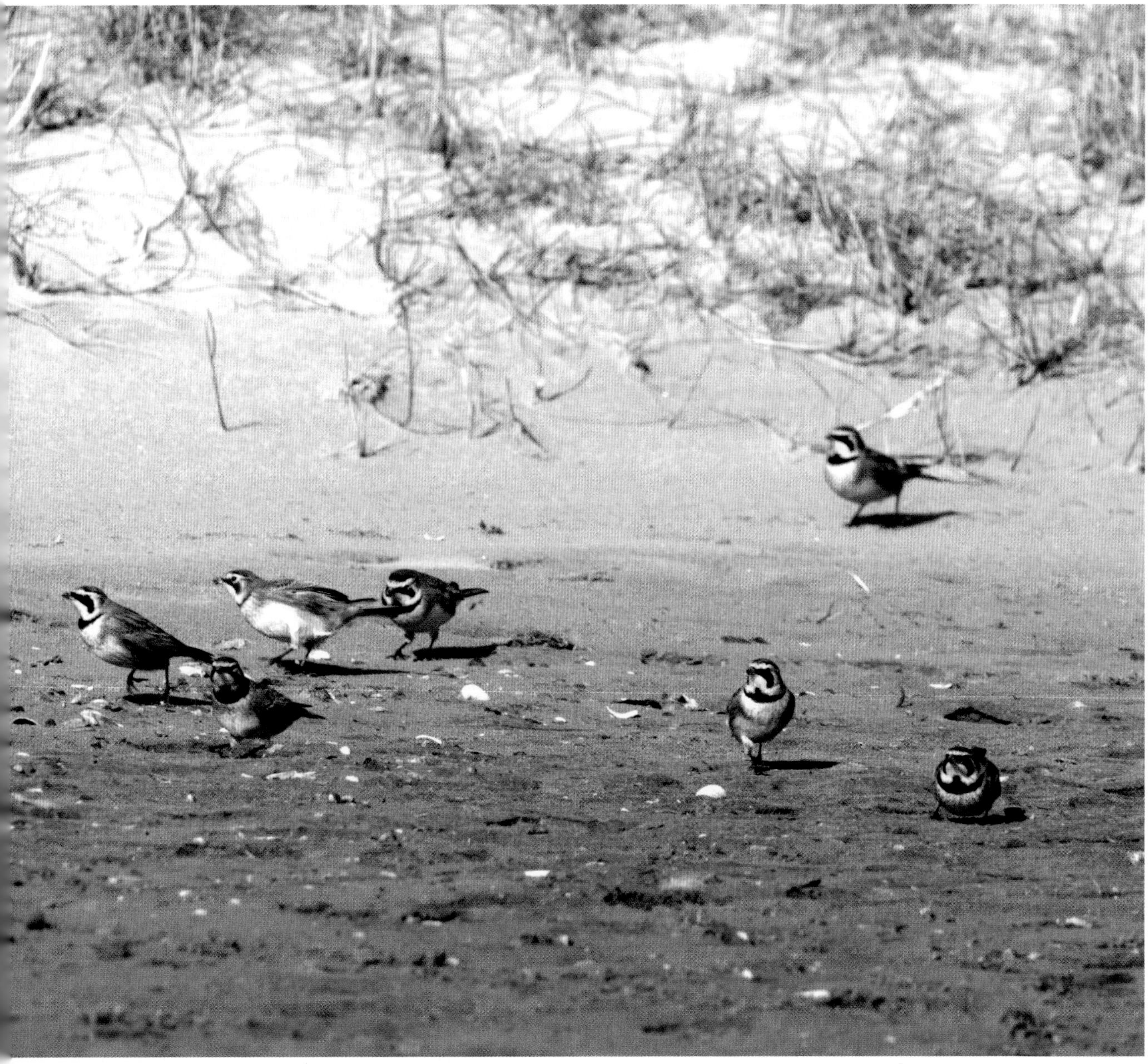

CHRIS KNIGHTS

'Despite their bright head markings their presence can easily be missed, as they often crouch or run rather than fly.'

Although most Shore Larks have left Norfolk by the end of March, some were reported in April and May, generally in similar locations to those used in winter, apart from a party of 28 at Horsey on 25th–26th April 2003. Possibly these same birds had been present on Scolt Head ten days earlier and might have included the 15 on Blakeney Point on 20th–25th April. The latest spring date during the NBA period was one at Happisburgh on 13th May 2000.

WINTER TOTALS

Winter count totals 1999–2007
(data from *NBR*)

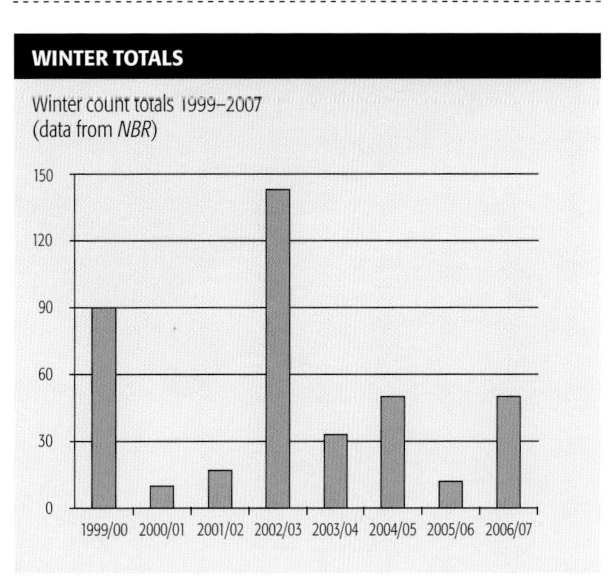

Sand Martin
Riparia riparia

NBA 1999–2007	SUMMER: ALL / BREEDING	WINTER
TETRADS OCCUPIED	199 (14%) / 83 (6%)	none
SUMMER/WINTER ONLY	199	none
MEAN PER OCCUPIED TETRAD	21 / 42	none
SUMMED MAX COUNTS	4,225 / 3,492	none
POPULATION ESTIMATE	3,000–4,000 bp	none

PREVIOUS ATLASES	SQUARES OCCUPIED	1999–2007	LOSSES	GAINS
1968–72 (10 KM)	59 (95%)	39 (63%)	21	1
1980–85 (TETRAD)	221 (15%)	83 (6%)	175	37
1980–85 (10 KM)	47 (76)	39 (63%)	13	5
1981–84 WINTER (10 KM)	1 (2%)	none	1	0
1988–91 (10 KM)	46 (74%)	39 (63%)	16	9

THE FIRST SAND MARTINS generally appear in Norfolk in mid March and are often among the earliest of all the spring arrivals. As colonial birds with specialist nesting requirements, their range has always been much more restricted than those of the other hirundines.

As new sand quarries were excavated during the 20th century, Sand Martins became more widespread as breeding birds in Britain but, after the 1960s, numbers declined over much of northwest Europe, due primarily to drought in their winter quarters in the Sahel region of West Africa. The autumn roosts estimated at 75,000 at Wiggenhall and 15,000 at Cantley in August 1965 seem inconceivable today.

DAVID TIPLING

Sand Martins are gregarious at all times of the year and nest in colonies, generally of 10–50 pairs. They excavate their nesting burrows in vertical banks of sand or loam, sited along rivers or streams, around working sand pits or on coastal cliffs. Birds breeding in sand quarries are not deterred by the presence of workers and heavy machinery and tend to favour active or recently excavated sites. At some sites, new nesting faces are specially created for the birds each spring.

In the mid 1960s a few Norfolk colonies held over a thousand pairs each but, during the NBA summers, the largest colonies were of 300 at Happisburgh and 290 at Sandy Hill in the Stanford TA, while up to 350 nested in several scattered colonies along the cliffs at Sheringham. Sand Martins have been nesting on the cliffs at Cromer since at least the 19th century. Occasionally, nests have been located in the drainage pipes along stone-embanked rivers.

The NBA summer map shows a sparse and scattered distribution, with colonies tending to follow the lines of the river valleys, where many of the sand pits are situated, and the sandy coastal cliffs around northeast Norfolk. The small concentration of occupied tetrads in west Norfolk largely relates to the gravel pits in the Nar valley.

The comparisons with earlier 10-km atlases show a progressive decline in range, from 59 occupied squares in 1968–72 to only 39 in the NBA period. The change map shows that, by comparison with the *1980–85 NBBS*, many previously occupied sites throughout the previous range no longer hold Sand Martins. Some new tetrads have been occupied, however, perhaps with pairs moving in as suitable sandy banks become newly available. Coastal erosion also has its effect in the turnover of tetrads, as previously occupied sites disappear in cliff falls and new, soft cliff faces are created. Losses of range, with no gains, are indicated in the Bure valley around Coltishall, around Norwich, on the Little Ouse and Thetford and in the upper Waveney valley. It may be that Norfolk Sand Martins no longer nest in drainpipes in concrete riverbanks, as they used to in Norwich and in Thetford.

During the NBA period, there were no winter records of Sand Martins, although there are five December records from earlier years, involving six birds.

SUMMER

Small dots 1–2, medium 3–12, large 13–300 ('pairs')
Shading – breeding proved or considered likely

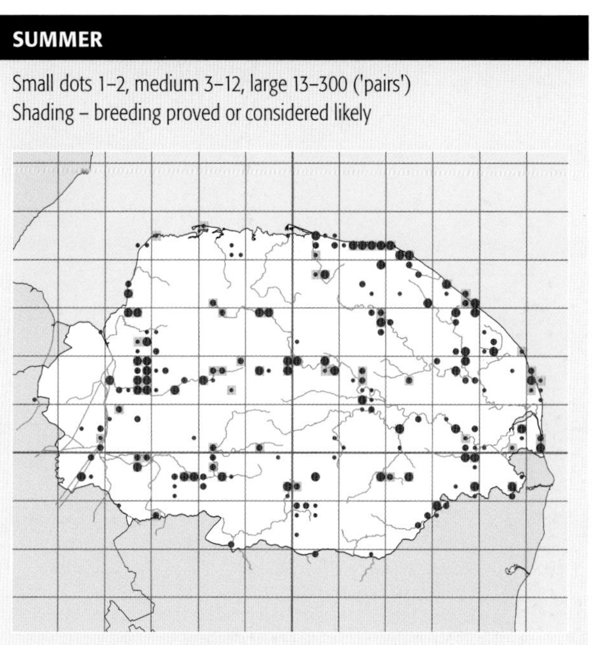

CHANGE SINCE 1980–85

+ Gain ✖ Loss ■ No change

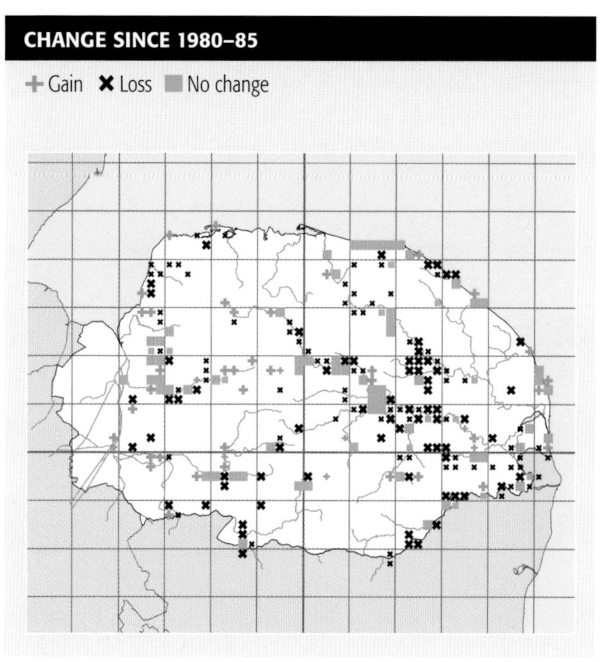

Swallow
Hirundo rustica

NBA 1999–2007	SUMMER: ALL/BREEDING	WINTER
TETRADS OCCUPIED	1,339 (92%) / 1,257 (86%)	20 (1%)
SUMMER/WINTER ONLY	1,320	1
MEAN PER OCCUPIED TETRAD	7 / 7	1
SUMMED MAX COUNTS	8,951 / 8,686	27
POPULATION ESTIMATE	10,000–12,000 bp	none

PREVIOUS ATLASES	SQUARES OCCUPIED	1999–2007	LOSSES	GAINS
1968–72 (10 KM)	62 (all)	62 (all)		
1980–85 (TETRAD)	1,372 (94%)	1,257 (86%)	160	45
1980–85 (10 KM)	62 (all)	62 (all)		
1981–84 WINTER (10 KM)	14 (23%)	14 (23%)	8	8
1988–91 (10 KM)	62 (all)	62 (all)		

THE SWALLOW, typically seen swooping low after flying insects, epitomises warm summer days. With its long, backswept wings and long tail streamers, it is the classic hirundine. It is a widespread breeding visitor throughout the western Palaearctic, except for the arctic tundra and southern deserts, the vast majority of European birds wintering in Africa south of the Sahara.

Although numbers have always tended to fluctuate, a widespread decline has been noted in recent years across much of Europe. This has been due to a combination of factors on the breeding grounds, including a loss of feeding habitats, a reduction in the supply of flying insects – secondary to changes in agricultural practice and the increasing use of insecticides – and the loss of nesting sites due to barn conversions. Wetter summer weather in Europe has had an adverse effect, while drought in the winter quarters has also taken its toll (*BWP5*).

The first spring migrants generally arrive back in Norfolk in March, although two were reported in mid February 2004. Typically, breeding Swallows are found around farms, especially those holding livestock and having a farm pond, and in other rural or semi-rural areas, such as villages or isolated dwellings. In Norfolk, their nests are almost invariably built inside open buildings, such as barns, stables, sheds, outhouses or garages, a single, suitable building sometimes supporting several breeding pairs.

The NBA summer map shows the species to be very widespread within the county, with particularly high numbers in Broadland. The only areas from

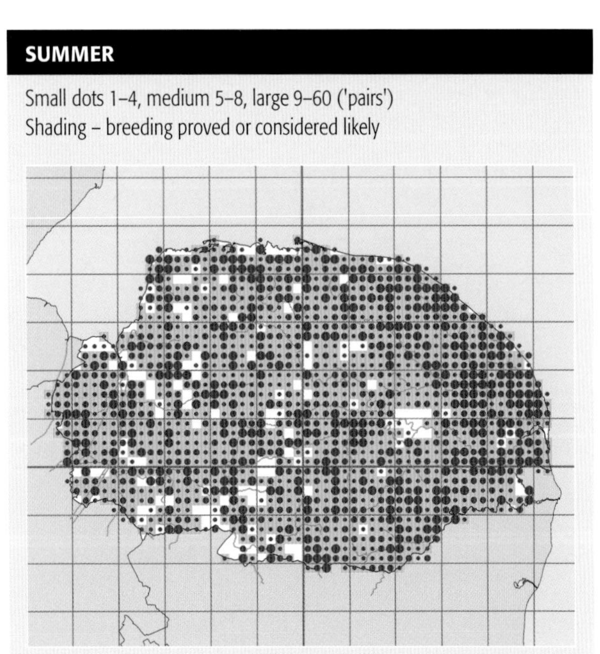

SUMMER

Small dots 1–4, medium 5–8, large 9–60 ('pairs')
Shading – breeding proved or considered likely

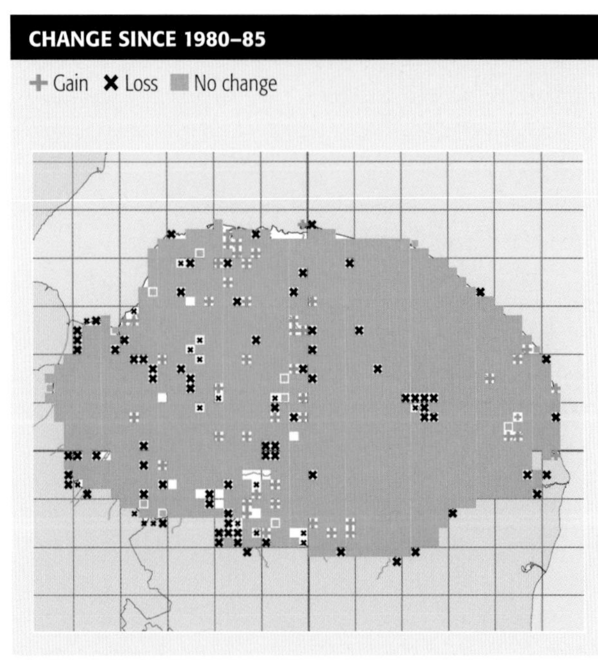

CHANGE SINCE 1980–85

+ Gain ✖ Loss ■ No change

DAVID TIPLING

which Swallows were absent were the heavily built-up parts of Norwich (the map almost exactly delineating the city boundaries) and King's Lynn, and sections of Thetford Forest.

With its many unoccupied buildings, the Stanford TA has always held a good population of nesting Swallows, surveys in 2004 and 2005 revealing the presence of over 100 breeding pairs. Welney, with its ideal feeding conditions for hirundines, held 40 nesting pairs in 2000, including many inside the birdwatching hides, although nest failure rates were high owing to Sparrowhawks entering the hides and taking the adults.

Comparisons with the previous atlases indicate that little range change has occurred at 10-km or at tetrad level. The change map, comparing occupied tetrads between the *1980–85 NBBS* and NBA, indicates that there have been losses, with no corresponding gains, in Norwich, in parts of Thetford Forest and the Fens, and along the River Waveney.

'The first spring migrants generally arrive back in Norfolk in March, although two were reported in mid February 2004.'

In recent years, occasional Swallows have been seen in Norfolk in the winter months, especially at coastal sites. Apart from one at Hunstanton on 4th January 2005 and singles in mid February 2004 at South Walsham and King's Lynn, which were probably exceptionally early spring migrants, all the rest during the NBA period were in December. Over half the December sightings were in 2000 or 2006 and all involved single birds, apart from three at Cromer on 13th December 2000.

House Martin
Delichon urbicum

NBA 1999–2007	SUMMER: ALL / BREEDING	WINTER
TETRADS OCCUPIED	1,114 (76%) / 974 (67%)	16 (1%)
SUMMER/WINTER ONLY	1,100	2
MEAN PER OCCUPIED TETRAD	9 / 10	5
SUMMED MAX COUNTS	10,076 / 9,495	77
POPULATION ESTIMATE	10,000–12,000 bp	none

PREVIOUS ATLASES	SQUARES OCCUPIED	1999–2007	LOSSES	GAINS
1968–72 (10 KM)	62 (all)	62 (all)		
1980–85 (TETRAD)	1,221 (84%)	974 (67%)	324	77
1980–85 (10 KM)	62 (all)	62 (all)		
1981–84 WINTER (10 KM)	13 (21%)	8 (13%)	8	3
1988–91 (10 KM)	62 (all)	62 (all)		

HOUSE MARTINS, ORIGINALLY a cliff-nesting species, have had a close association with man for at least the last four centuries, during which time the vast majority of their population in Britain have nested on buildings. The species occurs throughout much of the western Palaearctic and, although numbers fluctuate, it appears that a slow long-term decline has been taking place over a number of years (*Birdtrends*).

House Martins are migratory, wintering mainly in Africa south of the Sahara. The first spring migrants are normally recorded in Norfolk during the second half of March although the main arrival does not take place until late April or early May. The earliest spring arrival ever in Norfolk was noted on 29th February 2000, the year in which the earliest Sand Martin was also recorded.

House Martins are highly gregarious throughout the year and nest in colonies varying in size from a few pairs up to a hundred or more – although a colony's size depends on how its boundaries are drawn. Most nests are constructed under the eaves of houses or on bridges over rivers, the proximity of tree cover to houses with eaves being particularly attractive.

The NBA summer map shows that the species is widely distributed throughout the county, being absent from the more open agricultural parts of central Norfolk, the more heavily wooded areas in Breckland and open, flat areas such as parts of the Methwold Fens and the Halvergate Marshes.

SUMMER

Small dots 1–4, medium 5–10, large 11–84 ('pairs')
Shading – breeding proved or considered likely

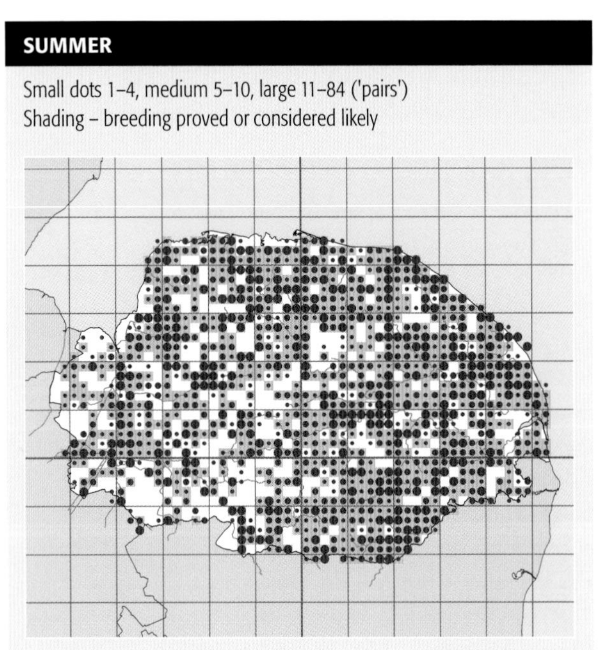

CHANGE SINCE 1980–85

+ Gain ✖ Loss ■ No change

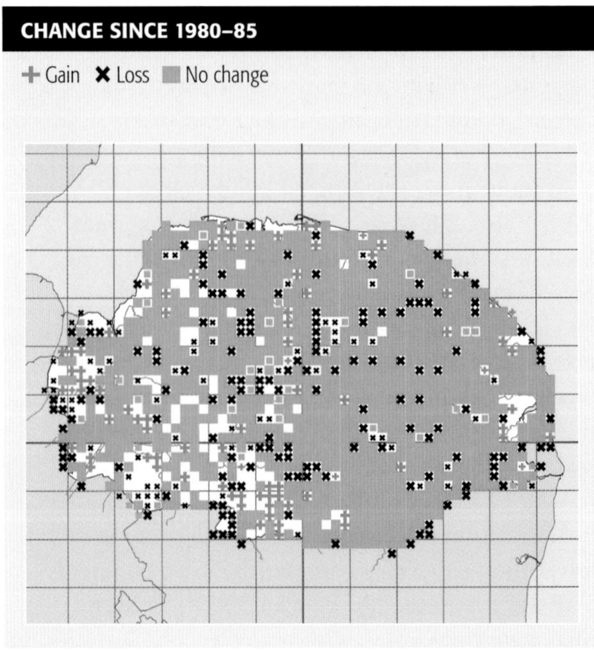

DAVID TIPLING

Nationally, colonies are generally smallest in urban areas and increase in size through suburban areas of towns to reach their largest in rural districts and small villages, with most large colonies being associated with farmyards or bridges over rivers (*1988–91 Atlas*). This certainly appears to hold true in Norfolk, with maxima of 132 nests on bridges over the Great Ouse Relief Channel, 43 at St George's School at Doddshill, near Dersingham, 35 on a farmhouse at Oby and 30 at Horning Hall during the NBA summers. The largest single colony count may have been of 48 nests at Magdalen Bridge over the RC in 2004. The highest tetrad count of occupied nests was of 84 at Lamas, and three tetrads at Cromer, Horsford and Hickling held over 60 breeding pairs.

Carefully constructed surveys are required to distinguish normal turnover of nesting sites at the local scale from population change at the county or national scale; for Norfolk, such data are currently lacking. The comparisons with previous atlases suggest that a net loss of occupied tetrads has occurred since the *1980–85 NBBS* but, since neither data set refers specifically to nests found, observer opinions about possible or likely breeding may be playing a significant part. The change map indicates that losses of occupied tetrads may have been most prevalent in Breckland and along the southern rivers.

Most House Martins have left the county by the end of October, with just a few stragglers remaining in November and occasional birds recorded in December. During the NBA period, the species was recorded in 17 tetrads in December, almost exclusively at coastal sites. Most of the records were made in 2000 or 2006. In December 2000, small parties of birds were noted feeding around the cliff-faces in northeast Norfolk between Waxham and Cromer, and presumably the same group of birds was involved. At the latter site they also fed around the seafront buildings near the pier, where a maximum of 13 was present on 6th–8th December. Cromer clearly holds a particular attraction for House Martins at this time of year, for one or two were also recorded here in December 2002 and 2006. The latest date was of one at Holkham GM on 16th December 2006.

Cetti's Warbler

Cettia cetti

NBA 1999–2007	SUMMER: ALL/BREEDING	WINTER
TETRADS OCCUPIED	116 (8%) / 109 (7%)	75 (5%)
SUMMER/WINTER ONLY	61	20
MEAN PER OCCUPIED TETRAD	3 / 4	3
SUMMED MAX COUNTS	395 / 388	188
POPULATION ESTIMATE	100–400 singing males	250–800

PREVIOUS ATLASES	SQUARES OCCUPIED	1999–2007	LOSSES	GAINS
1968–72 (10 KM)	none	22 (35%)	0	22
1980–85 (TETRAD)	37 (3%)	109 (7%)	6	78
1980–85 (10 KM)	11 (18%)	22 (35%)	2	13
1981–84 WINTER (10 KM)	7 (11%)	21 (34%)	0	14
1988–91 (10 KM)	8 (13%)	22 (35%)	2	16

WITH ITS SUDDEN outburst of brief song, the Cetti's Warbler betrays its presence deep in the tangled, waterside vegetation that it inhabits throughout the year. The first Cetti's Warbler in Norfolk was recorded in 1973, a Belgian-ringed bird dead in a Thorpe St Andrew garden, and breeding was proved the following year in the Yare valley. Since then the species has increased to become nowadays a characteristic bird of Broadland.

Male Cetti's Warblers are polygamous and noisy, and for the most part the map indicates the relative abundance of singing males. They inhabit inaccessible, scrubby areas bordering damp reed-swamp and alder carr, and they are difficult to see amongst the dense, low vegetation. Counting singing males and mapping these records is the only practical method of indicating the distribution and abundance of the species. Although the males' breeding territories are mutually exclusive, with clear-cut boundaries, they often extend for several hundred metres in linear scrub; each male patrols his territory, singing from different perches along the route (*BWP6*). Care must therefore be taken not to duplicate records.

The NBA summer map shows the extent of colonisation by 2007. There is a clear association with the Rivers Bure, Yare and to a lesser extent the Waveney, and their tributaries. During the NBA summers, the highest concentrations were along the Yare valley, where 90 singing males were recorded in 2003 (*NBR*), the River Ant and the Hickling/Horsey Broads area, where males favoured 'islands' of bramble and sallow scrub along dykes and in reedbeds (Cadbury 2005). The largest counts in 2000 were both made along the Yare, with 26 at Strumpshaw and 23 at Wheatfen, but by 2005 there were 31 breeding territories at Hickling Broad.

Despite occasional records in north Norfolk, it was not until 2003 that Cetti's Warblers were first proved to breed there. At Weybourne in that year, a male was paired to up to five females and three or four broods were successfully reared. Elsewhere in north Norfolk, three or four males were present at Titchwell and at least one brood was raised, while singing males were also present at several other localities. By the following year over ten males were present during the summer, although numbers fell in 2005, despite a mild winter. It is likely that about 250 territory-holding males were present in Norfolk by 2007, although the number could be considerably higher. The total of 176 singing males reported in 2006 was considered to be a gross underestimate, as only 137 were noted in the Broads, this region being hugely under-recorded.

Being resident insectivorous birds, Cetti's Warblers

BREEDING TOTALS

Breeding pairs in Norfolk for each of the NBA summers (data from *NBR*)

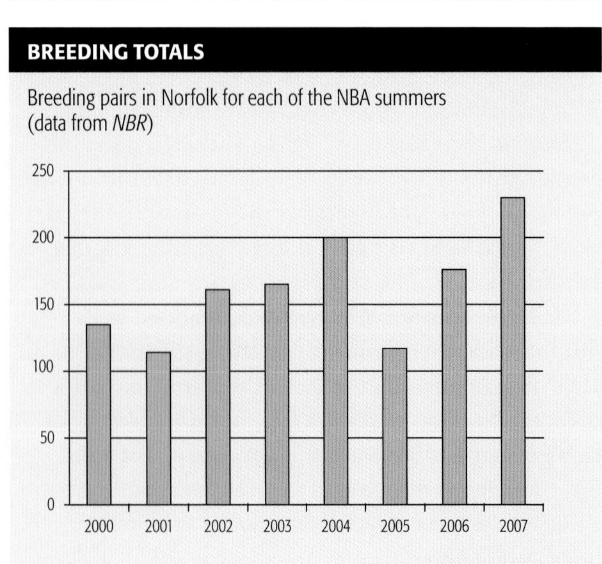

DAVID TIPLING

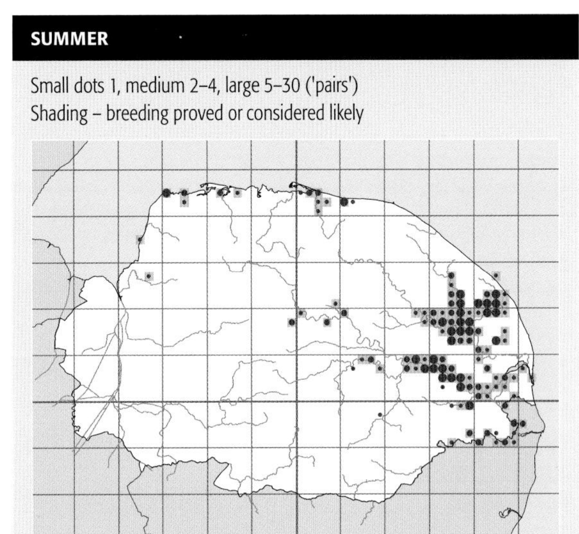

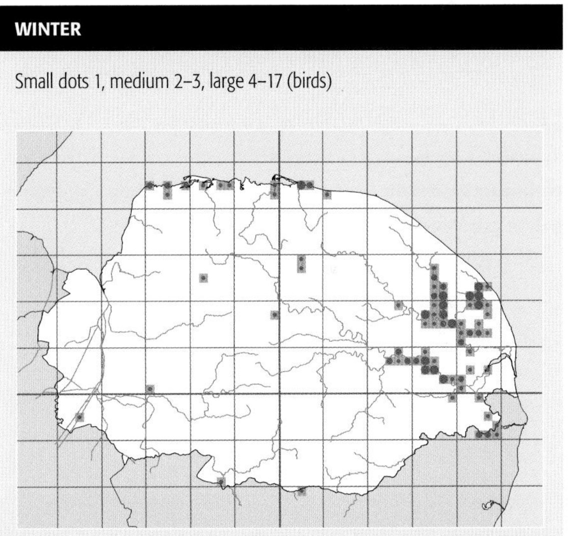

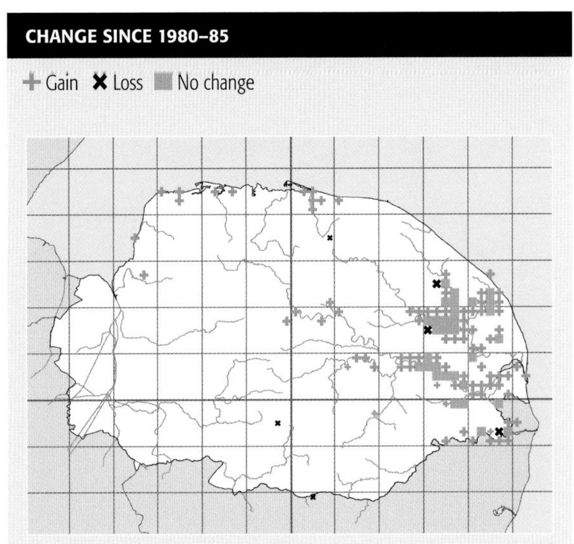

are susceptible to severe winter weather, particularly periods of prolonged freezing or snow cover. Fortunately, the series of mild winters that lasted throughout the NBA period has meant that the Norfolk population has thrived and spread beyond Broadland.

Males are quieter during winter and both sexes are hard to locate at this time of year as they feed on reed litter or creep through waterside vegetation. Nevertheless, the NBA winter distribution is a good match to the summer map, albeit with fewer tetrads recorded as occupied. The highest counts of singing males in winter were made at Hickling Broad (14), Horsey Mere (12) and Buckenham Marshes (10). The winter map also shows dispersal by some birds to localities well outside the current breeding range, such as Lopham Fen and Thetford Nunnery Lakes.

Comparing the current distribution map with that in the *1980–85 NBBS*, it is very apparent that Cetti's Warblers have spread throughout many parts of Broadland during the intervening 20 years, particularly along the lower reaches of the main rivers. The number of occupied 10-km squares has doubled and the number of tetrads almost trebled.

Cetti's Warblers have been very slow to spread along the Wensum valley, perhaps because the city of Norwich has been a barrier, but seven singing males were located beyond Norwich in 2004. Advance along the Waveney valley has also been very limited so far, with much apparently ideal habitat still unoccupied, and the complete lack of breeding records in Norfolk Fenland is surprising.

Long-tailed Tit
Aegithalos caudatus

NBA 1999–2007	SUMMER: ALL/BREEDING	WINTER
TETRADS OCCUPIED	1,129 (77%) / 1,095 (75%)	1,185 (81%)
SUMMER/WINTER ONLY	102	158
MEAN PER OCCUPIED TETRAD	3 / 3	15
SUMMED MAX COUNTS	3,695 / 3,646	17,780
POPULATION ESTIMATE	6,000–8,000 bp	25,000–40,000

PREVIOUS ATLASES	SQUARES OCCUPIED	1999–2007	LOSSES	GAINS
1968–72 (10 KM)	60 (97%)	62 (all)	0	2
1980–85 (TETRAD)	667 (46%)	1,095 (75%)	94	522
1980–85 (10 KM)	60 (97%)	62 (all)	0	2
1981–84 WINTER (10 KM)	59 (95%)	62 (all)	0	3
1988–91 (10 KM)	60 (97%)	62 (all)	0	2

DESPITE ITS SMALL size, the Long-tailed Tit draws attention by being continually on the move, either while foraging or flying line astern in winter flocks, as well as by its almost constant trilling contact notes.

It has always been a common resident in Norfolk. As it is a small, insectivorous bird, up to 80% of the population may succumb during hard winters, due to low temperatures and glazed frosts, but Long-tailed Tits have remarkable powers of recovery and within a couple of years will have returned to their former status.

Long-tailed Tits have a fascinating breeding strategy with failed breeders and siblings of the male parent acting as 'helpers at the nest', thus improving the chances of survival for the nestlings, to which they may be related. They are one of the earliest species to nest in the spring, their familiar dome-shaped nests being built in low prickly bushes, such as gorse, in dense hedges, amongst brambles or in the fork of a tree up to 20 metres off the ground. They are found during the breeding season along the edges of woodland and in clearings, along hedgerows, in patches of scrub, on commons and heathland, and even in large gardens.

The NBA summer map shows a very wide distribution, with the absence of any suitable cover accounting for the lack of records in the Fens and on marshlands inland from Breydon Water. The highest concentrations were of 24 and 18 pairs in the West Harling Common and

SUMMER

Small dots 1–2, medium 3–4, large 5–27 ('pairs')
Shading – breeding proved or considered likely

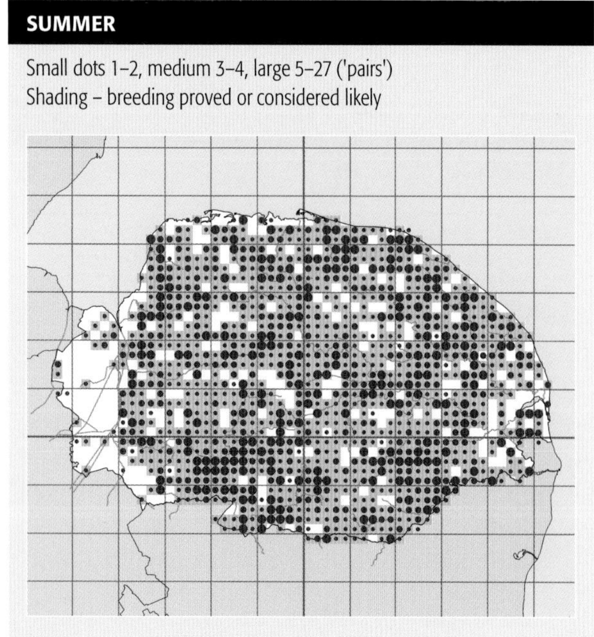

WINTER

Small dots 1–8, medium 9–16, large 17–127 (birds)

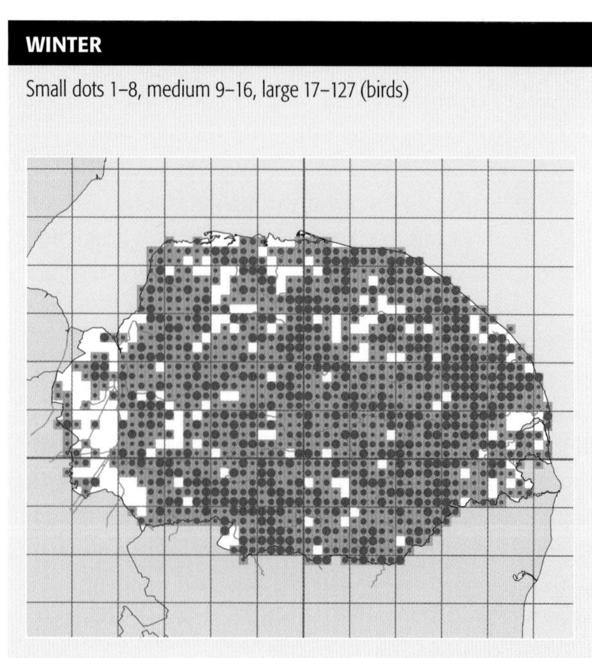

DAVID TIPLING

Neatishead tetrads respectively. Four other tetrads also held 15 or more pairs. Breckland shows a concentration of high tetrad counts.

After fledging, Long-tailed Tits remain in their family groups until the following spring, the winter flocks consisting of the parents, young and any additional helpers that joined them at the nest. These flocks generally wander around a fairly large, but defined area, throughout the winter, often following the same daily route and roosting in the same site each night. They join mixed flocks of tits and Goldcrests, and may also temporarily amalgamate with other family parties of Long-tailed Tits. Longer seasonal movements are occasional, including rare winter arrivals of white-headed continental races.

The NBA winter map, as expected, shows a very similar overall distribution to that in the summer, but with more being recorded in built-up areas, as Long-tailed Tits visited gardens to feed on fat and peanuts, a habit that has become widespread throughout the county. Groups consisting of several family parties accounted for the larger winter flocks that were recorded during the NBA period. The highest tetrad counts (but not single flocks) were 127 at Hockham Heath, 99 at Langmere, 86 near Honing and 81 at the eastern end of the Cromer to Holt ridge; in addition, several flocks totalling 100 birds were noted at Roydon Common. More than 25 tetrads produced counts of 50 or more Long-tailed Tits.

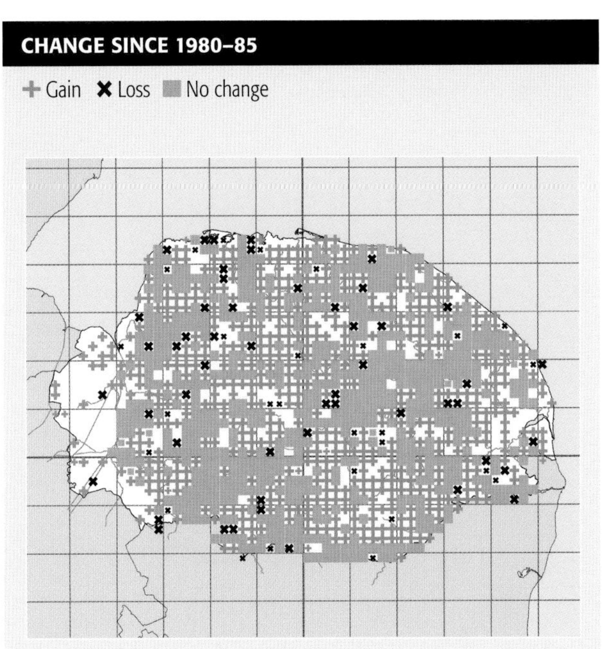

Comparisons with previous atlases indicate range extensions, in summer and in winter. The proportion of occupied tetrads increased from 46% in the *1980–85 NBBS* to 75% during the NBA summers. The change map shows that many of the previously unoccupied tetrads in Broadland and in the more extensively arable parts of Norfolk, particularly in the south, now host this species. Many more occupied tetrads were recorded in Fenland. Over the 25 years to 2007, the population in England is estimated to have risen by 72% (*Birdtrends*).

Wood Warbler

Phylloscopus sibilatrix

NBA 1999–2007	SUMMER: ALL/BREEDING	WINTER
TETRADS OCCUPIED	39 (3%) / none	none
SUMMER/WINTER ONLY	39	none
MEAN PER OCCUPIED TETRAD	1 / none	none
SUMMED MAX COUNTS	47 / none	none
POPULATION ESTIMATE	0–2 individuals	none

PREVIOUS ATLASES	SQUARES OCCUPIED	1999–2007	LOSSES	GAINS
1968–72 (10 KM)	16 (26%)	none	16	0
1980–85 (TETRAD)	63 (4%)	none	63	0
1980–85 (10 KM)	31 (50%)	none	31	0
1988–91 (10 KM)	20 (32%)	none	20	0

THE WOOD WARBLER is the largest of the European leaf-warblers. Its clean-cut appearance and sharp demarcation between the yellow breast and white belly are very distinctive, as is the trilling song.

The species is in strong decline across much of its European range. It has been in retreat in southeast England since before the *1968–72 Atlas*, and is now becoming increasing restricted to the sessile oak woods of western Britain.

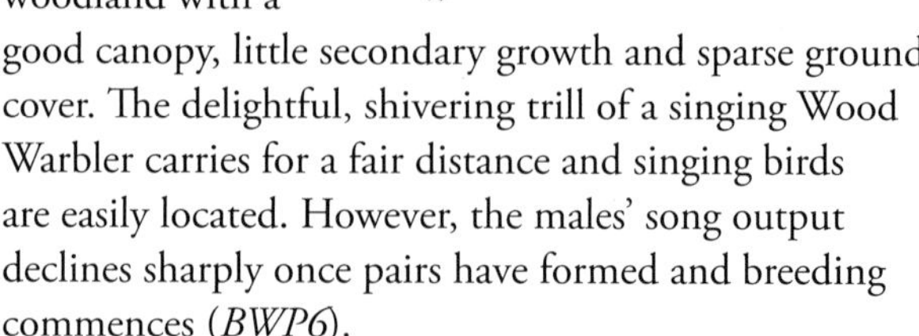

The first Wood Warblers arrive back from their sub-Saharan wintering grounds in the second half of April. For breeding they favour areas of woodland with a good canopy, little secondary growth and sparse ground cover. The delightful, shivering trill of a singing Wood Warbler carries for a fair distance and singing birds are easily located. However, the males' song output declines sharply once pairs have formed and breeding commences (*BWP6*).

In Norfolk, it was always a localised species, tending to favour beech woods, although oak, birch and sweet chestnut woods have all hosted breeding pairs in the past. A decline in the Norfolk breeding population was first noted in the mid 1950s, although there was a temporary upsurge in the 1980s, at the time of the *1980–85 NBBS*. Subsequently numbers once again began to fall and the species last bred in the county at Dersingham in 1995.

The NBA map shows that, despite having not bred in the county since 1995, the species was still being recorded at a surprising number of localities. Almost

SUMMER

Small dots 1, medium 2, large 3 ('pairs')

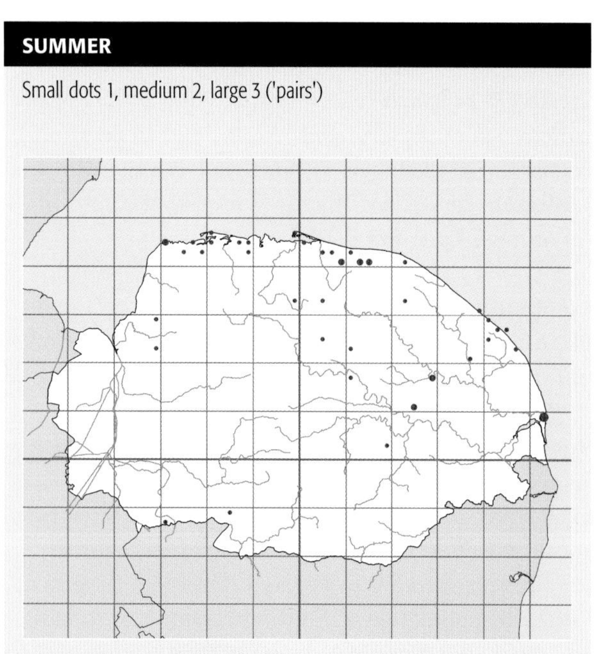

CHANGE SINCE 1980–85

+ Gain ✖ Loss ■ No change

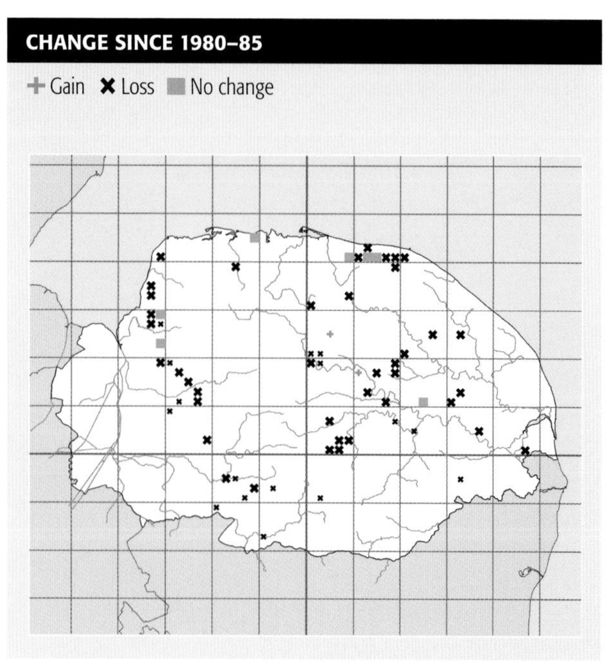

DAVID TIPLING

without exception, however, the records relate to birds on spring passage at sites where no suitable breeding habitat was present.

There was a cluster of tetrads temporarily hosting Wood Warblers along the Cromer to Holt ridge, where the species formerly bred. The other major concentration identified during the *1980–85 NBBS*, in west Norfolk, was not visited, however, even by birds on spring passage. The species was also noted at a few scattered woods in central Norfolk, some of which had previously been breeding sites. Most NBA records were of migrants resting at coastal sites, heading presumably for breeding sites in northern Britain or in Scandinavia.

Both Holme and Titchwell attracted migrant Wood Warblers in at least four years of the NBA period, while Great Yarmouth cemetery hosted three birds on the same days in the spring of both 2002 and 2004. In the final four NBA summers, only one or two Wood Warblers were recorded at inland localities, compared with up to six around the coast.

Males that pair successfully might conceivably still make a nesting attempt in the county, and be undetected. Conversely, males that sing for a couple of weeks or more, such as the birds at Sandringham in 2000 and Mousehold Heath in 2001, were most likely to be unpaired males that had failed to attract a mate. That formerly occupied sites have been abandoned, despite no apparent changes in the habitat, is evidence that pressures operating outside the breeding season have driven the decrease. For example, one or two Wood Warblers were recorded in three NBA summers at Pretty Corner, Sheringham, a previously regular nesting locality, but no breeding attempts have been made there in recent years.

'The delightful, shivering trill of a singing Wood Warbler carries for a fair distance and singing birds are easily located.'

Comparisons between previous atlases show that almost twice as many 10-km squares in Norfolk were occupied in 1980–85 as in the *1968–72 Atlas*, but that a decrease in range was already evident by 1988–91. The change map shows the total loss of breeding range since the *1980–85 NBBS*, with the only apparent gains being non-breeding migrants.

Chiffchaff

Phylloscopus collybita

NBA 1999–2007	SUMMER: ALL/BREEDING	WINTER
TETRADS OCCUPIED	1,215 (83%) / 1,188 (81%)	108 (7%)
SUMMER/WINTER ONLY	1,116	9
MEAN PER OCCUPIED TETRAD	7 / 7	1
SUMMED MAX COUNTS	8,223 / 8,186	142
POPULATION ESTIMATE	12,000–15,000 bp	25–50

PREVIOUS ATLASES	SQUARES OCCUPIED	1999–2007	LOSSES	GAINS
1968–72 (10 KM)	62 (all)	62 (all)		
1980–85 (TETRAD)	742 (51%)	1,188 (81%)	54	500
1980–85 (10 KM)	60 (97%)	62 (all)	0	2
1981–84 WINTER (10 KM)	14 (23%)	46 (74%)	0	32
1988–91 (10 KM)	61 (98%)	62 (all)	0	1

TO MANY NORFOLK birdwatchers, the distinctive song of the Chiffchaff is the sound that heralds the start of spring. It has always been a common summer visitor to Norfolk but in recent years has increased considerably and now greatly outnumbers the Willow Warbler, which was formerly by far the most abundant of the leaf-warblers.

Chiffchaffs are birds of mature deciduous and mixed woodland with a well-developed ground layer to conceal the nest. They are also found in more open areas, such as commons, heathland, parks, large gardens and along hedgerows, provided mature trees are present for use as song posts. In tetrads with few Chiffchaff pairs, it is notable that they typically occupy the same isolated habitat patches as pairs of Blackcaps. Although song output is reduced after pair formation, it continues strongly throughout the summer, ensuring that the species is unlikely to be overlooked.

The summer distribution map shows Chiffchaffs to be very widespread across the county. They are largely absent, however, from the Fens and from the more open areas of Broadland, such as Halvergate Marshes and Haddiscoe Island. Concentrations of birds were found in the more wooded regions, including Breckland and around Sandringham. A tetrad in the latter area held 44 pairs, while one in the Brecks, east of Brettenham, held 42 pairs.

Since the 1980s, increasing numbers of Chiffchaffs have been found wintering in Britain, mainly in southern and western England. In Norfolk, *Riviere* recorded only two such instances up to the 1930s but in the last 40–50 years Chiffchaffs have been recorded annually in winter. Winter birds in Britain originate from a wide area of the Eurasian breeding range (*Migration Atlas*). Chiffchaffs are insectivorous throughout the winter and so are often found near to waters that can support the insect life on which they depend. Many are recorded at or near sewage treatment works or old gravel workings. Their survival is dependent on the microclimate that is provided by thick hedges and reedbeds. They often join roving tit flocks and many of the records from the NBA winters concerned birds visiting both rural and urban gardens. However, they rarely take advantage of the artificial foods provided.

The winter distribution map shows a clear preponderance of records in the eastern half of the county, with many records scattered around the east and north coasts but the highest counts mostly spread along the Yare valley. Most records involved single birds but favoured sites held several Chiffchaffs, some on a

WINTER TOTALS

Winter count totals 1999–2007 (data from *NBR*)

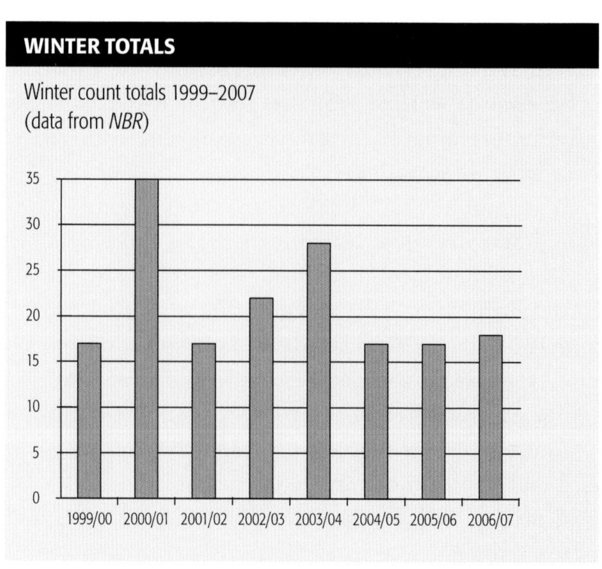

DAVID TIPLING

SUMMER

Small dots 1–4, medium 5–8, large 9–44 ('pairs')
Shading – breeding proved or considered likely

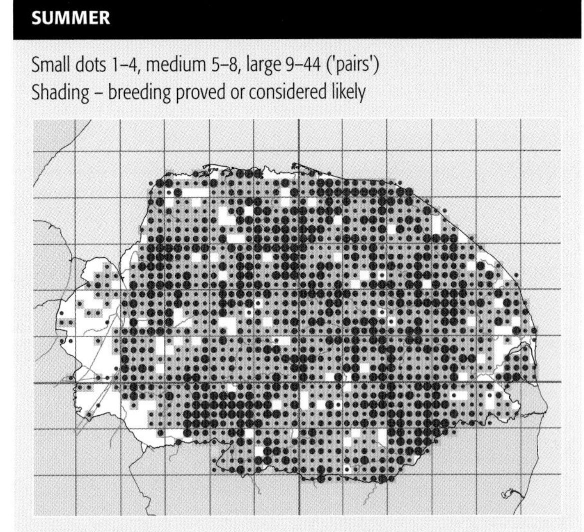

WINTER

Small dots 1, medium 2, large 3–5 (birds)

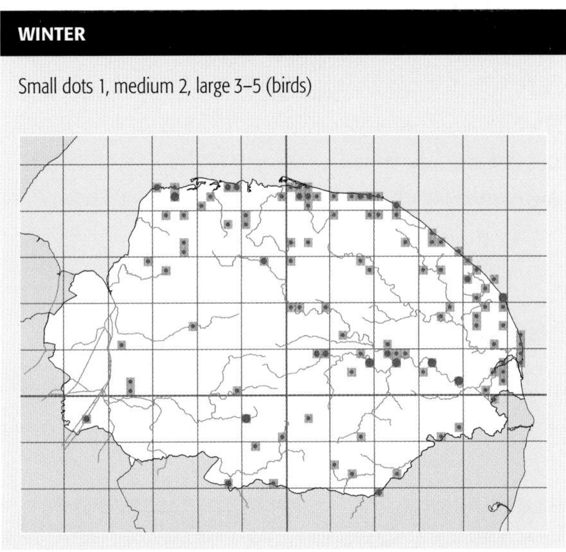

CHANGE SINCE 1980–85

+ Gain ✖ Loss ■ No change

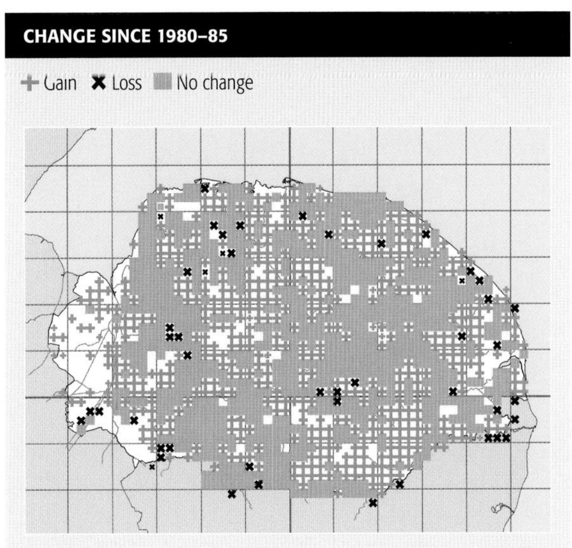

regular basis. Cley SF hosted at least one Chiffchaff in each NBA winter, with a maximum of six on 7th January 2001. Cantley BF was another favoured locality with a maximum of four also in January 2001, while Whitlingham CP hosted up to five in January 2005. As with Blackcaps, more Chiffchaffs were recorded in the second half of the winter, perhaps as they became more concentrated into better-watched habitats, such as gardens and wetlands. During the NBA winters, the number of Chiffchaffs recorded varied from 17 to a peak of 35, one of the highest winter totals ever for the county, during 2000/01.

During the 25 years 1982–2007, the CBC/BBS index of population size for England rose by a staggering 155% (*Birdtrends*). A strongly increasing trend is also evident for this period at the county scale. The number of occupied tetrads found by NBA was 60% higher than during the *1980–85 NBBS*. *BoN* indicated a population of up to 5,000 pairs in the county in 1998, whereas the NBA counts suggest that figures in the range 12,000–15,000 pairs applied during the NBA summers.

The change map shows that, in common with the *Sylvia* warblers, there are large areas of the county, especially in the southeast, the Fens, and parts of the Broads, where Chiffchaffs had been scarce or absent in 1980–85 and where the range has since been substantially filled.

Comparison with the *1981–84 Winter Atlas* shows a rise in 10-km squares occupied in winter from 14 to 46, a measure of the increase also in the winter population over this period.

Willow Warbler

Phylloscopus trochilus

NBA 1999–2007	SUMMER: ALL/BREEDING	WINTER
TETRADS OCCUPIED	1,038 (71%) / 965 (66%)	none
SUMMER/WINTER ONLY	1,038	none
MEAN PER OCCUPIED TETRAD	5 / 6	none
SUMMED MAX COUNTS	5,479 / 5,366	none
POPULATION ESTIMATE	4,000–6,000 bp	none

PREVIOUS ATLASES	SQUARES OCCUPIED	1999–2007	LOSSES	GAINS
1968–72 (10 KM)	62 (all)	62 (all)		
1980–85 (TETRAD)	1,103 (76%)	965 (66%)	273	135
1980–85 (10 KM)	62 (all)	62 (all)		
1988–91 (10 KM)	61 (98%)	62 (all)	0	1

THE BEAUTIFUL, CASCADING song of the Willow Warbler epitomises summer for birdwatchers in many parts of Britain. Indeed, it is one of the commonest and most widespread summer visitors throughout much of northern Europe.

The Willow Warbler favours less mature, more open areas of woodland than does its close relative the Chiffchaff, although both species may well be found on commons and heathland, where birches harbour the Willow Warbler's most accessible insect food (*BWP6*). Birches and sallows around areas of open water, such as lakes and old gravel workings, are also a favourite habitat.

The NBA summer map shows a wide, but rather patchy distribution around Norfolk, with the main concentration in Breckland, where young conifer plantations hold a special attraction for the species. Other favoured areas are the woodlands around

SUMMER

Small dots 1–2, medium 3–6, large 7–46 ('pairs')
Shading – breeding proved or considered likely

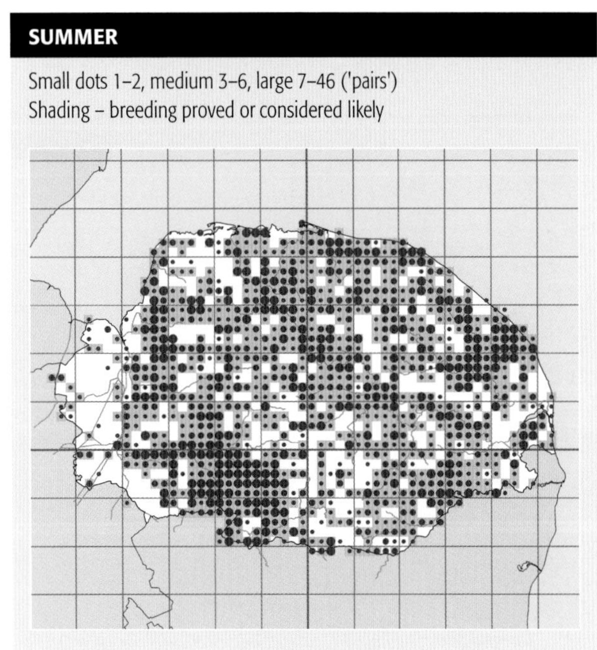

CHANGE SINCE 1980–85

+ Gain ✖ Loss ■ No change

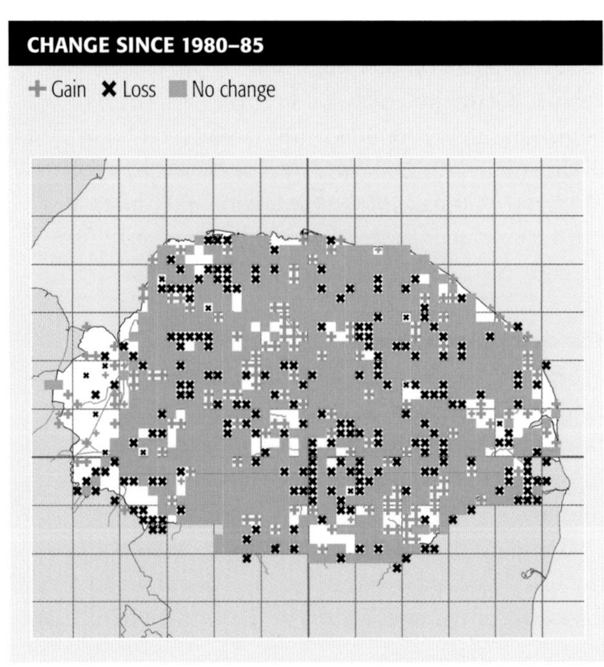

DAVID TIPLING

Sandringham, the woods and heaths in the northern half of the county, and the Broadland carrs in east Norfolk. During the NBA summers, four tetrads held 40 or more pairs of Willow Warblers: these were at Roydon Common, Salthouse Heath, Irstead and at Sandringham, where 46 singing males were located. The species was mostly absent from open arable land and from the treeless Fens. There is a clear tendency for birds to be drawn to river valleys, such as those of the Ant, Bure, Yare and Wissey.

Willow Warblers singing from near the top of a tree or bush are not easy to miss, but at both coastal and inland sites males sing while on spring passage. In many tetrads, the count on the visit during the second summer recording period was lower than that on the first. Whether this represented the onward movement of birds still on passage or a reduction in song due to successful pairing is unknown, but it may indicate that the breeding population in Norfolk is not as high as the summed tetrad maxima would suggest.

'There is a clear tendency for birds to be drawn to river valleys, such as those of the Ant, Bure, Yare and Wissey.'

The fate of the Willow Warbler population differs very sharply from that of its closest relative, the Chiffchaff. Whereas that species has more than doubled in population size in recent decades, Willow Warblers in England declined by 60% during 1982–2007. Although distribution is still complete at the 10-km scale, there has been a drop of 13% since the *1980–85 NBBS* in the number of occupied Norfolk tetrads. The change map shows that previous gaps along Norfolk's main watersheds have become more obvious. Range loss is also apparent along the southern borders of the county, along the rivers Little Ouse and Waveney. How far this loss of range and numbers will proceed remains to be seen.

Blackcap
Sylvia atricapilla

NBA 1999–2007	SUMMER: ALL / BREEDING	WINTER
TETRADS OCCUPIED	1,299 (89%) / 1,286 (88%)	81 (6%)
SUMMER/WINTER ONLY	1,225	7
MEAN PER OCCUPIED TETRAD	7 / 7	1
SUMMED MAX COUNTS	9,146 / 9,128	113
POPULATION ESTIMATE	12,000–15,000 bp	25–50

PREVIOUS ATLASES	SQUARES OCCUPIED	1999–2007	LOSSES	GAINS
1968–72 (10 KM)	62 (all)	62 (all)		
1980–85 (TETRAD)	640 (44%)	1,286 (88%)	30	676
1980–85 (10 KM)	60 (97%)	62 (all)	0	2
1981–84 WINTER (10 KM)	17 (27%)	39 (63%)	5	27
1988–91 (10 KM)	62 (all)	62 (all)		

THOUGH FORMERLY considered to be purely a summer visitor, the Blackcap has in recent decades become a regular Norfolk bird in winter also, albeit in mere dozens rather than in tens of thousands, as in summer.

In Norfolk, Blackcaps favour areas of mature deciduous and mixed woodland with a well-developed shrub layer for nesting, and are able to occupy small or fragmented woods. Blackcaps also breed in Broadland carrs, Fenland poplars, the sallows around gravel pits and in larger rural and suburban gardens with mature trees.

The NBA summer map confirms the Blackcap's status as a common and widespread breeding bird. Summer concentrations are evident not only in the best-wooded parts of the county, such as the Sandringham estate and in Breckland, but also around Norwich and in other areas of south Norfolk. More than forty tetrads each held over 20 pairs, with the highest counts being 44 at Swanton Abbot and 35 at both Ickburgh and Fritton. In 2004, a pair bred on Scolt Head for the first time, following unprecedented scrub growth there.

The first males arrive back on territory in late March, the females from a week or so later, and most birds have returned by early May. As male Blackcaps have an extended song period, often continuing until early July, it was not difficult to locate breeding pairs at any time throughout the survey period. In the most intensively farmed areas, however, where breeding habitat may be scarce, it would still be possible for some occupied tetrads to have been overlooked. Conversely, some of the smaller tetrad counts might have referred solely to birds recorded, perhaps in song, while still searching for suitable breeding habitat, and may not always indicate that breeding occurred within the tetrad.

Until the mid 1960s, only one or two overwintering Blackcaps were noted in Norfolk in most winters. Ten were recorded in 1966/67, however, and no fewer than 53 were reported in December 1992, although the actual total of birds present could have been far higher.

During the NBA winters, the number of Blackcaps reported varied from 13 to 26, the vast majority being in gardens. The winter distribution map shows concentrations around Norwich, in north Norfolk and to a lesser extent in Great Yarmouth – areas where sheltered gardens, or birdwatchers, or both, were most numerous. By contrast, very few wintering Blackcaps were reported from west Norfolk.

Ringing indicates that Blackcaps wintering in Britain originate mostly in Germany, the Netherlands or Belgium (*Migration Atlas*). A notable arrival into gardens occurs in late December, or with cold weather. It is surmised, but on little evidence, that most birds may

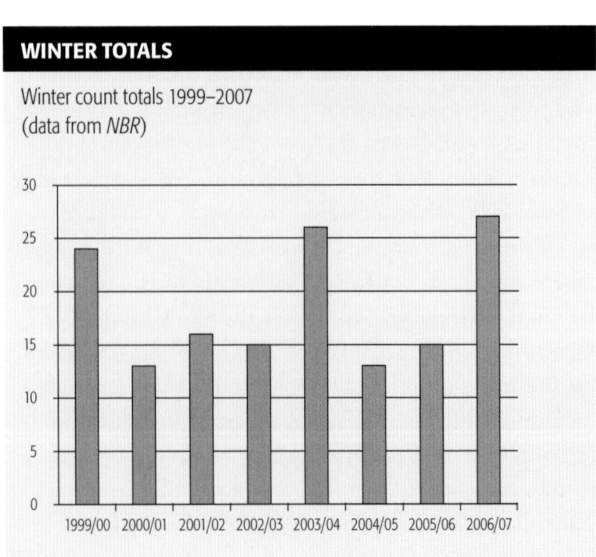

WINTER TOTALS

Winter count totals 1999–2007 (data from *NBR*)

have arrived in Britain weeks earlier, in late autumn, and spent the first part of the winter feeding on wild berries and other natural foods in woodlands and scrub (*1981–84 Winter Atlas*). Once in gardens, they join other birds, such as roving tit flocks, to feed on a wide variety of food items including peanuts, sunflower hearts, fat, cheese and bread, as well as the berries and nectar of exotic plants.

Some town gardens appear to be especially favoured by wintering Blackcaps, and ringing has demonstrated winter site fidelity between years. In contrast, some sites were known to have held Blackcaps in only one of the eight NBA winters. To some extent, therefore, the map might exaggerate the distribution likely to be observed in any single winter. More likely, however, since wintering Blackcaps proved so difficult to locate on NBA's set visits, the map underestimates the true winter distribution.

The strong growth of the English breeding population since the late 1970s (*Birdtrends*) is clearly reflected in the NBA results. In particular, the number of occupied tetrads has doubled since the *1980–85 NBBS*, and the NBA breeding estimate of 12,000–15,000 pairs is more than double that given by *BoN* in 1999.

The change map shows that nearly all of the large gaps in the 1980–85 distribution have since been filled, for example the Diss–Wymondham–Harleston triangle, where no confirmed breeding was noted in the first tetrad survey. It is probably the case, however, as Kelly (1986) himself suggested, that some breeding was overlooked there by the *1980–85 NBBS*.

Norfolk's wintering population has also become much more widespread. Winter Blackcaps were recorded by NBA in 63% of the 10-km squares in Norfolk, compared with only 27% during the *1981–84 Winter Atlas*.

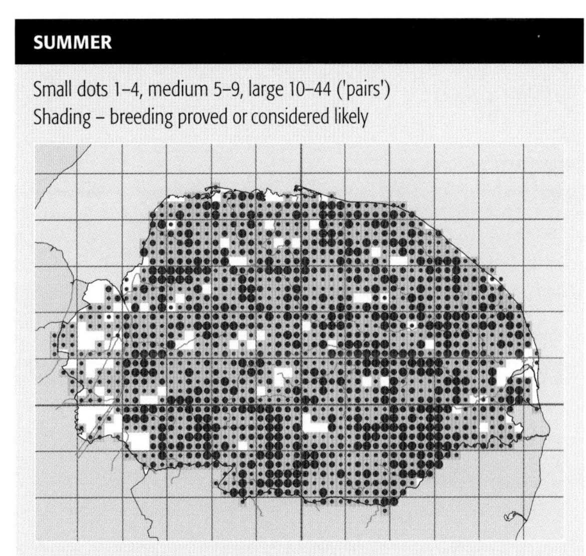

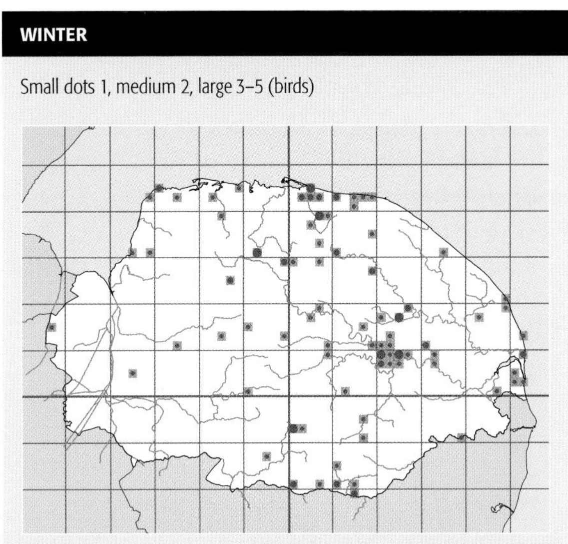

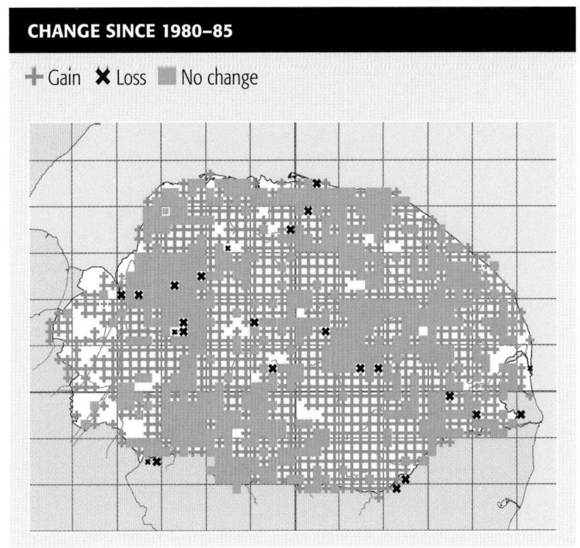

Garden Warbler
Sylvia borin

NBA 1999–2007	SUMMER: ALL/BREEDING	WINTER
TETRADS OCCUPIED	592 (41%) / 536 (37%)	none
SUMMER/WINTER ONLY	592	none
MEAN PER OCCUPIED TETRAD	2/2	none
SUMMED MAX COUNTS	1,267 / 1,195	none
POPULATION ESTIMATE	1,200–1,500 bp	none

PREVIOUS ATLASES	SQUARES OCCUPIED	1999–2007	LOSSES	GAINS
1968–72 (10 KM)	59 (95%)	58 (94%)	4	3
1980–85 (TETRAD)	361 (25%)	536 (37%)	172	347
1980–85 (10 KM)	57 (92%)	58 (94%)	2	3
1988–91 (10 KM)	55 (89%)	58 (94%)	3	6

THE GARDEN WARBLER is one of the last warblers to arrive in Norfolk in spring, often not being noted until early May. Its territorial song is distinctive but requires care and practice to separate from that of Blackcap.

Both *Stevenson* and *Riviere* described the species as less abundant and more localised than the Blackcap, a comment that holds true even more clearly today. Whereas that species is currently almost ubiquitous in Norfolk woodland of all types, Garden Warblers seem to select the patches of rich biological diversity. There they complete the breeding cycle with great efficiency and are among the first warblers to depart again in autumn.

The map shows that Garden Warblers were widely distributed throughout Norfolk but with a definite concentration in Breckland and the Fenland fringe. As well as these areas, the NBA also recorded concentrations of Garden Warblers in the other well-wooded parts of the county, such as parts of central Norfolk and along the Cromer to Holt ridge. The more open, arable areas of south Norfolk and the Fens held comparatively few, well-scattered pairs. Tetrads holding double-figure counts were confined to the Hockham and Ickburgh areas of the Brecks and Swanton Novers Great Wood.

SUMMER

Small dots 1, medium 2–3, large 4–13 ('pairs')
Shading – breeding proved or considered likely

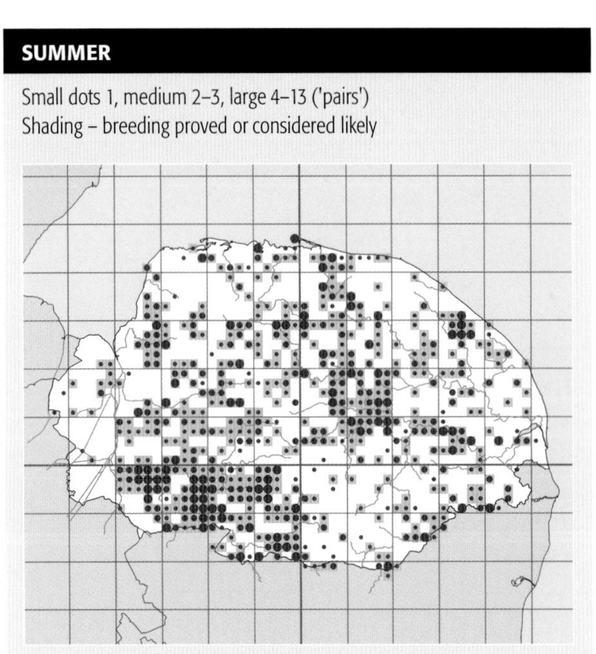

CHANGE SINCE 1980–85

+ Gain ✖ Loss ■ No change

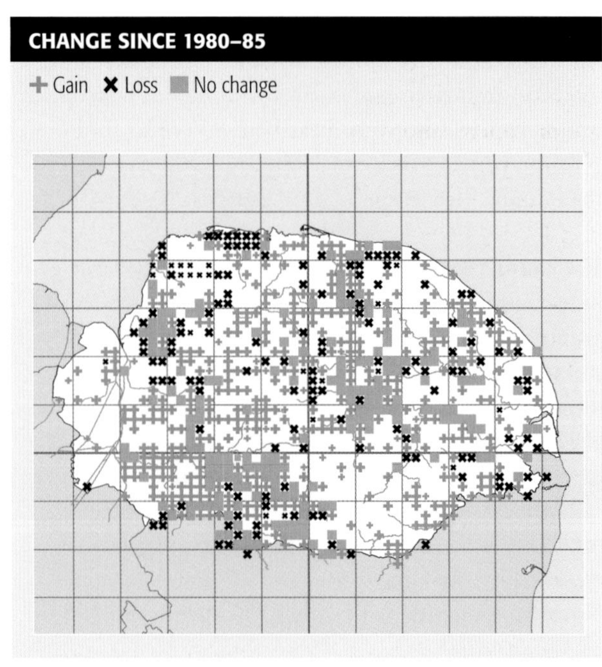

JIM ALMOND

While Garden Warblers are primarily a woodland-edge species, they favour deciduous areas with a more open canopy and fairly dense scrub and shrub layers, particularly tangles of bramble. They tend to be found on the woodland fringes and in the glades, as well as on commons and heathland, and in tall scrub around old gravel workings. Away from mature trees, they are also found in hawthorn and blackthorn thickets, clumps of rhododendrons and in young conifer plantations. There are parallels to the past and present distribution of the Nightingale in Norfolk, although that species has always been much less widespread. As elsewhere in its British range, it is in no sense a garden bird, except where gardens border its preferred habitats.

Comparison with previous 10-km atlases provides little evidence of any change in range.

'There are parallels to the past and present distribution of the Nightingale in Norfolk...'

Like all the *Sylvia* warblers in Norfolk, however, Garden Warblers were recorded in considerably more tetrads than in the *1980–85 NBBS*. In part, this could be due to better coverage, especially in the Brecks, and to the improved field skills of observers, as well as to a real spread in the distribution of the species. The change map shows strong gains in parts of south and central Norfolk, particularly the Feltwell and Methwold areas, and losses around Burnham Overy and Thetford.

There was very little population change in England over the 25 years 1982–2007 (*Birdtrends*).

Lesser Whitethroat
Sylvia curruca

NBA 1999–2007	SUMMER: ALL/BREEDING	WINTER
TETRADS OCCUPIED	594 (41%) / 524 (36%)	none
SUMMER/WINTER ONLY	594	none
MEAN PER OCCUPIED TETRAD	2 / 2	none
SUMMED MAX COUNTS	1,106 / 1,020	none
POPULATION ESTIMATE	1,000–1,500 bp	none

PREVIOUS ATLASES	SQUARES OCCUPIED	1999–2007	LOSSES	GAINS
1968–72 (10 KM)	57 (92%)	61 (98%)	1	5
1980–85 (TETRAD)	302 (21%)	524 (36%)	182	404
1980–85 (10 KM)	56 (90%)	61 (98%)	1	6
1988–91 (10 KM)	54 (87%)	61 (98%)	0	7

THE LESSER WHITETHROAT has a unique breeding distribution in southeast Britain and is the only common British breeding bird that migrates to eastern Africa and travels via the eastern part of the Mediterranean Basin.

On their return, normally in late April, male Lesser Whitethroats establish territories in tall, dense hedgerows on farmland and along country lanes, in blackthorn and hawthorn thickets, and in patches of tall scrub.

The distinctive rattling song is heard frequently until the final stages of nest building, after which the species may become extremely difficult to detect. The map may

DAVID TIPLING

thus omit some tetrads where breeding was successful, while including others where song was heard, but only from migrant or unpaired males.

The NBA map shows a patchy summer distribution, with Lesser Whitethroats largely absent from urban areas, the Broadland valleys and the Fens. A major concentration, previously undetected, was discovered in the southeast of the county, with highest densities around Pulham Market, Attleborough, Wymondham and Ditchingham. There were also smaller areas of high occupancy along the north Norfolk coast.

Counts in some areas would have been made during the peak song period for Lesser Whitethroats, or might have included non-breeding birds simply passing through. The two highest tetrad counts were both in southeast Norfolk, with 14 pairs at Kirstead Green on 3rd May and nine at Denton, but on the much later date of 20th June, when migration would not have been under way. There is no reason to doubt, therefore, that the concentration of Lesser Whitethroats in this part of the county is genuine.

Most of Norfolk's breeding Lesser Whitethroats have started on their autumn migration by early August. There were no reports of overwintering during the NBA period, although there are two earlier records of Lesser Whitethroats in Norfolk during the winter months.

Comparisons with previous atlas data suggest a range contraction between 1968–72 and 1988–91, followed by an expansion to 98% occupancy of 10-km squares by the end of the NBA period. The species is probably far more abundant in Norfolk now than it was in the 19th century.

There was a net gain of 222 tetrads since the 1980–85 NBBS, and the change map shows that the current area of highest density, in southeast Norfolk was then almost unoccupied. A preponderance of range gains is evident throughout the species' range within the county. It is not possible to know, however, how much of a part more thorough coverage for NBA, or an improvement in observers' identification skills, might have played in creating this pattern.

SUMMER

Small dots 1, medium 2, large 3–14 ('pairs')
Shading – breeding proved or considered likely

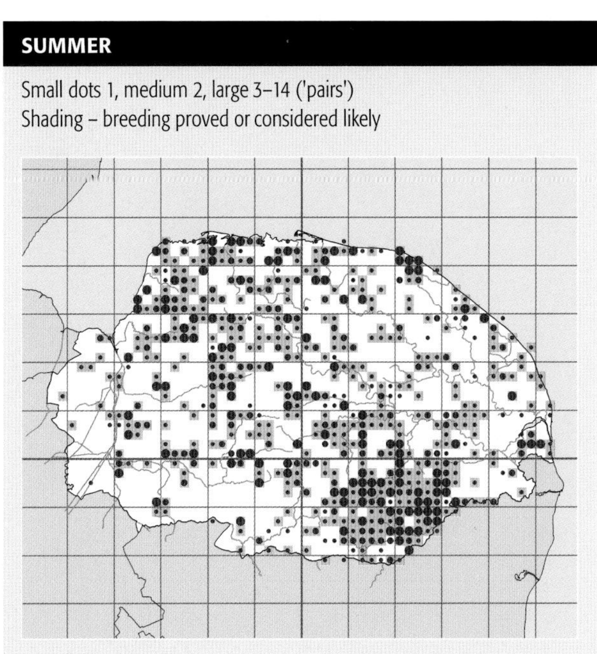

CHANGE SINCE 1980–85

+ Gain ✖ Loss ■ No change

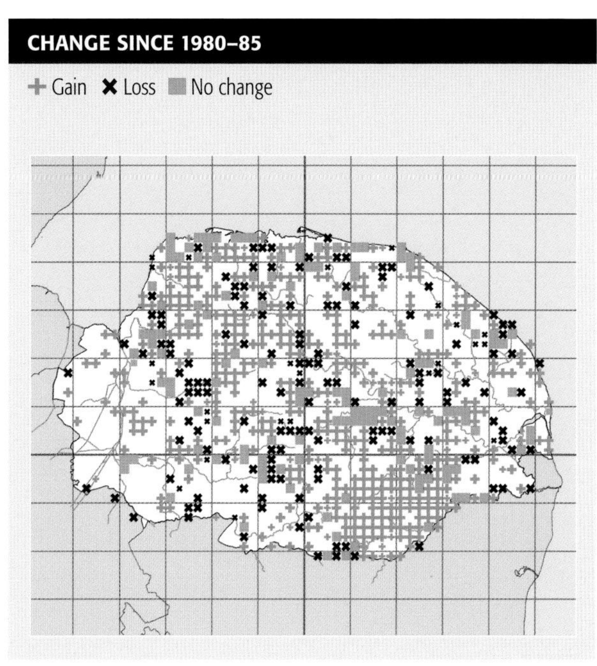

Whitethroat
Sylvia communis

NBA 1999–2007	SUMMER: ALL/BREEDING	WINTER
TETRADS OCCUPIED	1,340 (92%) / 1,333 (91%)	none
SUMMER/WINTER ONLY	1,340	none
MEAN PER OCCUPIED TETRAD	9 / 9	none
SUMMED MAX COUNTS	11,472 / 11,462	none
POPULATION ESTIMATE	13,000–15,000 bp	none

PREVIOUS ATLASES	SQUARES OCCUPIED	1999–2007	LOSSES	GAINS
1968–72 (10 KM)	62 (all)	62 (all)		
1980–85 (TETRAD)	775 (53%)	1,333 (91%)	46	604
1980–85 (10 KM)	60 (97%)	62 (all)	0	2
1988–91 (10 KM)	62 (all)	62 (all)		

THE WHITETHROAT prefers lower, younger scrub to most other British *Sylvia* warblers, and is a typical summer bird of farmland hedgerows. *Stevenson* described it as one of the most common summer visitors to Norfolk during the 19th century, and the NBA has confirmed it to be the most widespread warbler in the county, although Blackcap and Chiffchaff now rival it in abundance.

Whitethroats are characteristic birds of hedgerows, well-vegetated banks alongside ditches and other overgrown field margins, particularly where nettles or brambles are found. Although song output diminishes after pairing, males sing throughout the summer. The higher counts in each tetrad were more often made on the second visit, after mid May. Whitethroats often sing from low cover and often indulge in a distinctive song flight; they are active and inquisitive birds, and generally easy to locate during surveys.

It is not surprising that the NBA summer map shows concentrations of Whitethroats in arable regions of Norfolk, especially in the southwest and southeast. Even the Fens held concentrations in suitable habitat, for example up to 42 pairs at Eau Brink and 38 pairs at

SUMMER

Small dots 1–5, medium 6–11, large 12–61 ('pairs')
Shading – breeding proved or considered likely

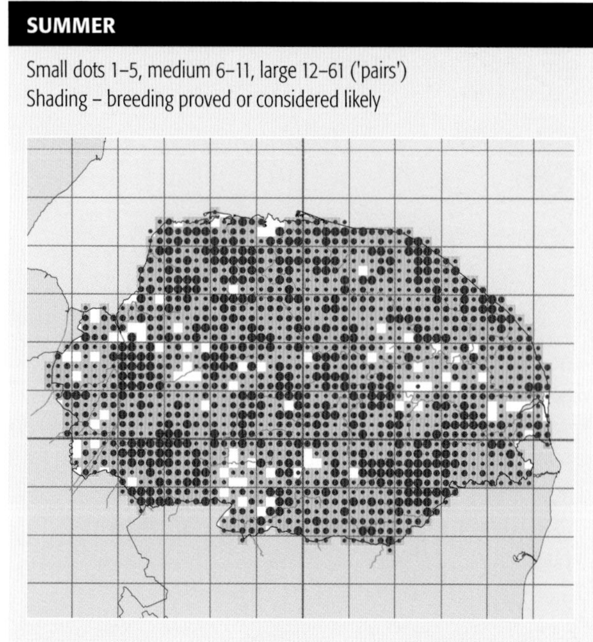

CHANGE SINCE 1980–85

+ Gain ✖ Loss ■ No change

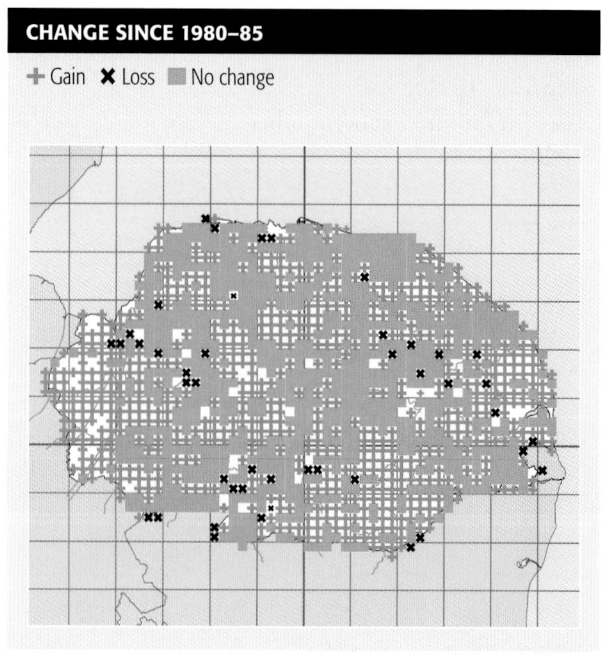

DAVID TIPLING

Welney, whereas relatively few were found in the more intensively farmed tetrads in Fenland. Whitethroats were also found in good numbers on commons and heathland, and the tetrad with the highest count, of 61 pairs, was the one that included Salthouse Heath. Woodland edges and broader glades are often occupied by breeding birds, provided there is a mixture of tall herbage and low bushes, as are young forestry plantations. The increase in scrub on Scolt Head has resulted in an expansion of the breeding population there to 14 pairs in 2006.

Between 1968 and 1969, Whitethroats suffered a devastating population crash in Britain as a result of the failure of West African rains (*Birdtrends*). With a return to more reliable rainfall, Whitethroat populations have increased, but remain well short of pre-crash levels. No range changes are evident in Norfolk at the 10-km scale since the *1968–72 Atlas*, but there has been a major increase at tetrad level since the *1980–85 NBBS*.

'Between 1968 and 1969, Whitethroats suffered a devastating population crash in Britain as a result of the failure of West African rains.'

During the NBA summers, Whitethroats were recorded in over 90% of the tetrads compared with only 53% in 1980–85. Over a similar period, the 25 years 1982–2007, an increase of 75% was recorded in England as a whole. The change map indicates that almost all gaps in the *1980–85 NBBS* distribution have since been filled, including large areas in the east and southeast, and in the Fens.

Grasshopper Warbler

Locustella naevia

NBA 1999–2007	SUMMER: ALL / BREEDING	WINTER
TETRADS OCCUPIED	151 (10%) / 99 (7%)	none
SUMMER/WINTER ONLY	151	none
MEAN PER OCCUPIED TETRAD	2 / 2	none
SUMMED MAX COUNTS	289 / 226	none
POPULATION ESTIMATE	150–200 bp	none

PREVIOUS ATLASES	SQUARES OCCUPIED	1999-2007	LOSSES	GAINS
1968–72 (10 KM)	51 (82%)	32 (52%)	20	1
1980–85 (TETRAD)	123 (8%)	99 (7%)	78	54
1980–85 (10 KM)	44 (71%)	32 (52%)	16	4
1988–91 (10 KM)	38 (61%)	32 (52%)	13	7

GRASSHOPPER WARBLERS ARE scarce summer visitors from wintering grounds in West Africa. Their mouse-like, unobtrusive behaviour means that their characteristic reeling song most often gives away their presence. Proof of breeding is very hard to obtain.

They favour rather drier habitats than Reed and Sedge Warblers and occur not only in thick, low, marshland vegetation, such as in Broadland, but also in drier areas like heathland, commons and sometimes young conifer plantations.

The NBA map shows that the main part of the Norfolk range is in Broadland, although the distribution is rather restricted there in comparison to other marsh-dwelling warblers. There is also an almost continuous coastal distribution from Snettisham to Overstrand, and several small patches of inland occurrence in the centre and southwest of the county. Many of the records from Broadland follow the routes of the Rivers Bure and Yare, and there are further clusters of river valley records along the Rivers Little Ouse and Wissey. There is a surprising lack of records from the Fens, where much suitable habitat appears to be available.

During the NBA summers, 155 singing males were reported to the *NBR* from 65 sites throughout Norfolk in 2004, including 32 in the mid-Yare RSPB reserves. The peak site counts included 16 at Strumpshaw and ten at Hickling Broad. In 2006, the county total was at least 177 singing males.

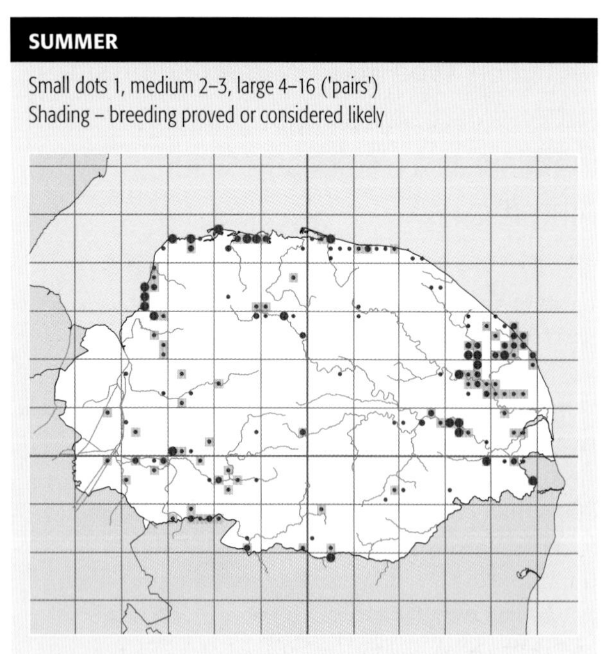

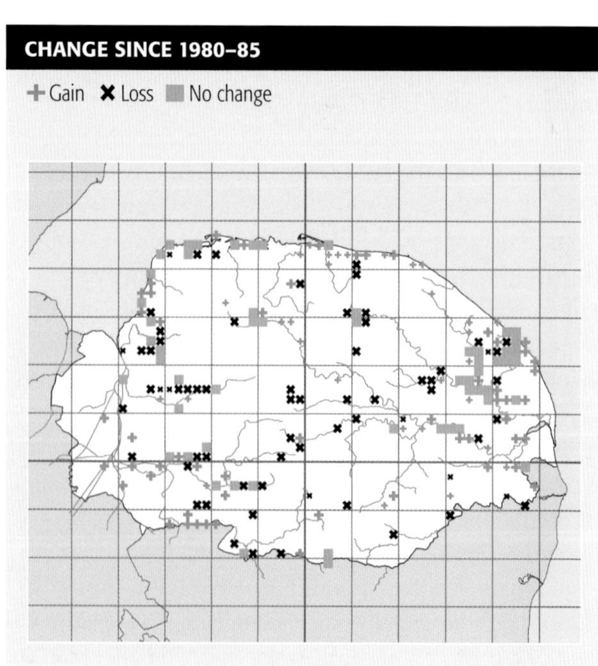

DAVID TIPLING

As the map is a compilation across all the NBA summers, the actual distribution in any single year may be less than that shown. Male Grasshopper Warblers also frequently sing while on spring passage, so that an unknown number of records, particularly around the coast, relate to migrants and not to summering birds. To a certain extent, this is counterbalanced by Grasshopper Warblers that were missed by the set visits, which were rarely made at dawn and dusk, when the species sings most persistently. As Grasshopper Warblers are often double brooded and the male sings between clutches, additional sites were commonly picked up on the second summer visit.

Numbers of this warbler have fallen widely across Europe in recent decades and, in the UK, a steep decline has occurred since the 1960s (*Birdtrends*). Interestingly, *Stevenson* also noted a decline in the county in the mid 19th century. Comparison with previous 10-km atlases shows a sequential decline in occupied squares from 51 in 1968–72 to only 32 during the NBA period.

Assessing change at tetrad scale is complicated by the natural tendency of suitable sites to change their distribution over time. An area suitable for breeding one year may become unsuitable the next, even on managed reserves, perhaps due to wetland drainage, the claiming of marginal land for agriculture, or natural succession, as on heathland and in conifer plantations.

The change map shows a broadly similar distribution to that in the *1980–85 NBBS*, although there is a rather poor match between the actual tetrads in which the species was recorded in the two surveys. Overall, however, there was a net loss amounting to 20% of the already depleted 1980–85 range.

Sedge Warbler
Acrocephalus schoenobaenus

NBA 1999–2007	SUMMER: ALL/BREEDING	WINTER
TETRADS OCCUPIED	442 (30%) / 418 (29%)	none
SUMMER/WINTER ONLY	442	none
MEAN PER OCCUPIED TETRAD	7 / 7	none
SUMMED MAX COUNTS	3,092 / 3,064	none
POPULATION ESTIMATE	3,000–3,500 bp	none

PREVIOUS ATLASES	SQUARES OCCUPIED	1999-2007	LOSSES	GAINS
1968–72 (10 KM)	61 (98%)	59 (95%)	3	1
1980–85 (TETRAD)	492 (34%)	418 (29%)	223	149
1980–85 (10 KM)	58 (94%)	59 (95%)	1	2
1988–91 (10 KM)	58 (94%)	59 (95%)	3	4

THE SEDGE WARBLER is a common summer visitor to favoured parts of Norfolk. Its inquisitive and confiding nature, combined with its habit of singing from exposed perches or during brief periods of song-flight, make it an easy species to survey.

Sedge Warblers are monogamous, and the males begin to sing as soon as they arrive back on their breeding territories. Once the females have arrived a week or so later and pairs have formed, the males sing less intensively for the rest of the breeding season (*BWP6*).

The NBA summer map shows distinct concentrations of birds along the county's river

DAVID TIPLING

systems, including smaller tributaries, and around the coastal dykes and reedbeds of north Norfolk. In the Fens, pairs were found occupying patches of nettles, willow herb and brambles, in fields of oil-seed rape, along hedgerows and in young conifer plantations, and were less attached to rivers. Without doubt, the favoured nesting habitats are the drier margins of reedbeds and reed-fringed marshland dykes, and it was in these situations that the highest counts were made. During the NBA summers, maximum counts of pairs included 55 at Dersingham, 57 at Holme and 59 at Holkham in north Norfolk, 75 at Eau Brink and 68 at Welney in the Fens, and 79 at Strumpshaw in Broadland. In 2002, and probably for the first time, two pairs of Sedge Warblers bred successfully on Scolt Head, despite the absence of any fresh water on the island.

The numbers of Sedge Warblers have shown a moderate long-term decline across England, but have changed little in the 25 years to 2007 (*Birdtrends*). Comparison of the numbers of occupied 10-km squares with previous atlases gives little indication of any change in range, but there has been a net loss of range at tetrad level since the *1980–85 NBBS*.

'The numbers of Sedge Warblers have shown a moderate long-term decline across England, but have changed little in the 25 years to 2007.'

The change map indicates a broad range extension in Fenland, but this has been outweighed at county level by losses in the upper reaches of many of Norfolk's river valleys.

SUMMER

Small dots 1–2, medium 3–7, large 8–79 ('pairs')
Shading – breeding proved or considered likely

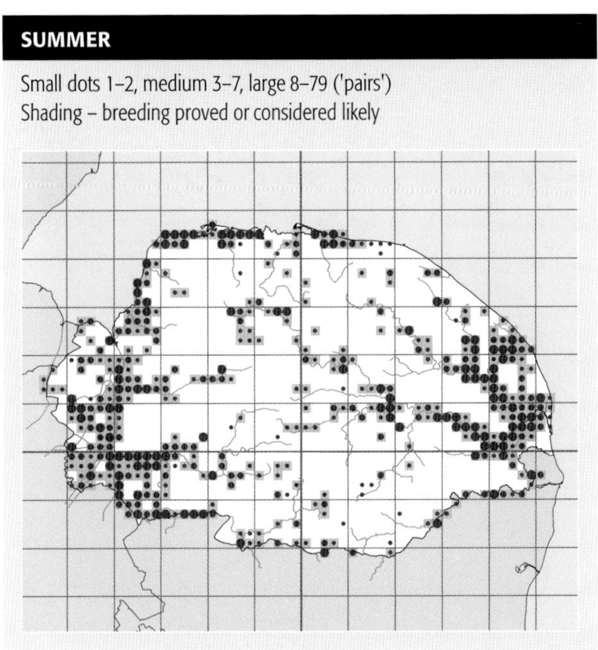

CHANGE SINCE 1980–85

+ Gain ✖ Loss ■ No change

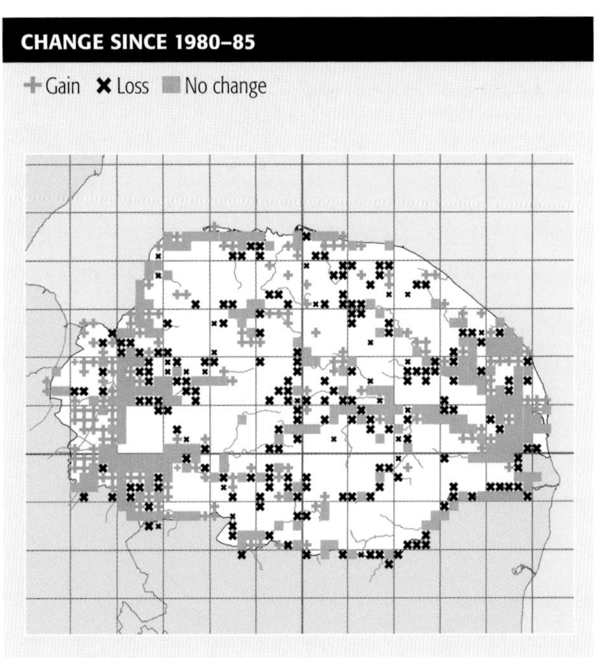

Reed Warbler

Acrocephalus scirpaceus

NBA 1999–2007	SUMMER: ALL/BREEDING	WINTER
TETRADS OCCUPIED	424 (29%) / 401 (27%)	none
SUMMER/WINTER ONLY	424	none
MEAN PER OCCUPIED TETRAD	7 / 8	none
SUMMED MAX COUNTS	3,152 / 3,129	none
POPULATION ESTIMATE	6,000–7,000 bp	none

PREVIOUS ATLASES	SQUARES OCCUPIED	1999–2007	LOSSES	GAINS
1968–72 (10 KM)	54 (87%)	56 (90%)	3	5
1980–85 (TETRAD)	335 (23%)	401 (27%)	105	171
1980–85 (10 KM)	55 (89%)	56 (90%)	5	6
1981–84 WINTER (10 KM)	1 (2%)	none	1	0
1988–91 (10 KM)	53 (85%)	56 (90%)	2	5

THE REED WARBLER is the most numerous of the *Acrocephalus* warblers in Norfolk's reedbeds, and can be easily distinguished from Sedge Warbler by its unstreaked plumage and more repetitive song. As its name implies, it is closely associated with reeds and its British distribution closely mirrors that of *Phragmites*.

Since the 1960s the species has shown a remarkable range expansion into Scotland, western Britain and even into Ireland. The Norfolk distribution has

probably changed relatively little since the time of *Stevenson*, and later *Riviere*, however, who both stressed the abundance of Reed Warblers in Broadland.

Reed Warblers return a couple of weeks later than Sedge Warblers, with the main arrival often being in early May. Therefore the species was sometimes still absent during early summer visits. Reed Warblers sing more persistently than Sedge Warblers later in the season, however, and there was good opportunity to record singing Reed Warblers in the second half of the summer recording period.

The prime breeding habitat is large reedbeds, where Reed Warblers nest semi-colonially, often at a density of more than ten pairs per hectare. Less favoured, but still widely used are the smaller stands of reeds along rivers, dykes and drainage ditches, and around ponds and old gravel workings. Here it is often far easier to count the number of pairs present. Reed Warblers

SUMMER

Small dots 1–2, medium 3–6, large 7–70 ('pairs')
Shading – breeding proved or considered likely

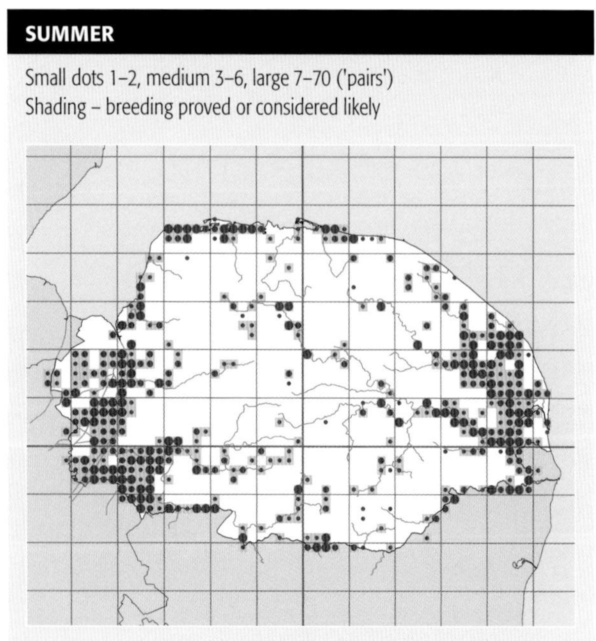

CHANGE SINCE 1980–85

+ Gain ✖ Loss ■ No change

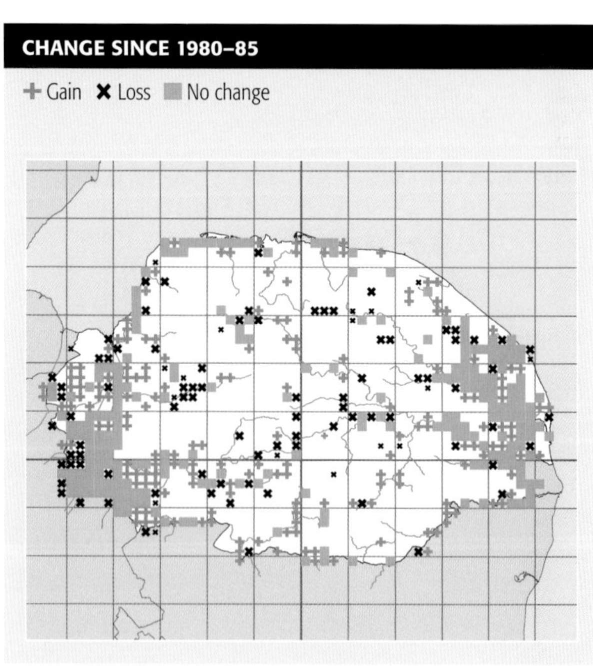

DAVID TIPLING

defend only a small territory and often feed or forage in drier vegetation adjacent to the reeds, such as sallows, willow herb or arable crops, and on occasion will even nest in such locations.

As well as the Broads, the NBA summer map also shows significant concentrations in the Fens and along the north Norfolk coast. Most of the records away from these three main areas follow the river systems that cross the county. On the Suffolk border, the special importance for the species of the isolated site at Lopham Fen is very evident on the map. During the NBA summers, Welney held the largest concentration in the Fens, with up to 95 pairs. In Broadland, a count of 188 pairs was made at Hickling Broad in 2005 and there were 186 pairs at the mid-Yare RSPB reserves in 2004; elsewhere the highest tetrad counts included 70 pairs at Blackfleet Broad and over 50 at Eau Brink, Burnham Norton, Cley and Salthouse.

Like many of our summer migrants, Reed Warblers sing while on spring passage, which continues into early June. Song may even be heard in areas totally unsuited for nesting, such as town gardens. For instance, in 2000, singing Reed Warblers were recorded in the centre of Norwich, in roadside hedges at Reepham and Pulham Market, and at Scolt Head, Blakeney Point, Beeston Bump and Paston, while one sang from a yew tree at Tasburgh in 2004 (*NBR*).

The tetrad totals show that Reed Warblers were a little less widely distributed than Sedge Warblers in Norfolk, but rather more abundant. For Britain as a whole, however, Sedge Warblers are estimated to outnumber Reed Warblers by a factor of about three (*APEP06*).

Comparison with the *1980–85 NBBS* indicates that the range in Norfolk has expanded, along with that in Britain as a whole, with a net gain of 66 tetrads. The change map shows many gains in Fenland, and there were noticeably more records along the Waveney valley and in isolated sites in mid county.

Waxwing
Bombycilla garrulus

NBA 1999–2007	SUMMER: ALL / BREEDING	WINTER
TETRADS OCCUPIED	8 (<1%) / none	185 (13%)
SUMMER/WINTER ONLY	none	177
MEAN PER OCCUPIED TETRAD	5 / none	10
SUMMED MAX COUNTS	37 / none	1,764
POPULATION ESTIMATE	none	10–300

PREVIOUS ATLASES	SQUARES OCCUPIED	1999–2007	LOSSES	GAINS
1981–84 WINTER (10 KM)	10 (16%)	52 (84%)	0	42

IN THE SPECIES' OCCASIONAL invasion winters, greedy flocks of Waxwings may be found devouring the berries and fruits in Norfolk's roadside hedges, gardens and parks. They are often remarkably tame and allow a close approach, feeding unconcerned beside the busiest of roads and roundabouts. In some winters, however, barely a handful of migrants arrive.

Waxwings breed in loose colonies in the taiga forests of northern Europe. During the summer months, they are insectivorous, feeding mainly on mosquitoes, but in the autumn they switch to a diet of fruits and berries. Their winter range is exceptionally responsive to food shortages. If the rowan crop is poor in northern Europe, more Waxwings move southwest towards Britain, where they occur mostly between October and April. In recent times, the largest invasion took place in the winter of 1965/66 when thousands of birds were involved. Although numbers are so volatile, there have been only two years since

CHRIS KNIGHTS

'Remarkably, there were notable influxes in four of the eight NBA winters, with major arrivals normally in December or January...'

1946 in which none at all was seen in Norfolk.

Amongst their favourite fare are the berries of rowan, cotoneaster and pyracantha. As many of their favourite trees and shrubs are planted in gardens, they are usually found in villages and towns, thus accounting for the distribution of occupied tetrads on the NBA winter map, with the main concentration being in and around the city of Norwich. Elsewhere many of the records were around the coastal strip, relating to birds stopping off temporarily on their way to the inland counties of England. Apart from Norwich, comparatively few penetrate into central Norfolk, where by midwinter most berries in rural areas have already been stripped by winter thrushes. Because the flocks move so freely around the county in search of new sources of food, there is clearly much duplication in the records.

Remarkably, there were notable influxes in four of the eight NBA winters, with major arrivals normally in December or January, but the largest took place in mid October 2003. During these four winters, between 150 and 300 Waxwings were recorded in the county, the largest numbers being in December 2003, when at least 200 were in Norwich alone. It was during that period that the count in one city-centre tetrad peaked at 160. Other high tetrad counts included 60 at both Titchwell and Acle.

The *1981–84 Winter Atlas* by contrast did not include any 'Waxwing winters'. Birds were recorded then in just ten of Norfolk's 10-km squares, compared with 52 during the NBA period.

While the vast majority of Waxwings have left the county by the end of March, in invasion years some parties remain into April and during the NBA summers there were even three sightings in May.

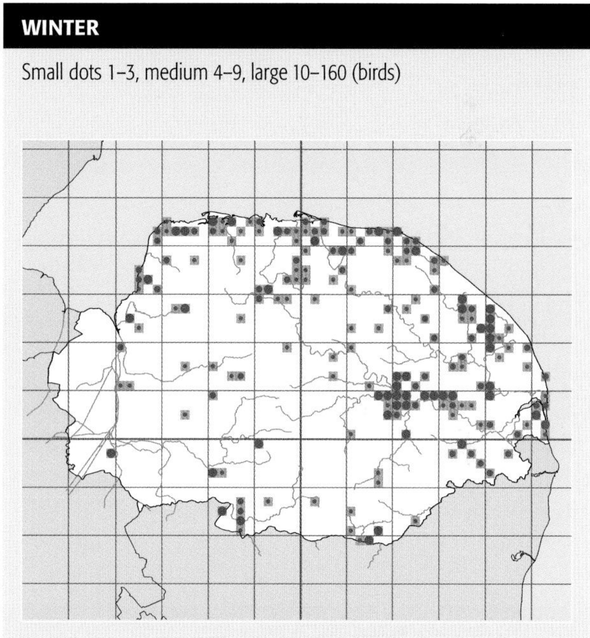

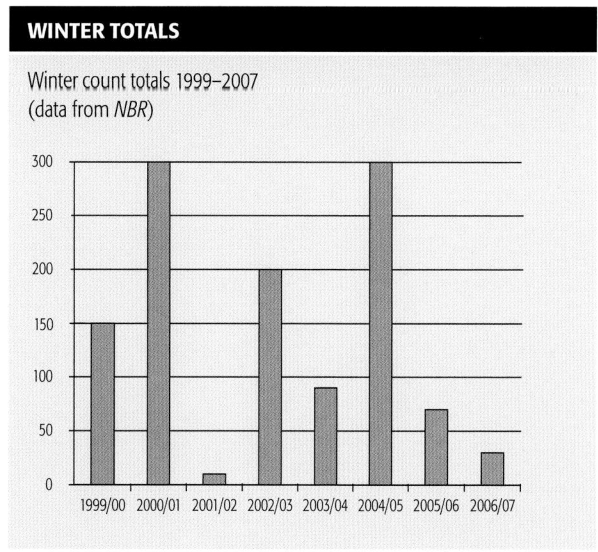

Nuthatch
Sitta europaea

NBA 1999–2007	SUMMER: ALL / BREEDING	WINTER
TETRADS OCCUPIED	341 (23%) / 317 (22%)	348 (24%)
SUMMER/WINTER ONLY	107	114
MEAN PER OCCUPIED TETRAD	2 / 2	2
SUMMED MAX COUNTS	676 / 652	767
POPULATION ESTIMATE	650–850 bp	1,400–1,800

PREVIOUS ATLASES	SQUARES OCCUPIED	1999–2007	LOSSES	GAINS
1968–72 (10 KM)	58 (94%)	51 (82%)	7	0
1980–85 (TETRAD)	386 (26%)	317 (22%)	211	142
1980–85 (10 KM)	56 (90%)	51 (82%)	5	0
1981–84 WINTER (10 KM)	55 (89%)	52 (84%)	7	4
1988–91 (10 KM)	53 (85%)	51 (82%)	5	3

NUTHATCHES ARE NOISY, excitable birds that draw attention to themselves and so are rarely missed, despite inhabiting the higher trunks and branches of trees.

They inhabit extensive tracts of mature deciduous and mixed woodland, and open parkland, favouring oak, beech and sweet chestnut. They remain in their pairs throughout the year, and generally stay within their territories, although they will visit gardens, especially in winter.

The NBA summer map shows a rather sparse and patchy distribution around the county. There is a clear concentration in Thetford Forest and surrounding Breckland, where birds are found mainly in old deciduous stands, especially those with oak or hornbeam. Further smaller pockets of continuous distribution are evident elsewhere, for example on the Sandringham estate, in some well-wooded areas around Norwich, and along the Cromer to Holt ridge, although some observers commented that Nuthatches have become less common in such places in recent years. Other fieldworkers were surprised to find the species absent from extensive areas of apparently suitable woodland. At Holkham this has been attributed to the felling of old trees, while at East Tuddenham in the 1980s and 1990s grey squirrels were implicated, having eaten the hazel nuts before they had

SUMMER

Small dots 1, medium 2, large 3–14 ('pairs')
Shading – breeding proved or considered likely

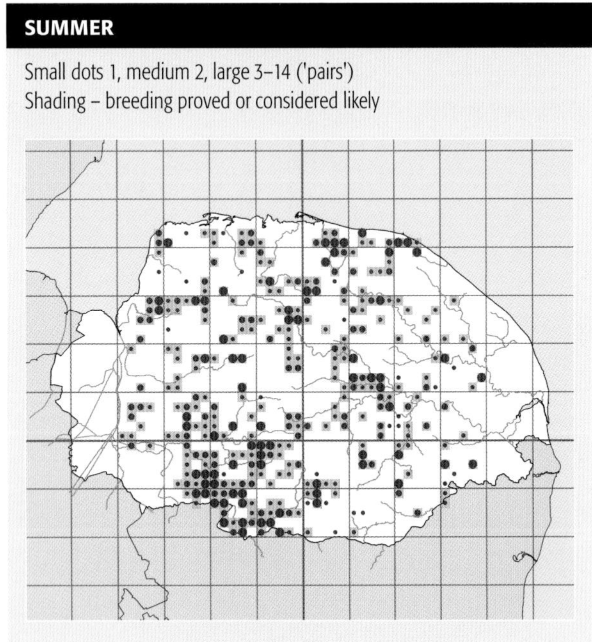

WINTER

Small dots 1, medium 2, large 3–11 (birds)

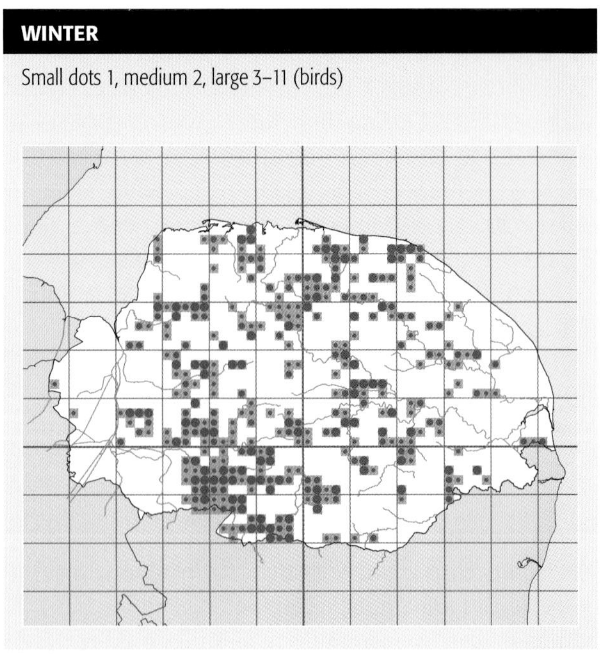

ripened. Not surprisingly, the species is absent in the relatively treeless Fens, but it is also absent from wide areas in central, southeast and east Norfolk. The highest individual tetrad counts of Nuthatches were of 14 pairs at Brettenham and ten at Coxford Wood.

As Nuthatches are normally resident within their territories throughout the year, it is not surprising that the NBA summer and winter maps are almost identical. Nuthatches sing from December onwards and so are almost as easily located during the winter as in the spring. They may temporarily join roving tit flocks that pass through their territories and will feed conspicuously on bird feeders or on beechmast and hazel nuts on the woodland floor. A count of 11 Nuthatches in the tetrad that included Merton Park was the only one to provide double figures during the winter.

CHANGE SINCE 1980–85

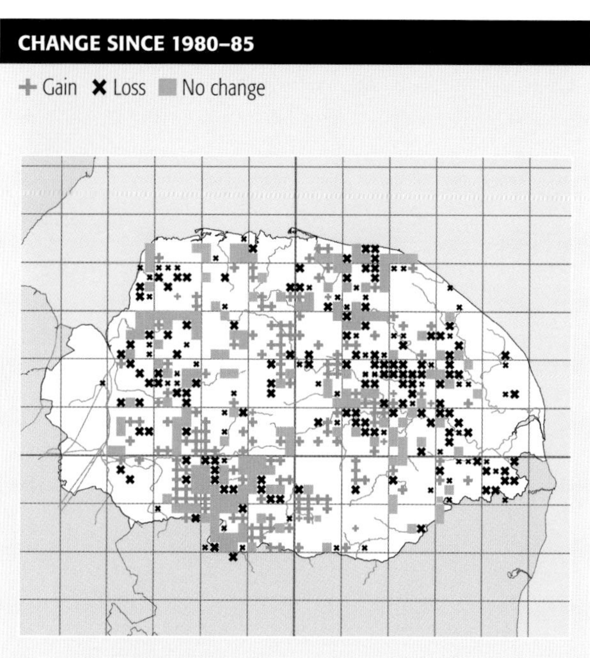

The national trend for Nuthatches has been a strong increase, with a rise of 84% noted in England between 1982 and 2007 (*Birdtrends*), and the breeding range has concurrently spread northwards into southern Scotland. The breeding range in Norfolk, by contrast, has shown a sequential reduction from 58 occupied 10-km squares in the *1968–72 Atlas* to 51 in the NBA period. The number of occupied tetrads in Norfolk has fallen by 18% since the *1980–85 NBBS*. The change map indicates a clear withdrawal from the eastern part of the former range, and many losses also in the northwest of the county, with limited gains in Breckland and some central areas of the county.

Nuthatches are now absent from some previously occupied areas that apparently remain as suitable habitat. Recolonisation of fragmented mature woodland in a largely agricultural landscape may be difficult for this species, as dispersal of first-year Nuthatches is very limited.

Treecreeper
Certhia familiaris

NBA 1999–2007	SUMMER: ALL/BREEDING	WINTER
TETRADS OCCUPIED	527 (36%) / 504 (35%)	613 (42%)
SUMMER/WINTER ONLY	170	256
MEAN PER OCCUPIED TETRAD	2 / 2	2
SUMMED MAX COUNTS	944 / 919	1,351
POPULATION ESTIMATE	3,000–4,000 bp	8,000–12,000

PREVIOUS ATLASES	SQUARES OCCUPIED	1999–2007	LOSSES	GAINS
1968–72 (10 KM)	58 (94%)	57 (92%)	3	2
1980–85 (TETRAD)	497 (34%)	504 (35%)	248	255
1980–85 (10 KM)	58 (94%)	57 (92%)	2	1
1981–84 WINTER (10 KM)	53 (85%)	59 (95%)	0	6
1988–91 (10 KM)	58 (94%)	57 (92%)	4	3

THE MOUSE-LIKE Treecreeper is a familiar bird in most areas of woodland in Norfolk, although its unobtrusive habits mean that silent birds can be easily overlooked.

Treecreepers are exclusively associated with trees, favouring broad-leaved and mixed woodland and nesting in crevices in trees or behind loose bark. Coniferous woods, parkland, churchyards and hedges with mature trees are also occupied, especially when population levels are high. The distinctive and piercing song of the Treecreeper, once learnt, enables breeding pairs to be located very easily. However, singing mainly occurs from February to early April and, if missed during the first summer recording period, it may be difficult to find a nesting pair later in the season.

The NBA summer map shows the species to be widely distributed across the county in summer, but absent from the levels near Breydon Water, and some smaller patches in mid county. Breeding was suspected at Welney in 2002 but nowhere else in Fenland. The highest concentrations were found in Breckland and it was here at West Harling and near Brettenham that the two highest tetrad counts were made in summer, with 16 and 13 pairs respectively.

Treecreepers tend to remain in the same general area all year, sometimes joining mixed flocks of tits and Goldcrests as they move through the woodland.

SUMMER

Small dots 1, medium 2, large 3–16 ('pairs')
Shading – breeding proved or considered likely

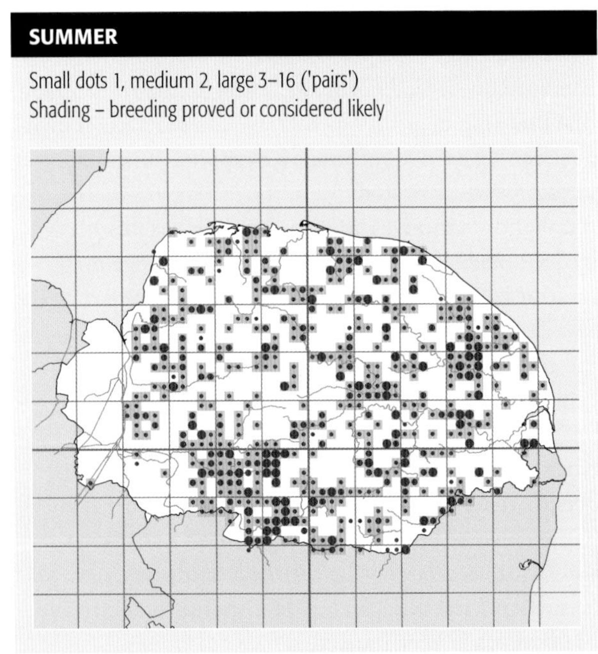

WINTER

Small dots 1, medium 2–3, large 4–21 (birds)

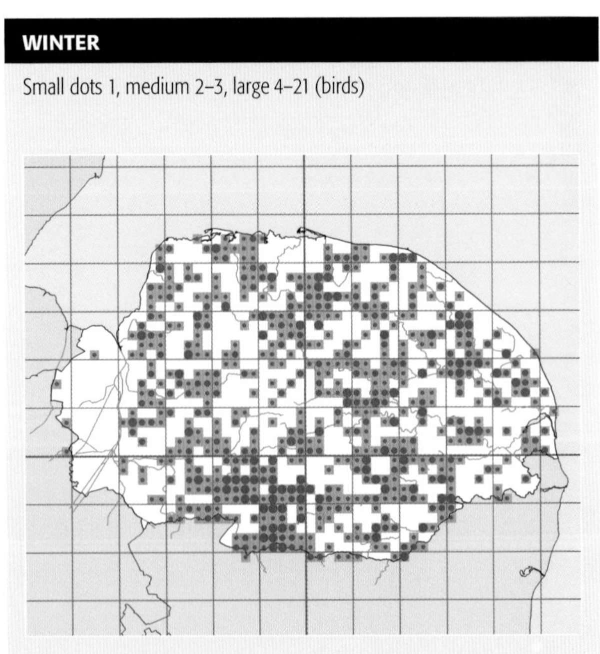

DAVID TIPLING

The NBA winter map is very similar to that of the summer, but Treecreepers are rather more widespread in the winter season, with wandering birds occasionally met with at considerable distance from breeding habitat, and even in Fenland. Two of the highest tetrad winter counts were of 18 at West Harling and 15 near Brettenham, in the same part of Thetford Forest in which the highest numbers of breeding pairs were located. In Broadland, the tetrad south of Rollesby held an impressive 16 birds.

'Comparison with previous atlases suggests there has been very little overall change in the species' range in the county since the 1960s.'

CHANGE SINCE 1980–85

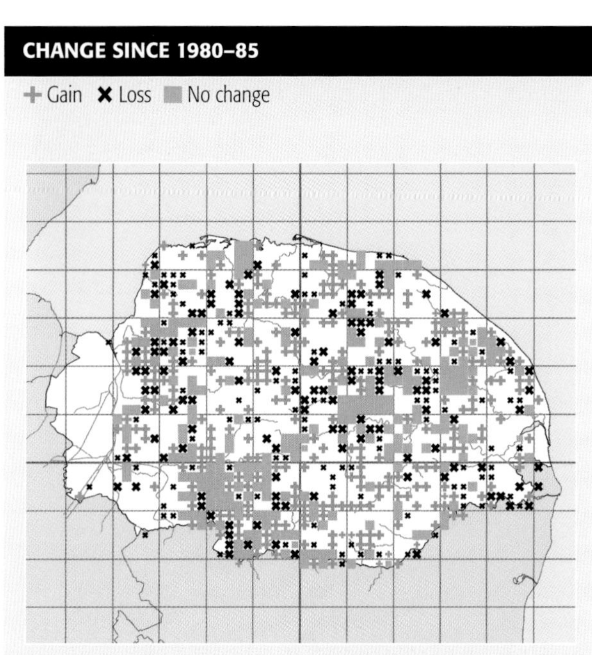

Like other small resident species, Treecreepers are susceptible to the effects of hard weather in winter, numbers being particularly badly affected by periods of freezing rain or glazed frosts. In addition to insects and spiders, Treecreepers take pine and spruce seeds in winter, and have occasionally been reported feeding in gardens on peanuts and sunflower seeds.

Comparison with previous atlases suggests there has been very little overall change in the species' range in the county since the 1960s. The change map shows an even mix of gains and losses since the *1980–85 NBBS* in almost all parts of the county.

Wren

Troglodytes troglodytes

NBA 1999–2007	SUMMER: ALL / BREEDING	WINTER
TETRADS OCCUPIED	1,418 (97%) / 1,418 (97%)	1,404 (96%)
SUMMER/WINTER ONLY	30	16
MEAN PER OCCUPIED TETRAD	20 / 20	11
SUMMED MAX COUNTS	28,100 / 28,100	15,443
POPULATION ESTIMATE	60,000–70,000 bp	140,000–160,000

PREVIOUS ATLASES	SQUARES OCCUPIED	1999–2007	LOSSES	GAINS
1968–72 (10 KM)	62 (all)	62 (all)		
1980–85 (TETRAD)	1,344 (92%)	1,418 (97%)	15	89
1980–85 (10 KM)	62 (all)	62 (all)		
1981–84 WINTER (10 KM)	62 (all)	62 (all)		
1988–91 (10 KM)	62 (all)	62 (all)		

THE WREN IS one of the most widespread and most numerous breeding birds in Britain. Although it is very vulnerable to periods of prolonged, severe winter weather, the population has remarkable powers of recovery and so numbers can fluctuate widely between years.

Wrens are extremely adaptable, inhabiting almost every type of habitat that provides low cover, amongst which the birds can forage and nest.

Although they are primarily a woodland species, they also particularly favour waterside vegetation. During the breeding season, pairs will nest in low scrub, hedgerows, gardens, parks, and manmade structures such as outhouses and stone walls.

During the NBA summers, Wrens were recorded in virtually every tetrad in Norfolk. Despite its small size, its loud and distinct song made confirmation of its presence easy. It was also one of the most numerous species encountered during surveys. The highest tetrad counts included 101 pairs at Bridgham and 92 near Brettenham, both localities in the Brecks, 95 at Surlingham and 92 at Ringstead Downs, while up to 135 pairs were present at the RSPB Reserve at Strumpshaw, and up to 40 males held territories on Scolt Head. Areas of highest density mostly related to well-wooded tetrads in or close to the upper sections of the river valleys.

During the winter months, Wrens inhabit similar habitats to those they use in the summer, except

SUMMER

Small dots 1–12, medium 13–23, large 24–101 ('pairs')
Shading – breeding proved or considered likely

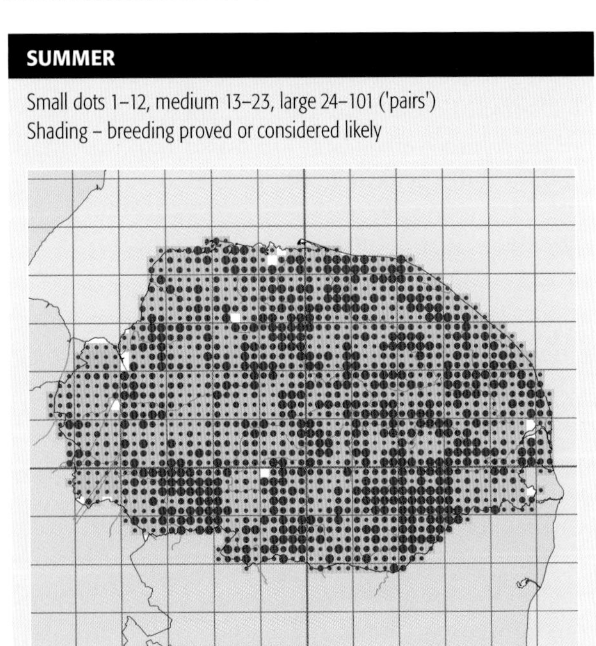

WINTER

Small dots 1–6, medium 7–12, large 13–100 (birds)

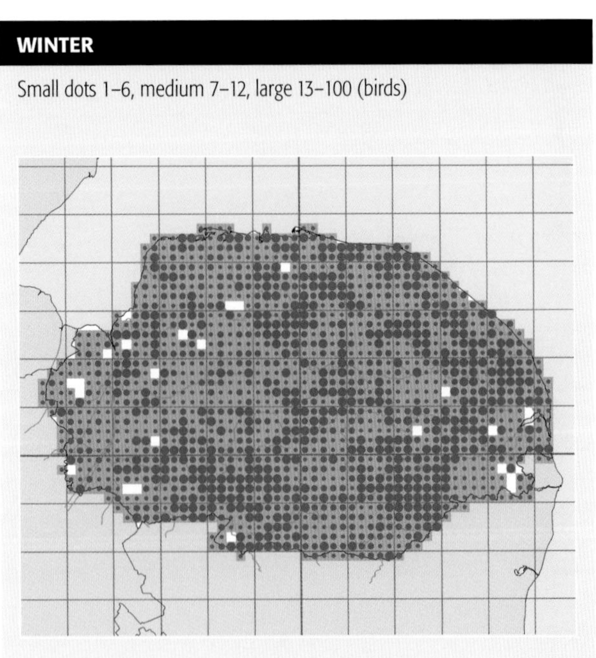

DAVID TIPLING

'At 10-km level, Wrens have been ubiquitous in Norfolk in all the atlas projects so far.'

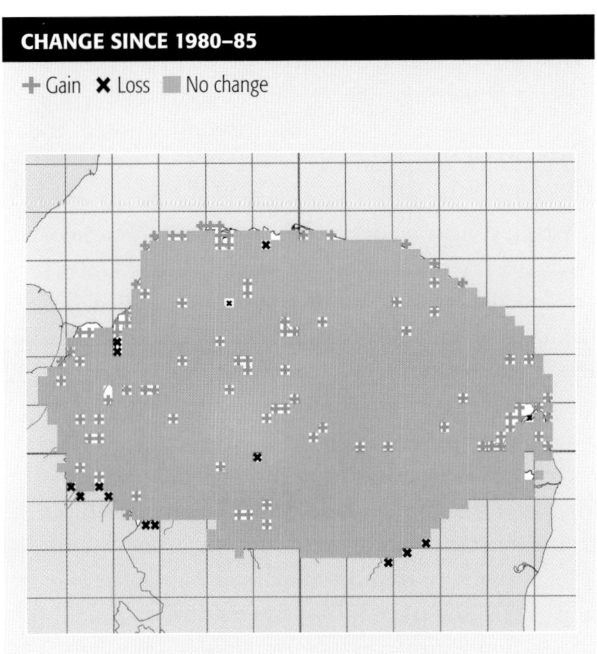

that hedgerows are frequently deserted, while reedbeds are often favoured. Being tiny-bodied and insectivorous, Wrens are susceptible to the effects of severe winter weather, but their small size and agility enable them to forage for insects and spiders in holes and crevices that are inaccessible to other birds. Wrens were recorded in 96% of Norfolk tetrads during the NBA winter fieldwork, with most of the missing tetrads probably relating to very low densities of Wrens where, by chance, not one was encountered. As Wrens are territorial in winter and continue to sing, however, they are comparatively easy to locate. The highest tetrad count was of 100 at Ringstead Downs. Patterns of high and low density were quite similar between summer and winter.

At 10-km level, Wrens have been ubiquitous in Norfolk in all the atlas projects so far. The change map shows some very limited expansion since the *1980–85 NBBS*, for example on Halvergate Levels and on Scolt Head. Given that across England the population rose by 44% between 1982 and 2007 (*Birdtrends*), some gains may be real and not simply an artefact of better coverage.

Starling
Sturnus vulgaris

NBA 1999–2007	SUMMER: ALL / BREEDING	WINTER
TETRADS OCCUPIED	1,294 (89%) / 1,216 (83%)	1,332 (91%)
SUMMER/WINTER ONLY	64	102
MEAN PER OCCUPIED TETRAD	16 / 16	207
SUMMED MAX COUNTS	20,258 / 19,760	275,370
POPULATION ESTIMATE	18,000–22,000 bp	250,000–280,000

PREVIOUS ATLASES	SQUARES OCCUPIED	1999–2007	LOSSES	GAINS
1968–72 (10 KM)	62 (all)	62 (all)		
1980–85 (TETRAD)	1,367 (94%)	1,216 (83%)	194	43
1980–85 (10 KM)	62 (all)	62 (all)		
1981–84 WINTER (10 KM)	62 (all)	62 (all)		
1988–91 (10 KM)	62 (all)	62 (all)		

THE STARLING – rakish, jaunty, gawky, domineering and bustling – is a bird once taken for granted but now becoming noticeably scarcer and starting to diminish in range, in Norfolk as in the rest of Britain.

Over the course of the last 200 years, both the distribution and abundance of Starlings in Britain have fluctuated widely, possibly in relation to agricultural changes or climate change. Since the mid 1960s, there has been a strong decline, which has placed Starling firmly on the red list of birds of conservation concern (*BoCC3*).

DAVID TIPLING

Traditionally, Starlings have been regarded as birds of both town and country, nesting wherever suitable holes are found in trees or buildings. They are semicolonial, the laying of the first clutches being synchronised over a period of four to ten days (*BWP8*). The NBA summer map, however, shows there to be some agricultural and woodland tetrads devoid of Starlings and clear concentrations of breeding pairs in and around Norwich, Great Yarmouth, Cromer and King's Lynn. At this time of year, the Starlings' preferred feeding habitat is grazed, permanent pasture, which provides high densities of the main breeding-season food item of leatherjackets, the larvae of crane flies. Loss of permanent pasture, and general intensification of livestock rearing, are likely to be having adverse effects on rural populations, but decline is also occurring in urban areas, where other reasons must be sought (*Birdtrends*).

In 2000, several observers reported a disquieting decline or absence of Starlings in many parts of Broadland, with virtually no late-summer flocks of juveniles feeding on the harvested fields. In the same year, it had also become a scarce breeder in the woods around Strumpshaw. Some NBA observers noted that the lack of any human habitation in a tetrad was associated with a total absence of Starlings. As adult Starlings wander quite widely in search of food for their nestlings, and as urban habitats are hard to survey, the number of pairs recorded within an individual tetrad does not necessarily give an accurate indication of the number of nesting pairs.

Starlings may gather into small communal roosts in summer, consisting of breeding males and non-breeders. Once the juveniles are on the wing, the roosts increase considerably in size. Within a week or so of fledging, the juveniles and post-breeding adults gather into flocks and begin to roam more widely, foraging in more open areas, such as grazing pastures or saltmarshes, and later in the summer on recently harvested fields. The presence of large flocks from late May onwards, often many miles from their nests, made it extremely difficult to assess the number of breeding pairs in any one tetrad.

Starlings were recorded much more abundantly in winter and were more widespread and less conspicuously urban at this season. The NBA map

suggests a highly clumped distribution during the winter months, with tetrad maxima ranging from zero to 50,000 birds. Winter feeding flocks were found in association with grazing livestock, around outdoor pig units, on stubble and on recently ploughed fields, often alongside plovers, corvids and thrushes, especially Fieldfares. In general, far fewer than expected were recorded as winter visitors in gardens. Excluding counts known to be of roosts and pre-roost gatherings, the largest flocks recorded during the NBA winters were of 6,000 on South Walsham Marshes and 5,000 at St Benet's Level and Foulden.

Winter visitors from the Continent, especially Russia and Finland, augment the Norfolk population of Starlings, but far fewer have been arriving in recent years. These immigrants greatly swell the size of the communal winter roosts of Starlings, which may be located in reedbeds, thorn thickets, and conifer plantations or on manmade structures. During the NBA winters, the largest roosts were in Broadland, with up to 80,000 at Strumpshaw and at How Hill/Reedham Marshes, and 70,000 at Rockland Broad. These pale into insignificance, however, when compared with estimates of three and a half million birds roosting at Egmere, near Holkham, in the 1950s and two million at Marham in 1984.

Because Starling has been so abundant and widespread, even the severe declines among both breeding and wintering birds that have been noted have had hardly any effect on occupancy, as measured by comparisons between the county's five atlas projects. At tetrad level, however, occupancy fell from 94% in the *1980–85 NBBS* to 83% in the NBA summers. During the *1980–85 NBBS*, the species was indeed found almost throughout the county with small, isolated pockets of absence in the Stanford TA and the treeless marshes by Breydon Water. By 2000–07, the change map shows that far more gaps had appeared, often in contiguous tetrads, especially in west Norfolk, with a much smaller number of tetrad gains.

SUMMER

Small dots 1–6, medium 7–17, large 18–135 ('pairs')
Shading – breeding proved or considered likely

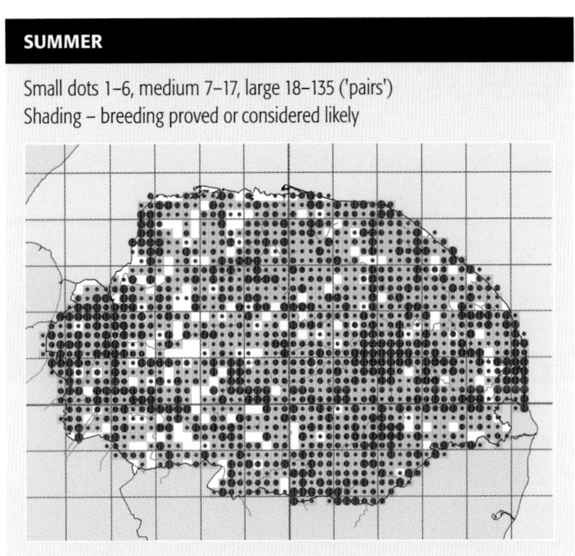

WINTER

Small dots 1–30, medium 31–106, large 107–50,000 (birds)

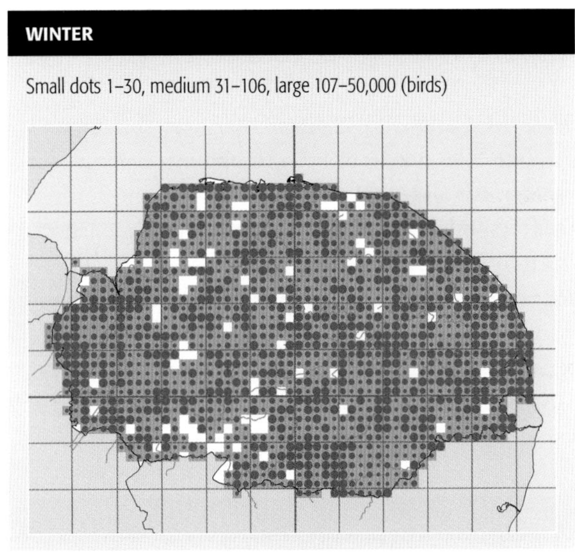

CHANGE SINCE 1980–85

+ Gain ✖ Loss ■ No change

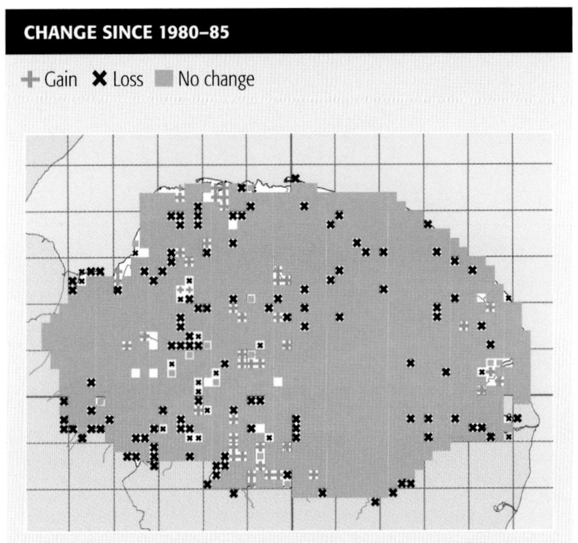

Blackbird
Turdus merula

NBA 1999–2007	SUMMER: ALL / BREEDING	WINTER
TETRADS OCCUPIED	1,413 (97%) / 1,408 (97%)	1,422 (97%)
SUMMER/WINTER ONLY	7	16
MEAN PER OCCUPIED TETRAD	26 / 26	41
SUMMED MAX COUNTS	36,806 / 36,800	58,925
POPULATION ESTIMATE	45,000–55,000 bp	120,000–150,000

PREVIOUS ATLASES	SQUARES OCCUPIED	1999–2007	LOSSES	GAINS
1968–72 (10 KM)	62 (all)	62 (all)		
1980–85 (TETRAD)	1,405 (96%)	1,408 (97%)	24	27
1980–85 (10 KM)	62 (all)	62 (all)		
1981–84 WINTER (10 KM)	62 (all)	62 (all)		
1988–91 (10 KM)	62 (all)	62 (all)		

THE BLACKBIRD IS one of our most familiar and recognisable songbirds, being found throughout the county in a wide variety of habitats.

The species began to spread into manmade habitats in the 19th century, thus expanding its range and increasing its numbers, such that by the early 1940s it had become more abundant as a breeding species across Britain than the Song Thrush (Holloway 1996). The British population probably stabilised during the 1950s,

and BTO monitoring since the 1960s has shown relatively little population change over that period (*Birdtrends*).

Blackbirds are the most adaptable of the thrushes and occupy a wide range of habitats throughout the year. Nowadays, gardens in both rural and urban settings provide optimum conditions, with areas of bare soil and short vegetation for foraging and plenty of suitable cover for nesting. Blackbirds are also found on farmland, in hedgerows, in woodland and on heaths and commons. Not surprisingly, therefore, the NBA summer map shows that they are one of the most widespread species in Norfolk, with records in almost every tetrad in the county. It is likely that the species was genuinely missing from the occasional square on the Halvergate Marshes, in the Fens and on

SUMMER

Small dots 1–15, medium 16–29, large 30–143 ('pairs')
Shading – breeding proved or considered likely

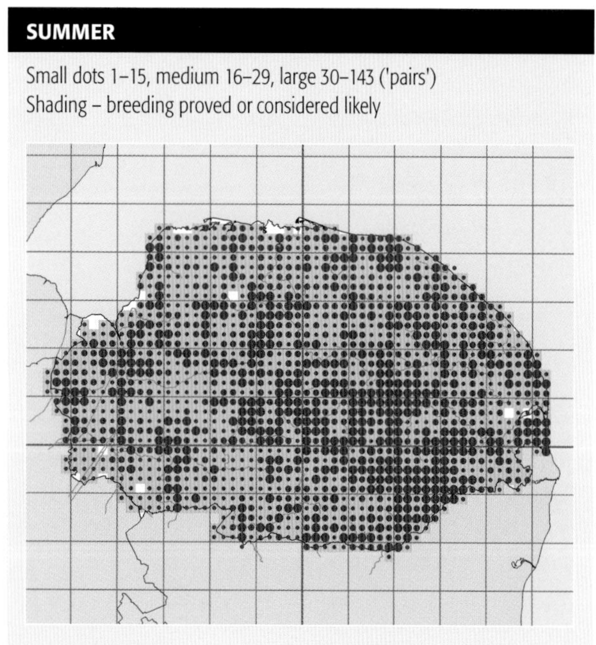

WINTER

Small dots 1–25, medium 26–48, large 49–200 (birds)

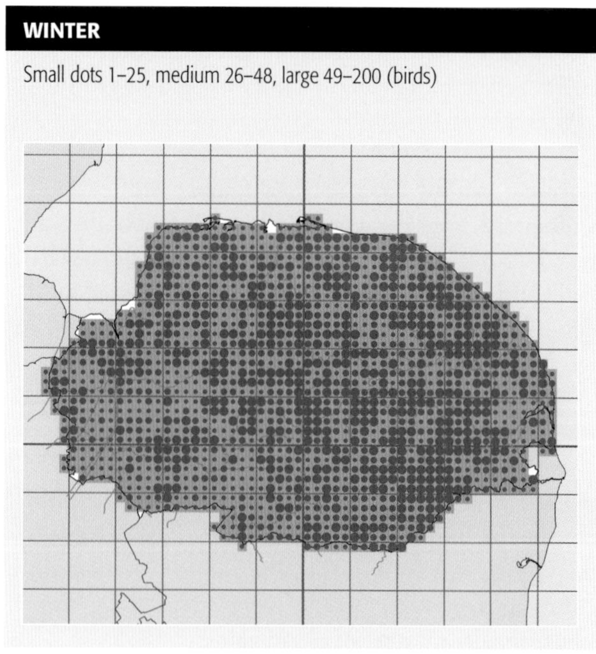

DAVID TIPLING

saltmarsh in north Norfolk and around the Wash. It is known that some of the highest densities of breeding Blackbirds are found in urban areas (Mason 2003) and this was the case during the NBA summers, with the highest tetrad count of 143 pairs being made at Thetford, while 120 pairs were found near West Winch. Five other tetrads also held over 100 pairs.

British Blackbirds cover the whole spectrum of migration strategies from being sedentary to being fully migratory, with the more northerly and upland populations showing the greater tendency to migrate in autumn. Established territory-holders often continue to defend their territory actively throughout the winter, perhaps especially in urban and suburban habitats. In the winter months, many visitors from northern and central Europe join the British population and these birds often remain in loose flocks and forage socially.

Blackbird was even more widespread in winter, being recorded in 97% of tetrads during NBA fieldwork, with a suggestion from the NBA winter map that it is more abundant inland than around the coast. Counts of over 150 Blackbirds were recorded in 11 tetrads, all of which were inland, with the highest counts at Harpley Dams (200), Newton Flotman (179) and Thetford (177). Away from towns and villages, the species particularly favoured small, irregularly shaped fields with untrimmed hedges, unimproved grassland and the presence of livestock. Although Blackbirds are little affected by severe winter weather and hard-weather movements are not common, some notable influxes were recorded during the NBA winters, including 500 in off the sea at California over a three-day period at the end of December 2005.

Previous atlas data for the county indicate an almost identical distribution to that recorded by NBA, in both summer and winter. The change map shows only minor changes since the *1980–85 NBBS*, including some infilling in mid Norfolk and a few apparent losses of range around the fringes of the county.

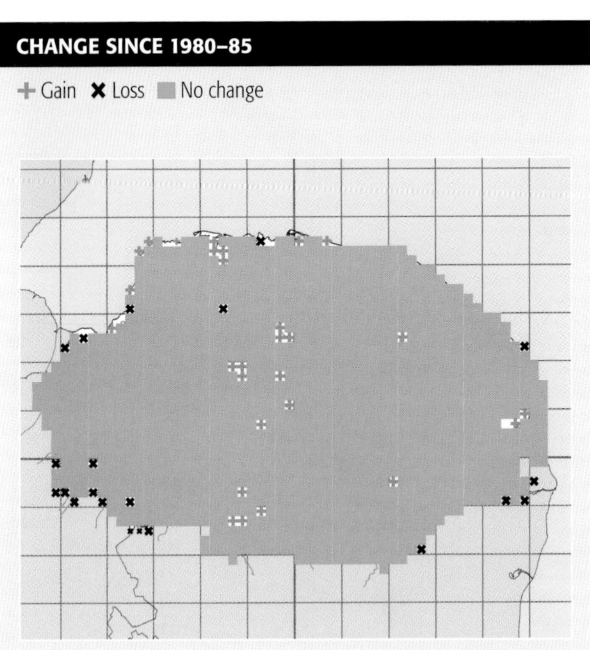

Fieldfare
Turdus pilaris

NBA 1999–2007	SUMMER: ALL/BREEDING	WINTER
TETRADS OCCUPIED	124 (8%) / none	1,202 (82%)
SUMMER/WINTER ONLY	7	1,085
MEAN PER OCCUPIED TETRAD	13 / none	111
SUMMED MAX COUNTS	1,577 / none	133,422
POPULATION ESTIMATE	none	40,000–50,000

PREVIOUS ATLASES	SQUARES OCCUPIED	1999–2007	LOSSES	GAINS
1980–85 (TETRAD)	13 (<1%)	none	13	0
1980–85 (10 KM)	10 (16%)	none	10	0
1981–84 WINTER (10 KM)	62 (all)	62 (all)		
1988–91 (10 KM)	2 (3%)	none	2	0

THE FIELDFARE IS one of the most abundant breeding birds in northern Europe and, following a marked expansion in range that began over 200 years ago, now breeds widely in many central and western European countries as well.

In Britain, the species first bred successfully in 1967, since when a few pairs have nested in most years, but it is as an autumn passage migrant and winter visitor that the Fieldfare is best known. Varying numbers arrive in autumn, the timing of their arrival depending partly on the depletion of rowan berries in Fenno-Scandia. The species is highly gregarious and during the winter months may be found in flocks, even of a thousand or more, on open farmland, along tall hedgerows, in orchards and on freshwater marshes, where they are often joined by small numbers of Redwings and by Starlings.

The NBA winter map shows that Fieldfares were recorded in a high proportion of tetrads throughout the county but, as this map is drawn from eight years' data, it may exaggerate the distribution in any one winter. Because flocks are nomadic, the sum of tetrad maxima is several times higher than the estimated county population, with the same birds inevitably recorded in more than one tetrad. Their relative abundance through the county indicates

DAVID TIPLING

that they favoured the central and southern half of Norfolk, with a distinct tendency to avoid coastal tetrads.

The highest NBA tetrad count was of 2,000 at Saham Park, with flocks of 1,500 at Snettisham CP, Rockland St Mary and Winfarthing. Flocks will often remain feeding in the same area for several weeks at a time, as was demonstrated at Saham Park where 1,050 were present on the first winter-period visit, increasing to 2,000 on the second visit three weeks later. While grazed meadows and ploughed fields are often favoured on farmland, one observer in Breckland found a flock of 200 feeding around a muckheap. Fieldfares feed mainly on terrestrial invertebrates, but they also take fruit and berries from the hedgerows, while apple orchards can prove particularly attractive in hard weather. It is often during spells of severe weather on the Continent that December/January influxes occur, usually resulting in the largest numbers in the west of the county.

'Although nearly all have left by the end of April, 100 were still present at Snettisham in early May 2000.'

Flocks of Fieldfares often linger well into spring, especially at sites, such as Felbrigg Park, where they can put on weight prior to migration. The NBA summer map shows that as many as 8% of tetrads hosted Fieldfares during the summer recording period, with maximum counts of up to 250 in the Kenninghall/Banham area and 200 at Toftrees. Although nearly all have left by the end of April, 100 were still present at Snettisham in early May 2000. The species has never been proved to breed in Norfolk but single pairs summered in the Winterton area during 1975–77 and four were present in the same area up to late June 1978. An intriguing record concerned two at Blakeney GM on 26th June 2006.

SUMMER

Small dots 1–2, medium 3–10, large 11–125 ('pairs')

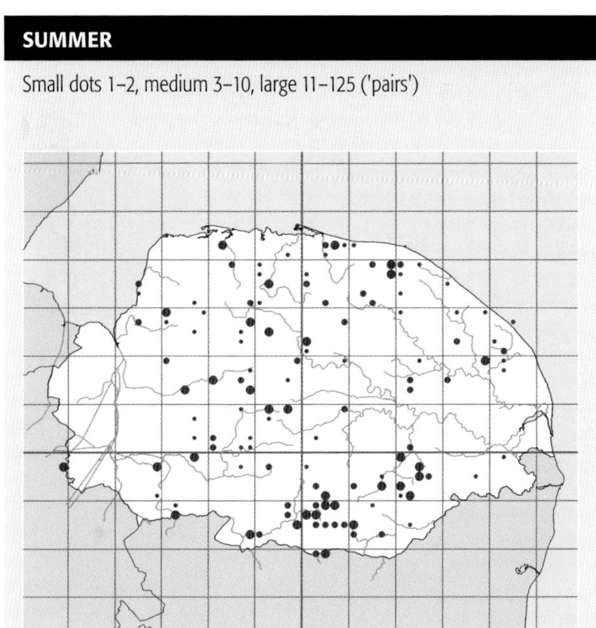

WINTER

Small dots 1–32, medium 33–100, large 101–2,008 (birds)

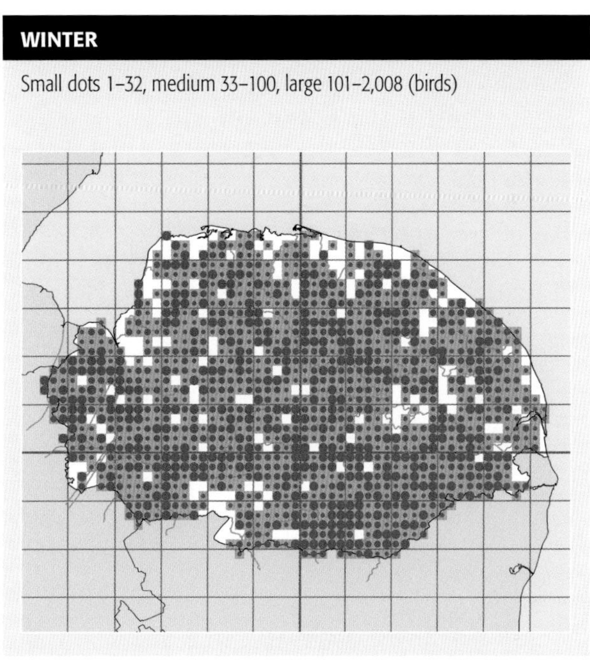

Song Thrush
Turdus philomelos

NBA 1999–2007	SUMMER: ALL/BREEDING	WINTER
TETRADS OCCUPIED	1,278 (88%) / 1,263 (87%)	1,270 (87%)
SUMMER/WINTER ONLY	104	96
MEAN PER OCCUPIED TETRAD	4 / 4	4
SUMMED MAX COUNTS	5,488 / 5,470	5,658
POPULATION ESTIMATE	6,000–8,000 bp	15,000–20,000

PREVIOUS ATLASES	SQUARES OCCUPIED	1999–2007	LOSSES	GAINS
1968–72 (10 KM)	62 (all)	62 (all)		
1980–85 (TETRAD)	1,377 (94%)	1,263 (87%)	143	29
1980–85 (10 KM)	62 (all)	62 (all)		
1981–84 WINTER (10 KM)	62 (all)	62 (all)		
1988–91 (10 KM)	62 (all)	62 (all)		

THE SONG THRUSH'S territorial song, well known for its repeating phrases, is still heard widely in Britain's towns and villages. During the early decades of the 20th century, however, this thrush was commoner in Britain than the Blackbird.

Song Thrushes may be found in most habitats that include trees or bushes and open areas where they can forage at a short distance from cover; they inhabit woodland edges, hedgerows, farms, commons and heathland, as well as

gardens, cemeteries and city parks. They sing mainly in the early morning and late evening, and their presence can also be inferred by finding a 'thrush's anvil' surrounded by broken snail shells. The CBC recorded a steep decline in Britain's farmland and woodland, beginning in the late 1960s (*Birdtrends*). Mason (1998) found that, in his study area in northeast Essex, gardens were far more important as breeding habitat than woodland, and that many of the woodland and farmland territories were within 100 metres of a garden.

The NBA summer map shows that, at tetrad level, Song Thrushes remained very widespread throughout the county. The highest counts of breeding pairs in a tetrad were near Gooderstone (24), King's Lynn (22), Swardeston (21) and Thetford (20), while conditions at Wayland

SUMMER

Small dots 1–2, medium 3–5, large 6–24 ('pairs')
Shading – breeding proved or considered likely

WINTER

Small dots 1–2, medium 3–5, large 6–31 (birds)

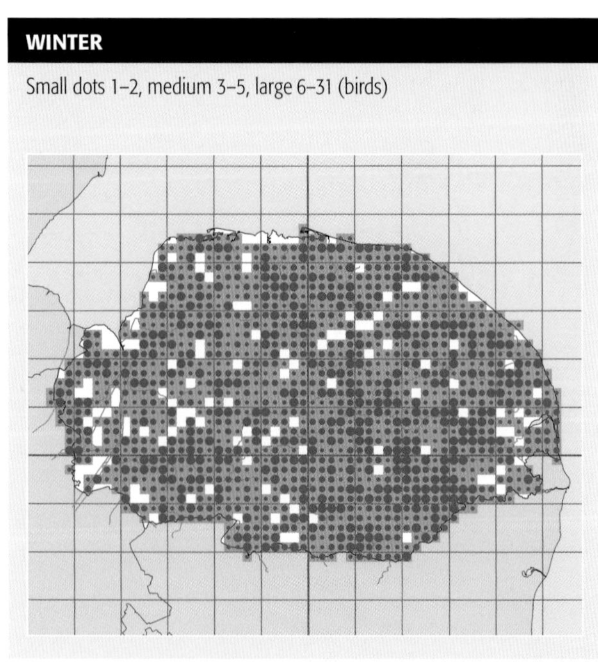

DAVID TIPLING

Wood were clearly to their liking as shown by the presence of 15 singing males in 2006. In Thetford Forest, the thicket stages of plantations 5–20 years old held thriving populations of Song Thrushes. The species was absent from much of the Halvergate Levels and adjoining marshes, the coastal saltmarshes and parts of the Fens and Brecks. In the more open rural tetrads, the association of Song Thrushes with gardens was often very striking.

Outside the breeding season, Song Thrushes are usually solitary or found in only small groups, and can more easily be overlooked. The NBA winter map also records high occupancy, however, even the Halvergate Marshes hosting small numbers. The main areas where the species was not encountered were along a narrow coastal strip, most obviously from the Wash west to Stiffkey, and in a few parts of the Fens. The highest winter tetrad count was of 31 at both Southrepps and North Runcton.

Winter birds in the county are likely to be almost entirely southeast English in origin (*Migration Atlas*). Very few of the migrants from southern Fenno-Scandia, which pass through Norfolk in autumn and spring, are thought to spend the winter in Britain. Severe weather on the Continent may prompt cold-weather influxes, including birds from the Netherlands and Belgium. The NBA winters were generally mild, however, and no large-scale influxes occurred.

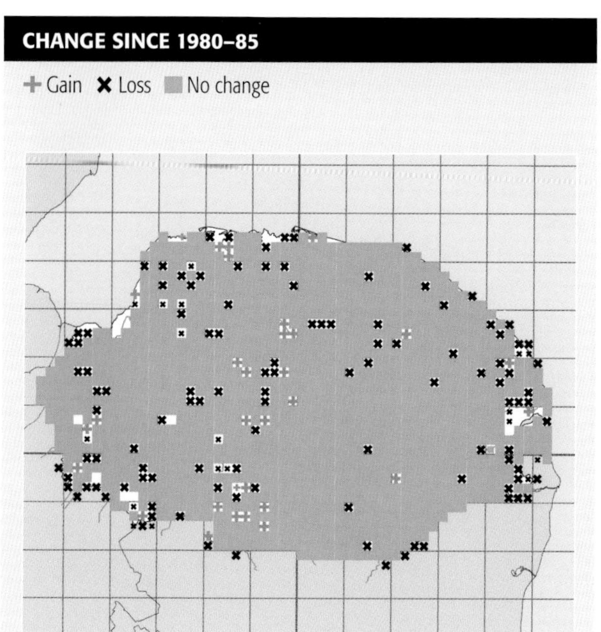

There is no doubt that the county population has fallen since the 1960s. As an example, one observer found a diary from 1965, where he had recorded finding 65 Song Thrush nests on the farm at Sparham Hall, compared with fewer than ten during NBA fieldwork. Only the comparison with the *1980–85 NBBS*, however, shows any evidence of loss in range. The change map shows thinly scattered losses of previously occupied tetrads, outnumbering gains in all regions, except perhaps in Thetford Forest.

Redwing
Turdus iliacus

NBA 1999–2007	SUMMER: ALL/BREEDING	WINTER
TETRADS OCCUPIED	75 (5%) / none	1,076 (74%)
SUMMER/WINTER ONLY	13	1,014
MEAN PER OCCUPIED TETRAD	6 / none	29
SUMMED MAX COUNTS	459 / none	31,235
POPULATION ESTIMATE	0–1 individual	10,000–15,000

PREVIOUS ATLASES	SQUARES OCCUPIED	1999–2007	LOSSES	GAINS
1980–85 (TETRAD)	6 (<1%)	none	6	0
1980–85 (10 KM)	4 (6%)	none	4	0
1981–84 WINTER (10 KM)	62 (all)	62 (all)		

THE REDWING'S distinctive nocturnal flight call is a sure sign that Norfolk's winter visitors are returning. Britain hosts only a few breeding birds but receives migrants from Iceland (race *coburni*) and from subarctic regions of Fenno-Scandia, the Baltic States and Russia.

As autumn migrants and winter visitors, Redwings frequent open fields, where they forage for invertebrates, often in association with Fieldfares and Starlings, and hedgerows and open woodland, where they take hawthorn and other berries. Generally they visit gardens only with the onset of hard weather.

The NBA winter map shows that the species was well distributed throughout the county, but was largely absent from the open Fens and, like other thrushes, from the coastal fringe. The eastern half of the county appears to be particularly favoured. Four of the five highest counts made during the NBA winters were of gatherings in open parkland, with 700 at Blickling Park, 380 at Costessey Park and 300 at both Holkham Park and Felbrigg Park.

SUMMER

Small dots 1, medium 2–5, large 6–143 ('pairs')

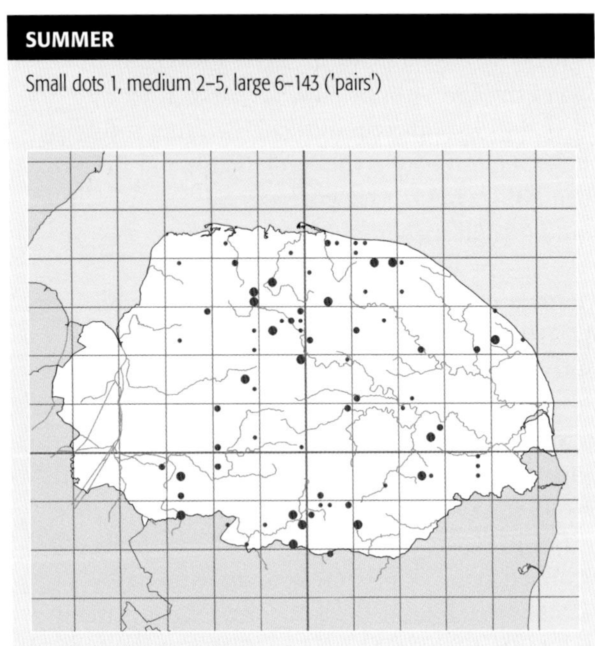

WINTER

Small dots 1–7, medium 8–25, large 26–700 (birds)

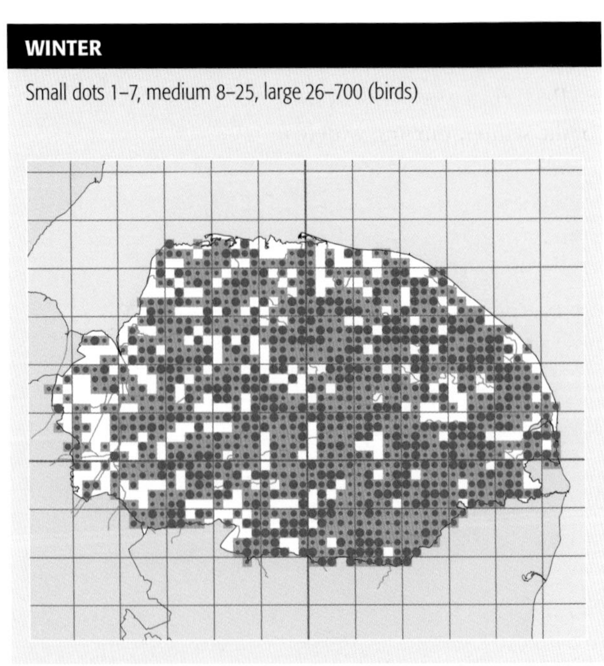

DAVID TIPLING

Redwings are highly nomadic during the course of the winter, moving widely in response to weather conditions and food availability. It is therefore extremely difficult to assess Norfolk's wintering population, which in any case varies between years. Ringing has demonstrated that occasional birds return to the same area in subsequent winters and that the Redwings wintering in England rarely, if ever, include *coburni* from Iceland (*Migration Atlas*).

In late March and early April, flocks of Redwings begin to gather prior to their return migration and, as for Fieldfares, Felbrigg Park hosted some of the largest groups, such as 200 in early April 2000. The NBA summer map shows that there was a good scattering of sightings during the summer recording period, the vast majority made during the first weeks of April. The latest spring records each year were generally in the last week of April or the first two weeks of May, but one in heavy wing moult, presumably an injured or sick bird that had been present since spring, was ringed at Weybourne on 10th July 2007 and retrapped in August having completed its moult.

'Redwings are highly nomadic during the course of the winter, moving widely in response to weather conditions and food availability.'

The species has never been proved to breed in Norfolk and would now be a most unlikely colonist. The *1980–85 NBBS*, however, recorded singing birds at Carbrooke and at Grimston and possible breeding in four other tetrads where late birds were seen.

Mistle Thrush

Turdus viscivorus

NBA 1999–2007	SUMMER: ALL / BREEDING	WINTER
TETRADS OCCUPIED	1,222 (84%) / 1,149 (79%)	1,269 (87%)
SUMMER/WINTER ONLY	81	128
MEAN PER OCCUPIED TETRAD	3 / 3	5
SUMMED MAX COUNTS	3,689 / 3,575	6,312
POPULATION ESTIMATE	3,500–4,000 bp	8,000–10,000

PREVIOUS ATLASES	SQUARES OCCUPIED	1999–2007	LOSSES	GAINS
1968–72 (10 KM)	62 (all)	62 (all)		
1980–85 (TETRAD)	946 (65%)	1,149 (79%)	131	334
1980–85 (10 KM)	62 (all)	62 (all)		
1981–84 WINTER (10 KM)	61 (98%)	62 (all)	0	1
1988–91 (10 KM)	62 (all)	62 (all)		

THE MISTLE THRUSH'S wild and far-carrying song is commonly heard from midwinter onwards. Large and strongly built, Mistle Thrushes defend large territories and rarely consort with other thrushes.

This species favours areas with tall trees and open grassland, and so is found along woodland edges, on parkland, farmland and in large gardens. The species mostly avoids treeless terrain, such as open farmland and wetlands.

The NBA summer map shows that Mistle Thrushes are very widely distributed throughout the county, although with more absences at tetrad level than Norfolk's other breeding thrushes. The main areas of absence are parts of Fenland, the more intensively farmed arable areas in northwest Norfolk and the treeless expanses of the Halvergate Marshes.

Male Mistle Thrushes sing from the topmost perches of tall trees. Their loud songs carry a considerable distance and make the birds easy to locate during survey work. They are one of the earliest nesters and some broods may have fledged before the summer recording period began. However, the birds remain in their family groups for several weeks and are very obvious as they feed on grassland and open fields. The largest post-breeding flocks recorded during the NBA summers were 33 at Hunworth and 30 at Holme, although parties of over 50 were recorded in autumn, in late

SUMMER

Small dots 1–2, medium 3–4, large 5–20 ('pairs')
Shading – breeding proved or considered likely

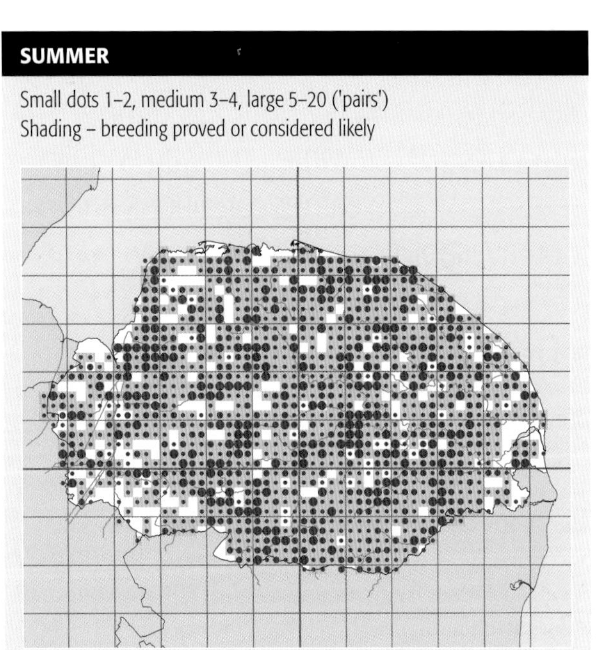

WINTER

Small dots 1–3, medium 4–6, large 7–47 (birds)

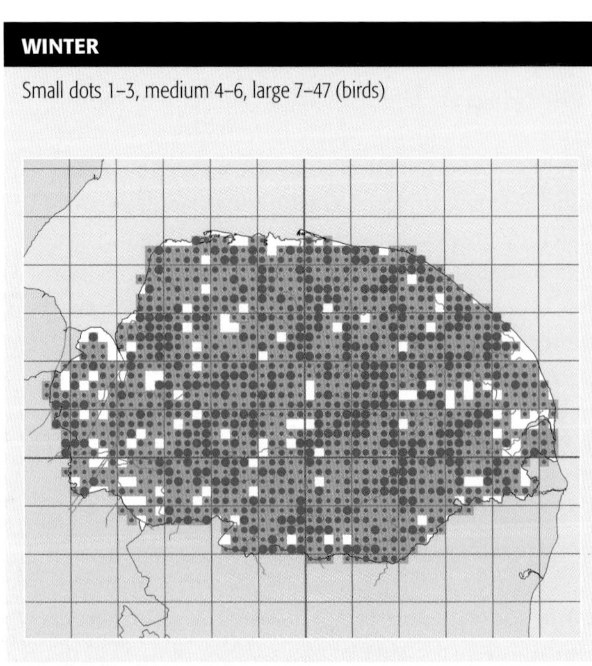

DAVID TIPLING

July and August. The highest numbers of pairs in a tetrad were 20 at Framingham Earl, 18 at Frettenham and 17 at Necton, but such high numbers were exceptional.

In winter, Mistle Thrushes are usually found alone or in pairs, but occasionally in single-figure flocks. To ensure an adequate food supply throughout the winter months, individuals may vigorously defend a berry-bearing tree, such as holly, guelder rose or yew, against other fruit-eating birds. The NBA winter map shows a slightly wider distribution than during summer, with some additional tetrads hosting small numbers, even in the Fens and on the marshes around Breydon Water. The highest winter tetrad counts were 47 at Stockton and 34 at East Winch.

'In winter, Mistle Thrushes are usually found alone or in pairs, but occasionally in single-figure flocks.'

CHANGE SINCE 1980–85

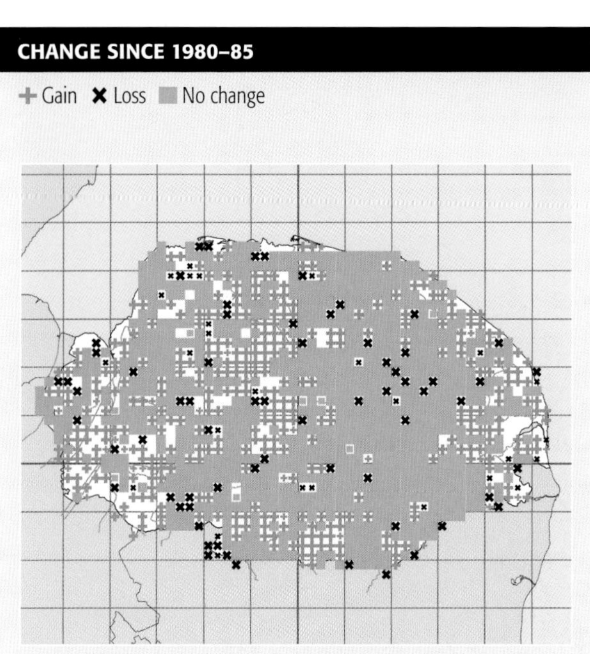

In Britain many first-year Mistle Thrushes are migratory, especially those reared in Scotland, but the scale of immigration from the Continent is small (*Migration Atlas*). The great majority of birds wintering in Norfolk are likely to be of very local origin.

Only the comparison with the *1980–85 NBBS* gives any evidence of change in Norfolk range, with a net gain of more than 200 tetrads. Mistle Thrushes have spread into the previously unoccupied swathe between Dereham and Fakenham, and other patches of previous absence, such as around North Lopham, and have become more widespread in Broadland and in the Fens.

Spotted Flycatcher
Muscicapa striata

NBA 1999–2007	SUMMER: ALL/BREEDING	WINTER
TETRADS OCCUPIED	518 (36%) / 467 (32%)	none
SUMMER/WINTER ONLY	518	none
MEAN PER OCCUPIED TETRAD	1 / 1	none
SUMMED MAX COUNTS	708 / 653	none
POPULATION ESTIMATE	500–700 bp	none

PREVIOUS ATLASES	SQUARES OCCUPIED	1999–2007	LOSSES	GAINS
1968–72 (10 KM)	62 (all)	57 (92%)	5	0
1980–85 (TETRAD)	683 (47%)	467 (32%)	428	212
1980–85 (10 KM)	62 (all)	57 (92%)	5	0
1988–91 (10 KM)	62 (all)	57 (92%)	5	0

SPOTTED FLYCATCHERS sallying out from a perch to catch a flying insect were once a common sight in Norfolk, but this popular bird is now in strong retreat. The species' long-term decline, since at least the early 1960s, has been widespread across Europe and has probably been driven by factors operating on migration or in the African winter quarters (*Birdtrends*).

The Spotted Flycatcher may be found in a variety of woodland-edge habitats and often in parkland and large gardens. Its requirements include raised perches from which it can launch its aerial forays and a suitable nesting site, such as a small hollow in a tree, creepers growing up trees or walls, a small ledge on a building or an open-fronted nest box. NBA observers found it to be strongly attracted to churchyards and cemeteries.

Their songs and calls are undistinguished and, despite the confiding nature of the species, it might sometimes have been overlooked during surveys. In addition, it returns very late from Africa, mainly in mid to late May, and was unlikely to have been present during the early summer set visits.

The NBA summer map shows a well-scattered distribution throughout much of the county but with a suggestion of denser occupation near the north coast and in a broader zone of south Norfolk between Breckland and the Broads. Spotted Flycatchers were largely absent from the Fens and

CHRIS KNIGHTS

from substantial parts of northwest and central Norfolk.

A few notable concentrations of breeding pairs were recorded, including up to seven pairs on the estates at Mannington and Horning Hall, and five pairs within a mile of the village of Roydon, near King's Lynn, while up to three pairs bred in Chapelfield Gardens in central Norwich in the early years of the survey.

The Spotted Flycatcher is one of the most steeply declining species in Britain. During the 25 years 1982–2007, the population in England fell by 82% (*Birdtrends*). Comparison with previous atlas data shows that substantial gaps are already apparent in the Norfolk distribution. The species was missing from five 10-km squares during the NBA period, although every square had been occupied in each of the earlier surveys. At tetrad level, almost a third of tetrads occupied during the *1980–85 NBBS* had lost their Spotted Flycatchers by 2000–07. The change map shows losses predominating in all parts of the county except the southeast, where gains were apparent in some regions. By 2007, the population may already have numbered as few as 500 breeding pairs.

'The Spotted Flycatcher is one of the most steeply declining species in Britain. During the 25 years 1982–2007, the population in England fell by 82%.'

SUMMER

Small dots 1, medium 2, large 3–7 ('pairs')
Shading – breeding proved or considered likely

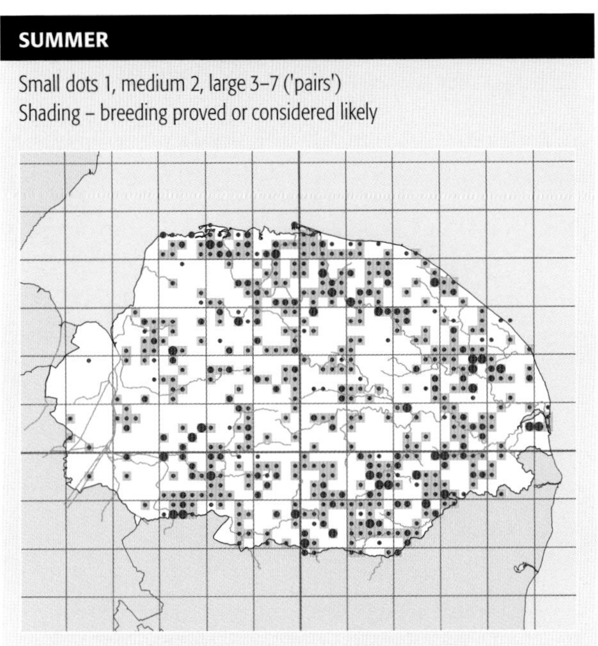

CHANGE SINCE 1980–85

+ Gain ✖ Loss ■ No change

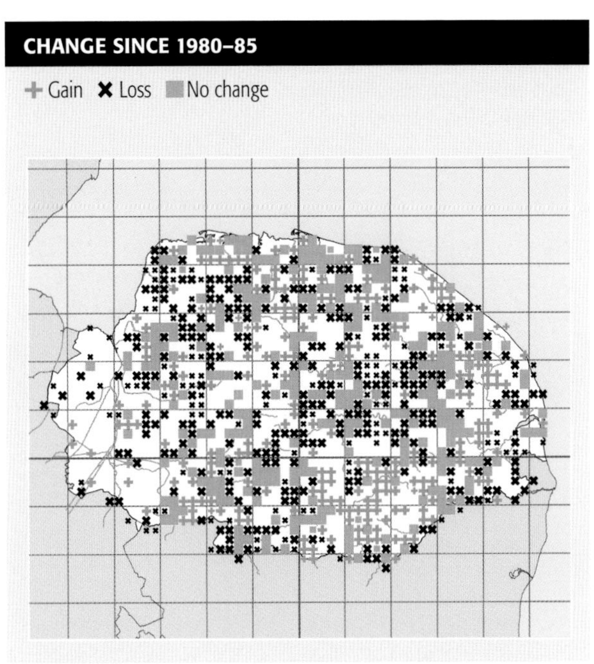

Robin
Erithacus rubecula

NBA 1999–2007	SUMMER: ALL / BREEDING	WINTER
TETRADS OCCUPIED	1,396 (96%) / 1,390 (95%)	1,390 (95%)
SUMMER/WINTER ONLY	25	19
MEAN PER OCCUPIED TETRAD	15 / 15	17
SUMMED MAX COUNTS	20,739 / 20,733	23,876
POPULATION ESTIMATE	40,000–50,000 bp	100,000–150,000

PREVIOUS ATLASES	SQUARES OCCUPIED	1999–2007	LOSSES	GAINS
1968–72 (10 KM)	62 (all)	62 (all)		
1980–85 (TETRAD)	1,329 (91%)	1,390 (95%)	27	88
1980–85 (10 KM)	62 (all)	62 (all)		
1981–84 WINTER (10 KM)	62 (all)	62 (all)		
1988–91 (10 KM)	62 (all)	62 (all)		

THE ROBIN'S SWEET song and confiding behaviour make it familiar to many people and it is probably Britain's best-loved bird. It is widely distributed throughout the western Palaearctic and is migratory in much of its range.

Robins may breed wherever a shrub layer is present, such as in broad-leaved woodland, in farmland hedges with trees, and in parks, churchyards and gardens.

Suitable conditions are met very widely in Norfolk. The NBA summer map shows that the species was found in almost every tetrad in the county, the only exceptions being a few coastal squares, and certain relatively treeless tetrads in the Fens. It is likely that Robins were overlooked, rather than absent, in the other inland tetrads where none was recorded.

NBA fieldwork showed that the species was most plentiful in the areas of mixed woodland, such as along the Cromer to Holt ridge, and in southeast Norfolk. Two adjacent Breckland tetrads each held 100 or more breeding pairs: Stow Heath (114) and Hockham Belt (100), while up to 102 pairs were present in the tetrads covering the Swanton Novers woods. Parts of Norfolk's river valleys, such as the Tas

SUMMER

Small dots 1-9, medium 10-17, large 18-114 ('pairs')
Shading – breeding proved or considered likely

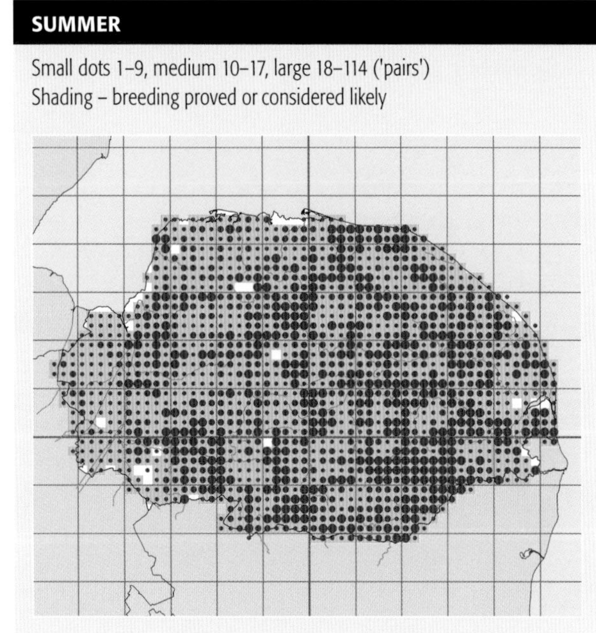

WINTER

Small dots 1-10, medium 11-20, large 21-106 (birds)

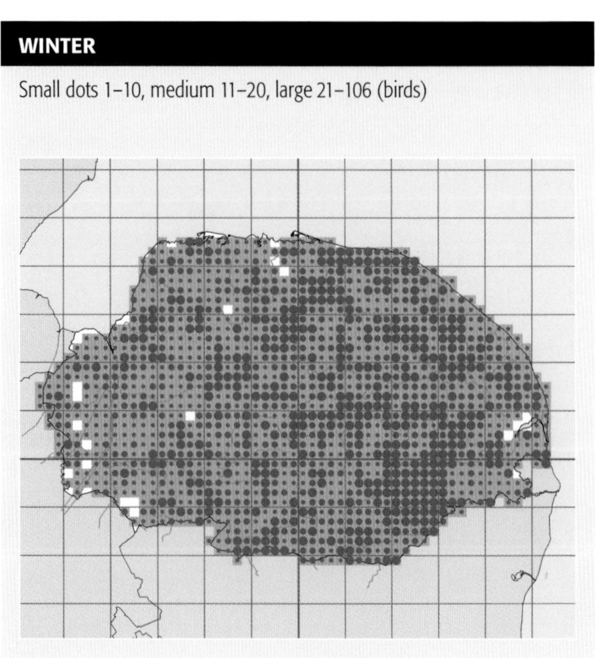

DAVID TIPLING

and the Thet, hold higher densities than areas nearby, perhaps because the habitat near the rivers is more varied and better wooded.

Robins are solitary and strongly territorial outside the breeding season, and both sexes sing. Indeed the Robin is often the only species to be heard singing in winter, and therefore they are easy to locate at this season. As British Robins are largely resident it is not surprising that the winter and summer maps are almost identical, with concentrations in the areas of mixed woodland and relative scarcity in the more open habitats, such as the Fens. However, in winter, Robins are also found in other sites, unsuitable for breeding, such as reedbeds, sand dunes and scrub. As in summer, the highest tetrad count was at Stow Heath (106 birds), while one at Woodton, in southeast Norfolk, held 100. Migrant Robins at the coast include many from Fenno-Scandia and elsewhere in northern Europe but nearly all of these migrants continue southward towards Iberia and very few are present during midwinter.

'NBA fieldwork showed that the species was most plentiful in the areas of mixed woodland, such as along the Cromer to Holt ridge, and in southeast Norfolk.'

CHANGE SINCE 1980–85

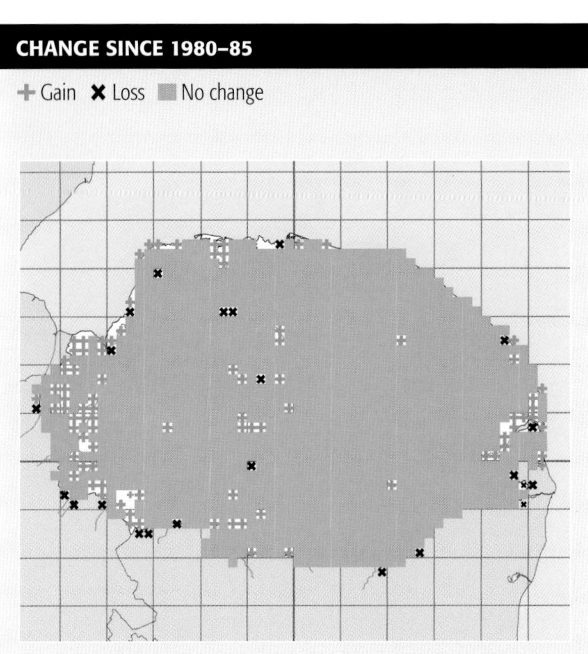

Comparison with the *1980–85 NBBS* shows some minor increase in tetrad occupancy, with infilling of range particularly in the Fens and near Breydon Water. The species is clearly thriving nationally, with an increase of 60% measured by the CBC/BBS index for England between 1982 and 2007.

Nightingale

Luscinia megarhynchos

NBA 1999–2007	SUMMER: ALL / BREEDING	WINTER
TETRADS OCCUPIED	173 (12%) / 142 (10%)	none
SUMMER/WINTER ONLY	173	none
MEAN PER OCCUPIED TETRAD	2 / 2	none
SUMMED MAX COUNTS	341 / 309	none
POPULATION ESTIMATE	200–300 bp	none

PREVIOUS ATLASES	SQUARES OCCUPIED	1999–2007	LOSSES	GAINS
1968–72 (10 KM)	45 (73%)	39 (63%)	12	6
1980–85 (TETRAD)	212 (15%)	142 (10%)	150	80
1980–85 (10 KM)	45 (73%)	39 (63%)	14	8
1988–91 (10 KM)	35 (56%)	39 (63%)	6	10

FAMED FOR ITS fabulously rich and varied song, the Nightingale is an inveterate skulker and is a very difficult bird to catch even a glimpse of. For a variety of reasons, its range has contracted and its population has been in decline in England since the early 20th century.

In Norfolk, Nightingales inhabit thick scrub in open woodland, on heaths and commons or near water, such as gravel pits or along the banks of watercourses. Many of the breeding sites are used by the species year after year, although other apparently suitable sites are no longer occupied. The males are site faithful and on return from their African winter quarters are often heard singing from exactly the same clump of bushes or blackthorn thicket as in the previous spring. Nightingales are most vocal at dusk and dawn, and have a comparatively short song period, with maximum output around mid May. For these reasons, it was very easy to miss the species during normal daytime NBA fieldwork; indeed it has been estimated that single visits to suitable locations may underestimate numbers by as much as half (*1988–91 Atlas*).

Throughout the 20th century, the most favoured areas for Nightingales in Norfolk have traditionally been the Brecks, the area between King's Lynn and Swaffham, and the Cromer to Holt ridge. As can be seen from the NBA summer map, the distribution has changed somewhat, with peak numbers now around the Fenland/Breckland border and far fewer in central Breckland and around Swaffham, and almost complete absence from the Cromer to Holt ridge. In addition, a few scattered sites in central Norfolk still hold Nightingales. During the NBA summers, the species was recorded in over 170 tetrads, although some of these were not occupied for breeding. Three tetrads hosted 11 singing males: at Feltwell, Methwold and Salthouse Heath, although at the last named site numbers had fallen to just two or three in the later years of the survey, a similar situation occurring at Roydon and East Winch Commons.

The first Nightingales are generally back on the breeding territories in the first half of April, although one was present at Pentney Heath from at least 28th March 2005 and constituted the earliest Norfolk record ever. Undoubtedly, some of the coastal records on the NBA summer map refer to birds on spring passage.

A BTO survey in 1999 recorded a major contraction of range across England since the previous survey in 1980, believed to be part of a longer-term decline in the British population (Wilson *et al.* 2002). Factors that may adversely affect the species are loss of habitat in their breeding areas, such as through scrub clearance and increased browsing by deer, and climate-driven changes in their wintering quarters. Habitat loss may be counterbalanced by the development of suitable scrub around disused gravel workings and along the banks of drainage channels. In the Fens it was the appearance of thick scrub along the banks of the Cut-off Channel which resulted in 26 singing males being counted along a 20-km stretch between Hockwold

EDMUND FELLOWES

and Wereham in 1999 (Wilson 2000). In the same year, 23% of the county's total was located in the two parishes of Feltwell and Methwold along the Fenland/Breckland border.

The change map indicates substantial loss in overall Norfolk range since the *1980–85 NBBS*. Redistribution away from many former haunts and towards the Feltwell and Methwold area is clearly evident and had already occurred by the time of the 1999 survey.

'The change map indicates substantial loss in overall Norfolk range since the *1980–85 NBBS*.'

The 1980 survey found 322 singing males in Norfolk, compared with 316 in 1999 (Wilson 2000). NBA data suggest that population decline has occurred since and the population could number well below 300 singing males.

SUMMER

Small dots 1, medium 2, large 3–11 ('pairs')
Shading – breeding proved or considered likely

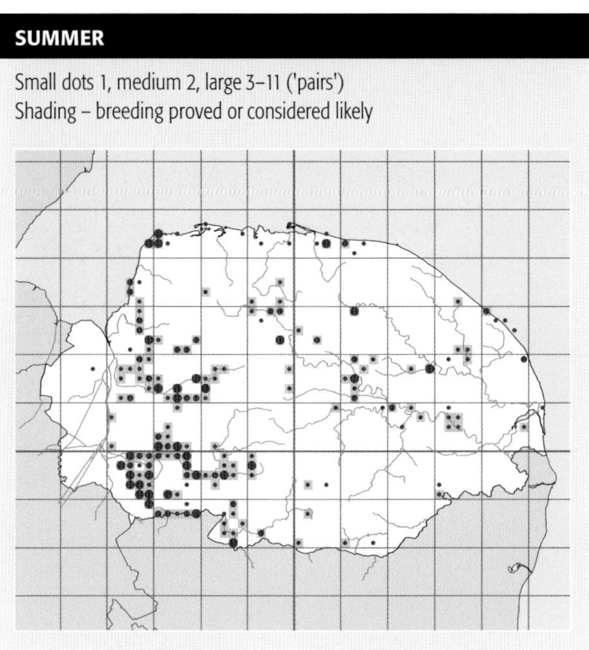

CHANGE SINCE 1980–85

+ Gain ✖ Loss ■ No change

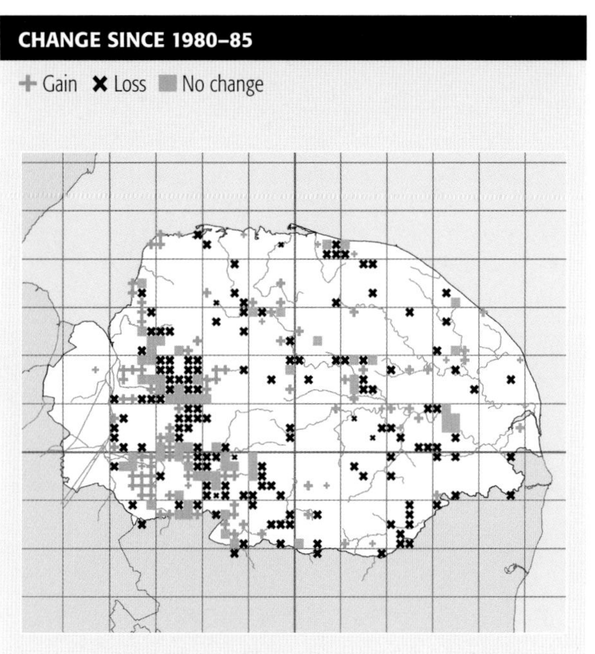

Black Redstart
Phoenicurus ochruros

NBA 1999–2007	SUMMER: ALL/BREEDING	WINTER
TETRADS OCCUPIED	63 (4%) / 5 (<1%)	21 (1%)
SUMMER/WINTER ONLY	57	15
MEAN PER OCCUPIED TETRAD	1 / 2	1
SUMMED MAX COUNTS	73 / 9	24
POPULATION ESTIMATE	4–10 bp	3–5

PREVIOUS ATLASES	SQUARES OCCUPIED	1999–2007	LOSSES	GAINS
1968–72 (10 KM)	5 (8%)	2 (3%)	3	0
1980–85 (TETRAD)	18 (1%)	5 (<1%)	15	2
1980–85 (10 KM)	11 (18%)	2 (3%)	9	0
1981–84 WINTER (10 KM)	7 (11%)	16 (26%)	2	11
1988–91 (10 KM)	8 (13%)	2 (3%)	7	1

BLACK REDSTARTS FIRST bred regularly in Britain on the Sussex cliffs from 1923 onwards and, although they have since bred in most English counties, there have never been more than about 100 singing males present in any one year. Traditionally, the species became associated with the London bombsites after the Second World War, and it was in bombsites that the first pairs bred in Norfolk, in Great Yarmouth and Gorleston, more than 50 years ago. In Norfolk, numbers peaked in the early 1970s, with up to 18 singing males in the Great Yarmouth area, and since then only a few have been located in the county each summer.

Black Redstarts in Norfolk have almost invariably nested in or on buildings, usually large and often derelict, and in inaccessible locations. The males require high song posts, typically 40 metres or more above the ground, from which to deliver their simple, rather quiet song. A third requirement for breeding is waste ground, colonised by weeds and with patches of bare soil. Black Redstarts are largely ground feeders, dropping down from low perches to catch their invertebrate prey. These conditions were all met in the industrial South Denes area of Great Yarmouth, which has been the species' stronghold in Norfolk.

The distribution in the NBA summers, as mapped, is much wider than the distribution of breeding, because of the many spring migrants that were

SUMMER

Small dots 1, medium 2, large 3–4 ('pairs')
Shading – breeding proved or considered likely

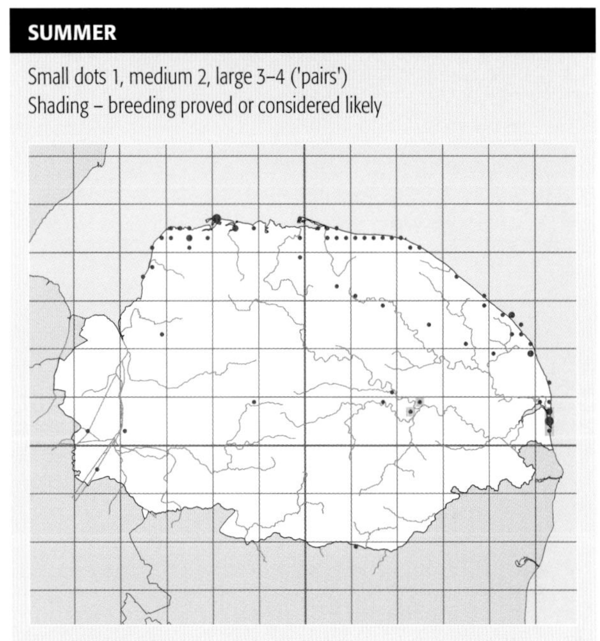

WINTER

Small dots 1, medium 2 (birds)

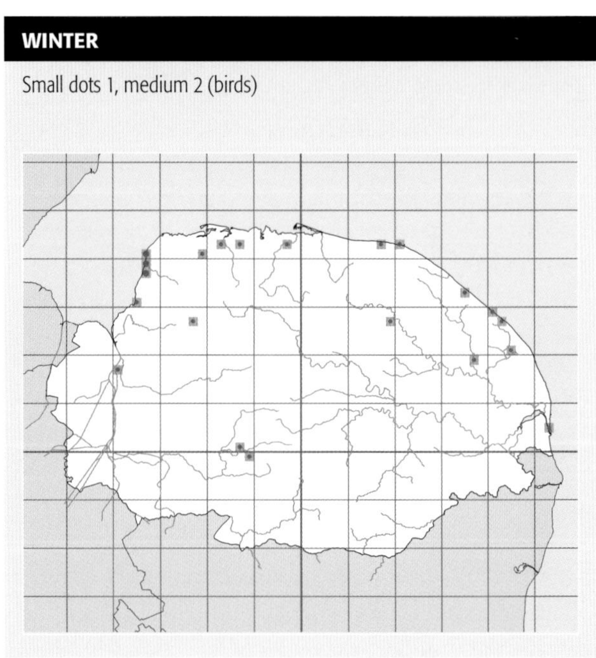

DAVID TIPLING

observed at coastal and at inland sites. Breeding was thought likely in only five tetrads, all in the Great Yarmouth and Norwich areas.

The picture is further complicated by the fact that additional, single, non-breeding, first-year male Black Redstarts are often present, singing and apparently holding territories, in potentially suitable nesting areas. Black Redstarts are often inconspicuous birds and it may be very difficult to prove breeding. As in other scarce breeding species at the limit of their breeding range, marked annual fluctuations occur (*1988–91 Atlas*). During the NBA period, the number of breeding pairs or singing males reported varied between nine in 2001 and none in 2004, although six males were once again present in Great Yarmouth in 2005.

Habitat change has affected some sites. At Great Yarmouth power station and the former army camp at Weybourne, the buildings used for nesting have simply been demolished, while areas of waste ground on which the birds feed have been tidied up and built on. Black Redstarts successfully raised two broods in the Riverside multi-storey car park near Norwich Station in 2001, but not subsequently during the NBA summers. Other potential breeding sites that have hosted singing males included the original buildings of the Norfolk and Norwich Hospital in south Norwich and a chemical works at King's Lynn. Black Redstarts thus have a very tenuous hold as a breeding species within the county, despite the strength of spring migration between early March and mid May.

Although normally recorded singly on passage, six were present on Scolt Head on 3rd April 2000 and up to four have been recorded together at Winterton.

The NBA winter map shows a mainly coastal distribution although also with a small scattering of records inland. Only seven inland winter sightings had ever been reported in Norfolk up to 1999, so the NBA map suggests a recent change in habit. Apart from two between Hunstanton and Heacham in February 2003, all winter records referred to single birds. As well as this area of west Norfolk, where the birds feed on the short turf and rough ground around the beach huts, Black Redstarts were noted in several winters at Sheringham, generally on the cliff slopes behind the promenade, and again around the beach huts. Winter records varied from none to six annually with the majority of birds first appearing in January and most remaining on site for a few weeks. It seems likely that winter birds are mainly visitors from the Continent, although occasional individuals might be resident throughout the year.

Comparison with previous atlases suggests considerable expansion in wintering distribution but a major loss in breeding range, especially since the *1980–85 NBBS*. In that survey, breeding was confirmed at Hunstanton, King's Lynn and Thetford in west Norfolk, and in Weybourne and Cromer in the north, in addition to Norwich and Great Yarmouth where birds were found during the NBA summers.

Redstart

Phoenicurus phoenicurus

NBA 1999–2007	SUMMER: ALL/BREEDING	WINTER
TETRADS OCCUPIED	66 (5%) / 23 (2%)	none
SUMMER/WINTER ONLY	66	none
MEAN PER OCCUPIED TETRAD	2 / 2	none
SUMMED MAX COUNTS	100 / 50	none
POPULATION ESTIMATE	50–100 bp	none

PREVIOUS ATLASES	SQUARES OCCUPIED	1999-2007	LOSSES	GAINS
1968–72 (10 KM)	22 (35%)	8 (13%)	14	0
1980–85 (TETRAD)	41 (3%)	23 (2%)	30	12
1980–85 (10 KM)	17 (27%)	8 (13%)	9	0
1988–91 (10 KM)	15 (24%)	8 (13%)	8	1

THE REDSTART IS one of our most brightly coloured small passerines, its attraction enhanced by its delightful habit of quivering its tail.

The species has been undergoing a long-term decline in Britain, which is probably related to loss of winter habitat and to drought in its trans-Saharan winter quarters. Increasingly it is a bird of woodlands on the fringes of upland regions, having been lost from many lowland parts of its former range. Its future as a breeding species in Norfolk is highly uncertain.

In Norfolk, Redstarts inhabit the more open areas of broadleaved and mixed woodland, as occur in clearings and along forest edges, and in parkland. In the Brecks, hawthorn hedges with standards and clumps of pines also hold small numbers of breeding pairs. Since at least the 1960s, the Stanford TA has held the majority of breeding pairs in Norfolk, and this is clearly demonstrated on the NBA summer map. Elsewhere in the Brecks, occasional pairs nest in Thetford Forest, mostly in old stands. During the NBA summers, a few pairs also bred intermittently outside Breckland, such as at Swanton Novers and along the Cromer to Holt ridge at Sheringham and Felbrigg Parks.

A full survey of the Stanford TA in 2000 located a total of 93 singing males, which was an increase of 20 over recent years, and there were thought to be only five more throughout the rest of Norfolk. In 2005, however, the Stanford TA held 55 singing males of a county total of 58.

SUMMER

Small dots 1, medium 2, large 3–12 ('pairs')
Shading – breeding proved or considered likely

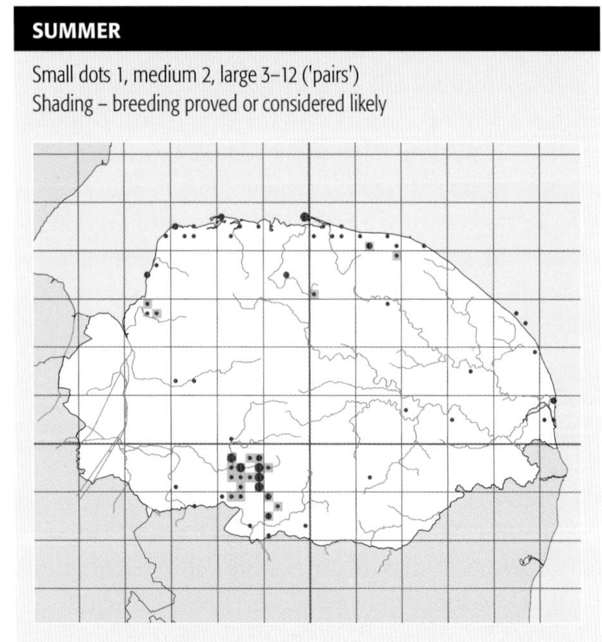

CHANGE SINCE 1980–85

+ Gain ✖ Loss ■ No change

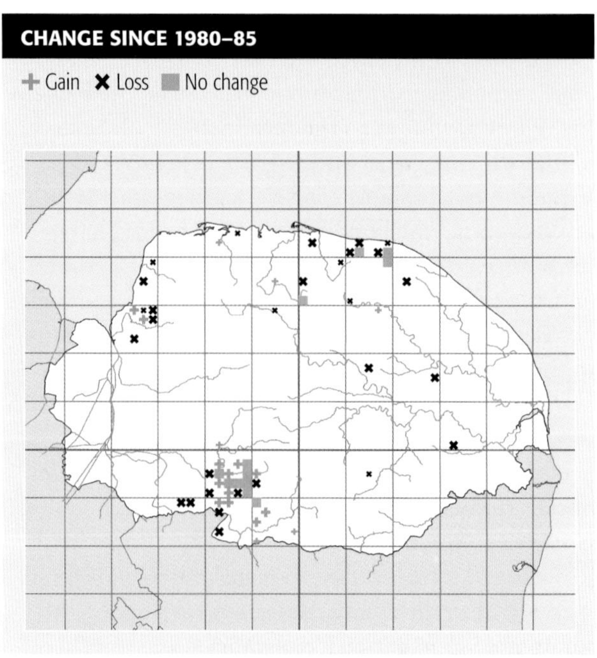

DAVID TIPLING

The highest number in a single tetrad was 12 at Sturston Warren. Redstarts usually sing from high in the canopy and might be overlooked if the song is not recognised; the song period can be short. Nevertheless, it is unlikely that many breeding pairs were missed.

The first spring Redstarts are normally recorded in the county during the first half of April, although one was present in the Stanford TA on 25th March 2000, the earliest county record ever. Another early bird was in Thetford Forest on 26th March 2005. Spring passage continues until the last week of May, with an annual average of about 30 Redstarts recorded on spring passage during the NBA period. The NBA summer map shows that a high proportion of the migrants were at coastal locations. Some may be heading for northern Britain and others for Fenno-Scandia.

'In Norfolk, Redstarts inhabit the more open areas of broadleaved and mixed woodland, as occur in clearings and along forest edges, and in parkland.'

Comparison with previous atlases shows a progressive loss of 10-km squares occupied by birds thought to be breeding, from 22 in 1968–72 to 17 in 1980–85, 15 in 1988–91 and just eight in the NBA period. The change map shows how the species has become more concentrated into Breckland since the *1980–85 NBBS*.

Whinchat
Saxicola rubetra

NBA 1999–2007	SUMMER: ALL/BREEDING	WINTER
TETRADS OCCUPIED	87 (6%) / none	1 (<1%)
SUMMER/WINTER ONLY	87	1
MEAN PER OCCUPIED TETRAD	1 / none	1
SUMMED MAX COUNTS	125 / none	1
POPULATION ESTIMATE	0–5 individuals	none

PREVIOUS ATLASES	SQUARES OCCUPIED	1999–2007	LOSSES	GAINS
1968–72 (10 KM)	18 (29%)	none	18	0
1980–85 (TETRAD)	27 (2%)	none	27	0
1980–85 (10 KM)	15 (24%)	none	15	0
1981–84 WINTER (10 KM)	2 (3%)	1 (2%)	2	1
1988–91 (10 KM)	7 (11%)	none	7	0

WHILE THE CLOSELY related Stonechat is currently thriving as a breeding species in Norfolk, the Whinchat has not bred in the county since 1992 and occurs now only as a spring and autumn passage migrant.

In Britain, a marked contraction of breeding range took place during the 20th century, especially in the south and east of England, so much so that the species was largely confined to the north and west by the turn of the century. In Norfolk, Whinchats were fairly common throughout the county during the 19th century, but as elsewhere, the number of breeding pairs thereafter fell steadily and the species last bred in the county at Horsey in 1992. BBS data indicate a continuing steep decline where the species stills occurs in England, with a 36% loss recorded between 1995 and 2007 (*Birdtrends*).

Although there are no breeding records on the NBA map, Whinchats are still occurring at many sites in Norfolk, albeit only on passage, with an estimated 50–80 birds annually on spring passage, bound either for northern Britain or for Scandinavia. The highest day counts during the NBA period were all made at coastal sites in north Norfolk, with a maximum of 14 at Holme on 22nd April 2000. On occasion, notable

DAVID TIPLING

influxes occurred simultaneously at several locations around the coast, for example eight at Old Hunstanton, ten at Holme and six at Scolt Head on 30th April 2003, and seven at Titchwell and nine at Scolt Head on 30th April 2005.

Unlike many migrant passerines, Whinchats occur widely inland as well as coastally, and might be encountered almost anywhere in the county. Many of the inland records were from sites where the species formerly bred, such as the Brecks and the heathy areas in west Norfolk.

The Whinchat has a much shorter breeding season than the Stonechat and is normally single brooded, taking advantage of the main summer peak of ground cover and insect abundance. The first spring arrivals appear in the county in the second half of April. During the breeding season it favours areas of tussocky grass, rough grazing and clumps of gorse with tall weeds or barbed wire fences from which it can sing and drop down to feed on its insect prey. It is less dependent on heathland than the Stonechat and will occupy agricultural areas and young conifer plantations, and lacks the Stonechat's association with coastal habitats.

On three occasions during the NBA period, male Whinchats were heard in song in potentially suitable nesting areas, but remained for only a single day. On 20th April 2002, a pair was displaying at Hunstanton GC, while in June 2004 and again in 2005, until chased off by a Stonechat, a male sang at Roydon Common.

Comparison with previous atlases shows a progressive loss of 10-km squares occupied by birds thought to be breeding, from 18 in 1968–72 to 15 in 1980–85, seven in 1988–91 and none at all during the NBA period. During the *1980–85 NBBS*, the species was recorded in possible breeding habitat in 27 tetrads, of which breeding was at least probable in 15. Breeding was confirmed in ten of these, all but one at Leziate being in the Brecks, and up to ten pairs were likely to have bred in any one year. All breeding sites have since been lost, although migrants appeared at some of them during the NBA period.

Winter records are rare in Britain but late migrants, within the respective winter periods, were recorded from two Norfolk 10-km squares in the *1981–84 Winter Atlas* and from one during the NBA winters.

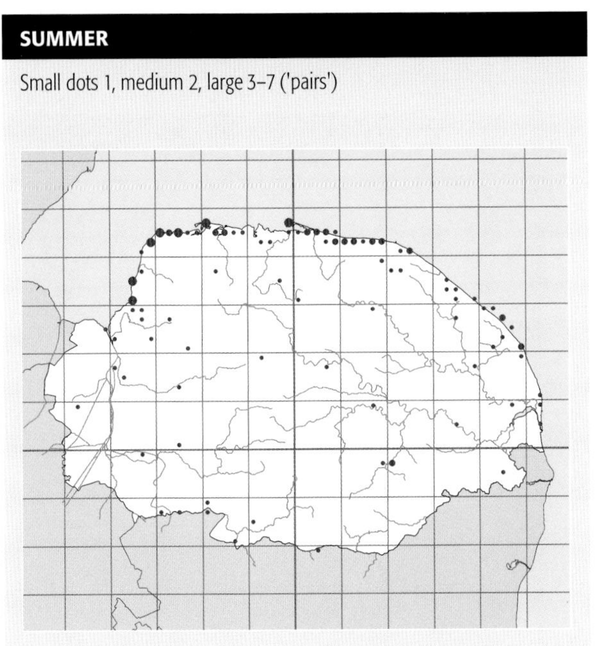

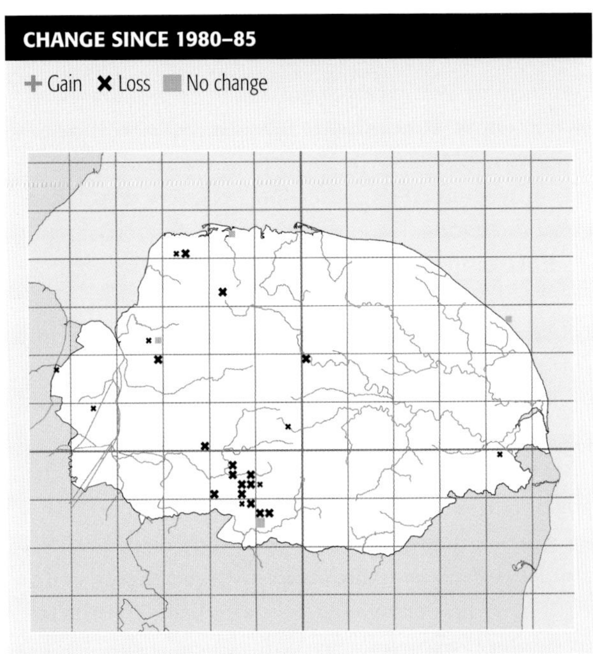

Stonechat

Saxicola torquatus

NBA 1999–2007	SUMMER: ALL / BREEDING	WINTER
TETRADS OCCUPIED	56 (4%) / 37 (3%)	152 (10%)
SUMMER/WINTER ONLY	20	116
MEAN PER OCCUPIED TETRAD	1 / 1	2
SUMMED MAX COUNTS	72 / 53	343
POPULATION ESTIMATE	13–60 bp	50–200

PREVIOUS ATLASES	SQUARES OCCUPIED	1999–2007	LOSSES	GAINS
1968–72 (10 KM)	10 (16%)	15 (24%)	4	9
1980–85 (TETRAD)	19 (1%)	37 (3%)	11	29
1980–85 (10 KM)	11 (18%)	15 (24%)	3	7
1981–84 WINTER (10 KM)	11 (18%)	37 (60%)	1	27
1988–91 (10 KM)	6 (10%)	15 (24%)	2	11

STONECHATS ARE constantly on the move and not easily overlooked as they sit sentinel-like on top of gorse bushes or on fence posts. The handsome males, with their black heads and distinctive white half-collars, are usually accompanied by a female as they patrol their territories.

The species has had a very chequered history in Norfolk. Writing in the 19th century, *Stevenson* suggested that Stonechats were fairly widespread in the county during the summer but that few remained in winter. However, by the early 1940s few pairs bred away from the Brecks and none bred anywhere in the county by 1946. It was not until 1958 that Stonechats once again nested in Norfolk, with a small breeding population being confined for many years to the coastal strip in the far east of the county. These changes reflected the wider picture in western Europe where the population had declined due to agricultural intensification, hedgerow destruction and afforestation. Nationally, there was widespread retreat from the east coast of England and Scotland between the *1968–72* and *1988–91 Atlases*, with very few pairs between Aberdeen and Norfolk by 1988–91, at least in part related to a run of cold winters. During the NBA period, however, numbers breeding in Norfolk reached their highest level since the 19th century.

In summer, Stonechats are closely associated with gorse on heathland and commons. Their requirements are perches, from which to sing and drop down to short ground vegetation to catch their invertebrate prey, and thick cover for nesting. The nests are usually constructed on or near the ground, often at the base of a gorse bush.

The breeding season lasts from mid March through to August.

The NBA summer map clearly shows three main areas within the county in which breeding Stonechats were concentrated, breeding occurring in these three general areas in most of the NBA summers. The coastal strip of dunes south from Waxham to Winterton held from four to eight pairs annually. Two or three pairs nested in most years in north Norfolk, on the heaths at the western end of the Cromer to Holt ridge or on the remnants of the coastal heathland between Weybourne and Morston, and up to seven pairs recently on the west Norfolk heaths, around Roydon and Dersingham. There has also been a strong recolonisation of the former stronghold in Breckland. Here, from a single pair in 2000, the breeding population expanded steadily and by 2005 a total of 27 pairs bred in the Norfolk Brecks, of which 19 were in Thetford Forest. In addition to heathland, Stonechats breed in young forestry plantations, especially where the ground cover is heather. Clearly, they are taking advantage of this type of habitat in Thetford Forest. There was a strong rise in the numbers of territories reported to the county recorders during the NBA period; it is likely that these totals represent a high proportion of the county population.

Unusually for a passerine, many Stonechats remain in pairs during the winter months, having paired

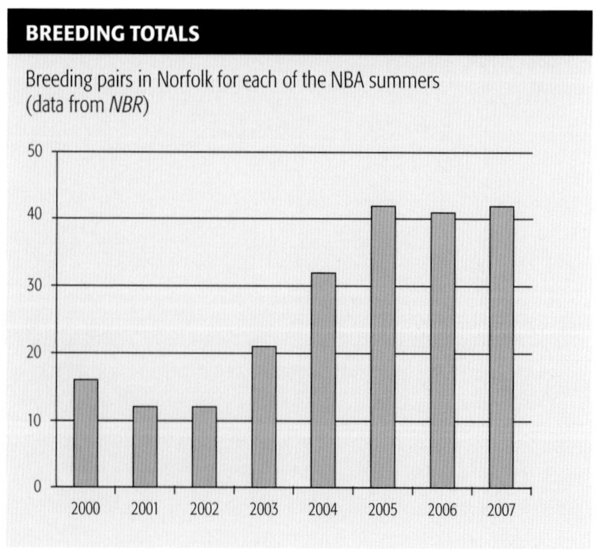

in the autumn. Whether solitary, in pairs or in small groups, many Stonechats have established their winter territories by October, often in areas of rough ground near the coast. They also frequent reedbeds at this time of year and up to four followed the reed cutters at Cley in February 2003. Some Stonechats remain within their breeding areas, however, particularly if these are situated on the coast, as is the case in east Norfolk.

The NBA winter map shows a surprisingly widespread distribution at this time of year, with birds present around most of the coastal breeding sites, as well as inland in Broadland, where many of the birds concentrate in the river valleys, in Breckland and around the eastern side of the Fens. The origin of Norfolk's wintering Stonechats is unclear. Some are likely to be birds dispersing within Norfolk, while a single ring recovery indicates that some originate from further north in England. The extent to which continental migrants may winter in Britain is poorly understood.

Stonechats are one of the earliest migrants, with passage often being apparent around the Norfolk coast from late February onwards. For example, counts of six at Northrepps on 28th February 2000 and 19 at Holme the following day clearly involved mainly migrants and not wintering birds, although they have been included in the NBA data. Midwinter counts of seven Stonechats were made at Titchwell, Winterton and Buckenham. Between 62 and 85 Stonechats were reported to the county recorders in each of the NBA winters.

Comparison with previous atlases suggests that the distribution during the NBA period, both in summer and in winter was exceptionally wide. The change map shows expansion of all the pockets of breeding distribution since the *1980–85 NBBS*.

The NBA winter data show a threefold increase in the number of occupied 10-km squares since the *1981–84 Winter Atlas*. The increase stems from the greatly increased number of pairs breeding in Norfolk, some of which will have raised two or even three broods, and from the winter weather being mild throughout during the NBA period. Being insectivorous, Stonechats are very susceptible to severe winter weather, as was demonstrated by the fall in the British population between 1968–72 and 1988–91.

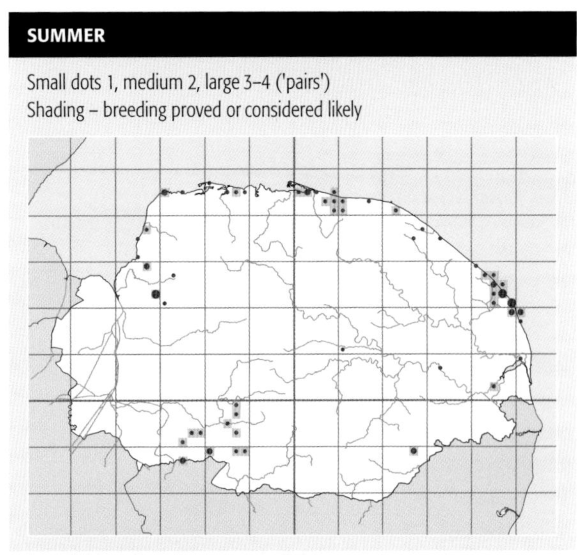

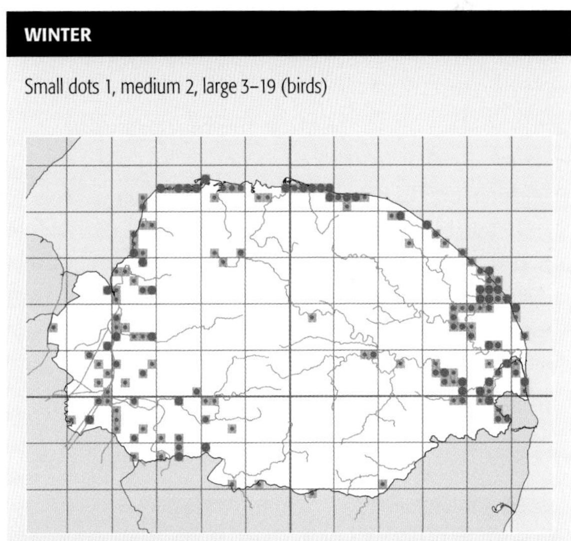

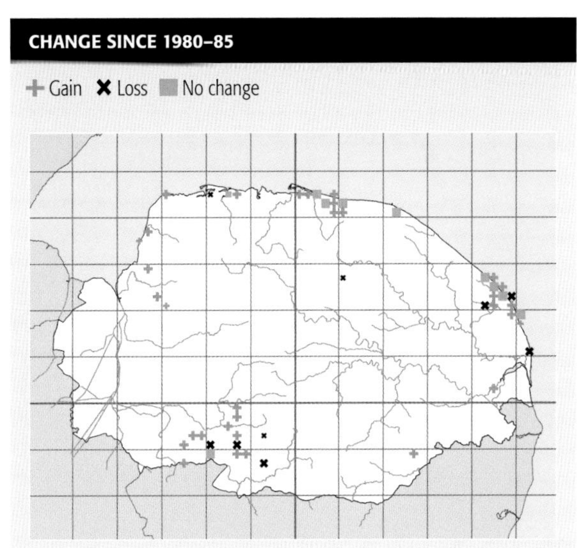

Wheatear
Oenanthe oenanthe

NBA 1999–2007	SUMMER: ALL / BREEDING	WINTER
TETRADS OCCUPIED	164 (11%) / 2 (<1%)	2 (<1%)
SUMMER/WINTER ONLY	164	2
MEAN PER OCCUPIED TETRAD	4 / 2	1
SUMMED MAX COUNTS	634 / 4	2
POPULATION ESTIMATE	2–4 bp	none

PREVIOUS ATLASES	SQUARES OCCUPIED	1999–2007	LOSSES	GAINS
1968–72 (10 KM)	23 (37%)	1 (2%)	22	0
1980–85 (TETRAD)	66 (5%)	2 (<1%)	64	0
1980–85 (10 KM)	23 (37%)	1 (2%)	22	0
1981–84 WINTER (10 KM)	none	2 (3%)	0	2
1988–91 (10 KM)	23 (37%)	1 (2%)	22	0

THE WHEATEAR IS often the first passerine to reach Britain in the spring. Prior to 1930, it was described as an abundant breeding species in Breckland but it is now on the brink of extinction in Norfolk as a breeding bird.

Wheatears winter in Africa south of the Sahara and have a protracted migration period in both the spring and the autumn. The first birds normally reach Norfolk during the first half of March; one at Holkham on 27th February 2000 equalled the earliest record ever for the county, established as long ago as 1926.

This has been one of the most strongly declining bird species in Europe since 1980. Its breeding population in central, southern and eastern England, already in retreat well before the *1968–72 Atlas*, has now collapsed, although it remains a common and widespread bird on passage.

A maximum of only six pairs have bred in Norfolk in any one year since 2000, in just two tetrads in the Stanford TA; all the other records on the NBA summer map almost certainly refer to spring passage migrants, many heading for Greenland or Fenno-Scandia. Passage is by no means confined to coastal tetrads, many inland sites also hosting single birds or small parties on

SUMMER

Small dots 1, medium 2-4, large 5-50 ('pairs')
Shading – breeding proved or considered likely

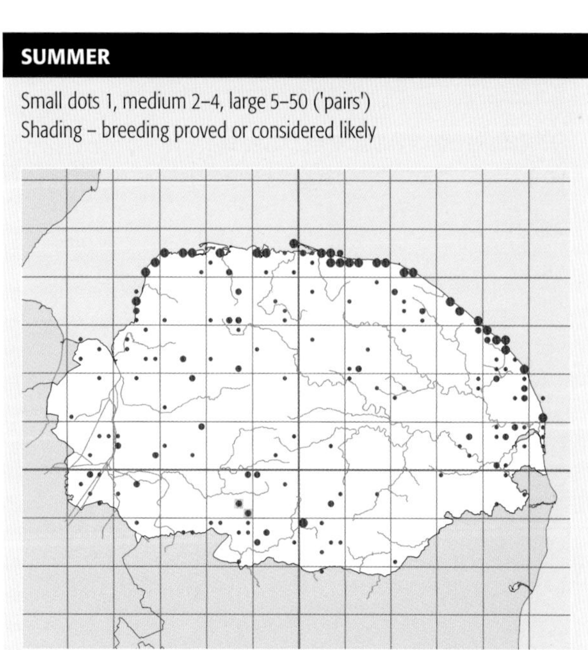

CHANGE SINCE 1980-85

+ Gain ✖ Loss ■ No change

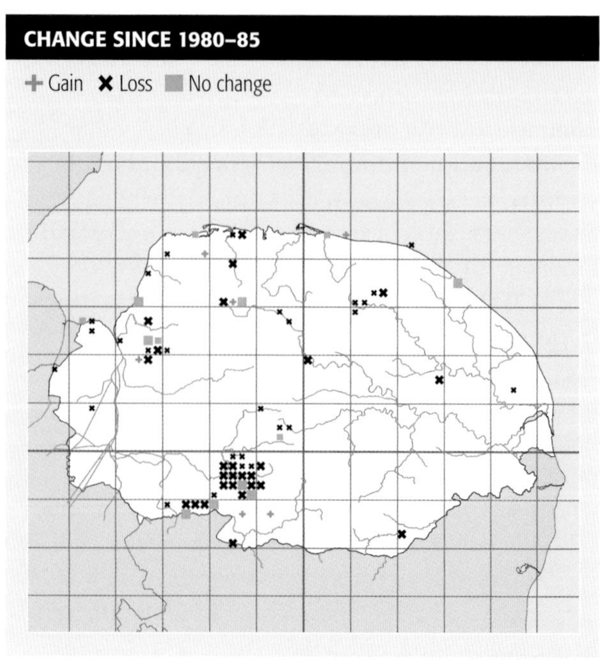

DAVID TIPLING

migration. The most notable passage during the NBA summers occurred on 30th April 2005, when 124 were recorded at Scolt Head, 100 in the cliff-top fields at West Runton and 90 at Sheringham.

By the 1960s, the Stanford TA was considered to be the most important centre in the Brecks. Although Weeting Heath held up to 36 breeding pairs in 1983, within ten years Wheatears had ceased to breed at that reserve, despite the habitat being managed appropriately for them. By 1992, the breeding population in the Stanford TA had fallen to 27 pairs and, four years later in 1996, only a single pair successfully fledged any young. During the NBA summers, between two and six pairs have bred annually.

Wheatears are mainly upland species and colonise lowland regions only where grazing by sheep or rabbits keeps the sward short. Undoubtedly, the myxomatosis epidemic that so drastically reduced the rabbit population took its toll, while many suitable breeding areas were ploughed up and conifers were planted on much of the heathland in Breckland. Habitat within the Stanford TA remains largely unaltered, however, and it is clear that the main reasons for the species' demise must lie outside the county.

Winter records in Britain are very unusual. In addition to the February migrant at Holkham, however, one other occurred during the NBA winter recording period: this was a male discovered in a sugar beet field at Dickleburgh on 11th December 2000.

'A maximum of only six pairs have bred in Norfolk in any one year since 2000, in just two tetrads in the Stanford TA.'

Comparison between the breeding atlases tells a sorry story. The change map indicates the extent of the loss of breeding range that has occurred since 1980–85. It remains to be seen how long the Wheatear can survive as a Norfolk breeding species.

BREEDING TOTALS

Breeding pairs in Norfolk for each of the NBA summers (data from *NBR*)

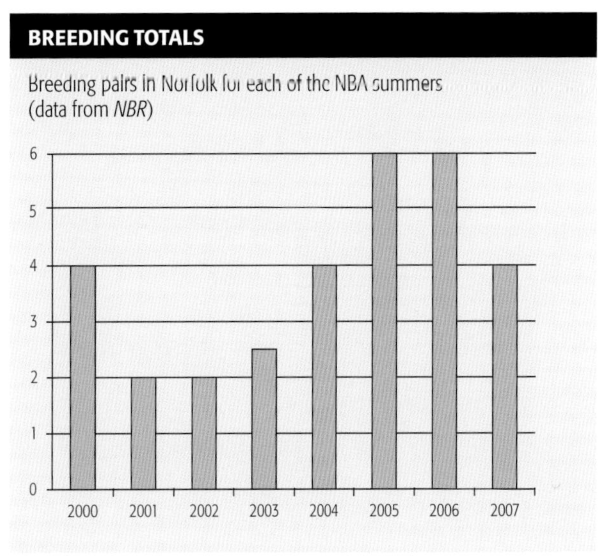

Dunnock

Prunella modularis

NBA 1999–2007	SUMMER: ALL/BREEDING	WINTER
TETRADS OCCUPIED	1,381 (95%) / 1,380 (95%)	1,383 (95%)
SUMMER/WINTER ONLY	34	36
MEAN PER OCCUPIED TETRAD	9 / 9	10
SUMMED MAX COUNTS	11,740 / 11,739	13,280
POPULATION ESTIMATE	20,000–25,000 bp	50,000–60,000

PREVIOUS ATLASES	SQUARES OCCUPIED	1999–2007	LOSSES	GAINS
1968–72 (10 KM)	62 (all)	62 (all)		
1980–85 (TETRAD)	1,368 (94%)	1,379 (95%)	48	59
1980–85 (10 KM)	62 (all)	62 (all)		
1981–84 WINTER (10 KM)	62 (all)	62 (all)		
1988–91 (10 KM)	62 (all)	62 (all)		

DESPITE THE DUNNOCK'S drab appearance and retiring habits, it belongs to a family of aristocrats, many members of which are sought-after species of Eurasia's highest mountain ranges. Though sometimes unknown by name, it is a familiar bird to many Norfolk householders as it shuffles, mouse-like around garden lawns and under bird tables.

Dunnocks are to be expected wherever low, thick undergrowth is present, such as hedgerows, thickets, woodland edges, gardens, parks, churchyards and the coastal fringe. The summer map confirms that the species is widespread throughout the county, the only contiguous unoccupied tetrads being in the Fens and the Halvergate Marshes. Breeding was considered likely wherever the species was found. Variation in density shows no strong pattern, although an association of higher densities with river valleys is discernible in some parts of the county. The highest tetrad counts were recorded in tetrads at Felbrigg (68 pairs), Thornage (64) and near Heacham (56). As an indication of the use of coastal habitats, such as dune scrub and *Suaeda*, Scolt Head Island held over 60 pairs in each of the NBA summers. Many of the 'pairs' recorded would have related to singing males and, because of the species' frequent polygyny and polyandry, not necessarily to a paired male and female.

As British Dunnocks are mostly sedentary, and winter immigration is very small in scale, it is not surprising that the NBA winter map is almost identical to the summer one, although there are a few tetrads occupied at only

SUMMER

Small dots 1–5, medium 6–10, large 11–68 ('pairs')
Shading – breeding proved or considered likely

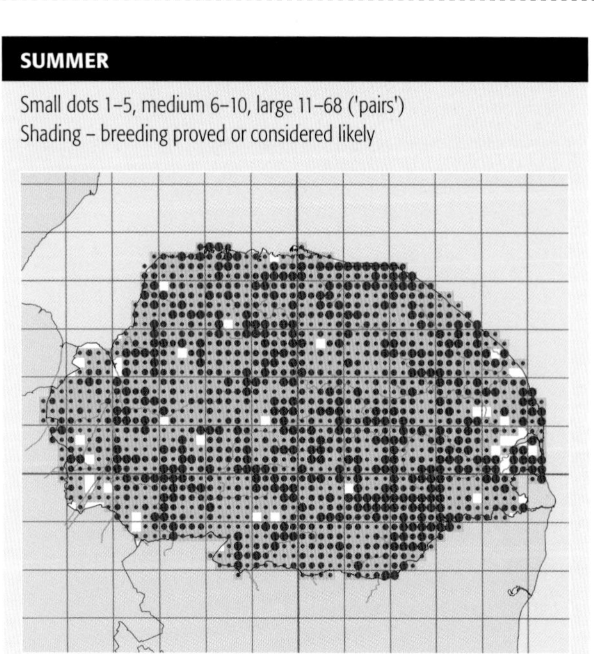

WINTER

Small dots 1–5, medium 6–11, large 12–62 (birds)

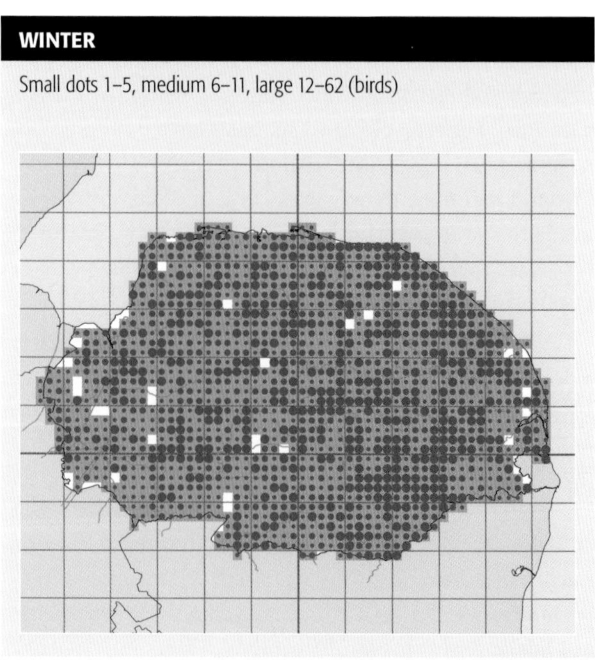

DAVID TIPLING

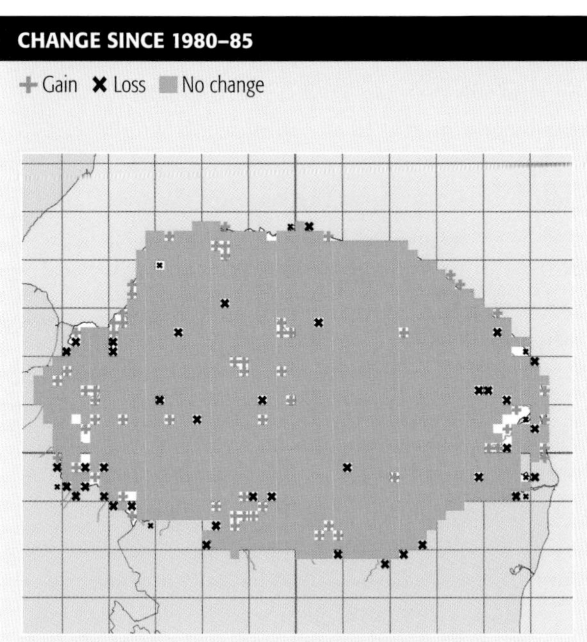

one of the two seasons. Outside the breeding season, Dunnocks are generally solitary, but can gather in areas where feeding is favourable. Such gatherings were noted by NBA observers around the periphery of fields of sugar beet prior to harvest and in game cover strips. The highest tetrad counts during the NBA winters were of 62 near Heacham and 52 at Newton Flotman, while a survey of Stiffkey saltmarsh in February 2004 found 80 Dunnocks.

The UK population of Dunnocks fell sharply after the mid 1970s, earning the species amber listing as a bird of conservation concern. There was little difference in population between the two Norfolk atlas periods, however (*Birdtrends*). The 1980–85 distribution was almost identical to that in 2000–07: the few tetrads gained and lost since then show no clear pattern, and probably relate to chance observations in tetrads with low Dunnock density.

House Sparrow
Passer domesticus

NBA 1999–2007	SUMMER: ALL / BREEDING	WINTER
TETRADS OCCUPIED	1,238 (85%) / 1,222 (84%)	1,200 (82%)
SUMMER/WINTER ONLY	74	36
MEAN PER OCCUPIED TETRAD	23 / 23	35
SUMMED MAX COUNTS	27,863 / 27,836	42,141
POPULATION ESTIMATE	40,000–50,000 bp	90,000–120,000

PREVIOUS ATLASES	SQUARES OCCUPIED	1999–2007	LOSSES	GAINS
1968–72 (10 KM)	62 (all)	62 (all)		
1980–85 (TETRAD)	1,354 (93%)	1,222 (84%)	165	33
1980–85 (10 KM)	62 (all)	62 (all)		
1981–84 WINTER (10 KM)	62 (all)	62 (all)		
1988–91 (10 KM)	62 (all)	62 (all)		

LONG GONE ARE the days when House Sparrows were considered agricultural pests, and they are no longer the common birds of many towns and cities. Several theories have been put forward to account for the decline and it is likely to have multiple causes, probably with differences between the rural and urban environments.

House Sparrows are gregarious birds throughout the year and breed in loose colonies, often chattering together while perched on guttering or concealed in a dense roadside hedge. Their nests are generally constructed in the roof spaces of older houses or barns. House Sparrows occasionally usurp House Martins' nests or utilise holes in hay and straw stacks. The untidy, ball-shaped, domed nests that the species builds in hedgerows and bushes are now rarely seen in the county (Williamson 2006).

The NBA summer map shows that, although the species is still widespread, House Sparrows are absent from many small parts of northwest Norfolk, often several tetrads across, and from much of Norfolk Breckland. The highest abundances, surprisingly, were found in Fenland towns and villages, with seven of the nine counts of 120 or more pairs being made in that area. Two of the highest tetrad counts, of 180 and 175, were made in King's Lynn. Elsewhere, 180 pairs were present at Mattishall in central Norfolk.

One observer taking part in the NBA fieldwork characterised suitable areas for breeding House Sparrows as containing old, unmodernised houses

(often council built) with tall, ivy-covered hedgerows and with allotments or some generally untidy land nearby. The value of dense hedges was clearly indicated at Honing Lock, where a colony of 35 pairs was lost when a mature, mixed-species hedge was removed and replaced by a wooden fence. Other observers commented that Norfolk pantile roofing seemed to be an additional attraction to nesting pairs.

During the winter months, House Sparrows are even more sociable than in the summer. Although they feed mainly on vegetable material in winter, taking advantage of whatever food is on offer, be it weed seeds, cereal grain, peanuts or sunflower seeds, they will also avail themselves of kitchen scraps. Gardens and the provision of food for wild birds certainly play an important role in the survival of the species in winter, as is shown by the presence of up to 60 House Sparrows in a Cley garden in December 2000 and up to 90 at a feeding station at Welney.

The NBA winter map shows a very similar distribution to that in the summer, as would be expected for a mainly sedentary species with limited dispersal. As in the summer the more open, undeveloped coastal areas do not host House Sparrows, nor do large parts of Breckland. Once again, the largest winter totals were found in the Fens, which held six of the eight tetrad counts of 200 or more, the other two being in Broadland.

A fascinating study of the House Sparrow population of Norwich was undertaken in November/December 2000 (Paston 2001). During this two-month period, most streets in the study area were visited at least once and the numbers of House Sparrows in each street were counted. The species was found at only a handful of places in the city centre, all of which were close to the River Wensum, where scrubby margins adjoined the

DAVID TIPLING

'The species continues to occupy every 10-km square, in summer and in winter.'

riverbank. Two-thirds of the population were found north of the River Wensum, a part of the city with more wild, open spaces, and the highest counts were in Mile Cross, in an area dominated by council houses, derelict land and allotments. Other features that appeared to attract House Sparrows were the presence of schools and their associated playing fields, and the provision of nuts and other food by householders.

The 1982–2007 CBC/BBS index has shown a 55% reduction in England, but effects of this population decrease on square occupancy in Norfolk have so far been limited. The species continues to occupy every 10-km square, in summer and in winter. During the *1980–85 NBBS* the species was recorded in 93% of the tetrads in Norfolk, however, and this fell to 84% during the NBA. The change map shows that the areas of west Norfolk from which House Sparrows were lacking have mostly enlarged over the intervening two decades. There are also many tetrads along the county boundary, shared with other counties, where House Sparrows could no longer be found in the Norfolk section.

SUMMER

Small dots 1–10, medium 11–25, large 26–180 ('pairs')
Shading – breeding proved or considered likely

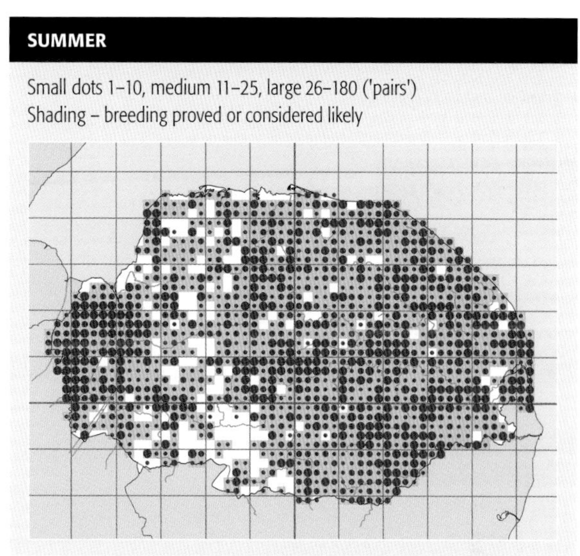

WINTER

Small dots 1–15, medium 16–37, large 38–288 (birds)

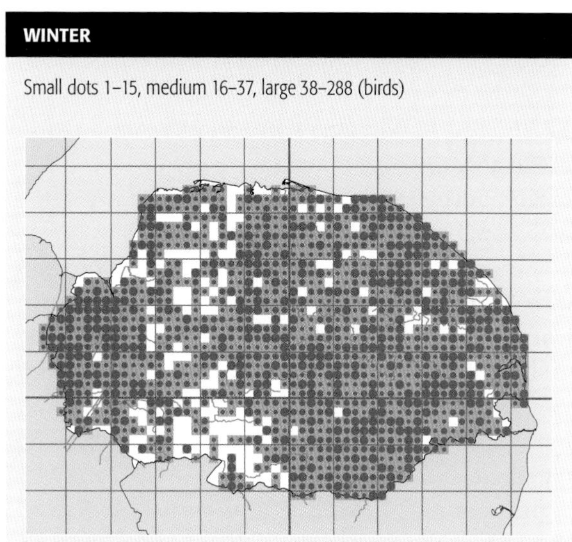

CHANGE SINCE 1980–85

+ Gain ✖ Loss ■ No change

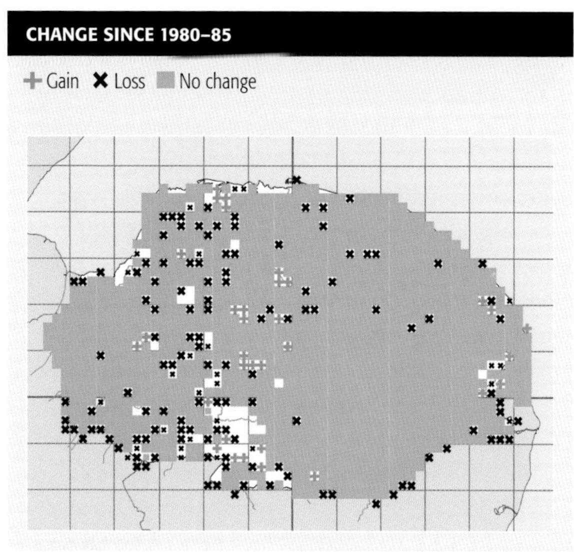

Tree Sparrow
Passer montanus

NBA 1999–2007	SUMMER: ALL/BREEDING	WINTER
TETRADS OCCUPIED	205 (14%) / 173 (12%)	211 (14%)
SUMMER/WINTER ONLY	99	105
MEAN PER OCCUPIED TETRAD	3 / 4	13
SUMMED MAX COUNTS	701 / 662	2,727
POPULATION ESTIMATE	700–800 bp	2,000–2,500

PREVIOUS ATLASES	SQUARES OCCUPIED	1999–2007	LOSSES	GAINS
1968–72 (10 KM)	61 (98%)	38 (61%)	24	1
1980–85 (TETRAD)	522 (36%)	173 (12%)	468	119
1980–85 (10 KM)	62 (all)	38 (61%)	24	0
1981–84 WINTER (10 KM)	60 (97%)	44 (71%)	17	1
1988–91 (10 KM)	57 (92%)	38 (61%)	20	1

TREE SPARROWS HAVE proved remarkably dynamic in their population size and distribution within Norfolk in recent decades (*BoN*). NBA has revealed a major withdrawal from east Norfolk since the 1980s.

Nationally, population levels had been high in the early 1960s but soon they entered a phase of decline, which accelerated strongly after 1977 (*Birdtrends*). By 2007, 97% of the population had been lost over a 40-year period. Recent years have shown that some recovery is under way, but relatively little progress had been made during the NBA period.

Tree Sparrows are sedentary, colonial, hole-nesters that in Norfolk are now living almost entirely in and around manmade structures, alongside their larger relative. Gone are the days when the species could be found along woodland edges and in parks. Most pairs in the county now nest under the tiles or in holes in the walls of buildings in villages or farmsteads, or in nest boxes that have been specifically erected for Tree Sparrows in rural gardens. As well as suitable nesting sites, they also require a reliable year-round supply of food. They feed more on weed seeds than on cereal grain and their decline was undoubtedly associated with the increased use of herbicides of farmland, and the loss of winter stubbles. In many of the localities where Tree Sparrows are currently thriving, artificial feeding is taking place throughout the year.

The NBA summer map shows a very clear-cut distribution within Norfolk, with only two isolated records in the eastern side of the county but a broad band running north–south through the centre and a smaller but more densely occupied area in the Fens. Away from the Fens, most Tree Sparrows were found on higher ground along Norfolk's main watershed, which runs from the Diss area towards Hunstanton.

Only a handful of locations could muster double-figure counts of breeding pairs during the NBA summers, at least three of which held colonies using nest boxes. The largest and most successful of these is at Fulmodeston, where at least 20 pairs have nested in a garden for a number of years, peaking at 34 pairs in 2004. Another garden site at Gooderstone has held up to 12 nesting pairs, and a site near Flitcham has hosted up to 16 pairs, also in nest boxes.

***BoN* described** the Tree Sparrow as a 'scarce resident' in the late 1990s, indicating a breeding population of up to 100 pairs. Data gathered for the NBA suggest that the breeding population was in the range 700–800 pairs, despite the tetrad distribution being very limited. It seems possible that some recovery in numbers is already in progress in the county.

Tree Sparrows are often encountered during the winter in flocks at favoured feeding sites. They are most often reported near abandoned outbuildings and run-down cottages, at garden feeders in rural areas and associating with finches and buntings in game cover strips. The NBA winter map shows a similar distribution to that in summer, although with a few more tetrads in the east of the county occupied in winter. The largest winter flocks were 75 at West Raynham in January 2000, 115 at Illington and 80 at Great Cressingham both in February 2000 and 80 at Sparham Hall in December 2004.

Comparison with previous atlas data shows a collapse of the 10-km summer distribution from 100% in the *1980–85 NBBS* to 92% in 1988–91 and then to just 61% during the NBA period. The winter distribution

DAVID TIPLING

'Only a handful of locations could muster double-figure counts of breeding pairs during the NBA summers...'

also fell from 97% in the *1981–84 Winter Atlas* to 71% in the NBA winters. At tetrad level, the number of occupied squares fell by two-thirds between 1980–85 and the NBA summers.

The change map shows a remarkable and intriguing pattern. Tree Sparrows have apparently colonised new areas of Fenland since the 1980s, especially near the Cambridgeshire border. Range loss has been much more pronounced, and has been concentrated into a number of broad areas: these are a large area east of King's Lynn, the area of Breckland northwest from Thetford, the environs of Norwich, particularly to the north and west, the area inland from Sheringham, the Waveney catchment, and Broadland more generally. All these areas, with extensive populations as recently as the 1980s, are now almost completely devoid of Tree Sparrows.

SUMMER

Small dots 1, medium 2–4, large 5–34 ('pairs')
Shading – breeding proved or considered likely

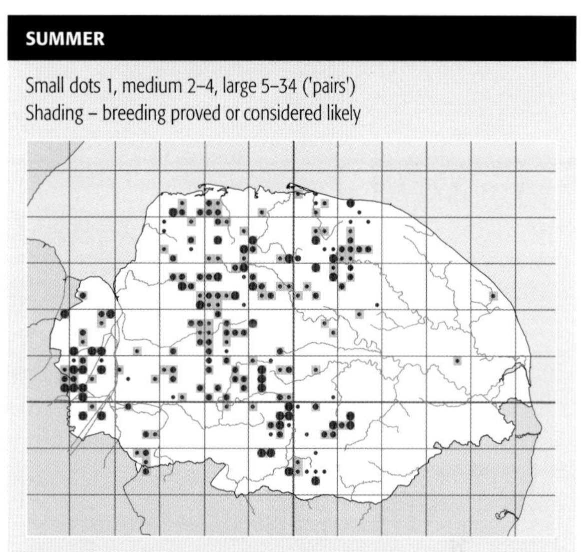

WINTER

Small dots 1–3, medium 4–10, large 11–115 (birds)

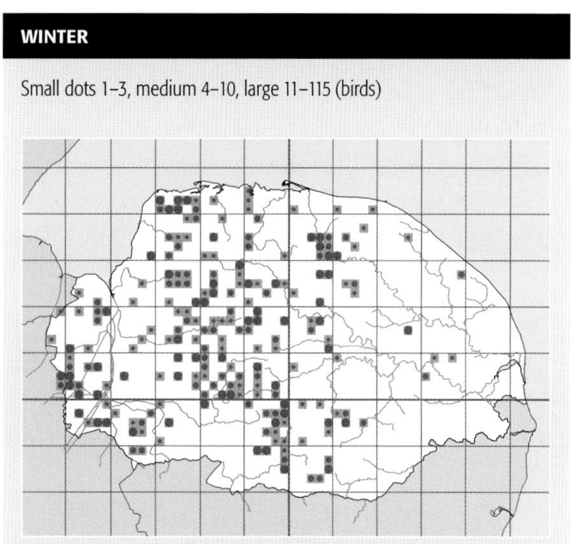

CHANGE SINCE 1980–85

+ Gain ✖ Loss ■ No change

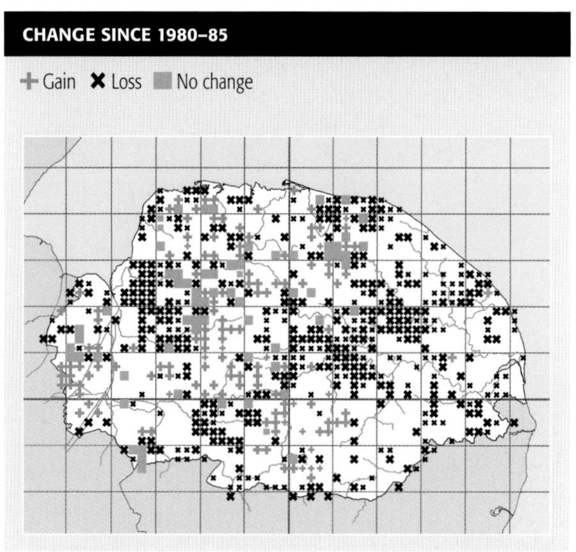

Yellow Wagtail
Motacilla flava

NBA 1999–2007	SUMMER: ALL/BREEDING	WINTER
TETRADS OCCUPIED	264 (18%) / 187 (13%)	none
SUMMER/WINTER ONLY	264	none
MEAN PER OCCUPIED TETRAD	3 / 3	none
SUMMED MAX COUNTS	922 / 644	none
POPULATION ESTIMATE	50–100 bp *flavissima*, 0–1 individual *flava*	none

PREVIOUS ATLASES	SQUARES OCCUPIED	1999–2007	LOSSES	GAINS
1968–72 (10 KM)	57 (92%)	38 (61%)	21	2
1980–85 (TETRAD)	272 (19%)	187 (13%)	192	107
1980–85 (10 KM)	48 (77%)	38 (61%)	16	6
1981–84 WINTER (10 KM)	2 (3%)	none	2	0
1988–91 (10 KM)	47 (76%)	38 (61%)	18	9

THE DAINTY AND brilliantly coloured Yellow Wagtail has been in strong decline across much of Europe since the 1980s, perhaps due to habitat change and droughts in its African winter quarters. Typically, it is a bird of damp, grazing marshes and in both its breeding and wintering ranges exhibits a close association with cattle and other grazing animals. During the breeding season it inhabits marshy fields, water meadows, and the fringes of wetlands, reservoirs and gravel pits, where there is low, luxuriant ground cover. In recent years, as wetlands have been drained and grassland has been lost to arable, Yellow Wagtails have increasingly turned to arable fields for nesting.

The NBA summer map suggests a breeding population that is now largely confined to the extreme east and west of the county, with a few pairs along a narrow coastal strip in north Norfolk. Even this sparse map overstates the distribution, however, since some tetrads, especially

DAVID TIPLING

> 'The NBA summer map suggests a breeding population that is now largely confined to the extreme east and west of the county, with a few pairs along a narrow coastal strip in north Norfolk.'

in coastal areas, would have held spring passage migrants and not breeding pairs. In southwest Norfolk, the Ouse Washes and adjacent parts of the Fens held the largest numbers of breeding pairs, with a peak at Welney of 62 in 2002, a spring with unusually low water levels. In the east, the Halvergate Marshes and the Bure valley were particularly favoured. Elsewhere, odd pairs nested in fields of peas, sugar beet and rape.

BTO data show the population trend to have been very strongly downward, especially by Britain's rivers and canals, where an estimated 94% of the population was lost between 1982 and 2007 (*Birdtrends*). It is clear that this decline has been strongly evident in Norfolk. The number of occupied 10-km squares has fallen sequentially, with 57, 48, 47 and 38 occupied across the four atlas projects. In comparison with the *1980–85 NBBS* map, it is readily apparent that many inland sites, particularly in central Norfolk, have been deserted, as have most of the coastal grazing marshes in the northwest of the county. For example, at Holkham GM 22 pairs bred in 1990, falling to 12 in 1996 and to a maximum of three during the NBA summers. In some areas, constant grazing by wildfowl in the winter months and late-season livestock grazing on the coastal marshes have resulted in too short a sward for nesting Yellow Wagtails. Gains are evident, too, especially on farmland in the Fens, though some of the gains shown on the change map related to spring passage birds, rather than territory-holding pairs.

The reporting of territory-holding pairs to the county recorders may have become more complete during the NBA period, but the higher numbers of 2002 were not repeated and the apparent rate of fall since then has been alarming. It is likely the county population could have fallen to as few as 50 pairs by 2007.

Most migrants were of the British race *flavissima*. Twelve tetrads held spring migrant Blue-headed Wagtails, nominate *flava*, which are widespread in continental Europe, and seven held Grey-headed Wagtails *M.f. thunbergi*, from northern Fenno-Scandia.

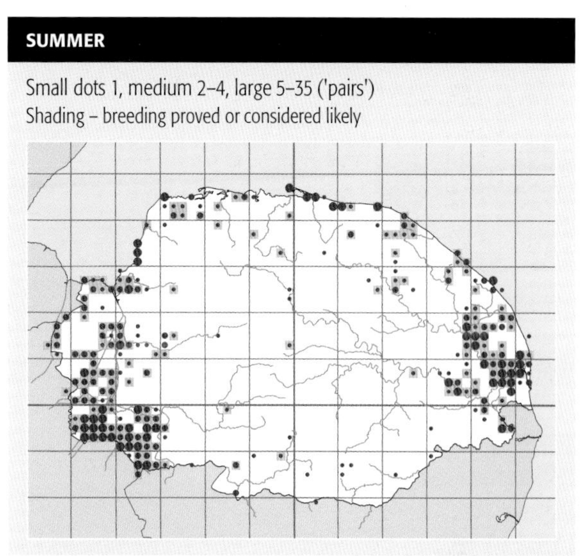

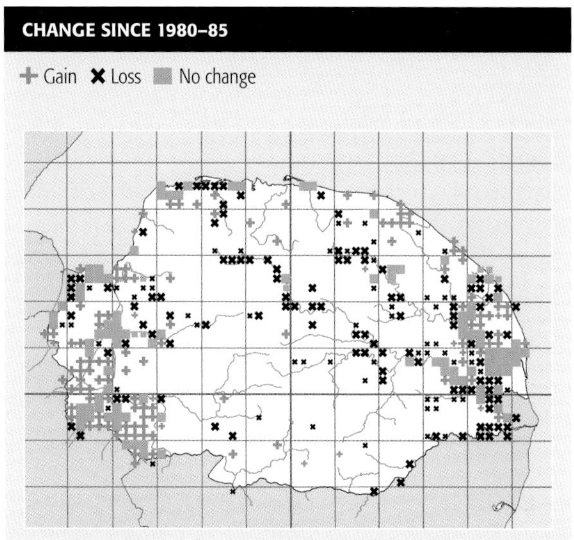

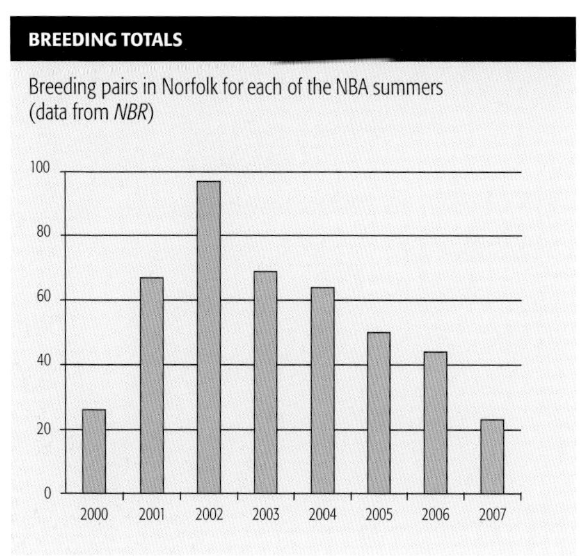

Grey Wagtail
Motacilla cinerea

NBA 1999–2007	SUMMER: ALL / BREEDING	WINTER
TETRADS OCCUPIED	142 (10%) / 97 (7%)	221 (15%)
SUMMER/WINTER ONLY	88	167
MEAN PER OCCUPIED TETRAD	1 / 1	1
SUMMED MAX COUNTS	161 / 112	275
POPULATION ESTIMATE	80–120 bp	150–200

PREVIOUS ATLASES	SQUARES OCCUPIED	1999–2007	LOSSES	GAINS
1968–72 (10 KM)	11 (18%)	38 (61%)	2	29
1980–85 (TETRAD)	57 (4%)	97 (7%)	29	69
1980–85 (10 KM)	23 (37%)	38 (61%)	3	18
1981–84 WINTER (10 KM)	24 (39%)	57 (92%)	1	34
1988–91 (10 KM)	20 (32%)	38 (61%)	4	22

WITH ITS VERY long tail and slim build, the Grey Wagtail is the most characterful of the wagtails, always recognisable by the brilliant yellow beneath the tail. As a result of its distinctive flight call and strict habitat requirements, it is a reasonably easy bird to locate at any season.

Grey Wagtails are characteristic of fast-flowing, rocky, upland rivers and streams, but also breed beside lowland waters, especially where fast-flowing stretches have been created by weirs, mill-races or outflows from lakes. The nests are often built in holes in the masonry of bridges, culverts or riverside buildings, or amongst tree roots overhanging the riverbank. It is a fairly widespread species in Britain, but its distribution is more restricted in the lowland counties of central and eastern England.

Grey Wagtails first nested successfully in Norfolk in 1923, since when varying numbers have bred in the county, but the species has always remained quite scarce.

The NBA summer map shows the rather sparse but widespread distribution throughout the county and a clear association with the upper reaches of the river systems. In the west, the Rivers Nar, Wissey and Little Ouse were favoured, in central Norfolk the River Wensum, and in the east the Rivers Yare, Tas and Waveney. A comprehensive survey of breeding Grey Wagtails in the Wensum valley in 2003 found a total of 13 confirmed breeding pairs and two possible pairs, confirming the importance of this area in the county context (Williamson 2003b, 2004). The survey also suggested that other potential sites were not used due

SUMMER

Small dots 1, medium 2, large 3 ('pairs')
Shading – breeding proved or considered likely

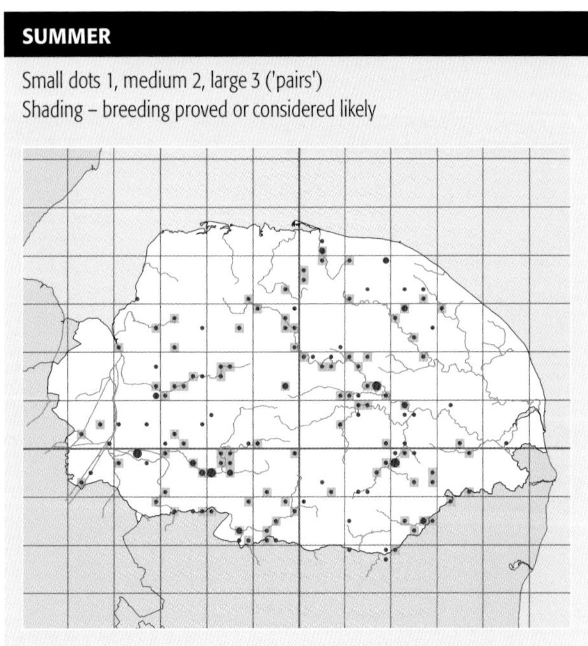

WINTER

Small dots 1, medium 2, large 3–4 (birds)

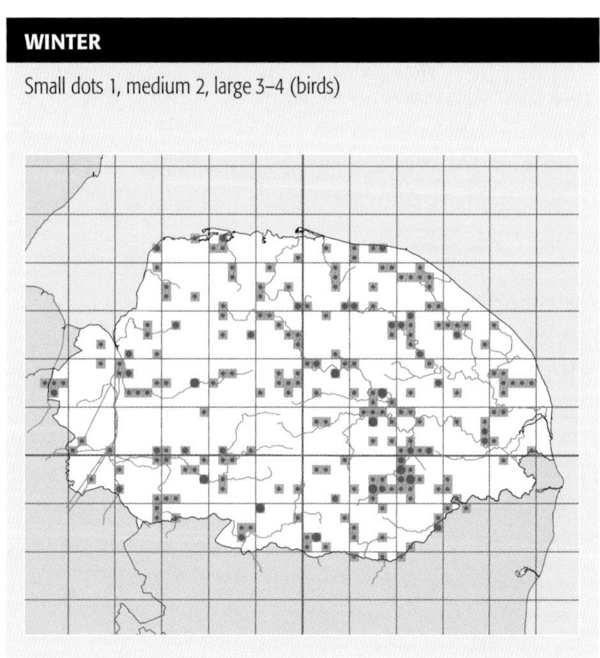

CHRIS KNIGHTS

to disturbance by anglers, picnickers and bathers. Four tetrads, well scattered around the county on the Rivers Wissey, Wensum and Tas, each held three breeding pairs. The number of territorial pairs reported annually to the county bird recorders during the NBA period remained fairly constant in the range 25 to 37, but appears to be a considerable underestimate of the whole county population.

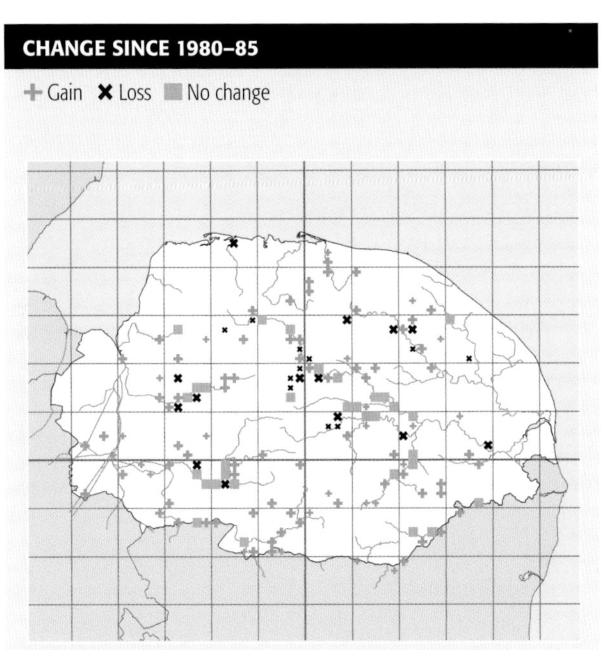

'In winter, Grey Wagtails from Scotland, northern England and the Continent occur in lowland Britain.'

In winter, Grey Wagtails from Scotland, northern England and the Continent occur in lowland Britain. Although at that season they are also found mainly alongside rivers and streams, others visit lakes, sewage works and farmyards, especially where slurry pits and manure heaps are located. This wider distribution is clearly shown on the NBA winter map, although most birds are still found along the river valleys. Grey Wagtails are very susceptible to freezing of rivers and streams during severe winter weather. In this situation, they may move to the coast or onwards towards milder regions. That so few coastal tetrads were occupied during the NBA winters may be a reflection of the generally mild winters during that period.

It is likely that Norfolk's population of Grey Wagtails is at an all-time high. The number of 10-km squares recorded as occupied rose from just 11 in 1968–72 to 38 in the NBA summers. In winter, the number of 10-km squares has more than doubled since 1981–84. Grey Wagtails were recorded in well over twice as many tetrads during the NBA summers as during the *1980–85 NBBS*, with range gains widespread but especially evident in the south of the county.

Pied Wagtail

Motacilla alba

NBA 1999–2007	SUMMER: ALL / BREEDING	WINTER
TETRADS OCCUPIED	1,309 (90%) / 1,260 (86%)	1,238 (85%)
SUMMER/WINTER ONLY	138	67
MEAN PER OCCUPIED TETRAD	4 / 4	12
SUMMED MAX COUNTS	4,665 / 4,571	15,412
POPULATION ESTIMATE	5,000–6,000 bp *yarrellii*, 2–5 individuals *alba*	12,000–18,000

PREVIOUS ATLASES	SQUARES OCCUPIED	1999–2007	LOSSES	GAINS
1968–72 (10 KM)	62 (all)	62 (all)		
1980–85 (TETRAD)	762 (52%)	1,260 (86%)	83	581
1980–85 (10 KM)	61 (98%)	62 (all)	0	1
1981–84 WINTER (10 KM)	60 (97%)	62 (all)	0	2
1988–91 (10 KM)	62 (all)	62 (all)		

THE PIED WAGTAIL is the commonest and most familiar of the British wagtails. The race *yarrellii* that nests almost exclusively in Britain and Ireland is one of the many races of the White Wagtail that occur across the Palaearctic.

In Britain, Pied Wagtails breed in a wide variety of habitats, ranging from waterside sites through farmland to urban areas. In agricultural settings, they favour mixed farming and often associate with livestock.

The NBA summer map shows that the Pied Wagtail is a very widespread breeding species in the county, the largest pockets of absence being in the Tilney area of the Fens, on Terrington Marsh and in the heavily forested Thetford Warren. During NBA fieldwork, it became apparent that in rural areas the species was almost invariably associated with buildings during the breeding season, such as barns and farmhouses. In more urban settings, Pied Wagtails favoured parks, school playing fields, large gardens, sewage treatment works and industrial estates, again usually choosing to nest in the nearby buildings. The three tetrads with the highest numbers of breeding pairs of Pied Wagtails during the NBA summers were all in the Brecks, with 26 at Grimston, and 19 and 20 in two tetrads in the Stanford TA, where no doubt they are attracted to the many small deserted buildings.

Norfolk's Pied Wagtails are very largely resident but are joined by winter visitors from elsewhere in Britain. During the winter months, Pied Wagtails are often found feeding in loose flocks on farmland, being particularly attracted to livestock, both penned and grazing in the open, to fields in which sugar beet is being lifted and to winter stubbles. In winter, the filter beds of sewage treatment works offer a ready supply of insect prey, as indicated by up to 100 birds near Saxlingham Nethergate and 60 at Crownthorpe. In less rural situations, they are also found in the same general areas where breeding occurs. As in summer, they occur throughout the county, except for parts of the Fens and the more heavily wooded areas in Breckland.

Communal winter roosts of Pied Wagtails can on occasion be spectacular and hold considerable numbers of birds. During the NBA winters, the largest roost occupied three plane trees in Brigg Street, in the centre of Norwich, where 2,213 birds were counted by streetlight in January 2001. For some reason this site was deserted the following winter and smaller numbers of Pied Wagtails gathered in Rampant Horse Street, a short distance away. Subsequently, the largest known roost in the county built up at the Thickthorn Service Station at Hethersett, peaking at 1,250 in December 2003. Up to 250 also roosted in or on buildings at the Bacton Gas Terminal, although numbers were well down on earlier winters. Other sites where 200 or more birds were counted entering or leaving the roost were in a tidal reedbed at Brancaster Staithe, in the freshwater reedbeds at Titchwell and Horsey Mere, and at Threxton SF, near Watton. Before entering the roost, Pied Wagtails gather in a variety of habitats to take a last-minute feed, and these have included a beet field at Sheringham, a ploughed field at Waxham and the South Beach at Great Yarmouth.

DAVID TIPLING

Observations at Pied Wagtail roosts in other parts of England have indicated that most of the roosting birds feed during the day within 12 km of the roost site and that catchment areas of roosts may overlap (*1981–84 Winter Atlas*). During the NBA winters, the known roosts accounted for at most about 3,000 roosting Pied Wagtails, which is less than a quarter of the estimated wintering population of the county. Whether the missing roosts are large or small ones is unknown.

Since the *1980–85 NBBS*, the species has clearly thrived and expanded its range within the county, the previously deserted areas in the Fens, in Broadland and in the arable parts of northwest and south Norfolk once again hosting this now-ubiquitous species.

In addition to the Pied Wagtails that are mapped, 34 White Wagtails of the nominate race *alba*, from continental Europe or from Iceland, were also logged as migrants, in 25 tetrads. These were mainly around the coast, with highest numbers between Blakeney and Kelling, but some occurred inland. This race has nested once in Norfolk as a pure pair, at Cley in 1997. During the NBA summers, likely breeding, presumably as a mixed pair with *yarrellii*, was reported only from Beachamwell.

SUMMER

Small dots 1–2, medium 3–4, large 5–26 ('pairs')
Shading – breeding proved or considered likely

WINTER

Small dots 1–3, medium 4–9, large 10–1,650 (birds)

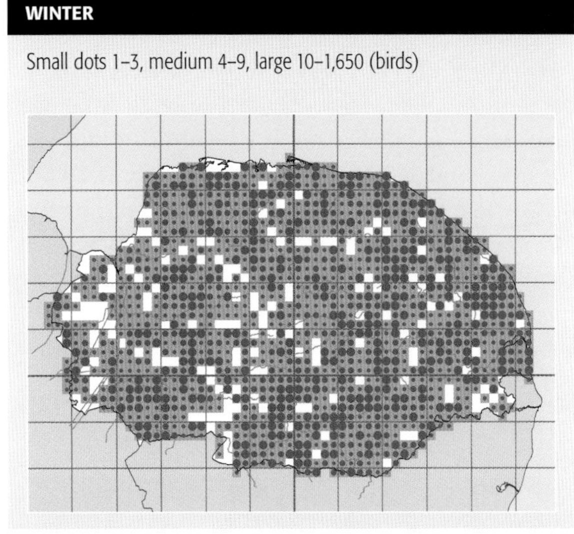

CHANGE SINCE 1980–85

+ Gain ✖ Loss ■ No change

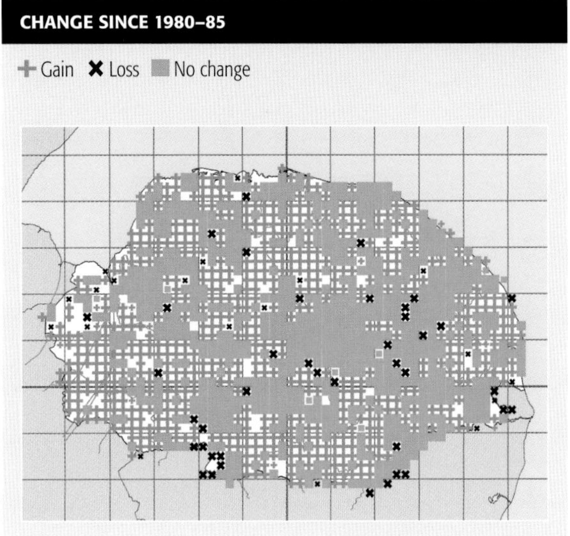

Tree Pipit
Anthus trivialis

NBA 1999–2007	SUMMER: ALL/BREEDING	WINTER
TETRADS OCCUPIED	97 (7%) / 81 (6%)	none
SUMMER/WINTER ONLY	97	none
MEAN PER OCCUPIED TETRAD	3 / 3	none
SUMMED MAX COUNTS	246 / 228	none
POPULATION ESTIMATE	200–250 bp	none

PREVIOUS ATLASES	SQUARES OCCUPIED	1999–2007	LOSSES	GAINS
1968–72 (10 KM)	24 (39%)	18 (29%)	11	5
1980–85 (TETRAD)	87 (6%)	81 (6%)	53	47
1980–85 (10 KM)	26 (42%)	18 (29%)	11	3
1988–91 (10 KM)	27 (44%)	18 (29%)	13	4

THE TREE PIPIT is sleeker and more elegant than the more familiar Meadow Pipit, but best distinguished by its songs and flight calls. It is a red-listed bird of conservation concern in the UK, having suffered a decline in population of 84% in England during the 25 years 1982–2007 (*Birdtrends*).

All populations of the Tree Pipit are strongly migratory, wintering in Africa south of the Sahara, with the first spring migrants generally recorded in Norfolk in the first few days of April. Although it both feeds and nests on the ground, the Tree Pipit requires trees or bushes to use as refuges and song posts. During the breeding season, it inhabits heathland, commons, parkland, woodland glades and conifer plantations up to about four years old, and only low-grade agricultural land is likely to be visited.

The NBA summer map confirms the species' status as a rather scarce, localised breeding bird in the county with its main stronghold in Breckland, as has been the case for at least the last 30 years. Here the conifer plantations, restocked on a regular cycle, provide an ideal habitat during the first years after planting, while the more mature areas of mixed woodland and clearings are also favoured. The highest tetrad counts of singing males during the NBA summers were all made in the Brecks, with a maximum of 12 at Santon Downham and eight or nine in the

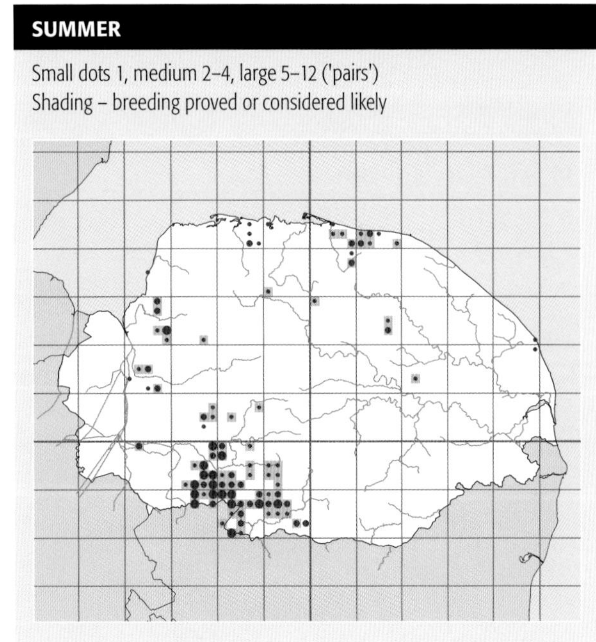

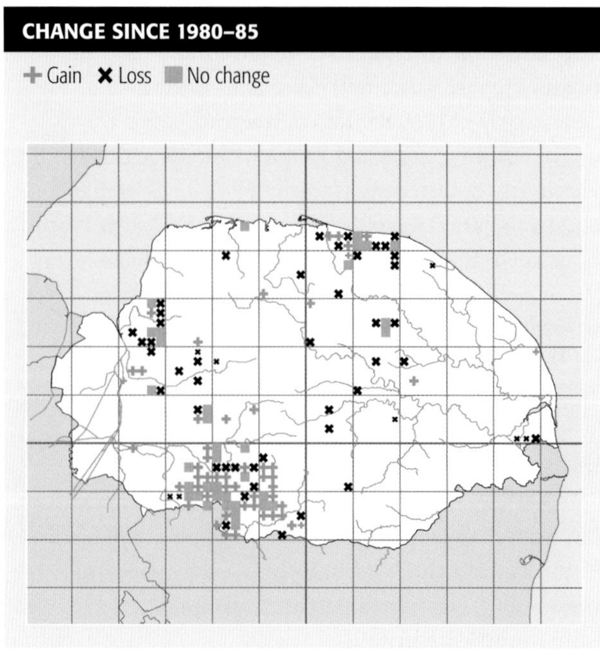

CHRIS KNIGHTS

Mundford/Cranwich and Croxton areas. Other parts of the county in which Tree Pipits were regularly recorded during the breeding season were the heaths along the Cromer to Holt ridge and on the Sandringham estate and southeast of King's Lynn. Undoubtedly, most of the coastal reports referred to passing migrants, but it was likely to have been the same male that returned to Cley in three successive summers to spend several weeks each year singing along the shingle bank or over the West Bank.

There are very strong parallels between the Norfolk breeding distributions of Tree Pipit and Woodlark, although the latter species is more widespread and probably more numerous in the county.

Despite frequent comments by observers that Tree Pipits have become less numerous in the county over recent years, numbers at the main sites appear to be holding up. For instance, at Roydon Common, seven pairs were present in 2000 and the same number in 2006, having peaked at nine pairs in 2004, while at Dersingham Bog eight pairs were present in 2006 compared with 11 in 1994.

Comparison with previous 10-km atlases shows a sharp drop from 27 squares occupied in 1988–91 to 18 during the NBA period. At tetrad level, the map of change since the *1980–85 NBBS* indicates that many outlying tetrads have been lost, but that considerable extension of range has occurred in Thetford Forest. During the NBA summers, Tree Pipits were recorded in over 50 tetrads in Breckland.

The sum of pair totals from likely breeding tetrads was well over 200 but, in view of the ongoing national decrease, the current breeding population is likely to be much lower than this. The Tree Pipit now needs a full and thorough county survey that would set a baseline for further numerical change.

Meadow Pipit
Anthus pratensis

NBA 1999–2007	SUMMER: ALL / BREEDING	WINTER
TETRADS OCCUPIED	485 (33%) / 346 (24%)	937 (64%)
SUMMER/WINTER ONLY	79	531
MEAN PER OCCUPIED TETRAD	5 / 6	13
SUMMED MAX COUNTS	2,330 / 2,029	12,580
POPULATION ESTIMATE	1,500–2,000 bp	15,000–20,000

PREVIOUS ATLASES	SQUARES OCCUPIED	1999–2007	LOSSES	GAINS
1968–72 (10 KM)	50 (81%)	59 (95%)	3	12
1980–85 (TETRAD)	389 (27%)	346 (24%)	213	170
1980–85 (10 KM)	54 (87%)	59 (95%)	3	8
1981–84 WINTER (10 KM)	57 (92%)	62 (all)	0	5
1988–91 (10 KM)	45 (73%)	59 (95%)	3	17

THE MEADOW PIPIT is the most abundant pipit in western Europe and is by far the commonest nesting passerine in the British uplands. Like many members of its genus, it is more easily identified from its voice than its appearance.

Meadow Pipits can breed in Britain at all altitudes between sea level and mountain tops at over 1,000 m, wherever there is sufficient low vegetation to conceal the nest. In Norfolk, they nest in rough grassland, on heathland and commons, around the unploughed edges of arable fields, in young forestry plantations (up to five years old), among sand dunes and on marshland, both inland and around the coast.

The NBA summer map shows a breeding distribution that is extraordinarily patchy. There is a strong attraction to the coast, where there is a thin band of almost continuous occupation. The tetrads around Breydon Water, including most of the marshland inland to Buckenham on the Yare and Burgh St Peter on the Waveney, are almost all occupied. There is strong occupation too of Fenland, where again damp grazing marshes, as for example at Welney, are a main attraction. Elsewhere, though, there is a strong presence east of Mundford, but not elsewhere in Breckland, and further dry, inland areas are occupied, notably north of Harleston, for reasons that are unclear.

There are wide variations in breeding density, with concentrations on the Ouse Washes, around the inner Wash, along the north Norfolk coastal strip from Hunstanton to Sheringham, where the majority of Meadow Pipits are found on the grazing marshes, coastal dunes and heaths, and on the marshes around Breydon Water.

During the NBA summers, the best-monitored sites were the reserves at Scolt Head, Blakeney Point and Welney. At Scolt Head the number of singing males has varied from 86 to 103, at Blakeney Point from 54 to 119 and at Welney from 40 to 121, where the highest counts have been made during the years with low spring water levels. At both coastal and inland sites, some counts may well have included some birds on spring passage, which continues strongly throughout April and into early May.

In winter, Meadow Pipits gather into loose winter flocks, although these rarely exceed 50–60. The NBA winter map shows that the species is much more widespread at that season, with concentrations in northwest Norfolk, in Broadland and in a broad band across the southern part of the county. During the winter months, Meadow Pipits can be found in a variety of habitats, such as sewage works, saltmarshes and cliff-top fields, but are particularly attracted to recently ploughed land, harvested sugar beet fields and to enclosed areas where livestock, such as sheep, are being fed on root crops. In these places, they are often to be found feeding alongside Pied Wagtails.

DAVID TIPLING

The origin of Norfolk's wintering population is unclear. A minority may well be local breeders and their offspring, while many others are probably winter visitors from further north in Britain; there is no evidence yet that birds from Greenland, Iceland, the Faeroes or Scandinavia winter in Britain, although they certainly occur abundantly as migrants (*Migration Atlas*). Cold-weather influxes swell the numbers in the county, for example in late January 2003, when 450 were counted flying west at Sheringham; 400 were present at Holme on 2nd February that year. Winter counts in individual tetrads are normally well below 100, but five other tetrads hosted three-figure counts during the NBA winters: 200 near Croxton and 140 near Bodney, both in the Brecks, and 148 at Reedham, 111 at Skeyton and 106 at Marsham, in east Norfolk. As Meadow Pipits may begin their spring migration in late February, some of those recorded during the late-winter recording period may have been on passage, rather than overwintering.

Occupation of 10-km squares shows an erratic trend across the four breeding atlas projects, being lowest in 1988–91 and highest during the NBA.

The change map suggests a complex pattern of range shifts in northwest Norfolk and in Breckland since the 1980–85 NBBS. Meadow Pipits appear to have largely deserted the North Creake/South Creake/Syderstone area and Thetford Warren. Perhaps, in the latter area, the occupied plantations had matured beyond the stage at which the habitat was suitable for breeding. In southeast Norfolk around Harleston and Long Stratton, on the other hand, there has been extensive colonisation in areas never previously known to hold the species. The Fenland and coastal distributions, however, showed relatively little change.

SUMMER

Small dots 1–2, medium 3–5, large 6–100 ('pairs')
Shading – breeding proved or considered likely

WINTER

Small dots 1–4, medium 5–14, large 15–200 (birds)

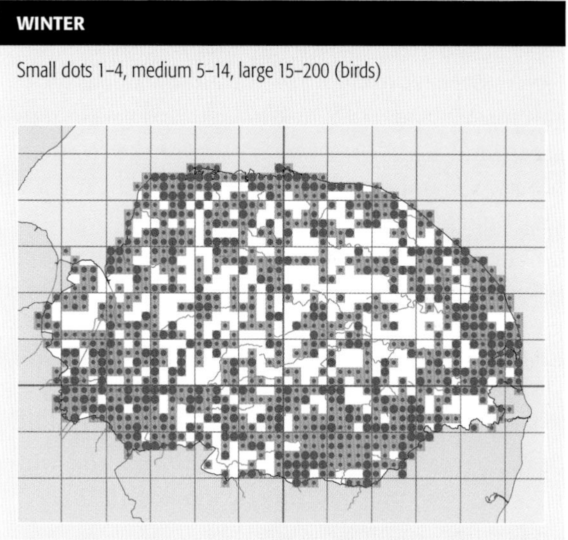

CHANGE SINCE 1980–85

+ Gain ✖ Loss ■ No change

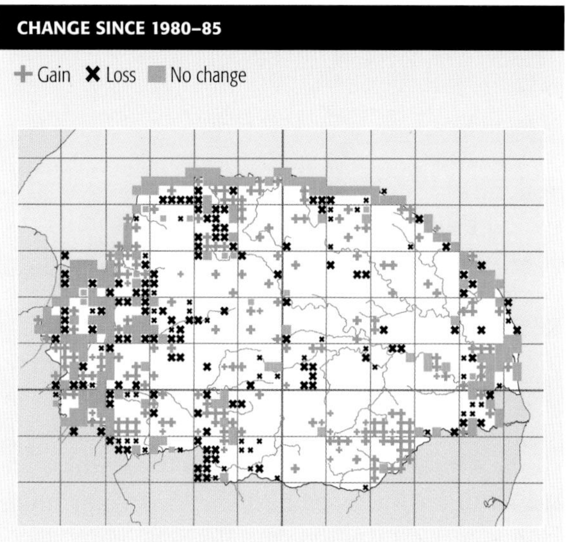

Rock Pipit

Anthus petrosus

NBA 1999–2007	SUMMER: ALL / BREEDING	WINTER
TETRADS OCCUPIED	6 (<1%) / none	68 (5%)
SUMMER/WINTER ONLY	2	64
MEAN PER OCCUPIED TETRAD	1 / none	31
SUMMED MAX COUNTS	6 / none	2,132
POPULATION ESTIMATE	none	1,800–2,200

PREVIOUS ATLASES	SQUARES OCCUPIED	1999–2007	LOSSES	GAINS
1981–84 WINTER (10 KM)	17 (27%)	14 (23%)	4	1

IT WAS ONLY in 1986 that Rock Pipits, formerly considered to be races of Water Pipit *A. spinoletta*, were given specific status by the BOU Records Committee. Although there are some apparently suitable nesting cliffs in Norfolk, this species nests all around Britain's coasts except for the stretch between Flamborough Head in Yorkshire and east Kent.

The British race of Rock Pipit, nominate *petrosus*, has been confidently identified in Norfolk on only a few occasions, the most recent being one in song at Scolt Head in May 2000. The vast majority of Rock Pipits recorded in Norfolk are of the migratory race *littoralis* that breeds in Fenno-Scandia and the Russian Kola Peninsula and winters south to Morocco and Algeria (Taylor 1997).

The first autumn migrants begin to appear along the Norfolk coast in mid September, with passage peaking in the second half of October. Numbers of Rock Pipits build up in tidal saltmarshes and harbours, where they feed on small marine molluscs. The NBA map shows that three separate areas hold virtually all the wintering Rock Pipits in Norfolk: these are the southern Wash, the north Norfolk coast from Holme to West Runton, and Breydon Water and the Halvergate Marshes.

Counting Rock Pipits during NBA set visits proved to be extremely difficult. The terrain that they occupy is often tricky or impossible to survey, due to the numerous tidal channels. Double-figure counts were obtained on only eight out of the 72 occasions that Rock Pipits were found on set visits, and many of the higher counts that were used to construct the map came from supplementary visits or from totals that appeared in *NBR*. The greatest concentration of Rock Pipits is undoubtedly in the saltmarshes between Thornham and Holkham, and from Wells to Blakeney, with peak tetrad counts of 250 at Wells and 210 at Burnham Overy Staithe. In December 1997, a coordinated low tide count of the entire intertidal zone between Holme and Weybourne resulted in a grand total of 2,010 Rock Pipits. This confirmed suspicion that the number of wintering birds had been grossly underestimated in the recent past – although 400 had been recorded at Blakeney as early as October 1884. In December 2001, a WeBS count in the Scolt Head/Brancaster Harbour area produced just over 500. While they are not generally considered social birds, a loose flock of 85 was encountered around the high-tide mark on Holkham beach in early December 2005.

Rock Pipits are rarely recorded away from intertidal areas in Norfolk except in the Breydon Water and Halvergate Marshes area. Here they extend onto the fresh marshes that border the lower reaches of the Rivers Yare and Bure, as well as further upriver along the Yare valley at Cantley and Buckenham, although only small numbers occur so far inland.

As winter progresses, the population begins to decline as birds start to return to their breeding areas. Those that remain into late February and early March, however, begin to assume their more attractive and

DAVID TIPLING

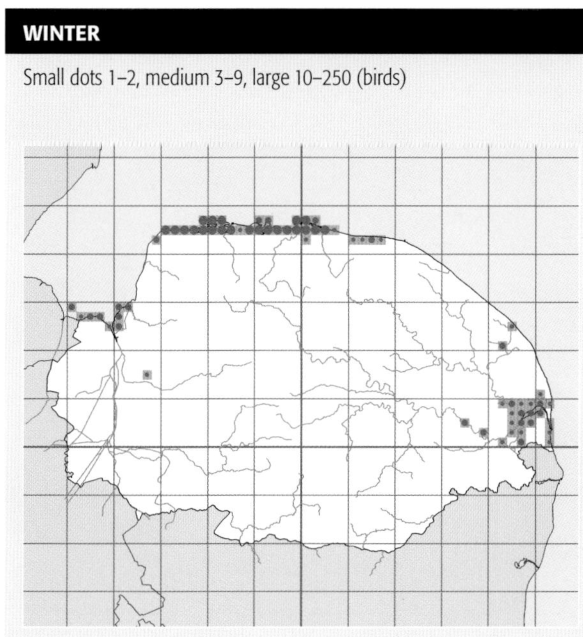

'As winter progresses, the population begins to decline as birds start to return to their breeding areas.'

Water-Pipit-like spring plumage, through a partial late-winter body moult. During the NBA summers, a few records were made in April, all but one involving single birds and all at coastal locations, apart from an inland migrant at Pentney GP.

Comparison with the *1981–84 Winter Atlas* is not straightforward, because some Water Pipits may have been included in the early data. There were winter records then from parts of the Wash and northeast Norfolk where neither species was reported to the NBA, however, suggesting that some range decrease may have occurred among Rock Pipits.

Water Pipit
Anthus spinoletta

NBA 1999–2007	SUMMER: ALL/BREEDING	WINTER
TETRADS OCCUPIED	14 (1%) / none	33 (2%)
SUMMER/WINTER ONLY	5	24
MEAN PER OCCUPIED TETRAD	1 / none	6
SUMMED MAX COUNTS	20 / none	193
POPULATION ESTIMATE	none	20–120

PREVIOUS ATLASES	SQUARES OCCUPIED	1999–2007	LOSSES	GAINS
1981–84 WINTER (10 KM)	6 (10%)	13 (21%)	1	8

ALTHOUGH THEIR identification during the winter months is usually fairly straightforward, Water Pipits can easily be confused with the Fenno-Scandian race of the Rock Pipit, *littoralis,* in spring, as both species attain their breeding plumage. Water Pipits breed abundantly in the mountains of central and southern Europe, descending in autumn to winter at lower elevations, some moving northwest to winter in the Low Countries and England.

Water Pipits are scarce winter visitors to Norfolk and other parts of southern England, the first autumn birds arriving in October. Within the county, certain sites are favoured by the species; indeed, there is evidence from elsewhere in England that some individuals exhibit site fidelity in consecutive winters. Favoured habitats

DAVID TIPLING

'Water Pipits are scarce winter visitors to Norfolk and other parts of southern England, the first autumn birds arriving in October.'

include coastal freshwater or brackish pools and flooded water meadows, while watercress beds are commonly utilised in other parts of England. The species tends to avoid saltwater habitats.

The NBA winter map shows a very sparse and localised distribution, based mainly around the freshwater reserves along the north Norfolk coast and in Broadland, the majority of locations there being alongside the Rivers Yare and Bure. During the NBA period, the numbers of overwintering Water Pipits have been very variable, with 40–50 birds in most winters. Maximum winter counts, however, were recorded in January/February 2004, when over 100 were present in the county. In recent years, the highest numbers have generally been at Buckenham and Cley, where the maximum counts have been 19 and 17 respectively, while two other locations, Rockland Marsh (15) and Burnham Norton (11) have also hosted double-figure counts.

Peak numbers have generally been noted in March, after the close of the NBA winter recording period, when birds tend to gather into flocks prior to migration. By April, only a few are still present in Norfolk, by which time many have attained their attractive spring colours. At this time of year, most records refer to single birds but up to six have been recorded at Buckenham and five at Burnham Norton in April. The latest spring date during the NBA period was 28th April in 2000.

There has apparently been substantial range increase at 10-km scale since the *1981–84 Winter Atlas*. The extent of this increase is perhaps an artefact, however, because some Water Pipits in 1981–84 may have been treated as Rock Pipits.

WINTER

Small dots 1, medium 2–5, large 6–25 (birds)

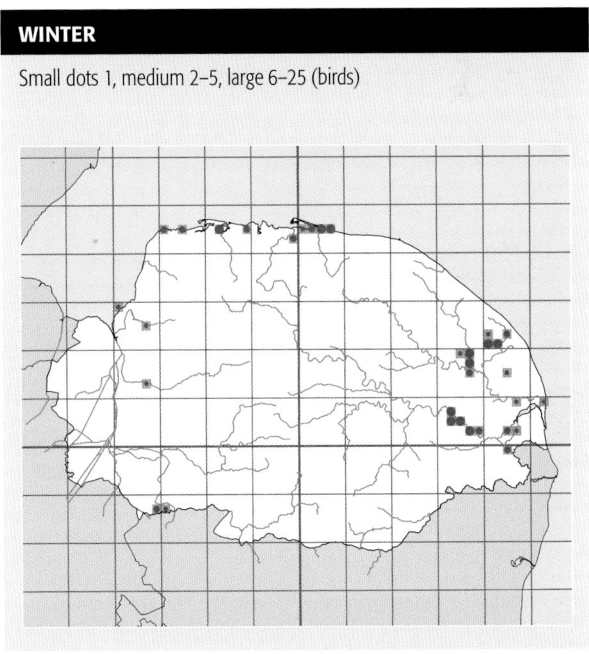

WINTER TOTALS

Winter count totals 1999–2007 (data from *NBR*)

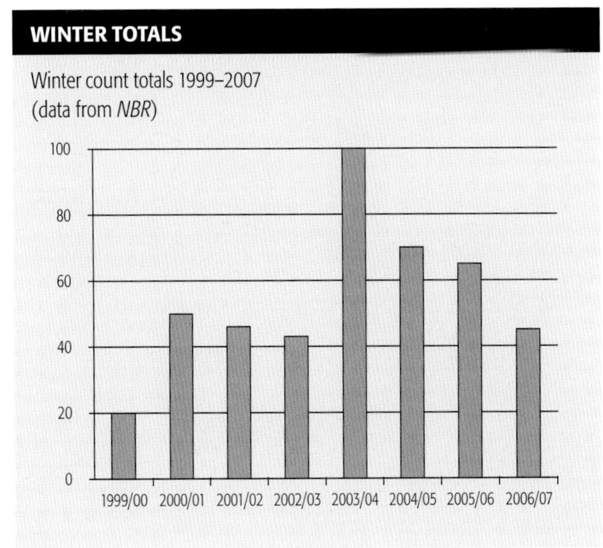

Chaffinch

Fringilla coelebs

NBA 1999–2007	SUMMER: ALL/BREEDING	WINTER
TETRADS OCCUPIED	1,412 (97%) / 1,407 (96%)	1,395 (96%)
SUMMER/WINTER ONLY	25	8
MEAN PER OCCUPIED TETRAD	27 / 28	58
SUMMED MAX COUNTS	38,771 / 38,764	81,303
POPULATION ESTIMATE	50,000–70,000 bp	120,000–160,000

PREVIOUS ATLASES	SQUARES OCCUPIED	1999–2007	LOSSES	GAINS
1968–72 (10 KM)	62 (all)	62 (all)		
1980–85 (TETRAD)	1,331 (91%)	1,407 (96%)	13	89
1980–85 (10 KM)	62 (all)	62 (all)		
1981–84 WINTER (10 KM)	62 (all)	62 (all)		
1988–91 (10 KM)	62 (all)	62 (all)		

MALE CHAFFINCHES are among the most colourful of British finches, and in Norfolk the species is one of the most widespread and most abundant breeding birds.

During the breeding season, Chaffinches are found in a wide variety of habitats, wherever trees, scrub or bushes are found. All types of woods are occupied, with mixed deciduous woodland being favoured. Chaffinches also nest along hedgerows, in scrubby areas, parks and gardens, even in the middle of urban developments.

Males sing from high perches within their territories and so breeding pairs are easy to locate, although they become less vocal once they have attracted a mate.

The NBA summer map confirms how widespread the species is within Norfolk, with likely breeding records from 96% of tetrads. As might be expected, the highest concentrations of breeding pairs in a single tetrad were recorded in the heavily wooded Brecks, with maximum counts of 133 at Hockham, 131 at Stow Heath and 126 near West Harling. Five other tetrads in the county held over 90 breeding pairs. Southeast Norfolk, north of Harleston, apparently holds another concentration of breeding pairs.

In the autumn, large numbers of Scandinavian Chaffinches migrate to Britain, some of which remain to overwinter in Norfolk. These continental birds may form larger flocks than do our native Chaffinches, and are more likely to be found in open areas, such as large

SUMMER

Small dots 1–18, medium 19–33, large 34–133 ('pairs')
Shading – breeding proved or considered likely

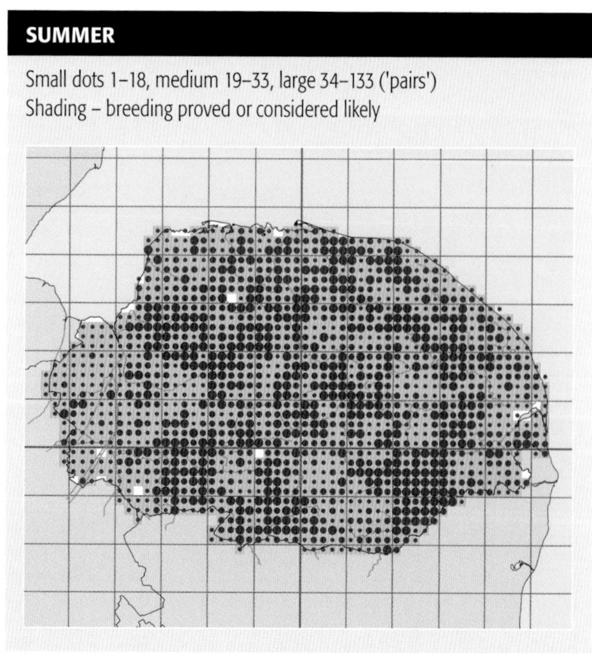

WINTER

Small dots 1–27, medium 28–60, large 61–1,000 (birds)

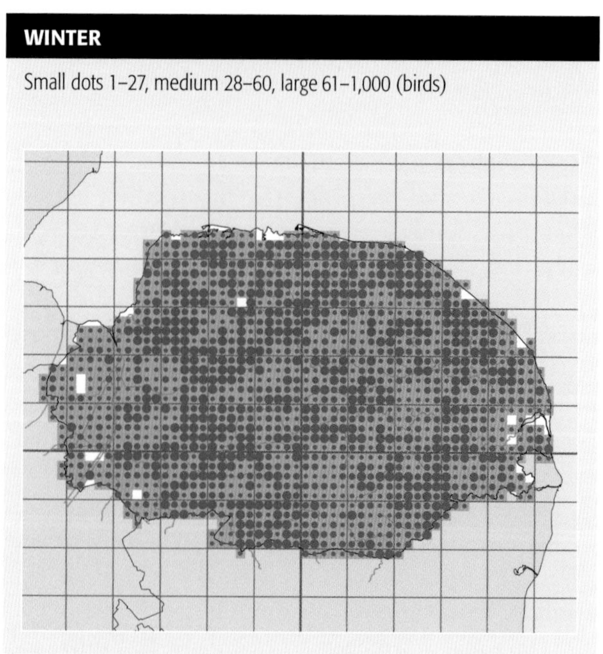

DAVID TIPLING

arable fields (*1981–84 Winter Atlas*). Browne (2004), however, analysing a ringing study at Hilborough, found that few, if any, continental immigrants supplemented the local winter population within that study area.

The NBA winter map shows a similarly widespread distribution to that recorded in summer, although with imperfect correspondence between the areas of highest density. The largest winter flocks at this season were noted in the west of the county, many being in Breckland. The highest counts consisted of 600–1,000 in woodland near Croxton, 590 on stubble at Grimston Carr and 500 at West Tofts Heath. By far the largest count in east Norfolk was of 450 on St Benet's Level. Other habitats that proved attractive to Chaffinches in winter included maize game-cover strips, recently ploughed fields, outdoor pig units, rubbish tips, and gardens providing a regular supply of seeds and nuts.

'In the autumn, large numbers of Scandinavian Chaffinches migrate to Britain, some of which remain to overwinter in Norfolk.'

Large winter flocks were often in different places between winters, so that some duplication of counts during the survey was inevitable. In mild winters, such as prevailed throughout the NBA period, flocks of local breeders often dispersed in February to begin establishing their breeding territories.

CHANGE SINCE 1980–85

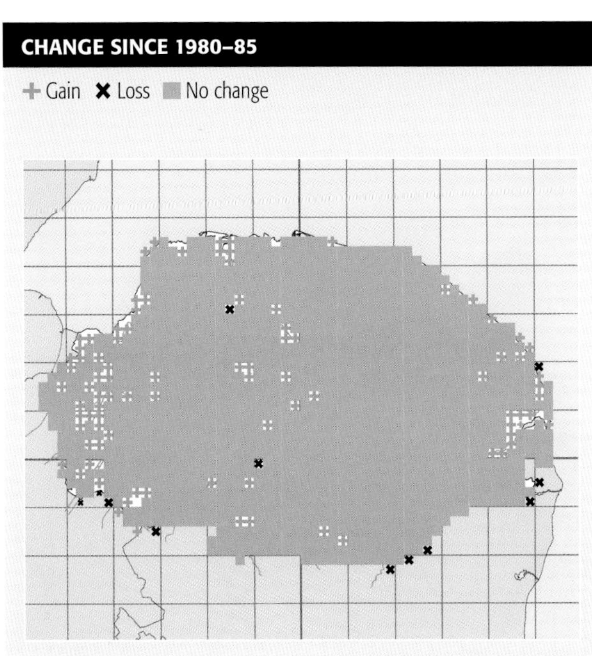

Comparison with the *1980–85 NBBS* indicates there has since been some limited range expansion at tetrad level. The change map shows there have been gains especially in the Fens, but also a few in mid county and near the east coast. Even the most open expanses of the Halvergate Levels, unoccupied during the *1980–85 NBBS*, now host small numbers of breeding Chaffinches.

Brambling
Fringilla montifringilla

NBA 1999–2007	SUMMER: ALL/BREEDING	WINTER
TETRADS OCCUPIED	52 (4%) / none	370 (25%)
SUMMER/WINTER ONLY	22	340
MEAN PER OCCUPIED TETRAD	3 / none	34
SUMMED MAX COUNTS	144 / none	12,414
POPULATION ESTIMATE	none	2,000–5,000

PREVIOUS ATLASES	SQUARES OCCUPIED	1999-2007	LOSSES	GAINS
1981–84 WINTER (10 KM)	44 (71%)	55 (89%)	2	13

THE BRAMBLING IS a winter visitor from the birch woods and conifer forests of Fenno-Scandia and northern Europe. In winter, it is often found in association with its close relative, the Chaffinch.

The winter distribution in Britain is largely dictated by the availability of beechmast across Europe (*1981–84 Winter Atlas*); good crops occur only at intervals of a few years, and therefore Bramblings are present in largest numbers in widely different areas from one winter to the next.

The first Bramblings are seen in Norfolk from around the end of September. Migrants cross the county on a broad front, often heading north of west, having perhaps taken a short sea-crossing from the Netherlands or Belgium, and westward coastal movements can be substantial.

The NBA map shows that the species was recorded during December to February across much of the county but that by far the largest numbers were in the west and north, with few migrants having stopped to winter near eastern arrival points. Breckland held the highest numbers, with maxima of 1,800 at St Helen's picnic site near Santon Downham in January 2003, up to 500 amongst a mixed finch flock of 2,000 birds on stubble at Grimston Carr in December 2001, and 350 at both Cranwich and Two Mile Bottom, near Thetford. The highest count in the north of the county was of 375 at Barrow Common, near Brancaster. In the east, only Fritton Warren held appreciable numbers.

Flocks of Brambling were recorded in beech woods, in open arable areas and in strips of game cover, especially if maize was included. In recent years, Bramblings have become increasingly frequent visitors to garden feeders and there were many such records during the NBA winters, albeit only involving up to about 20 birds at any one site. Bramblings form communal roosts in winter, often with Chaffinches, occupying areas of thick cover such as rhododendrons; one such roost in the NBA period was of 85 birds at Beeston Regis.

The NBA map indicates that many of the less wooded parts of Norfolk are not favoured by Bramblings; this includes much of the Fens, the

central part of the county and the southeast. Such a patchy winter distribution was not expected.

During the *1981–84 Winter Atlas* the species was found in 44 of the 10-km squares in the county, this figure rising to 55 in the NBA winters. This difference may suggest that Bramblings were more widespread than 20 years ago, but might follow at least partly from better coverage: the *1981–84 Winter Atlas* covered only three winters, against the NBA's eight, and fieldwork was not tetrad-based. The number of Bramblings wintering in Norfolk varies considerably from year to year. There is little information on which to base a county population estimate but, because of the birds' mobility, there will certainly have been many fewer birds during the NBA winters than the total of tetrad maxima, and perhaps as few as 2,000 in some of the winters.

Although the vast majority of Bramblings have left the county by the end of March, a few are generally recorded in early April and in some years quite substantial parties arrive during the month. In early April 2004, counts of 140 and 120 were made in the Stanford TA and at Swaffham respectively, while 100 were still present at Dersingham Bog on 11th April 2005, including several singing males. Even as late as 26th April 2003, 40 were still present in the Aylmerton/Felbrigg area and singles were noted in north Norfolk as late as 18th May. Spring migrant males are often heard in song.

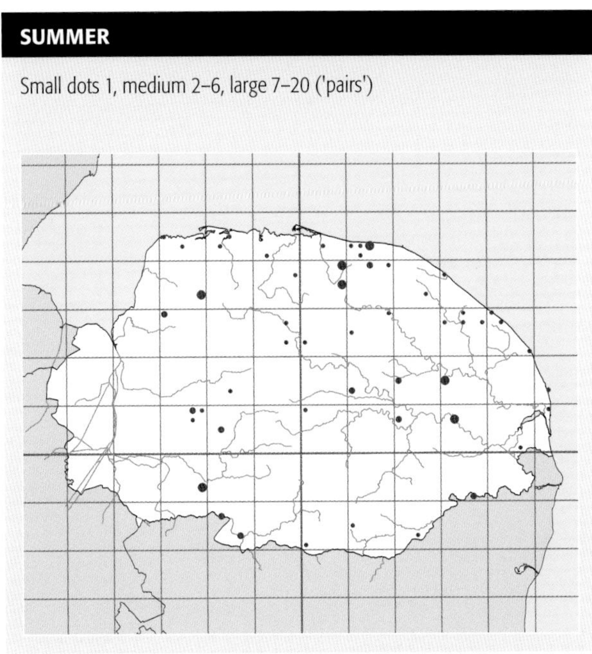

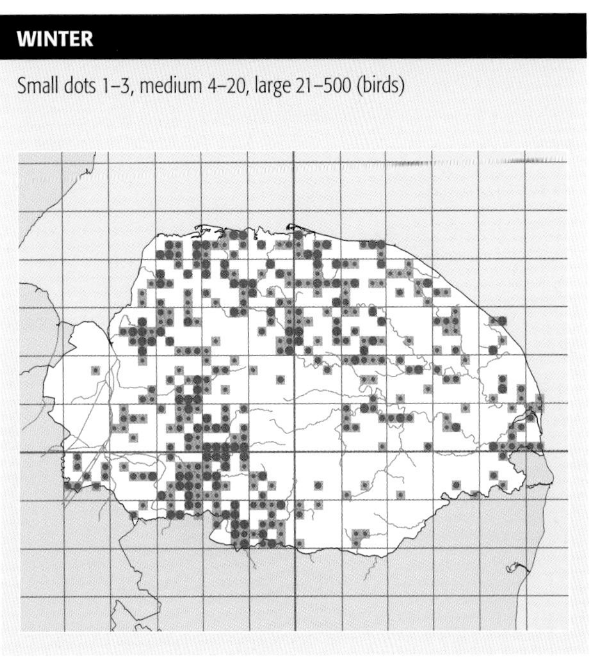

Greenfinch
Carduelis chloris

NBA 1999–2007	SUMMER: ALL/BREEDING	WINTER
TETRADS OCCUPIED	1,347 (92%) / 1,319 (90%)	1,323 (91%)
SUMMER/WINTER ONLY	68	44
MEAN PER OCCUPIED TETRAD	13 / 14	29
SUMMED MAX COUNTS	18,113 / 18,067	38,263
POPULATION ESTIMATE	18,000–22,000 bp	50,000–70,000

PREVIOUS ATLASES	SQUARES OCCUPIED	1999–2007	LOSSES	GAINS
1968–72 (10 KM)	62 (all)	62 (all)		
1980–85 (TETRAD)	1,234 (85%)	1,319 (90%)	65	150
1980–85 (10 KM)	62 (all)	62 (all)		
1981–84 WINTER (10 KM)	62 (all)	62 (all)		
1988–91 (10 KM)	61 (98%)	62 (all)	0	1

THE GREENFINCH IS one of the most widespread and abundant garden finches. Its eye-catching, bat-like display flight and familiar, nasal wheezing song are unmistakable.

The Greenfinch inhabits woodland edges, farmland spinneys and patches of thorny scrub, being often encountered along tall hedgerows, in young conifer plantations, orchards, parks, churchyards and gardens. Alongside an expansion of range during the 20th century, it has become more characteristic of villages and suburbs, where it is familiar at garden feeders.

The NBA summer map shows a very widespread distribution throughout the county, with some tiny pockets of absences on the grazing marshes around Breydon Water, in parts of the Brecks, and in scattered, mainly very open areas elsewhere. Greenfinches often breed in small, loose colonies, without territorial boundaries, and range widely in search of food. Counts of pairs may include feeding birds from other tetrads, sometimes in substantial flocks. Tetrads at Tasburgh and Wellingham returned counts of 60 pairs of Greenfinches, while an unusual spring concentration of 120 birds was present at Wiggenhall St Peter on 8th May 2004. An area of the southeast of the county, mainly between Long Stratton and the Suffolk boundary, appeared to be particularly densely occupied.

After the breeding season, Greenfinches gather

SUMMER

Small dots 1–7, medium 8–16, large 17–61 ('pairs')
Shading – breeding proved or considered likely

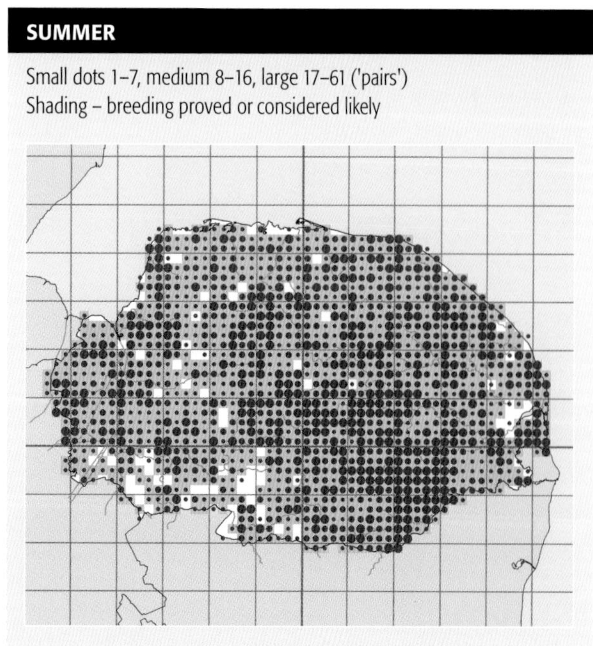

WINTER

Small dots 1–11, medium 12–29, large 30–420 (birds)

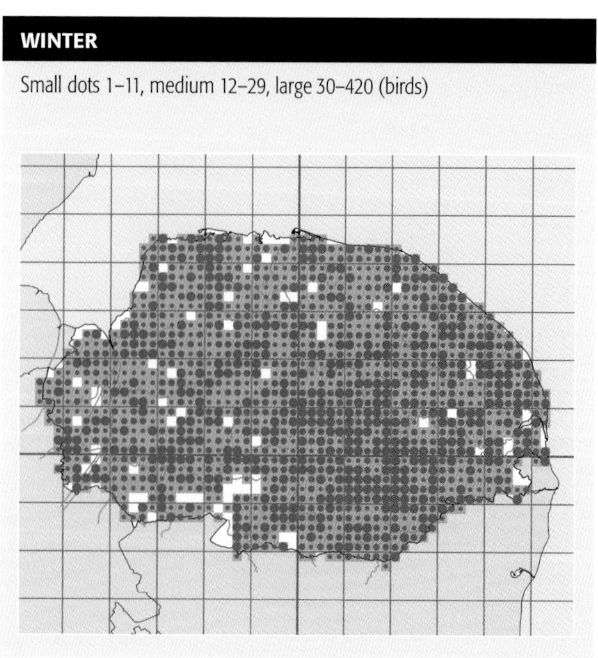

DAVID TIPLING

into feeding flocks, often accompanied by Chaffinches and, in more rural areas, by Linnets and Yellowhammers. There is substantial long-range dispersal within Britain and a small and variable amount of immigration from the near Continent. Movements of ringed birds show that Norfolk is especially well placed to receive such migrants; many of those arriving in the county originate from southern Norway (*Migration Atlas*).

The NBA winter map shows a very similar distribution of occupied squares to that in the summer, although the patterns of high and low abundance are rather different.

CHANGE SINCE 1980–85

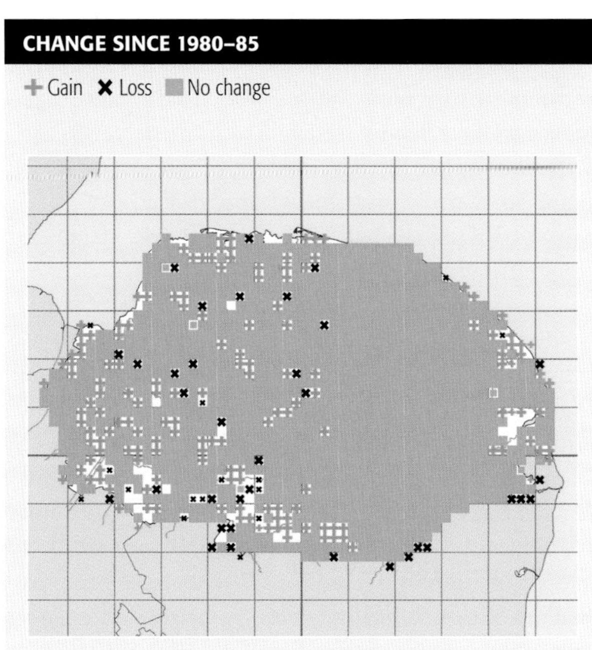

'After the breeding season, Greenfinches gather into feeding flocks, often accompanied by Chaffinches...'

In the early part of the winter, the flocks are generally found in the open countryside, feeding on stubble fields (including oilseed rape), in game-cover strips (especially of sunflowers), on areas of set-aside, where wild flowers have been allowed to set seed, or around the coast, feeding on seeds along shingle banks and on saltmarshes. As winter progresses and available food becomes more localised, the flocks often increase in size. Flocks of 200–300 Greenfinches were reported from several well-scattered localities during the NBA winters, with up to 400 at Holme in two of the years and an impressive 1,000 in the Stanford TA.

In recent years, Greenfinches have relied ever more heavily on garden feeding stations. By taking advantage of the bountiful supply of sunflower seeds and peanuts offered in many gardens, Greenfinches are able to augment or even totally replace the more natural foods, the supply of which dwindles during the second half of the winter and the early spring.

Comparison with the *1980–85 NBBS* indicates a small rise in the number of occupied tetrads. This has occurred alongside a population increase of 42% in England between 1982 and 2007 (*Birdtrends*). The change map shows that tetrad gains have been made in west and central Norfolk, and near the eastern coasts, but not elsewhere in east Norfolk, where the 1980–85 distribution was already almost complete.

Goldfinch
Carduelis carduelis

NBA 1999–2007	SUMMER: ALL / BREEDING	WINTER
TETRADS OCCUPIED	1,306 (90%) / 1,238 (85%)	1,137 (78%)
SUMMER/WINTER ONLY	246	77
MEAN PER OCCUPIED TETRAD	6 / 6	16
SUMMED MAX COUNTS	7,201 / 7,016	17,678
POPULATION ESTIMATE	7,000–8,000 bp	20,000–24,000

PREVIOUS ATLASES	SQUARES OCCUPIED	1999–2007	LOSSES	GAINS
1968–72 (10 KM)	62 (all)	62 (all)		
1980–85 (TETRAD)	1,231 (84%)	1,238 (85%)	157	164
1980–85 (10 KM)	62 (all)	62 (all)		
1981–84 WINTER (10 KM)	60 (97%)	62 (all)	0	2
1988–91 (10 KM)	62 (all)	62 (all)		

THE GOLDFINCH IS well known for its colourful plumage, with a unique red face and broad yellow wingbars, and for its cheerful, liquid voice.

Goldfinches declined considerably in late Victorian times because of their popularity as cage birds. By the 1970s, numbers were again high but there was a steep drop in population between the mid 1970s and mid 1980s, perhaps as declining natural food sources on farmland became limiting. Since 1986, however, the English population has been consistently on the rise (*Birdtrends*).

During the breeding season, Goldfinches favour areas with scattered trees and tall shrubs, often in or near villages or farmsteads, and preferably with patches of open ground where wild flowers grow; groundsels, thistles and dandelions, all in the family *Compositae*, provide their main sources of natural food. Goldfinches are found along mature hedgerows on farmland, in parks, orchards and gardens, and on commons and heathland where patches of hawthorn, gorse or other scrub are found. They often breed in loose colonies, with nests usually placed fairly high in a tree or tall bush. Breeding birds may forage at distances up to 800 m from the nest (*BWP8*).

The NBA summer map shows a widespread but somewhat patchy distribution, with a similar pattern of high and low densities to that of Greenfinch. Some Goldfinches remain in flocks of up to about 50 during April, and both these and summer feeding flocks would have been included in the summer counts.

Throughout the summer and autumn, Goldfinches feed almost exclusively on *Compositae*, choosing seeds that are in a milky, half-ripe state. They are the only birds able to extract teasel seeds. Flocks of Goldfinches move around from one patch of suitable plants to another as the various seeds develop (*BWP8*).

During the winter, flocks of Goldfinches, sometimes 100 birds or more, range over a wide area, visiting a larger variety of habitats than in summer, including weedy fields, neglected allotments, rubbish dumps, and coastal areas such as shingle banks and saltmarshes. At this season, Goldfinches often join flocks of Lesser Redpolls and Siskins to feed on the seeds of alder and birch.

The NBA winter map shows that Goldfinches were a little less widely distributed than in summer. A narrow coastal strip in north Norfolk was well favoured, as was the border of Breckland and Fenland. Seven of the eight tetrads in which 150 or more Goldfinches were recorded lay in west Norfolk, with maxima of 200 at Didlington and near Narborough, and there were 200 also at Filby Broad in the east. Fenland proper held many fewer occupied tetrads in winter than in summer, however, as did parts of the northeast coast. Goldfinches appear to have been less attracted to game-cover strips than other finches, although there were 70 in a strip of maize near Blackborough End. At Spixworth Hall, a small field of sunflowers attracted 75 Goldfinches.

Up to at least the 1980s, more than 80% of British Goldfinches moved south in autumn to winter in Belgium, France and Spain (*1988–91 Atlas*), a partial migration that involved mainly female and first-winter birds. As breeding populations have risen over recent years, it appears that far fewer birds may now be undertaking this southerly movement in autumn. A rise in numbers wintering in Norfolk is most evident in gardens, where Goldfinches have become regular visitors to feeding stations, being particularly attracted to niger seeds and sunflower hearts.

DAVID TIPLING

'During the winter, flocks of Goldfinches, sometimes 100 birds or more, range over a wide area, visiting a larger variety of habitats than in summer...'

These are both products only recently on the bird food market and perhaps instrumental in enabling Goldfinches to overwinter in such numbers.

It may be significant that there were two additional winter 10-km squares occupied by Goldfinches in the NBA winters, compared with the *1981–84 Winter Atlas*. There were no major differences in the distribution of breeding Goldfinches between the NBA and the *1980–85 NBBS*. The change map shows a mixture of tetrad gains and losses, which is hard to interpret: in some areas, the pattern may arise from chance observations in squares occupied at low density.

SUMMER

Small dots 1–3, medium 4–6, large 7–53 ('pairs')
Shading – breeding proved or considered likely

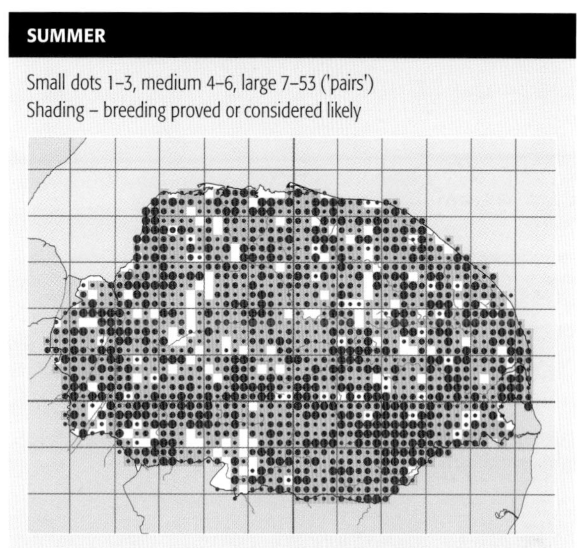

WINTER

Small dots 1–5, medium 6–15, large 16–200 (birds)

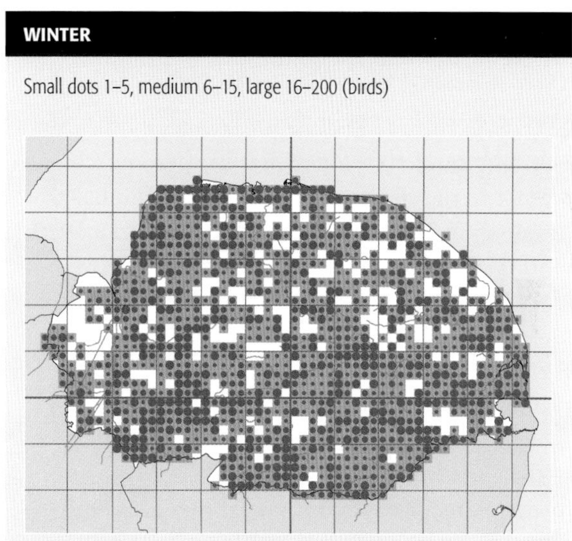

CHANGE SINCE 1980–85

+ Gain ✖ Loss ■ No change

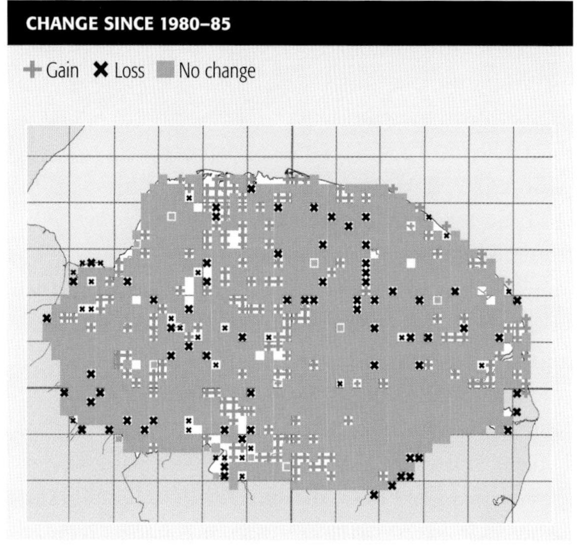

Siskin
Carduelis spinus

NBA 1999–2007	SUMMER: ALL/BREEDING	WINTER
TETRADS OCCUPIED	120 (8%) / 49 (3%)	420 (29%)
SUMMER/WINTER ONLY	40	340
MEAN PER OCCUPIED TETRAD	2/2	29
SUMMED MAX COUNTS	234 / 90	12,054
POPULATION ESTIMATE	100–200 bp	8,000–15,000

PREVIOUS ATLASES	SQUARES OCCUPIED	1999–2007	LOSSES	GAINS
1968–72 (10 KM)	8 (13%)	23 (37%)	2	17
1980–85 (TETRAD)	27 (2%)	49 (3%)	19	41
1980–85 (10 KM)	15 (24%)	23 (37%)	6	14
1981–84 WINTER (10 KM)	46 (74%)	58 (94%)	2	14
1988–91 (10 KM)	14 (23%)	23 (37%)	6	15

THE SISKIN USED to be just a winter visitor to Norfolk's coniferous forests but has become a regular breeder in the county, and much more familiar to people through its habit, developed since the 1970s, of visiting garden feeders in winter.

Throughout its European range, the Siskin breeds in lowland and mountain forest, inhabiting coniferous and mixed woodland. In Britain, breeding was thought to be confined to the Caledonian pine forests of Scotland until the mid 19th century, since when its range has spread greatly, aided by afforestation, including the planting of Thetford Forest in the 1920s.

Since 1959, the county population has been regularly boosted by irruptions from northern Europe. It was not until 1961, however, that breeding was first proved in the county, at Ringland, since when the population in Norfolk has grown to more than a hundred pairs. Siskins breed in loose colonies in tall conifers, especially spruce, fir and pine.

The NBA summer map shows that the species has a sparse and well-scattered distribution, with many tetrads recording birds thought likely to be migrants rather than breeding pairs. Three main areas regularly held small numbers of breeding Siskins, and show as local concentrations on the map: the main cluster of occupied tetrads was in the northern part of Thetford Forest, with additional concentrations around the Sandringham estate and along the Cromer to Holt ridge. All three areas are characterised by extensive tracts of mixed conifers.

Numbers of breeding birds are very hard to assess: many winter visitors are still present, often in song, in April, and autumn influxes begin as early as late June in some years. Hidden in dense cover at great height, their nests are amongst the most difficult to find of all British passerines. The presence of young juveniles in June is generally the best evidence that can be obtained for local breeding, though some of these birds may already have migrated from outside the county.

In winter, flocks of Siskins, frequently joined by Lesser Redpolls and Goldfinches, feed on the seeds of alders and birches, especially those in streamside or wetland locations. As the crop becomes depleted, generally from January onwards, Siskins begin to visit garden feeders, where they feed voraciously on niger, peanuts and sunflower hearts. This habit of using feeders during late winter and early spring was first noted in Norfolk in 1971, having been first described eight years earlier in Surrey. Since then variable, sometimes very large, numbers of Siskins have been reported in Norfolk gardens. High numbers of Siskins were present in the county's gardens in four of the eight NBA winters. Ringing has demonstrated that many arrive from northeast England, Scotland, Fenno-Scandia and western Russia. Favoured gardens generally have some tall, mature trees and a pond, and are close to more natural food sources such as an alder wood or conifer plantation.

The NBA winter map demonstrates that the species was far more widespread at this time of year, with an additional 300 tetrads being occupied. It remains a very patchy distribution, however. As in the summer, there are clear concentrations of records in the Brecks and around the Sandringham estate. Elsewhere, there

DAVID TIPLING

is a clear tendency to gather by riversides, typically in places where alders are abundant. Siskins were absent in winter from more than two-thirds of tetrads, especially the more open, agricultural squares on higher or better-drained ground.

Siskins are highly gregarious birds in winter and dense feeding flocks of 50 or more are not uncommon. They are mobile within and between winters and, undoubtedly, the same flocks will sometimes have been recorded in more than one tetrad. The largest counts were of 400 near Brettenham, 300 at Thetford and 200 at Lynford Arboretum, all three sites being in Breckland, and 200 at Roydon Common. Siskins roost communally in conifers, thorn scrub, alders and reedbeds (*1981–84 Winter Atlas*), but the only roost reported during the NBA winters was of 150 in bushes in a supermarket car park at Fakenham.

Comparisons with previous atlases show a strong range increase, in summer and in winter. The change map shows a substantial gain since the *1980–85 NBBS* in tetrads thought to hold breeding birds. In Thetford Forest, some tetrads have also been lost, presumably through felling and replanting. Despite its long-term range increase, however, the Siskin remains relatively scarce as a breeding bird in Norfolk.

SUMMER

Small dots 1, medium 2–3, large 4–22 ('pairs')
Shading – breeding proved or considered likely

WINTER

Small dots 1–5, medium 6–26, large 27–400 (birds)

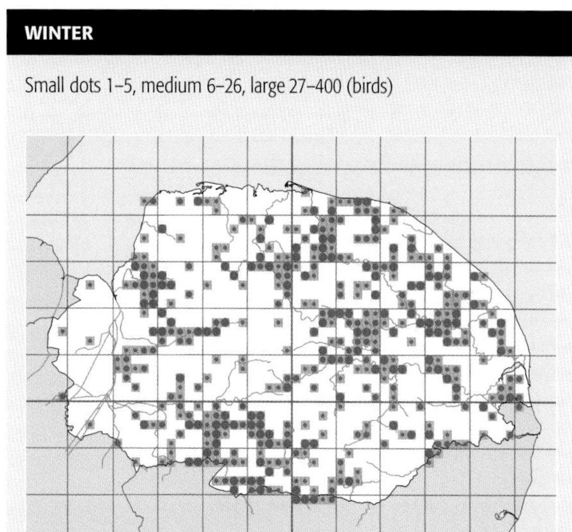

CHANGE SINCE 1980–85

+ Gain ✖ Loss ■ No change

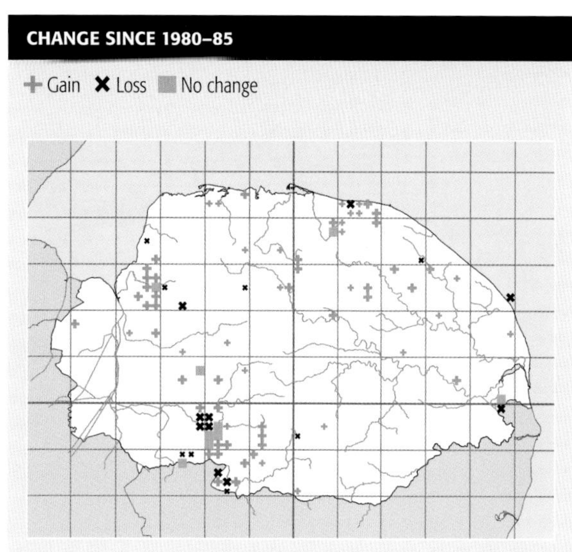

Linnet

Carduelis cannabina

NBA 1999–2007	SUMMER: ALL / BREEDING	WINTER
TETRADS OCCUPIED	1,130 (77%) / 1,007 (69%)	702 (48%)
SUMMER/WINTER ONLY	512	84
MEAN PER OCCUPIED TETRAD	6 / 6	40
SUMMED MAX COUNTS	6,575 / 6,188	28,035
POPULATION ESTIMATE	6,500–7,500 bp	18,000–22,000

PREVIOUS ATLASES	SQUARES OCCUPIED	1999–2007	LOSSES	GAINS
1968–72 (10 KM)	62 (all)	62 (all)		
1980–85 (TETRAD)	1,200 (82%)	1,007 (69%)	368	175
1980–85 (10 KM)	62 (all)	62 (all)		
1981–84 WINTER (10 KM)	59 (95%)	62 (all)	0	3
1988–91 (10 KM)	62 (all)	62 (all		

WITH ITS DELICATE pinkish-red breast and pleasing song, it is hardly surprising that the Linnet was a favourite cage bird in Victorian times. It was so popular that the activities of bird trappers brought about a marked decline in its numbers during the 19th century.

Linnets breed in loose colonies of four to six pairs in a variety of open habitats. On commons and heathland, gorse thickets are often used for nesting, and hedgerows on farmland. Other areas that host breeding Linnets include scrub and bushes along railway embankments and on golf courses, young conifer plantations and sea buckthorn and *Suaeda* around the coast. Throughout the year, Linnets are dependent on weed seeds, especially those of fat hen and chickweed, gleaned from the ground. These are most readily available after land has been cultivated. The population is under severe pressure from agricultural changes, however, and a rapid decline in the UK since the late 1960s has placed this species firmly on the red list of birds of conservation concern (*BoCC3*).

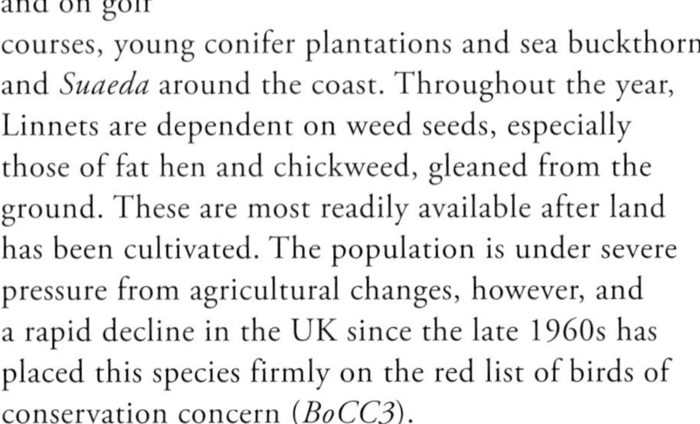

The NBA summer map shows a widespread but rather patchy distribution, with Linnets present in good numbers around the coast and southeast from the A11, but unrecorded from most of Broadland, the Norwich area and from many smaller patches of inland Norfolk. Linnets are often found in flocks of 50 or more well into April, and some of the higher tetrad counts may have been of birds on spring passage.

SUMMER

Small dots 1–3, medium 4–6, large 7–102 ('pairs')
Shading – breeding proved or considered likely

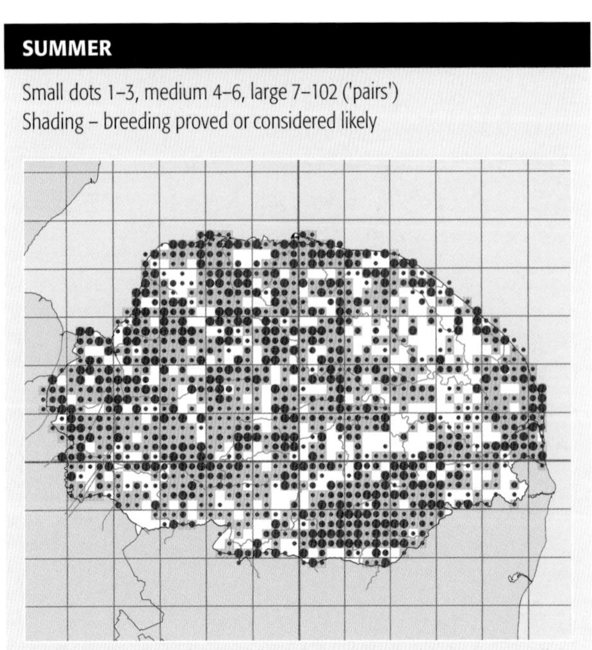

WINTER

Small dots 1–9, medium 10–37, large 38–800 (birds)

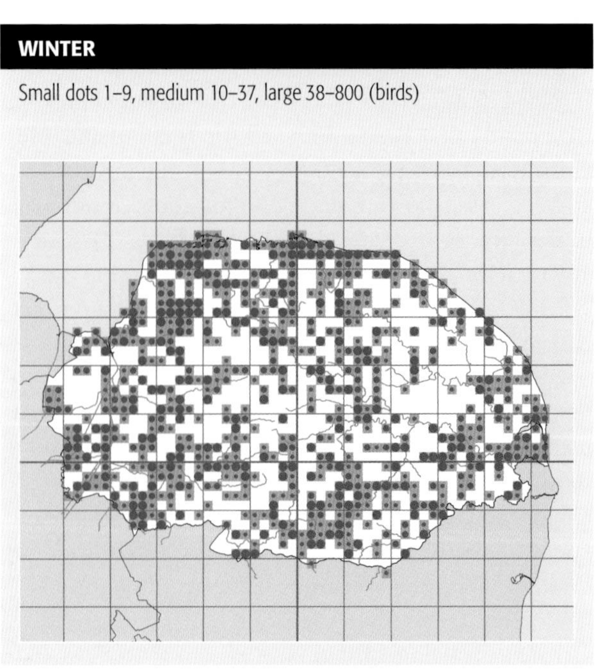

DAVID TIPLING

Linnets are highly gregarious after breeding, gathering into flocks of 200 or more. They often form mixed flocks with other seed-eaters, such as finches and buntings, although each species tends to remain as a separate unit within the larger flock. On farmland, stubble fields and set-aside are favoured locations and, in recent years, harvested oilseed rape fields have attracted the species, as do the seed-bearing plants on coastal saltmarshes and shingle banks.

CHANGE SINCE 1980–85

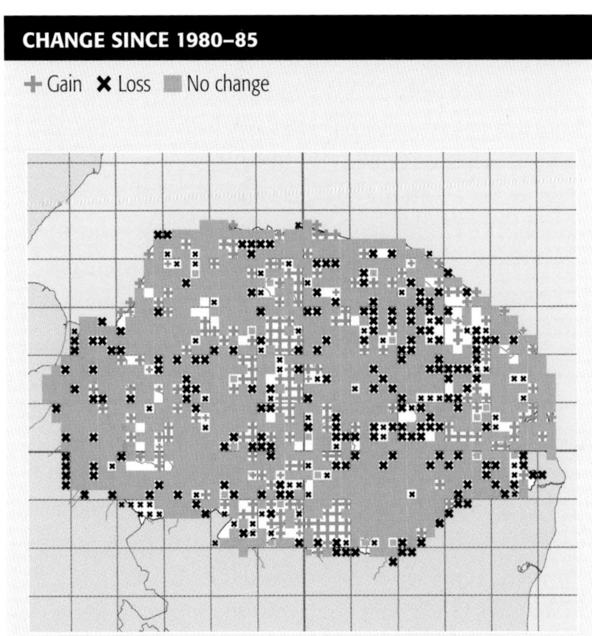

'Throughout the year, Linnets are dependent on weed seeds, especially those of fat hen and chickweed, gleaned from the ground.'

Many Linnets that breed in southeast England migrate south to winter in France or Spain and there is considerable dispersal within Britain and across the North Sea (*Migration Atlas*).

The NBA winter map demonstrates the sparser and more clumped distribution of Linnets at this season, with a notable withdrawal from many inland arable areas. There is a notable cluster of records along the saltmarshes and coastal fields between Wells and Cromer in north Norfolk, with for example a winter flock of 500 in cliff-top fields between Sheringham and Weybourne. The highest count during the NBA winters was of 800 on stubble at Grimston Carr, while flocks of 400 were also reported from Beachamwell and Pensthorpe.

Comparison with the *1980–85 NBBS* shows appreciable loss of breeding range since then. During a similar period, 1982–2007, the breeding population in England is estimated to have fallen by 44% (*Birdtrends*). The change map shows that, although some gaps in the 1980–85 distribution have since been filled, others have enlarged, particularly in Broadland and in other parts of east Norfolk.

Twite
Carduelis flavirostris

NBA 1999–2007	SUMMER: ALL / BREEDING	WINTER
TETRADS OCCUPIED	1 (<1%) / none	41 (3%)
SUMMER/WINTER ONLY	none	40
MEAN PER OCCUPIED TETRAD	35 / none	45
SUMMED MAX COUNTS	35 / none	1,856
POPULATION ESTIMATE	none	250–700

PREVIOUS ATLASES	SQUARES OCCUPIED	1999-2007	LOSSES	GAINS
1981–84 WINTER (10 KM)	14 (23%)	14 (23%)	5	5

THE TWITE IS an upland relative of the Linnet and has an extraordinary world distribution, being found most extensively in the mountains of southern Asia but also in Norway and the Kola Peninsula, northern Britain, and parts of western Ireland.

The species was only an occasional visitor to the county in the 19th century and *Riviere*, writing in 1930, described it as an irregular passage migrant and winter visitor, although he did mention a flock of 300 at Hunstanton. Peak numbers were recorded in Norfolk in the 1970s and 1980s with 500–1,000 at Scolt Head and up to 500 at Titchwell, Wells and Blakeney Point in most winters. Numbers began to decline during the

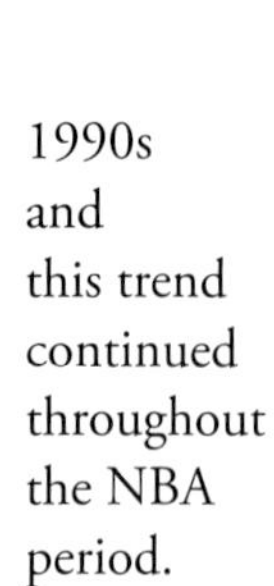

1990s and this trend continued throughout the NBA period.

Ringing has demonstrated that most, if not all Twite that winter in Norfolk are from breeding grounds in northern Britain, especially the south Pennines, and are of the race *pipilans* which is found only in Britain and Ireland (*Migration Atlas*). Norwegian birds, constituting the nominate race, winter mainly in Germany, the Netherlands and Belgium. A marked contraction occurred in the breeding range of the Twite in Britain during the 20th century and this is likely to be the reason for the decline in numbers visiting Norfolk in winter.

The NBA map shows the clear coastal distribution of this species, with most of the birds concentrated in north Norfolk between Holme and Blakeney. Here flocks of Twite gather on the saltmarshes, as well as amongst the sand dunes and on the shingle banks, to feed on the seeds of *Salicornia* and sea-aster. Occasionally Twite are recorded on coastal fields, as were 18 at Happisburgh. Sometimes, single birds or small groups join flocks of Linnets. On being disturbed, however, the two species usually form separate flocks in flight.

During the early NBA winters, there were two areas of northwest Norfolk that regularly held three-figure counts of Twite, but even at these sites the numbers rarely exceeded 50 in the later winters. It is likely that Twite in the Holme to Scolt Head stretch of coastline mainly involved the same roving flocks and these peaked at 230 in the winter of 2000/01, while a maximum of 130 was recorded at Holkham Bay.

Twite have always been less numerous in east Norfolk, although the saltmarshes around Breydon Water regularly held 70–100 up to 1994. Up to 40 were present in 2002/03, but the species was absent from this area for most of the NBA winters. On the Wash, traditionally a very important wintering ground, 270 were counted on Wootton Marsh in December 2004 and 130 the following month, while a flock of 170 was located in the Terrington/Ongar Hill/Lynn

WINTER

Small dots 1–15, medium 16–50, large 51–270 (birds)

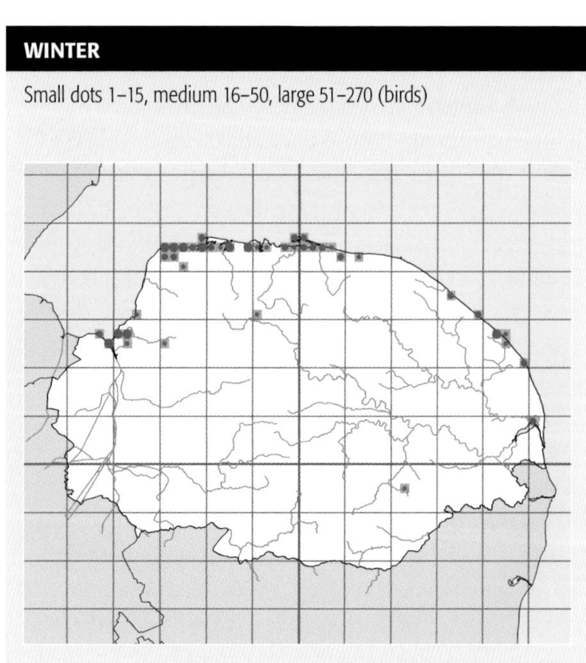

DAVID TIPLING

Point area in the following winter. Large areas of prime Twite habitat around the Wash are normally inaccessible to birdwatchers, or are very remote, so numbers here can easily be underestimated. An unexpectedly high count of 615 birds was made in the Terrington area in December 2006.

Occasional small parties of Twite are recorded inland in Norfolk in most years and, during the NBA winters, these included five in a large mixed finch flock near Sculthorpe, two with Chaffinches near Hillington, and two in south Norfolk at Hempnall.

Twite leave the county for their breeding areas during March and very few normally remain into April. Most unusually, 35 were still present on the saltmarsh at Holme on 4th April 2003, where a male was in full song on 14th April.

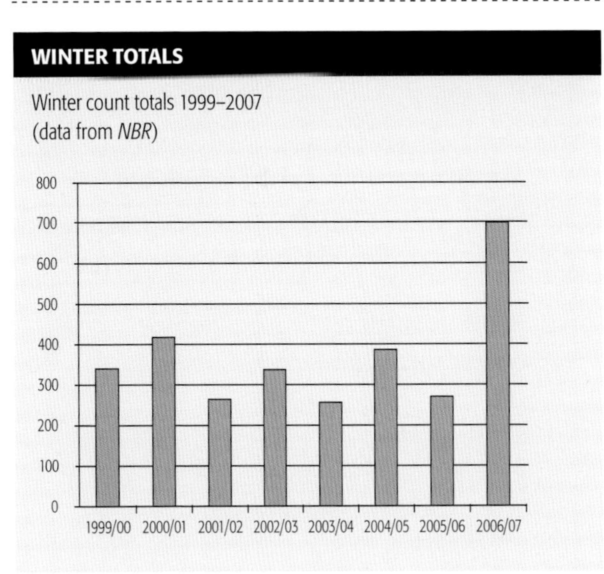

WINTER TOTALS

Winter count totals 1999–2007 (data from *NBR*)

Lesser Redpoll
Carduelis cabaret

NBA 1999–2007	SUMMER: ALL / BREEDING	WINTER
TETRADS OCCUPIED	92 (6%) / 41 (3%)	239 (16%)
SUMMER/WINTER ONLY	46	193
MEAN PER OCCUPIED TETRAD	3 / 4	12
SUMMED MAX COUNTS	277 / 163	2,851
POPULATION ESTIMATE	10–30 bp	2,000–4,000

PREVIOUS ATLASES	SQUARES OCCUPIED	1999–2007	LOSSES	GAINS
1968–72 (10 KM)	61 (98%)	23 (37%)	38	0
1980–85 (TETRAD)	441 (30%)	41 (3%)	421	21
1980–85 (10 KM)	59 (95%)	23 (37%)	36	0
1981–84 WINTER (10 KM)	53 (85%)	51 (82%)	7	5
1988–91 (10 KM)	54 (87%)	23 (37%)	34	3

LESSER REDPOLLS ARE smaller and darker than their northerly circumpolar relative, the Common Redpoll, and occupy a very restricted breeding range between Ireland, the Alps and south Sweden.

Lesser Redpolls frequent heathland, alder carr and young woodland, including conifer plantations, often nesting in small, localised groups. Pairs often range widely from the immediate nesting area in order to exploit suitable food sources. Although they are rather timid birds when breeding, their characteristic hard, mechanical calls, given almost continuously in flight, mean that they are fairly easily located.

For over 100 years, the species has shown marked fluctuations in numbers, with the first noticeable increase being recorded during the first decade of the 20th century. This was followed by a decline and it was only in the 1950s that the population once more began to expand as the establishment of conifer plantations gathered pace. At the same time, birches began to proliferate in the lowland woodlands that had undergone wartime felling during 1939–45. Numbers were at a high level in 1975 but have since collapsed across much of lowland Britain, with no signs so far of any recovery. Woodland succession, reducing the prevalence of birches, may have contributed locally to this change.

The NBA summer map indicates a very sparse and scattered distribution in Norfolk. Many birds mapped, perhaps including most of those in the 41 tetrads where

SUMMER

Small dots 1, medium 2–3, large 4–31 ('pairs')
Shading – breeding proved or considered likely

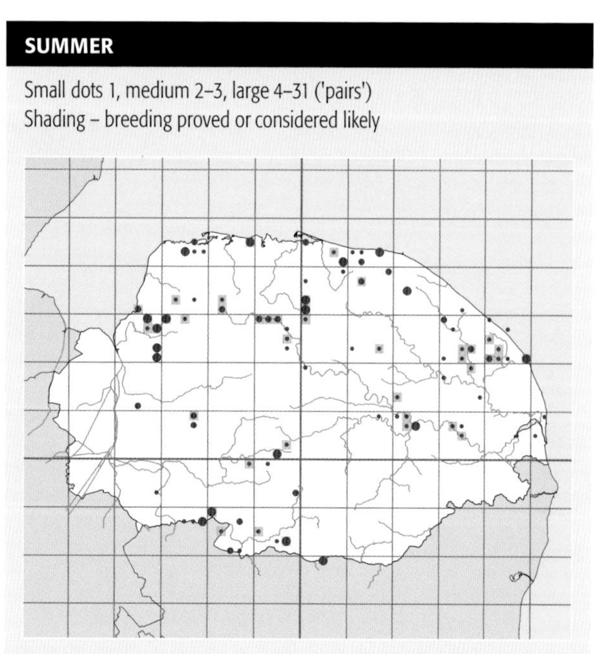

WINTER

Small dots 1–2, medium 3–10, large 11–160 (birds)

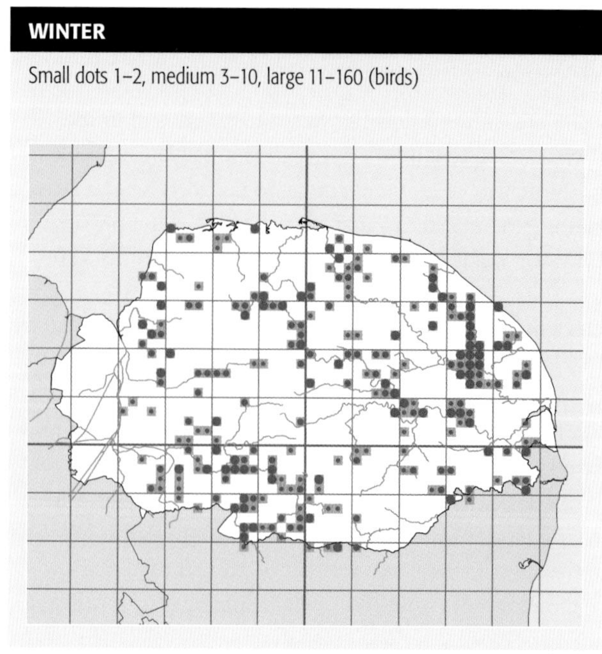

DAVID TIPLING

breeding was recorded as being likely, were late winter visitors or spring migrants. Breeding is exceptionally hard to detect in this species, as in Siskin, but there were no confirmed instances of breeding anywhere in the county in 2006, and only one in 2007. It is clear that Lesser Redpoll was a rare breeding bird in Norfolk throughout the NBA period.

In winter, Lesser Redpolls continue to feed on small seeds, especially those of birch, and later in the winter on alder cones, frequently with flocks of Siskins and Goldfinches. Irregular influxes occur in some winters from nearby continental Europe and from northern Britain. The winter distribution is largely determined by the presence or absence of birch trees (*1981–84 Winter Atlas*).

The NBA winter distribution is far wider than that in summer, with records from 16% of tetrads at that season. The map shows two main areas of concentration, in Breckland and parts of Broadland. Many of the other, smaller clusters of occupied tetrads were associated with birch, for example where young trees were colonising heathland. The largest winter parties recorded were of 160 at Barton Turf, 91 at Croxton, 80 at Stanford Church and 70 at Fulmodeston.

Comparison between the four breeding atlas projects reveals alarmingly how the Norfolk breeding range has contracted during recent decades. In the *1968–72 Atlas*, 61 of Norfolk's 62 10-km squares were occupied, but this fell to 54 by 1988–91 and then sharply to 23 during the NBA summers. These changes have occurred against the background of a 95% decrease of breeding Lesser Redpolls in England as a whole between 1982 and 2007, as measured by CBC and BBS (*Birdtrends*).

CHANGE SINCE 1980–85

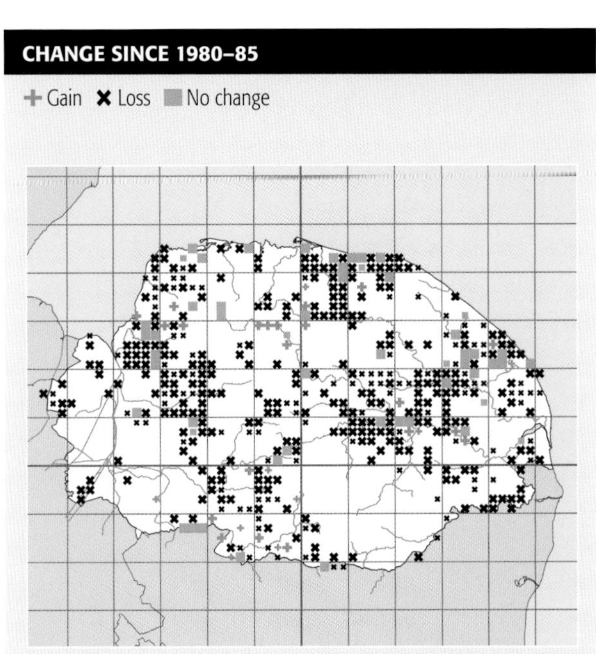

There was a net loss of 400 occupied tetrads between the *1980–85 NBBS* and the NBA summers, as shown on the change map. The concentrations of Lesser Redpolls at that time, between Hunstanton and Breckland, along the Cromer to Holt ridge and in Broadland, have all but disappeared.

Perhaps surprisingly, there was very little difference between the 10-km square distributions in the *1981–84 Winter Atlas* and the NBA winters, even though Norfolk's current wintering population is derived almost entirely from outside the county.

Common Redpoll
Carduelis flammea

NBA 1999–2007	SUMMER: ALL / BREEDING	WINTER
TETRADS OCCUPIED	1 (<1%) / none	36 (2%)
SUMMER/WINTER ONLY	none	35
MEAN PER OCCUPIED TETRAD	1 / none	5
SUMMED MAX COUNTS	1 / none	176
POPULATION ESTIMATE	none	1–65

PREVIOUS ATLASES	SQUARES OCCUPIED	1999-2007	LOSSES	GAINS
1981–84 WINTER (10 KM)	?	22 (35%)	?	?

THE OFFICIAL designation, by the BOU Records Committee, of Common and Lesser Redpolls as separate species dates only from 2001, and there are still many taxonomic uncertainties and unresolved identification problems in the redpoll complex. The Common Redpoll, as now defined, comprises two races that visit Britain: these are the Mealy Redpoll, nominate *flammea*, from Fenno-Scandia and Russia, and the Greenland Redpoll *rostrata*, which arrives in much smaller numbers from Greenland. Norfolk hosts birds of the nominate race in most winters, but in highly variable numbers.

Common Redpolls from Fenno-Scandia normally migrate in autumn in a southeasterly direction towards central Europe, but small numbers appear in Britain in most winters. Occasional larger influxes occur, normally to the east coast, related to the size of the source populations and the local availability of their favourite seeds. The last major influx into Norfolk took place in autumn 1995, when flocks of up to 500 were seen at locations throughout the county and several thousands of birds may have passed through.

The winter map reflects the fact that only small numbers of Common Redpolls were recorded during the NBA winters, from just a few locations around Norfolk. Although Common Redpolls often join flocks of Lesser Redpolls, not all the tetrads in which Common Redpolls were recorded also had records of Lessers. The winters of 2001/02 and 2005/06 were the only ones during the NBA survey in which over 50 Common Redpolls were recorded in the county. The most reliable flock in the earlier winter was at Titchwell, where up to 30 were present from 12th January to 23rd February 2002; a flock of 24 at Holme on 2nd January probably involved the same birds. The only other double-figure counts concerned 25 at Holt Lowes on 18th February 2001, 15 at Brundall Church Fen on 11th January 2002, 25 at West Walton on 9th January 2006 and 27 at Swaffham two days later. No other flock exceeded seven birds during the NBA winters,

WINTER

Small dots 1, medium 2–3, large 4–30 (birds)

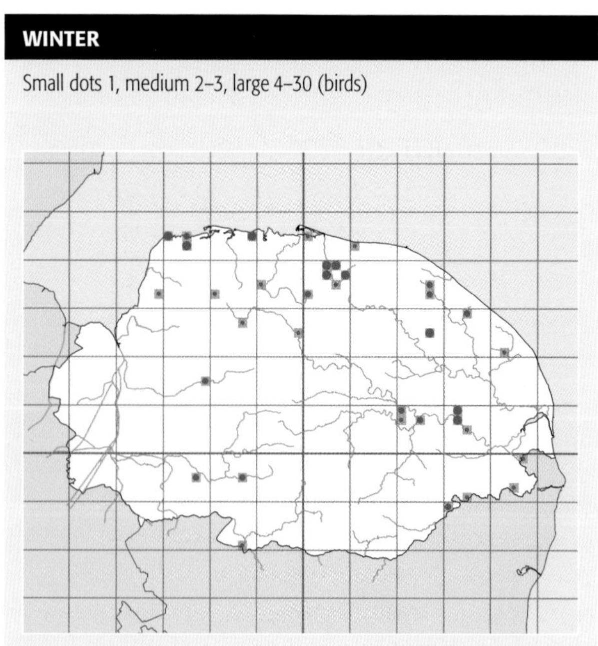

DAVID TIPLING

'Common Redpolls from Fenno-Scandia normally migrate in autumn in a southeasterly direction towards central Europe, but small numbers appear in Britain in most winters.'

although other Common Redpolls were recorded on autumn migration.

There is no valid comparison unfortunately with the *1981–84 Winter Atlas*, birds of the nominate *flammea* race observed during that survey not being recorded separately from Lesser Redpoll, which was at that time treated as conspecific.

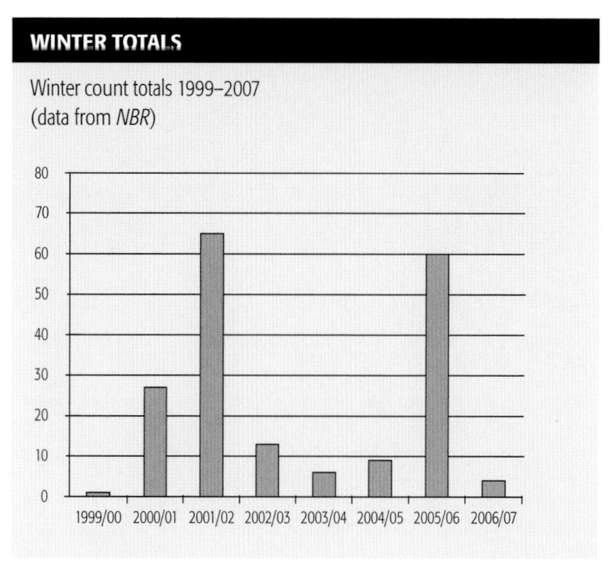

WINTER TOTALS

Winter count totals 1999–2007 (data from *NBR*)

Crossbill
Loxia curvirostra

NBA 1999–2007	SUMMER: ALL / BREEDING	WINTER
TETRADS OCCUPIED	77 (5%) / 29 (2%)	71 (5%)
SUMMER/WINTER ONLY	48	42
MEAN PER OCCUPIED TETRAD	6 / 7	13
SUMMED MAX COUNTS	460 / 202	902
POPULATION ESTIMATE	10–50 bp	100–500

PREVIOUS ATLASES	SQUARES OCCUPIED	1999–2007	LOSSES	GAINS
1968–72 (10 KM)	20 (32%)	13 (21%)	12	5
1980–85 (TETRAD)	49 (3%)	29 (2%)	41	21
1980–85 (10 KM)	18 (29%)	13 (21%)	9	4
1981–84 WINTER (10 KM)	16 (26%)	28 (45%)	1	13
1988–91 (10 KM)	16 (26%)	13 (21%)	9	6

CROSSBILLS ARE ALMOST exclusively associated with conifers, usually Scots pine or spruce. Their taxonomy is complex and controversial, with three species currently accepted as breeding in Britain. Only the Common Crossbill occurs regularly in Norfolk, although Parrot Crossbills nested in Holkham Meals in 1984 and 1985, during the *1980–85 NBBS*.

This species has always been remarkable for the scale of its fluctuations in population. Irregular influxes

from the Continent occur at intervals of a few years, depending on breeding success and on the strength of the conifer seed crop. It was after a major irruption in 1909 that the species was first recorded breeding in East Anglia. Since then, extensive conifer forests such as Thetford Forest have become Norfolk's stronghold for the species. Nevertheless, their occurrence in the county remains remarkably erratic.

Crossbills are gregarious throughout the year, and sometimes breed in loose groups. They are one of the earliest species to nest in Britain, with eggs being laid from late December onwards, although February to April is more usual. Many young have already fledged by the time that breeding-season surveys begin. By mid April, family groups can amalgamate and disperse over a considerable distance, with influxes from northern Europe often beginning in June and including many birds still in streaky juvenile plumage.

The NBA summer map shows a sparse and scattered distribution, representing the post-breeding distribution and not necessarily the localities at which breeding took place. The main concentration of occupied tetrads was,

SUMMER

Small dots 1, medium 2–5, large 6–50 ('pairs')
Shading – breeding proved or considered likely

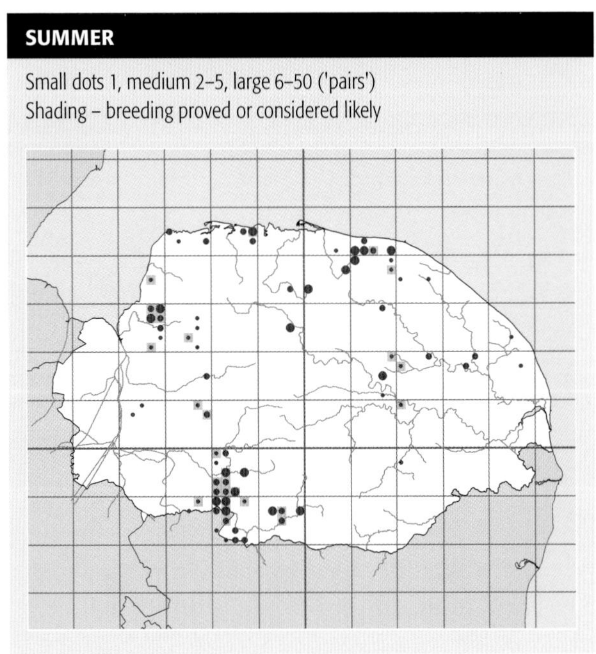

WINTER

Small dots 1–3, medium 4–12, large 13–128 (birds)

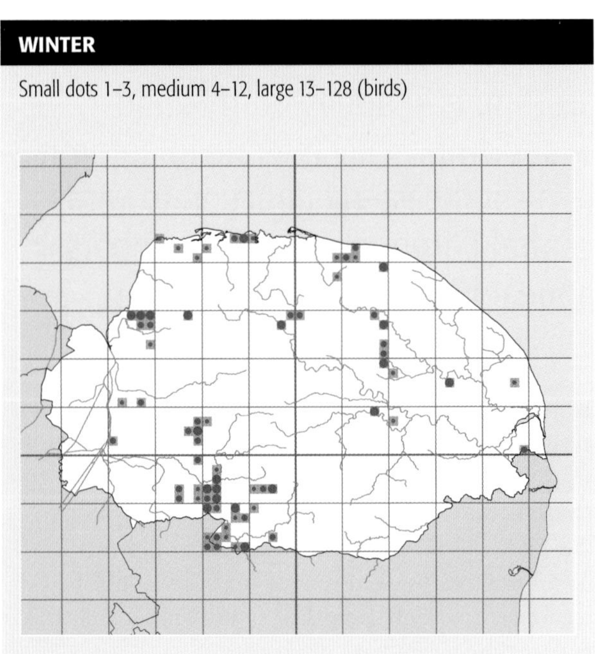

DAVID TIPLING

as expected, in Thetford Forest, with smaller groups around Sandringham, in Holkham Meals, along the Cromer to Holt ridge and in certain established conifer plantations around the outskirts of Norwich. Crossbills occupy mainly the more extensive tracts of conifer forests, but may also be seen in Breckland's Scots pine shelterbelts. The highest counts of Crossbills during the NBA summers were in Thetford Forest, with 100 at Lynford Arboretum and Santon Warren, while 70 were recorded at Swanton Novers.

Surprisingly few records of confirmed, or even suspected, breeding are received each year by the county recorders, but this is certainly due to under-recording. No more than five breeding pairs were reported in any NBA year. Outside the Brecks and the Sandringham area, sites that have held breeding Crossbills have included Holkham Meals, Sheringham, Aylmerton,

CHANGE SINCE 1980–85

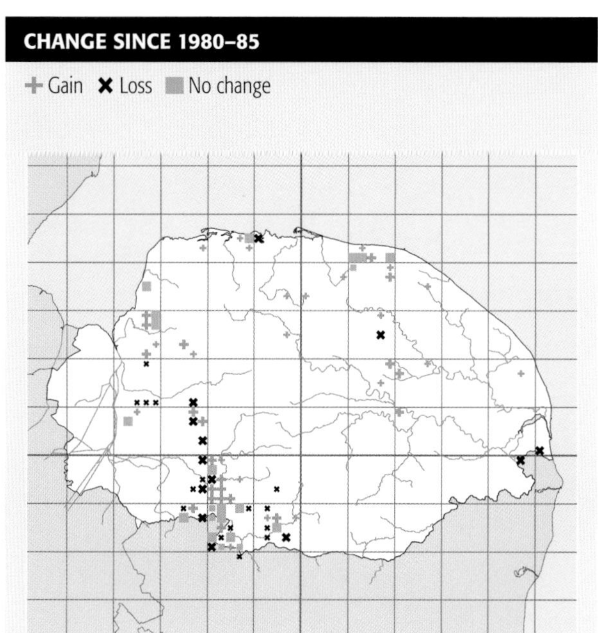

Horsford and Earlham cemetery, Norwich.

A minor Crossbill irruption took place in August/September 2002. Such an event leads to far higher numbers being present in winter and, during January/February 2003, at least 360 were reported in Norfolk, compared with an average reported winter population of about 100 birds or fewer. After an irruption, it is normal for many immigrant Crossbills to remain to nest, but despite the relatively large numbers present in the county between January and August 2003, the county recorders received only three records indicative of breeding that year.

The NBA winter map shows that slightly fewer tetrads were occupied at that season but with a very similar distribution to that in summer. Breckland was again the county's stronghold, with smaller concentrations in the conifer woods around Sandringham, along the north Norfolk coast and at scattered localities in central Norfolk. Numbers in winter are often eclipsed by late summer counts and the largest winter counts during the NBA winters were of 128 at Houghton, 60 at Aylmerton and 50 at Hockham. Arguably, the winter range is a better descriptor of the breeding distribution than that in summer, when the birds are more mobile.

Comparisons with previous atlases indicate a range extension in winter since 1981–84 but a sequential contraction of breeding range from 20 10-km squares in 1968–72 to 13 in the NBA summers. Because numbers fluctuate so widely between years, however, it would be unwise to conclude there was a directional trend at either season.

Crossbills were recorded in more tetrads overall during the NBA summers than in the *1980–85 NBBS*, but a comparison of breeding status is unsafe. Breeding was then confirmed in the Waveney Forest, near Fritton, from where NBA records were received only for the winter period.

Bullfinch
Pyrrhula pyrrhula

NBA 1999–2007	SUMMER: ALL / BREEDING	WINTER
TETRADS OCCUPIED	641 (44%) / 605 (41%)	914 (63%)
SUMMER/WINTER ONLY	92	365
MEAN PER OCCUPIED TETRAD	2 / 2	4
SUMMED MAX COUNTS	1,124 / 1,081	3,673
POPULATION ESTIMATE	1,500–2,000 bp	4,000–5,000

PREVIOUS ATLASES	SQUARES OCCUPIED	1999–2007	LOSSES	GAINS
1968–72 (10 KM)	61 (98%)	59 (95%)	2	0
1980–85 (TETRAD)	864 (59%)	605 (41%)	422	163
1980–85 (10 KM)	59 (95%)	59 (95%)		
1981–84 WINTER (10 KM)	62 (all)	62 (all)		
1988–91 (10 KM)	62 (all)	59 (95%)	3	0

BULLFINCHES ARE FOUND almost throughout the county, but their soft calls and unobtrusive nature can make them easy to overlook. Unlike most small passerines, they remain in pairs throughout the year, sometimes keeping the same partner for successive breeding seasons.

Bullfinches inhabit broadleaved woodland, often being found along edges and rides, and in clearings and glades, and are farmland birds where there is sufficient cover. For nesting, they favour thorn thickets, scrub, tall dense hedgerows, churchyards and large gardens, while old railway cuttings and embankments with unkempt bushes and scrub often hold Bullfinches.

Bullfinches feed mainly on seeds, particularly those of ash, bramble and dock, and on fruits and buds. As seeds and fruits become depleted as winter progresses, they turn their attention to developing buds. They have in the past been subject to shooting and trapping in commercial orchards, mainly in late winter and spring. A strong population decline has been evident across England since the mid 1970s, however (*Birdtrends*), and the perception of the species as a serious pest to fruit growers has consequently faded.

The NBA map shows that the species has a scattered pattern across most of the county, but is generally very thinly distributed, with a mean count of just two pairs

SUMMER

Small dots 1, medium 2, large 3–11 ('pairs')
Shading – breeding proved or considered likely

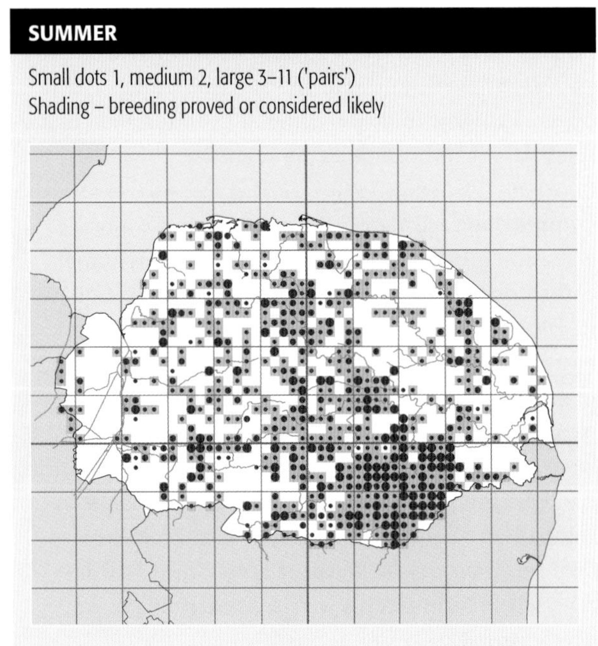

WINTER

Small dots 1–2, medium 3–5, large 6–28 (birds)

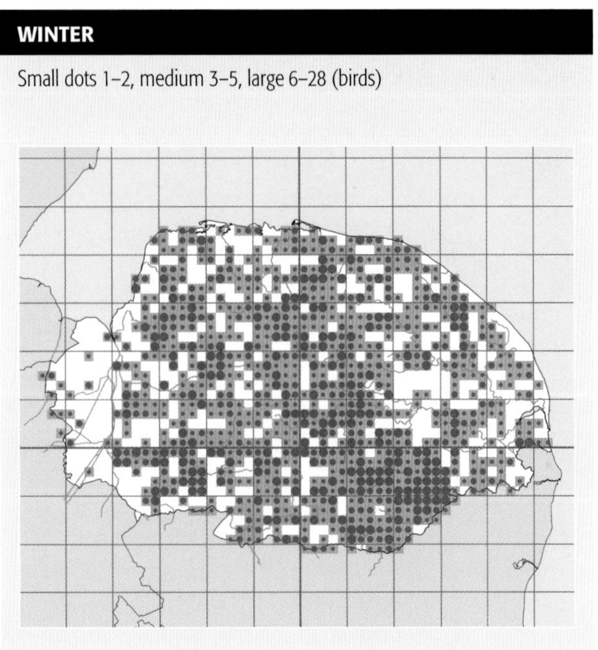

DAVID TIPLING

per tetrad. An unexpected concentration was revealed in southeast Norfolk, where there was a large area of continuous distribution at tetrad level and where many of the higher tetrad counts were located. Bullfinches were absent in summer from much of the Fens, the flat grazing marshes in east Norfolk and much mainly open, arable farmland. The highest numbers of pairs were 11 in tetrads east of Hempnall and near Thompson, and nine at Upton. A count of 14 pairs at Swanton Novers in 2005 represented a major increase there over the previous five years.

CHANGE SINCE 1980–85

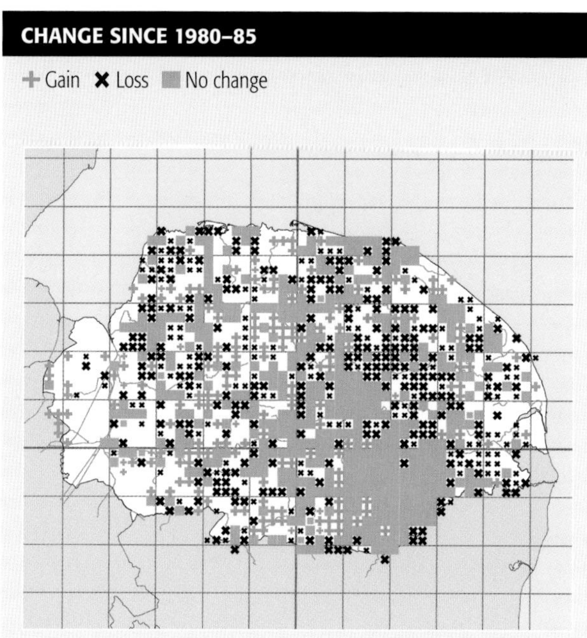

'The change map indicates that losses have been noticeable in all parts of the county except the southeast...'

Bullfinches are often found in small groups in winter, remaining in touch with each other through their distinctive contact notes. They are rather sedentary and rarely move more than a few tens of kilometres. The winter distribution was considerably wider than the summer one, however, although with a similar general distribution. Once again the greatest concentration was in southeast Norfolk and the largest tetrad counts were also there, with 28 at Shelton, 26 at Woodton and 23 east of Hempnall.

Nominate-race northern Bullfinches mounted an unprecedented invasion into Britain in autumn 2004, and up to three birds were reported from a scattering of locations around the county during the subsequent winter, with higher counts of nine near Holt and five at Titchwell.

Comparisons with previous breeding atlases suggest that there has been some fluctuation of the Norfolk breeding range, with a decrease since 1988–91. Since the *1980–85 NBBS*, there has been a net loss of more than 250 occupied tetrads. The change map indicates that losses have been noticeable in all parts of the county except the southeast, where the range has been maintained or even extended.

Hawfinch

Coccothraustes coccothraustes

NBA 1999–2007	SUMMER: ALL/BREEDING	WINTER
TETRADS OCCUPIED	17 (1%) / 2 (<1%)	24 (2%)
SUMMER/WINTER ONLY	11	18
MEAN PER OCCUPIED TETRAD	1 / 1	5
SUMMED MAX COUNTS	21 / 2	113
POPULATION ESTIMATE	0–5 bp	20–50

PREVIOUS ATLASES	SQUARES OCCUPIED	1999–2007	LOSSES	GAINS
1968–72 (10 KM)	24 (39%)	2 (3%)	24	2
1980–85 (TETRAD)	27 (2%)	2 (<1%)	27	2
1980–85 (10 KM)	17 (27%)	2 (3%)	17	2
1981–84 WINTER (10 KM)	10 (16%)	15 (24%)	8	13
1988–91 (10 KM)	13 (21%)	2 (3%)	13	2

DESPITE BEING THE largest of the finches, the Hawfinch is remarkably shy and it is one of the most secretive and enigmatic of Norfolk's birds.

Hawfinches inhabit deciduous woodland, parkland and occasionally large gardens, especially areas containing trees producing the large, hard seeds on which they feed, such as hornbeam, beech, wych elm and cherry. They forage unobtrusively in the tree canopy, and are very wary when feeding on the ground under trees or dense bushes. Their presence is often only detected by hearing their piercing, Robin-like 'tic' contact calls. Because the species is so hard to detect, it will inevitably be under-recorded by any survey.

Not a single Hawfinch was located during any of the almost 3,000 summer set visits that were made for the NBA. All records on the NBA summer map were added to the database as supplementary visits, the majority being obtained via the county bird report. There were just two records of confirmed breeding, at Brettenham Heath in 2006 and by three pairs in the west of the county in 2007, and no more than eight birds were reported in the county in any of the NBA summers. Records near the main winter gatherings at Lynford Arboretum and Thetford may have related to winter visitors remaining into early April, rather than to local breeding. Spring migrants also occurred, presumably returning to breeding sites on the Continent: at Ormesby and Narborough, single Hawfinches were recorded at bird feeders in gardens in May, and another was recorded in an Aylsham garden in late April.

SUMMER

Small dots 1, medium 2, large 3 ('pairs')
Shading – breeding proved or considered likely

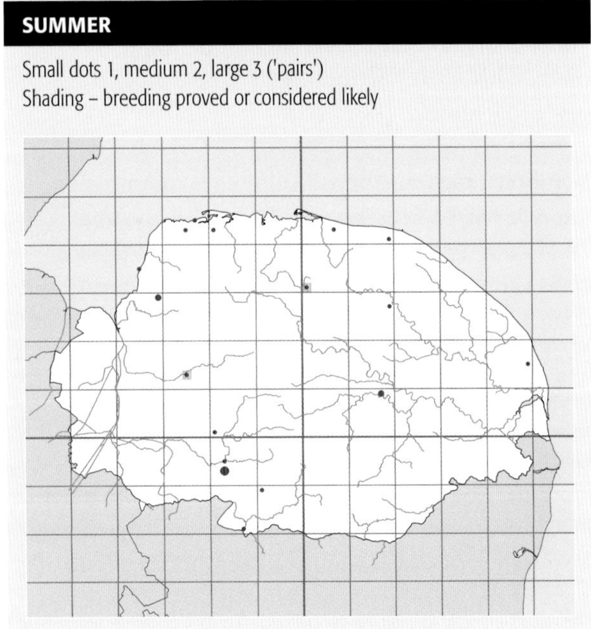

WINTER

Small dots 1, medium 2, large 3–47 (birds)

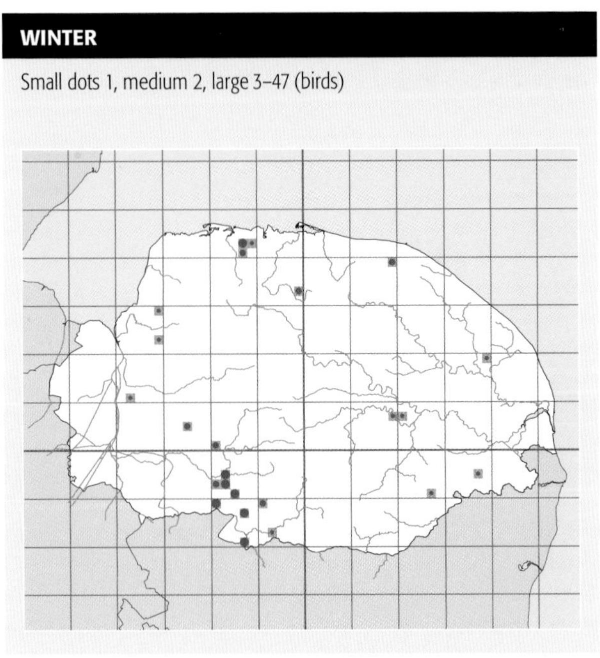

DAVID TIPLING

Hawfinches gather into small flocks outside the breeding season and usually one or two localities in the county host the majority of the wintering birds. Up to the late 1980s, East Wretham Heath was the favoured site, as was Holkham Park up to the mid 1990s.

The NBA winter map shows that, as in the summer, Hawfinches are well scattered at only a few sites, with a concentration in Breckland. Only six 10-km squares in the county hosted the species in both summer and winter. The main gatherings during the NBA winters were at Barnhamcross Common in Thetford, peaking at 17 birds in 2002/03, and at Lynford Arboretum, especially under hornbeams in an adjacent paddock. At the latter site, double-figure counts were made in the winters of 2003/04 and 2004/05, but were overshadowed during 2006/07 as numbers gradually built up to 47 in mid January. This was the highest count in Norfolk for more than 25 years, since 151 Hawfinches roosted at East Wretham Heath in February 1980.

The origin of these Norfolk wintering flocks is unknown. Some may be local breeding birds, but the erratic counts are sometimes much higher than could be accounted for by the local population. No likely sources for winter immigrants are known within Britain. The occasional presence of migrants at coastal sites is a strong indication that they come from the Continent.

CHANGE SINCE 1980–85

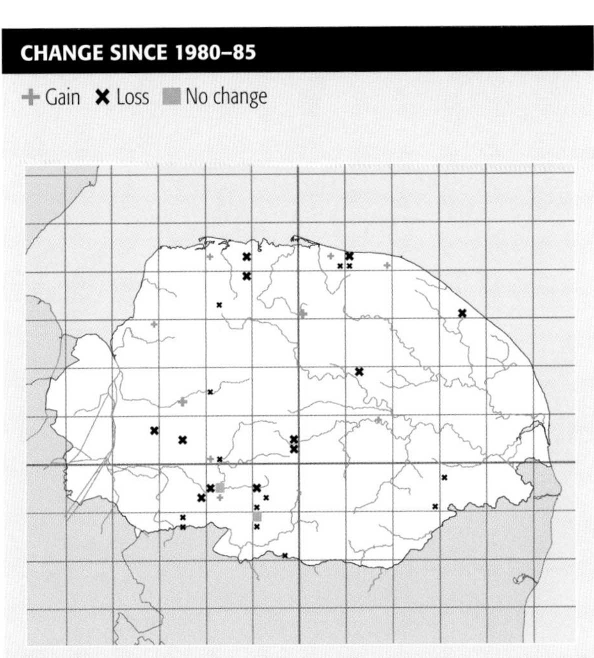

Although always scarce and localised in Britain, erratic fluctuations in its numbers were noted throughout the 20th century. Hawfinch is now a red-listed bird of conservation concern in the UK, having declined steeply during recent decades (*BoCC3*). National atlas data indicate a substantial loss of range since the *1968–72 Atlas*. For Norfolk, comparisons between the atlases indicate a sequential loss of breeding range at the 10-km level, from 24 squares in 1968–72 to 13 in 1988–91 and only two squares during the NBA summers.

During the *1980–85 NBBS*, the distribution was a little more extensive, although breeding was known only from Breckland. Many of the gains and losses shown on the change map refer to chance observations of migrant birds.

Snow Bunting
Plectrophenax nivalis

NBA 1999–2007	SUMMER: ALL/BREEDING	WINTER
TETRADS OCCUPIED	2 (<1%) / none	75 (5%)
SUMMER/WINTER ONLY	1	74
MEAN PER OCCUPIED TETRAD	2 / none	85
SUMMED MAX COUNTS	3 / none	6,370
POPULATION ESTIMATE	none	400–2,000

PREVIOUS ATLASES	SQUARES OCCUPIED	1999-2007	LOSSES	GAINS
1981–84 WINTER (10 KM)	13 (21%)	20 (32%)	1	8

THE HARDY SNOW Bunting is the most northerly breeding passerine in the world. Inland wintering is the norm across the major continents. In England, however, most wintering birds are found around the coast, and Norfolk is one of the most important counties for them.

The number wintering in Britain has always shown great fluctuations, peak numbers occurring for a series of years, followed by a decline for a similar period (*1981–84 Winter Atlas*). Such variability has been noted in Norfolk since at least the 19th century (*Stevenson*). In

DAVID TIPLING

more recent times, high numbers were present in the county during the 1960s, with flocks of over 500, while in the 1990s few parties exceeded 100.

The NBA winter map shows a distinctly coastal distribution, although with a few scattered records inland, some involving substantial numbers of birds. Snow Buntings seek out the seeds on which they feed on shingle and sandy beaches, saltmarshes and sand dunes, foraging along the tideline or amongst low-growing plants, as well as occasionally visiting coastal stubble fields. Although they tend to avoid beaches backed by cliffs, they were recorded during the NBA around most parts of the Norfolk coast. However, the highest concentrations were generally along the flatter stretches of beach.

Some stretches of coast held large numbers of Snow Buntings during each of the NBA winters, and the maximum counts at these sites were as follows: Snettisham 180, Thornham/Titchwell 195, Scolt Head 170, Holkham Bay 200, Blakeney Point/Cley/Salthouse 300 and Caister 450. At the last site 518 were ringed in November/December 2004 and 570, including ringed birds, were trapped during the same two-month period in 2005, having been attracted to the trapping area using grain. Although Snow Buntings often remain in the same general area for much of the winter, they can also be highly mobile. Estimating the wintering population in the county is never easy, but over 1,000 would appear to have wintered annually in Norfolk during the NBA period, except for 2000/01 when there may have been as few as 400.

Away from the beaches and saltmarshes, up to 70 were present regularly on stubble fields to the west of Wells and behind the dunes at Waxham. Other less likely coastal locations to hold Snow Buntings included the esplanade and a car park at Sheringham, the recently seeded cliff-top car park at Cromer, where 152 were found feeding, and a cliff-top garden at Overstrand. Particularly high numbers were recorded inland during 2004/05, a winter in which the county total approached 2,000. Notable counts included up to 120 at Choseley, 150 at Syderstone Common, 80 at Wighton and 50 at East Ruston.

'Although Snow Buntings often remain in the same general area for much of the winter, they can also be highly mobile.'

Comparison with the *1981–84 Winter Atlas* indicates an expansion of the winter range since then. Coverage for NBA was undoubtedly more thorough, and took place over a longer period of years, however, and these factors might have influenced the comparison.

Almost all Norfolk's wintering Snow Buntings have left by the end of March, but occasional migrant birds were recorded during the NBA summer recording period, including two at Scolt Head on 12th April 2000 with one remaining until 18th, and a male in breeding plumage on Winterton beach on 27th May 2004.

WINTER

Small dots 1–40, medium 41–100, large 101–450 (birds)

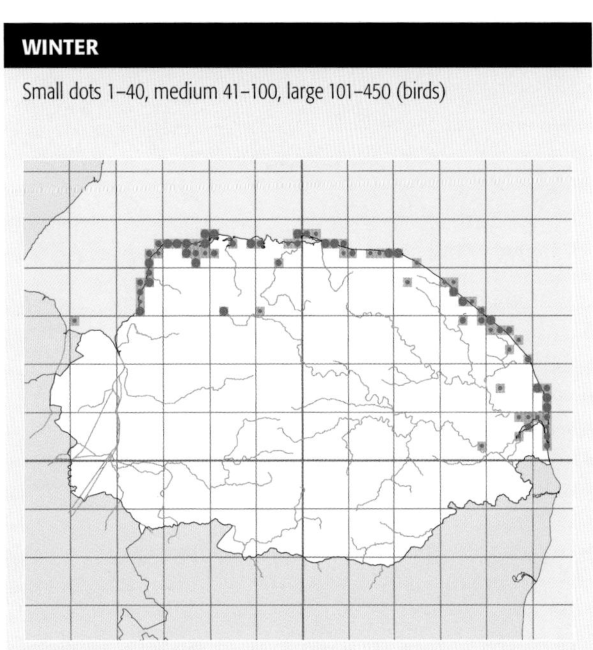

Lapland Bunting
Calcarius lapponicus

NBA 1999–2007	SUMMER: ALL/BREEDING	WINTER
TETRADS OCCUPIED	6 (<1%) / none	47 (3%)
SUMMER/WINTER ONLY	2	43
MEAN PER OCCUPIED TETRAD	2 / none	5
SUMMED MAX COUNTS	14 / none	241
POPULATION ESTIMATE	none	25–100

PREVIOUS ATLASES	SQUARES OCCUPIED	1999-2007	LOSSES	GAINS
1981–84 WINTER (10 KM)	11 (18%)	19 (31%)	2	10

THE COASTAL FIELDS, marshes and beaches of Norfolk are nationally important for Lapland Buntings, of which only a few hundred winter each year in Britain, as visitors from the mountains of Norway and the Russian tundra.

Up to 1892, only five Lapland Buntings had been reported in Norfolk, but in that year over 50 were shot or netted in the county. Since then it has been known as a regular but scarce winter visitor, with generally more recorded on autumn passage than during the winter months. The first arrivals are sometimes in mid September, although the main arrival is generally a month or more later.

Wintering Lapland Buntings frequent the fringes of saltmarshes, coastal grazing marshes and adjoining winter stubble fields, where they are often to be found in the company of Skylarks or finches, and less frequently with Snow Buntings. Lapland Buntings are often very confiding yet, unless the distinctive flight calls are known, they can very easily be overlooked. County wintering totals vary quite widely from year

DAVID TIPLING

to year, with the higher counts occurring after good numbers on autumn passage.

The NBA winter map shows the main distribution to be along the north Norfolk coast, especially between Holme and Stiffkey, with smaller numbers at scattered locations along the northeast coast. Lapland Buntings are usually found singly or in small groups, and during the NBA winters double-figure counts were distinctly unusual. However, up to 54 were present at Holme on 23rd January 2003, all having left by 27th, and up to 46 throughout December of the same year. The only other counts during the NBA that approached these totals were up to 30 on the cliff-top fields at Sheringham during the winter of 2004/05. During the earlier part of the NBA survey, the winter total was always fewer than 30, but in the later years there were up to 100 birds each winter.

WINTER

Small dots 1–2, medium 3–9, large 10–31 (birds)

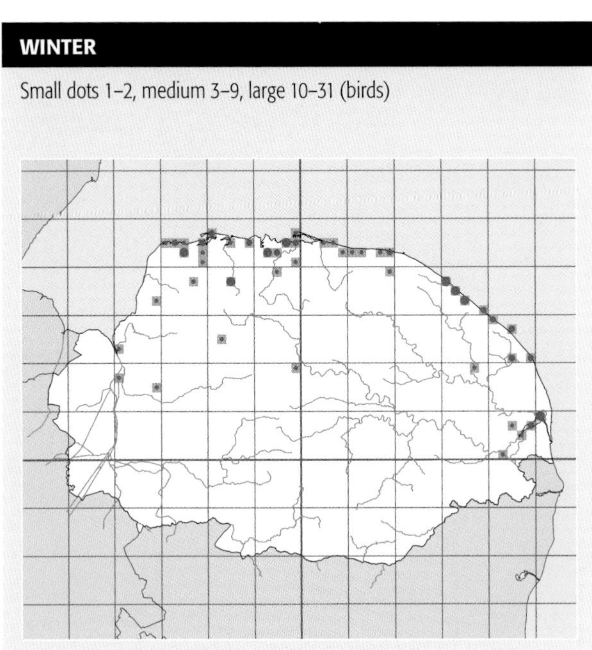

'Lapland Buntings are often very confiding yet, unless the distinctive flight calls are known, they can be very easily overlooked.'

The species is strongly associated with the coast, yet several inland localities hosted the species during the NBA winters. Most inland birds were found on stubble fields, where the birds' habit of running along the furrows, rather than flushing, at the approach of an observer made them particularly difficult to see. Up to 18 were present at Choseley but elsewhere inland only one or two birds were involved. Regular wintering has occurred on the Breydon Water and Halvergate Marshes since 1960, but numbers have fallen since the rough marshes were converted to arable use in the 1980s, and during the NBA winters no more than 12 were recorded there.

Comparison with the *1981–84 Winter Atlas* indicates an expansion of the winter range since then, although to some extent this may be an artefact. Coverage for NBA was more thorough and took place over a longer period of years; these factors are likely to be more important for a species that is hard to find, and one that is mobile between winters.

Lapland Buntings were recorded a little more often during the NBA summer period than Snow Buntings, including a male in breeding plumage that was singing at Weybourne on 23rd–26th April 2003, and a male at Blakeney Point as late as 11th May 2003. Such birds are more likely to be migrants from further south than birds that wintered in Norfolk, most of which have already departed during March.

Yellowhammer
Emberiza citrinella

NBA 1999–2007	SUMMER: ALL / BREEDING	WINTER
TETRADS OCCUPIED	1,206 (83%) / 1,186 (81%)	1,088 (75%)
SUMMER/WINTER ONLY	190	72
MEAN PER OCCUPIED TETRAD	7 / 7	21
SUMMED MAX COUNTS	8,495 / 8,462	22,924
POPULATION ESTIMATE	10,000–15,000 bp	25,000–35,000

PREVIOUS ATLASES	SQUARES OCCUPIED	1999–2007	LOSSES	GAINS
1968–72 (10 KM)	62 (all)	62 (all)		
1980–85 (TETRAD)	1,289 (88%)	1,186 (81%)	172	69
1980–85 (10 KM)	62 (all)	62 (all)		
1981–84 WINTER (10 KM)	62 (all)	62 (all)		
1988–91 (10 KM)	62 (all)	62 (all)		

THE YELLOWHAMMER is by far the most abundant British bunting, but its population is under severe pressure from agricultural and climatic change and it is becoming scarcer and more restricted as a Norfolk bird.

Yellowhammers are characteristic birds of the kinds of open country that Norfolk provides, especially heathland, commons and farmland hedgerows. They are also found along woodland edges, in young forestry plantations and on railway embankments. During the summer, males are easily located as they deliver their familiar song from the top of a bush or hedge.

The NBA summer map shows that Yellowhammers are well distributed throughout the county, although they are largely absent from the marshes inland from Breydon Water and along the lower Yare and Waveney valleys, from the most open parts of the Fens and from urban Norwich. They are also missing from many parts of the coastal fringe. Of the five tetrads in the county that held 30 or more breeding pairs during the NBA summers, four were in southeast Norfolk, with maximum counts of 39 pairs at North Lopham and 38 each at Hempnall and Forncett; in 2001, 45 singing males were counted around the village of Long Stratton, nearby. NBA figures indicate that, despite decline, the county breeding population probably still numbered more than 10,000 pairs.

In winter, Yellowhammers gather into loose flocks to feed on cereal grain and grass seeds, which they glean from stubble fields, weedy margins and waste ground, often in association with Chaffinches and smaller numbers of Reed Buntings. They are uncommon

SUMMER

Small dots 1–4, medium 5–8, large 9–39 ('pairs')
Shading – breeding proved or considered likely

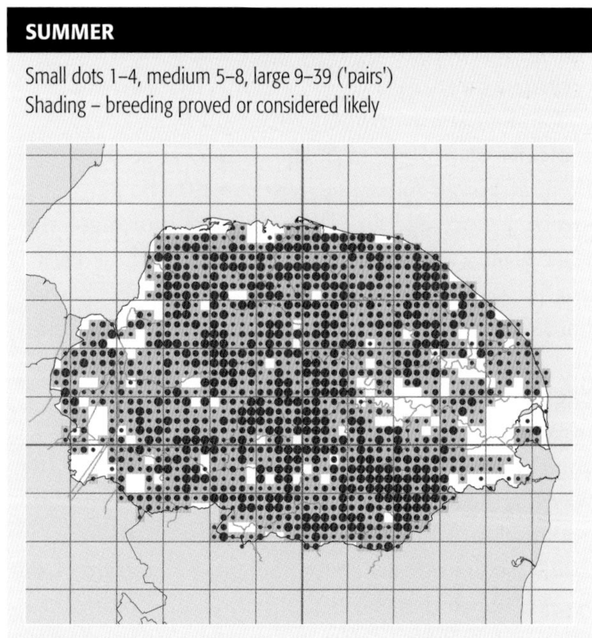

WINTER

Small dots 1–5, medium 6–19, large 20–485 (birds)

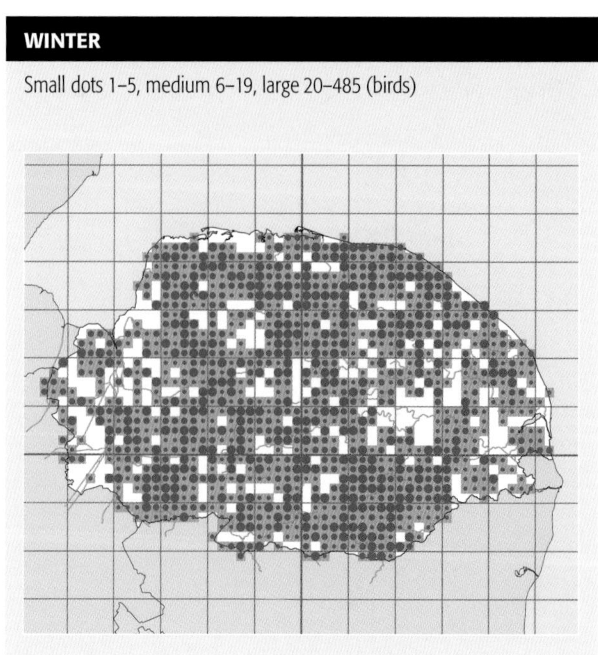

DAVID TIPLING

visitors to gardens, even those in rural settings. Most Yellowhammers appear to be sedentary, occupying similar areas in summer and winter, but ranging more widely in search of food during the winter months.

The NBA winter map shows a very similar distribution to that in summer, although with fewer tetrads occupied. Some additional tetrads, such as on the marshes around Halvergate and the lower Waveney, hosted small numbers during the winter. On the other hand, there were many breeding tetrads that did not hold a winter flock.

'Most Yellowhammers appear to be sedentary, occupying similar areas in summer and winter, but ranging more widely in search of food during the winter months.'

CHANGE SINCE 1980–85

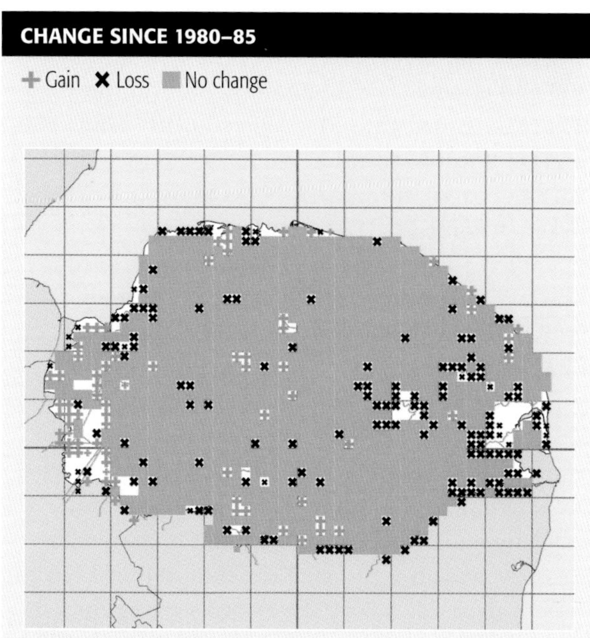

Most winter flocks of Yellowhammers held fewer than 50 birds. At Clenchwarton, 485 birds were found feeding along a strip of set-aside and other counts exceeding 400 were made during the NBA winters at Forncett (445) and North Pickenham (417 on wheat stubble). Flocks of 100–200 were also reported in strips of game cover, especially maize, and on recently ploughed fields.

Comparison with previous atlases shows no change from full occupancy at 10-km level. There has been some net loss at tetrad level since the *1980–85 NBBS*, however. The change map shows that there have been many losses around the fringes of the county and that the previous gaps in distribution around Norwich, the Breydon Water area and King's Lynn have all expanded. To a limited extent, losses have been offset by a range gain in Fenland. During a similar period, 1982–2007, the population in England fell by 57% (*Birdtrends*).

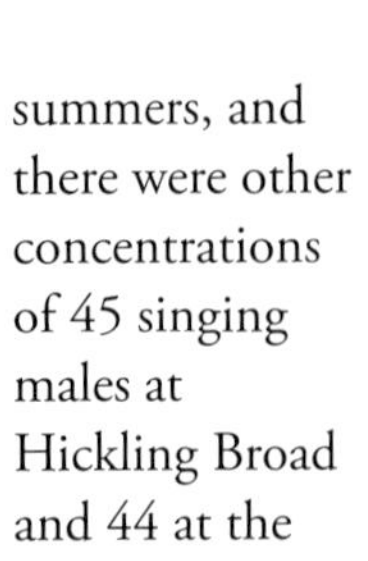

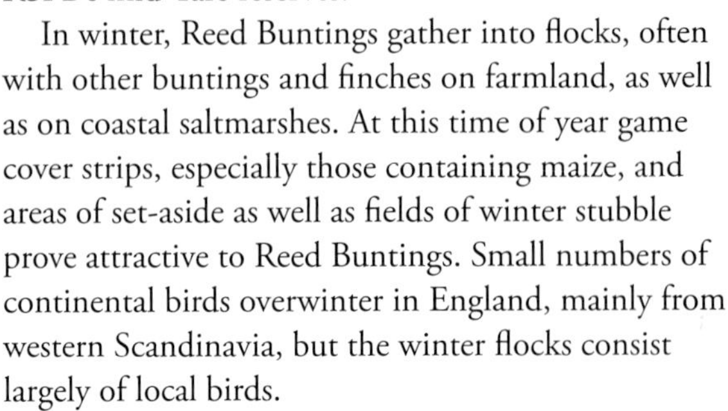

Reed Bunting

Emberiza schoeniclus

NBA 1999–2007	SUMMER: ALL/BREEDING	WINTER
TETRADS OCCUPIED	553 (38%) / 497 (34%)	552 (38%)
SUMMER/WINTER ONLY	214	213
MEAN PER OCCUPIED TETRAD	4 / 5	8
SUMMED MAX COUNTS	2,391 / 2,326	4,304
POPULATION ESTIMATE	2,500–4,500 bp	7,000–10,000

PREVIOUS ATLASES	SQUARES OCCUPIED	1999–2007	LOSSES	GAINS
1968–72 (10 KM)	62 (all)	58 (94%)	4	0
1980–85 (TETRAD)	475 (33%)	497 (34%)	178	200
1980–85 (10 KM)	57 (92%)	58 (94%)	2	3
1981–84 WINTER (10 KM)	55 (89%)	61 (98%)	0	6
1988–91 (10 KM)	57 (92%)	58 (94%)	2	3

REED BUNTINGS are commonly encountered in Norfolk's many reedbeds, as coastal migrants, or on farmland, but their distribution has always been very patchy.

Traditionally, Reed Buntings have been associated with waterways and marshy areas, breeding in reedbeds, along marshland dykes and rivers, in the scrub around old gravel workings and on the saltwater marshes around the coast. In addition, pairs can be found on marginal land on farms, and in young conifer plantations. Increasingly since the 1960s, birds have been nesting in drier habitats on farmland, being particularly attracted to fields of oilseed rape.

The NBA summer map shows a remarkably sharp-edged pattern of distribution. There is a broad distribution across Fenland, a complete coastal distribution between the cliffs at Hunstanton and at Weybourne, and solid occupation across Broadland wetlands. Away from these areas, there is a clear association with Norfolk's river systems, as there is in Broadland, although a few squares were occupied away from the rivers, even on the higher parts of the main watershed.

The highest number of breeding pairs in a single tetrad was 59 at Lopham Fen, although at Scolt Head a maximum of 88 singing males was located in 2005 on the reserve as a whole. Nearby, 31 pairs were counted at Burnham Overy Staithe, while 33 pairs were found in another tetrad at Saddlebow, in the Fens. Holkham NNR held a maximum of 58 pairs during the NBA summers, and there were other concentrations of 45 singing males at Hickling Broad and 44 at the RSPB's mid-Yare reserves.

In winter, Reed Buntings gather into flocks, often with other buntings and finches on farmland, as well as on coastal saltmarshes. At this time of year game cover strips, especially those containing maize, and areas of set-aside as well as fields of winter stubble prove attractive to Reed Buntings. Small numbers of continental birds overwinter in England, mainly from western Scandinavia, but the winter flocks consist largely of local birds.

Although just as many tetrads were occupied in winter as in summer, there was a very substantial turnover of occupied tetrads between seasons and the NBA winter map looks rather different from the summer one. The three main areas of distribution, in the Fens, the Broads and the north coast are the same, but the distribution across the rest of the county is broader and includes more tetrads away from the rivers.

While winter flocks usually number fewer than 50 birds, tetrad counts in excess of 90 were made at Hilgay (150), Runcton Holme (142), Hilborough (97) and Cranwich (93), all in the west of the county. In Broadland, Martham regularly holds 100 or more Reed Buntings in winter, as do the north Norfolk coastal saltmarshes between Scolt Head and Blakeney Point.

Since the 1980s, increasing numbers of Reed Buntings have been visiting gardens in winter, particularly in Broadland. In the Hickling area, it has become difficult to find Reed Buntings on arable land in winter due to the absence of stubble and general lack of weed seeds, and the birds are tending to commute between their wetland roosts and daytime feeding sites in the gardens of Potter Heigham and Hickling. One garden in particular regularly attracts up to 30 Reed Buntings at a feeding station, the birds having developed a liking for a particular seed mix containing the small seeds of

DAVID TIPLING

'Since the 1980s, increasing numbers of Reed Buntings have been visiting gardens in winter, particularly in Broadland.'

various grasses and other plants, including millet, which few other birds eat (Hampshire 2003).

Occupancy at 10-km level was recorded as complete in the *1968–72 Atlas*, but not subsequently, the NBA figure being 94%. Winter occupancy of 10-km squares has risen since 1981–84 from 89% to 98%. At tetrad level, the overall pattern of the NBA summer map is similar to that recorded during the *1980–85 NBBS*, although the proportion of occupied tetrads has increased. The change map shows particular range gains in Fenland and in the Tas valley. The *1980–85 NBBS* observed that the Norfolk breeding ranges of Reed Bunting and Sedge Warbler were very similar; the match is less clear in the NBA, owing to the expansion of Reed Buntings into arable fields, especially in the Fens.

SUMMER

Small dots 1, medium 2–4, large 5–59 ('pairs')
Shading – breeding proved or considered likely

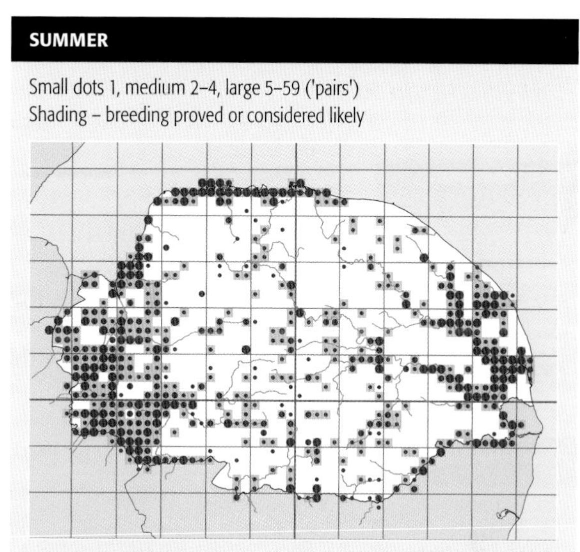

WINTER

Small dots 1–2, medium 3–6, large 7–150 (birds)

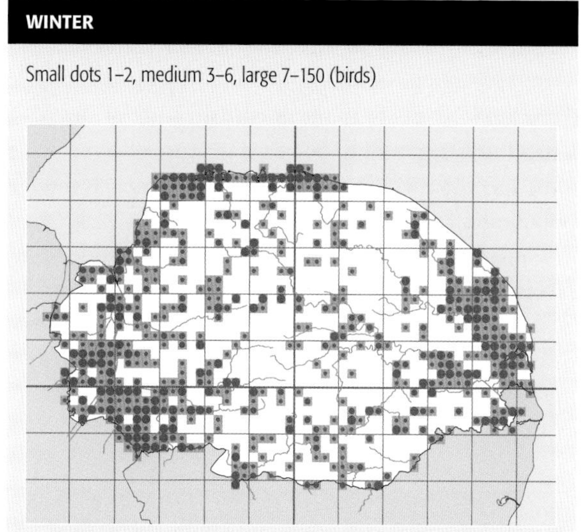

CHANGE SINCE 1980–85

+ Gain ✖ Loss ■ No change

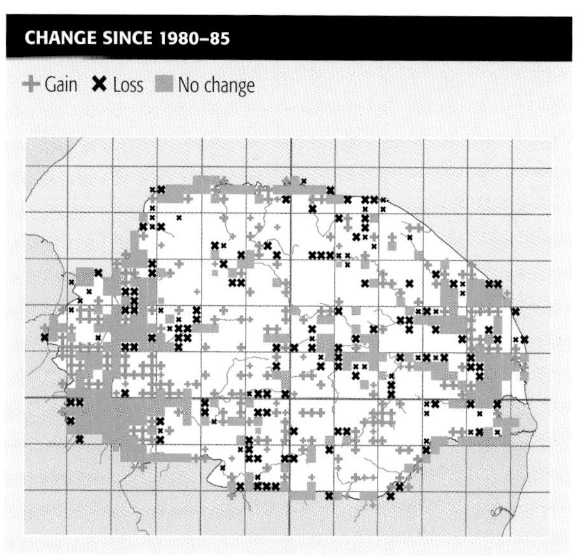

Corn Bunting
Emberiza calandra

NBA 1999–2007	SUMMER: ALL/BREEDING	WINTER
TETRADS OCCUPIED	99 (7%) / 80 (5%)	68 (5%)
SUMMER/WINTER ONLY	59	28
MEAN PER OCCUPIED TETRAD	3 / 4	25
SUMMED MAX COUNTS	324 / 303	1,697
POPULATION ESTIMATE	150–200 bp	400–700

PREVIOUS ATLASES	SQUARES OCCUPIED	1999–2007	LOSSES	GAINS
1968–72 (10 KM)	36 (58%)	19 (31%)	20	3
1980–85 (TETRAD)	117 (8%)	80 (5%)	86	49
1980–85 (10 KM)	32 (52%)	19 (31%)	16	3
1981–84 WINTER (10 KM)	23 (37%)	23 (37%)	9	9
1988–91 (10 KM)	29 (47%)	19 (31%)	14	4

THE DISTINCTIVE but discordant song of the Corn Bunting is still to be heard in parts of Norfolk, although at a dwindling number of locations as the UK population falls.

Corn Buntings are birds of open countryside, favouring cereal-growing areas with few hedges. Males, which are often polygamous, use bushes, fences or cables as song-posts, as well as singing from low perches or the ground. In a study site in northeast

Essex, there was little preference shown for any particular crops or other land uses during the breeding season (Mason & Macdonald 2000); some birds showed strong territory fidelity between years, and sites with water-filled ditches or weedy farm tracks were preferred.

This has been one of the most strongly declining birds on British farmland, having entered a steep decline in the early 1970s (*Birdtrends*). In England, the population fell by 81% in the period 1982–2007 alone. It is considered that the reduction in the availability of winter food, through loss of winter stubbles and the lack of weed seeds, owing to herbicide usage on the remaining stubbles, has been the most serious factor affecting Corn Bunting populations (Donald & Evans 1994).

The NBA summer map shows a very limited and fragmented distribution within the county, with a large group of occupied tetrads in southwest Norfolk, particularly the higher sections of the Fens, and a smaller cluster in the northwest, in the Choseley/Ringstead area. Breeding was also thought likely in a few scattered tetrads between Morston and Breydon Water around the

SUMMER

Small dots 1, medium 2–3, large 4–35 ('pairs')
Shading – breeding proved or considered likely

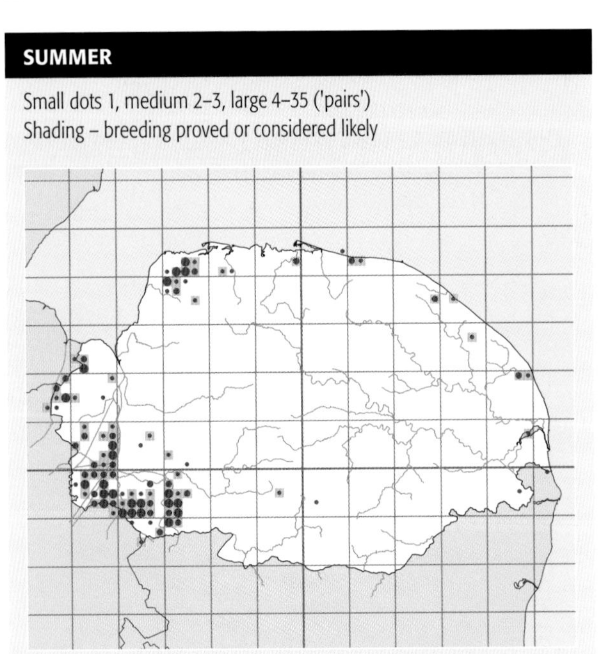

WINTER

Small dots 1–4, medium 5–23, large 24–150 (birds)

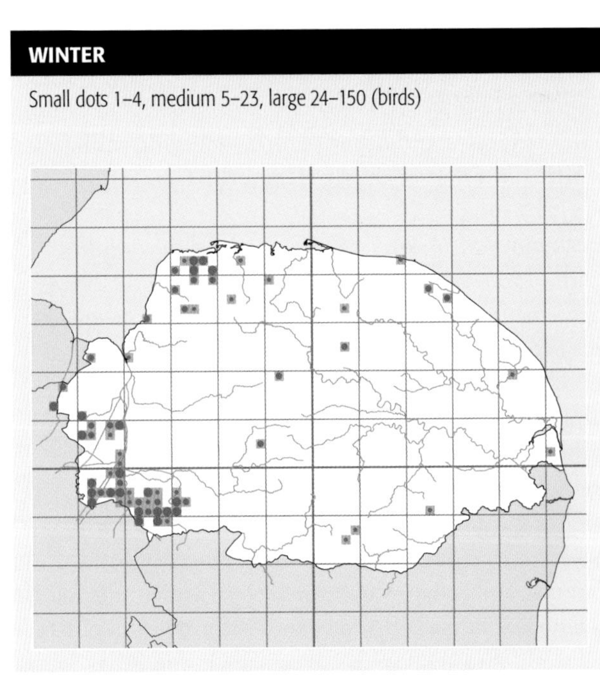

DAVID TIPLING

coastal zone, and at a single tetrad at Stow Bedon. Males return to the breeding territories as early as January and during the summer sing persistently throughout the day. The species is a late breeder, however, with nesting activity peaking in July. Females often remain in their winter flocks until April or May (*1968–72 Atlas*) and thus the spring and early summer counts include late-dispersing flocks as well as breeding birds.

CHANGE SINCE 1980–85

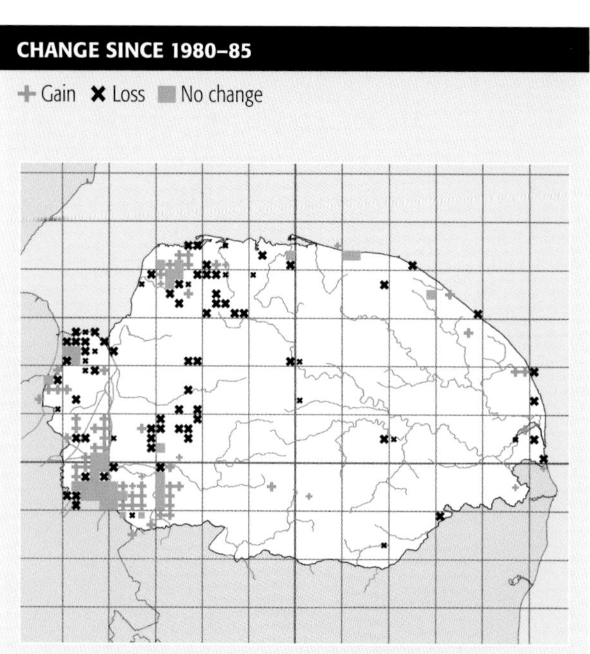

Corn Buntings are highly gregarious outside the breeding season but, as the flocks tend to roam around quite widely, they are not always easy to locate. Many Corn Buntings feed on stubble fields in winter, seeking out weed seeds; a flock of 70 in the Fens was found feeding on seeding weeds in an arable field that had been abandoned and allowed to go wild.

The NBA winter map shows a similar pattern to that in the summer, but the occupied tetrads are fewer and more localised; significant counts were made in a few squares well away from the summer distribution. Tetrads at Choseley and at Brandon Bank held 150 Corn Buntings in winter, while 90 were found at Hilgay. However, these counts are well down on some made in the 1990s, when 341 were at Denver Sluice in 1991 and 309 at Welney in 1997. Corn Buntings roost communally in winter, typically in reedbeds, but no roosting groups were reported during the NBA winters.

Comparison with the previous atlases shows an accelerating rate of loss of summer occupancy at the 10-km scale, from 36 squares occupied in 1968–72 to 32 in 1980–85, 29 in 1988–91 and just 19 during the NBA summers. At tetrad level, there has been a 32% reduction in the number of occupied tetrads between the *1980–85 NBBS* and the NBA. The change map shows that the two current areas of main distribution were then less clearly separated and that patches of former breeding on Terrington Marsh, southeast of Docking and west of Swaffham have been lost, although with gains in some parts of southern Fenland.

CHAPTER 3

DAVID TIPLING

Additional species recorded

IN ADDITION TO THE SPECIES ALREADY reported in detail in the main taxonomic section of this book, there were a large number of further species recorded during the NBA's eight summer and winter periods for which we did not consider a full species text to be warranted. Each of these is tabulated below, with a summary of its occurrence in the NBA period, and for selected species there is also a brief discussion of the NBA data and any changes noted since previous atlases.

The species are dealt with under two major headings. The first section (3.1) covers species on BOU's official *British List* as naturally occurring visitors, or as long-standing introductions that are now fully established and self-supporting (BOU categories A–C), and a much shorter second section (3.2) relates to species occurring in Britain solely as escapes or as non-established introductions (BOU categories D–E). Each section comprises a comprehensive table, including all the species recorded, and accompanying texts for a subset of species.

These two groups of species overlap broadly, however. Partly this is because the BOU categories refer to Britain as a whole, whereas a different status may apply at county level. Also, there are many Norfolk records of category A–C species that are known or suspected to refer to individuals that have escaped or been released. We have resolved these difficulties by including species that occur both as wild and suspect individuals in Table 3.1, marking their name with an asterisk, and by relegating Hooded Merganser, which has records of wild vagrants in Britain but not in Norfolk, to Table 3.2. Section 3.1 thus deals only with species that are on the Norfolk List, with all other species relegated to section 3.2.

3.1 Additional species on the Norfolk List

The species that are commonest in Norfolk during the April–June and December–February periods all have their own pages in the main systematic list. All additional species on the Norfolk List that were recorded during the NBA period are listed in Table 3.1. These include some species that neither breed nor spend the winter in Norfolk, but occur solely as passage migrants. National and local breeding atlas projects have generally excluded passage migrants, in the past: NBA has included them in its data collection, as has *Atlas 2007–11*, on the basis that these are species whose distribution as grounded migrants needs better documentation. For some migrant species, however, not every *NBR* record has found its way into the NBA database.

This book does not record every migrant species that occurred during 1999–2007. Many further species were recorded in Norfolk in these years during March or during the autumn months July–November, but were not recorded during the NBA summer and winter recording periods. Details of these can be found in the *NBR* or in the national reports on rarities.

Table 3.1 provides a cross-tabulation of species and their occurrence in the 16 summer and winter NBA periods. For species marked with an asterisk, some records, or for some species all records, are likely to have been of individuals that were not truly wild. Dots or numbers in the cells of Table 3.1 indicate presence during each NBA season and an empty cell indicates that no record was received: numbers are the numbers of individuals recorded, according to the database. The total numbers of tetrads with records in the NBA database are also given, where known, for winter and summer; dots indicate that NBA cannot provide a valid figure, and blank cells that the species did not occur at that season. The order of species and the scientific names that are used are those currently recommended by BOU.

Lesser White-fronted Goose*
Anser erythropus

LESSER WHITE-FRONTED GEESE have historically been rare winter vagrants to Britain and, from the mid 1950s to the late 1960s, the species was recorded almost annually in Norfolk, especially in the Yare valley. Since then, however, the Fenno-Scandian breeding population has declined almost to extinction and sightings of genuinely wild birds in Norfolk have virtually ceased.

A few individuals were recorded during each of the NBA winters, including both adult and immature birds, but all were likely to have been escapes from captivity rather than genuinely wild vagrants. NBA records were received from five tetrads in winter and one in summer. The only previous atlas records were from three 10-km squares in the *1981–84 Winter Atlas*.

Snow Goose*
Anser caerulescens

INTRODUCED SNOW GEESE bred ferally in Norfolk at several locations during the 1990s, including groups of a dozen or so white-morph birds at Sandringham and in the Holkham area, but were poorly reported by birdwatchers at the time. Although no breeding was noted in the county during the NBA years, a few birds continued to spend the summer in Norfolk.

WINTER – Snow Goose

Small dots 1, medium 2, large 3–18 (birds)

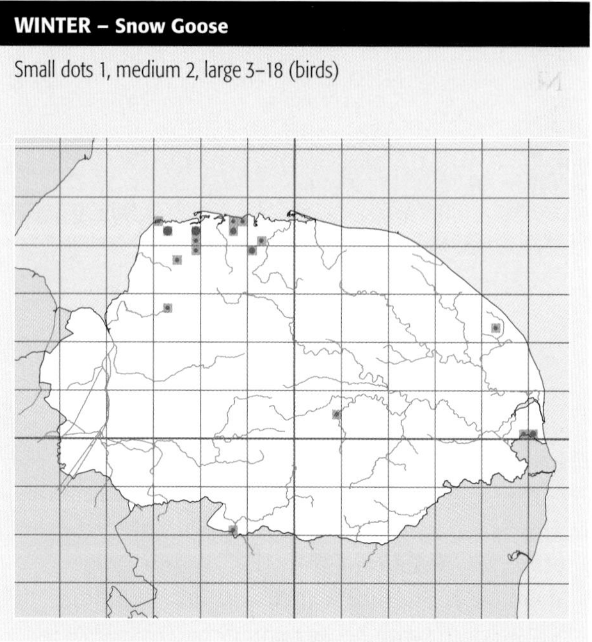

Since the demise of the breeding colonies, it has become increasingly likely that birds seen in winter are winter immigrants, perhaps originating from the native breeding grounds in Canada or northwest Greenland. Native North American populations have increased rapidly in recent years.

Undisputed immigrants were recorded during the 2004/05 and 2006/07 winters. A first-winter bird was found at Holkham GM in January 2005 and remained in northwest Norfolk with the Pink-footed Geese until 3rd May, when it flew off north, flying past

*Species marked with an asterisk occur in the county as wild birds and as escapes or non-established introductions.

four Yorkshire coastal sites with 60 Pinkfeet and past Tyneside in the evening. In October 2006 an adult white morph and an adult blue morph arrived separately at Holkham with Pink-footed Geese, the white morph having been seen flying south over Spurn Point and then Mablethorpe in Lincolnshire earlier in the day. They both remained in the large flocks of Pinkfeet in northwest Norfolk until January 2007, often being seen together.

Whether winter immigrants were hatched in the native range is another question. It is entirely possible that some escapes, or the progeny from feral populations, now accompany the wild flocks north to the Arctic for the summer and occur in Britain as winter immigrants. Birds in first-winter plumage are now the ones most likely to be truly wild.

Because the goose flocks are so mobile, a small handful of individual birds has given rise to records in 17 winter tetrads. The 11 occupied 10-km squares during the NBA winters represent a big increase from just two during the *1981–84 Winter Atlas*. Only one NBA summer record was received and there are no previous summer atlas records.

Red-breasted Goose*
Branta ruficollis

RED-BREASTED GEESE are rare vagrants to Britain from their breeding grounds on the tundra in northern Siberia. It is likely that they arrive in western Europe as a result of joining migrating flocks of Dark-bellied Brent Geese. It is also a very popular avicultural subject in western Europe and frequently occurs as an escape.

Prior to the NBA years, only seven Red-breasted Geese had been recorded in the county. During the 1999/2000 winter a first-winter Red-breasted Goose was present with the Brent Geese in the Wells/Holkham area and in the following winter single adults were located in northwest Norfolk (associating with Pink-footed Geese) and in east Norfolk. However, the picture was complicated when up to three feral birds were found at Berney Marshes in May 2001 and one, first seen at Titchwell in August, roamed around the northwest of the county and almost certainly overwintered in the area. Diss Mere held a free-flying individual, alongside a pinioned one, from 2003 to 2005 and another feral bird was in the Yare valley in 2006 and 2007.

In all, there were NBA winter records from 13 tetrads (six 10-km squares) and summer records from one tetrad. The only previous atlas records were from two 10-km squares in winter during 1981–84.

Ruddy Shelduck
Tadorna ferruginea

RUDDY SHELDUCKS ARE characteristic of wetlands in desert and mountainous regions of southern Asia, but also nest in similar habitats in southeast Europe and the Atlas Mountains. They are common in captivity and, in recent decades, substantial populations have become naturalised in Switzerland, Germany and the Netherlands. While occasional feral pairs nest in Britain and in France, no self-sustaining populations have yet established.

WINTER – Ruddy Shelduck

Small dots 1, medium 2–4, large 5–17 (birds)

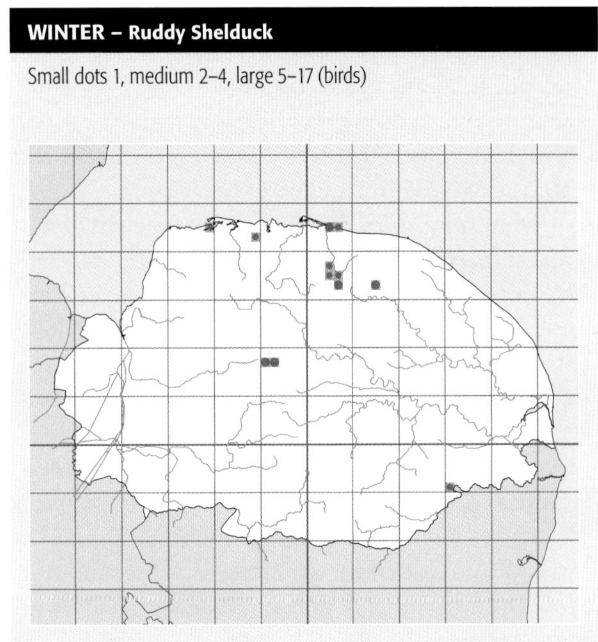

In Norfolk, suspected escapes have been recorded since at least 1869 (*BoN*). A bird washed up dead on the beach at Snettisham in 1892 during a major influx into western Europe, and thought to have originated in the native range, is the county's best candidate for a genuinely wild bird.

Feral birds have been reported annually in Norfolk since 1990, and breeding was first proved in 1996. In the following year, a pair bred at Bayfield Lake, another inland north Norfolk locality. Further instances of breeding already suggest that a population might be on the verge of establishing in the county.

During the NBA period, Ruddy Shelducks were recorded from at least 12 tetrads in winter and 18 during the summer months. Most records came from north or central Norfolk, but birds were also reported from the Fens, Brecks, south Norfolk and Broadland. Breeding occurred in at least three of the NBA summers: 2002, with a pair and four young at Thornage; 2004, with a pair and five ducklings at Bayfield Lake; and 2005, when pairs bred successfully at Bayfield Lake and Kettlestone and there were three sites and three or four breeding pairs in total. The highest winter count was of 17 at Bittering GP on 28th January 2004.

The NBA population estimates are 5–20 birds in the winter period and 0–3 breeding pairs. No birds were recorded in Norfolk by any of the previous atlases.

American Wigeon
Anas americana

AMERICAN WIGEON HAVE been recorded almost annually in Norfolk since the mid 1990s. The vast majority of records refer to drakes, as females are difficult to locate and identify amongst the flocks of Eurasian Wigeon, their usual companions.

The species was recorded in five of the eight NBA winters, most birds being initially located in January or February and often remaining at the same locality until March. No site in the county appeared to be particularly favoured, although single drakes were recorded at Welney in the winters of 2002/03 and 2005/06. A first-winter female present at Holme from January to March 2003 was subsequently seen at several sites along the north Norfolk coast between Brancaster and Cley, remaining until August. There were NBA records from six tetrads in winter and from three in summer; there were no records from any of the previous atlases.

Green-winged Teal
Anas carolinensis

GREEN-WINGED TEAL, the New World counterpart of the Eurasian Teal, was first recorded in Norfolk in 1964 but has been reported annually in the county since 1993. All records have referred to drakes.

The species was recorded in all but one of the NBA winters, with up to three individuals in any one winter. Despite the species being predominantly a winter visitor, birds were reported during five of the NBA summers, mainly in April and May, with Stiffkey Fen being particularly favoured.

Green-winged Teal are renowned for returning to the same localities in subsequent winters. A drake returned to Buckenham Marshes for three consecutive winters and another returned to the Upper Thurne area for six winters up to 2007/08. While Broadland has hosted the majority of birds, records have also come from Welney and several sites on the north coast. There were NBA records from nine tetrads (five 10-km squares) in winter and from four tetrads in summer; there were previous atlas records from three 10-km squares in winter during 1981–84.

Also recorded (Table 3.1): Blue-winged Teal

Red-crested Pochard*
Netta rufina

RED-CRESTED POCHARD is primarily a south Asian species but it also nests in scattered wetlands across Europe, westward to Denmark, the Netherlands and Spain. In Britain, it occurs as a vagrant from migratory wild or naturalised populations on mainland Europe, as unintended escapes from captivity and as an introduced nesting species in scattered localities, and it is virtually impossible to distinguish birds in these categories.

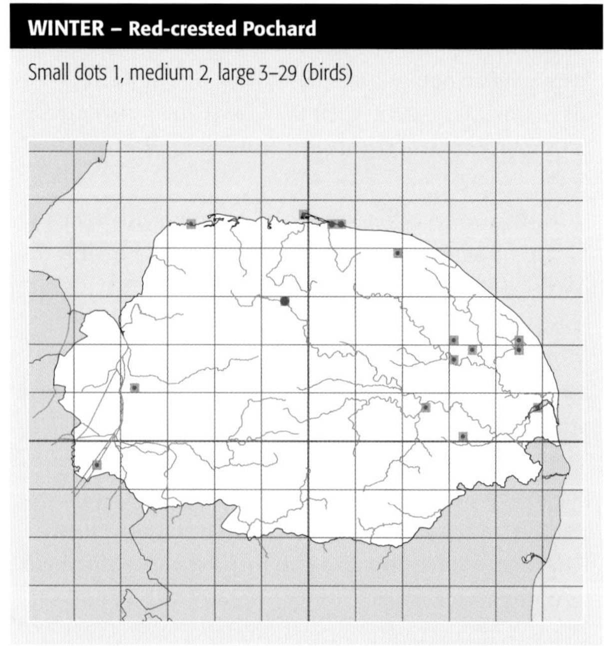

A female shot at Breydon Water in July 1818 was the first British record of the species. Over 20 further birds were recorded in Norfolk up to 1929, most of them also shot by collectors. There were no more reports until 1954 but, since 1980, the species has been recorded annually in the county.

The species was recorded in single Norfolk 10-km squares by the *1981–84 Winter* and *1988–91 Atlases*. During the NBA years, it was recorded in 16 tetrads in winter and in ten during the summer months. These were mainly in the Fens, Broadland or in north Norfolk, although the most reliable sites during the summer were in the Wensum valley, where a feral breeding group is centred upon Pensthorpe. In 2001, at least five broods of full-winged birds were reared at Pensthorpe, while a pair raised seven young at Pentney GP in 2004 and in 2006 a pair reared three young at Hickling Broad. Single birds were reported from a few scattered inland sites each winter and two drakes were seen flying west offshore at Mundesley and Salthouse on 23rd December 2006; presumably it was one of these individuals that was found in the scoter flock off Blakeney Point five days later.

The NBA population estimates are 40–60 birds in the winter period and 5–10 breeding pairs.

Also recorded (Table 3.1): Ring-necked Duck

Ferruginous Duck*
Aythya nyroca

FERRUGINOUS DUCK is a rare visitor to Britain from wild populations on the Continent, although undoubtedly many records relate to escapes or releases from captivity, as the species is widely kept in collections both in Britain and abroad.

The species was recorded in three consecutive NBA winters from 2001/02 to 2003/04 and one of the drakes at Welney may well have been the same returning bird each winter. Each year it followed a similar pattern of being first seen at Welney in January and subsequently reported at Fowl Mere, Stanford Water or Lynford GP. A second drake and a female were also recorded at Welney in the winter of 2003/04, in addition to a drake at Tottenhill GP and Watlington.

Four Ferruginous Ducks were reported during the NBA summer recording periods, including a drake at Fowl Mere from April to July in 2001. NBA records were received from 14 tetrads (ten 10-km squares) in winter and from three tetrads in summer. The only previous atlas record was from the *1981–84 Winter Atlas*, when a single 10-km square was occupied.

King Eider
Somateria spectabilis

KING EIDER IS A very rare vagrant to Norfolk from the Arctic. Prior to the NBA period it had been recorded in the county on only four occasions. The fifth county record was provided by a first-winter drake offshore at Holkham Bay from 19th January to 3rd April 2002. Another first-winter drake was present intermittently off Titchwell between 11th December 2004 and 3rd January 2005.

Surf Scoter
Melanitta perspicillata

THE SURF SCOTER is an abundant breeding species in Alaska and northern Canada, and is a rare vagrant east of the Atlantic. It was recorded in Norfolk on three occasions during the NBA period. None had been reported by previous atlas projects.

There were two winter records, of a drake off Winterton, Cley, Blakeney Point and Holkham in December 2001 and an immature female off Sea Palling and Waxham in December 2002. A first-summer drake with a raft of Common Scoters off Titchwell in June 2002 was a highly unusual summer record for the county.

*Also recorded (Table 3.1): Lady Amherst's Pheasant**

White-billed Diver
Gavia adamsii

WHITE-BILLED DIVERS were formerly rare vagrants to Britain but in recent years have been detected more regularly, especially in the far northwest of Scotland. The species remains a rare vagrant in Norfolk.

Although several were recorded in the county during 1999–2007, only one occurred during an NBA recording period, at Titchwell on 14th January 2001. It represented only the sixth Norfolk record and the first since 1996.

Also recorded (Table 3.1): Black-browed Albatross, Sooty Shearwater, Manx Shearwater, Balearic Shearwater, Leach's Storm-petrel

Gannet
Morus bassanus

GANNETS OCCUR OFF Norfolk coasts for much of the year but are seen mainly on autumn and spring passage and are comparatively scarce in midsummer and midwinter.

Even outside the passage seasons, the birds concerned roam very widely within and beyond the North Sea and do not really represent a summering or wintering population within the county.

There are NBA records from four tetrads in summer and five in winter, with no overlap between these two seasons. The *1981–84 Winter Atlas* recorded Gannets from four of Norfolk's 10-km squares, in comparison to NBA's five. It is very likely, however, that both atlases have underestimated the full distribution.

Also recorded (Table 3.1): Little Bittern

Night-heron*
Nycticorax nycticorax

THE TRUE STATUS of the Night-heron as a rare vagrant in Norfolk, mainly occurring as a spring overshoot, was obscured during the NBA period by the existence of a poorly known feral breeding colony at a wildlife park near Great Witchingham, in the Wensum valley. The birds began to nest outside the confines of their original enclosure, among a colony of Grey Herons, reportedly after their enclosure was damaged in the 1987 storm. Numbers and breeding success were little known but birds from this site have almost certainly accounted for most of the winter records in the county. Eight pairs nested there in 2003 but this may have been the last year in which the colony was active.

During the NBA summers, three Night-herons were probably wild vagrants from the Continent: these were a second-summer or adult that roosted in willows at Titchwell on 20th–29th May 2002, a second-summer at Holkham on 15th May 2005 and at Thornham the following day, and one at Santon Downham on 29th May 2005.

In total, birds were recorded from five tetrads in summer and one in winter. The only previous atlas records came from two 10-km squares in winter during 1981–84.

Squacco Heron
Ardeola ralloides

THIS SOLITARY CREPUSCULAR heron is a rare vagrant to Britain from southern Europe, with only two Norfolk records since the 1960s prior to the NBA period.

A juvenile found at Bacton Gas Terminal on 27th September 2001 subsequently moved to the Horsey/ Waxham area, where it remained until 10th December. The only other record of a wintering bird, the first for the county, concerned one accidentally trapped in a drying bow-net near Ormesby Broad in December 1820.

*Also recorded (Table 3.1): Cattle Egret**

Great White Egret
Ardea alba

UNTIL THE LATE 1990s, the Great White Egret was a rare spring and summer vagrant to Britain from the Continent, but it is now far more frequently recorded, even during the winter months, and must now be regarded as a likely future breeding species.

There were sightings during two of the NBA winters and during the summer recording periods in 2002 and 2007. In winter 2001/02 one was present at various Broadland sites from 28th January to 23rd February and in the following winter singles were recorded at Hickling Broad and roosting with the Little Egrets at Holkham GM on 11th January and at Snetterton GP on 13th–14th February. In 2002, three were noted at Hickling Broad on 10th May (at the time a record count for the county) and were seen the next day in Essex, while singles were at Holkham GM for six days in mid May and at Breydon in mid June. In spring 2007, singles were seen in flight over East Carleton and Cromer.

In all, there were NBA records from 11 tetrads in winter and from five in summer. No birds were recorded in Norfolk by any of the previous atlas projects.

Also recorded (Table 3.1): Purple Heron, Black Stork

White Stork*
Ciconia ciconia

WHITE STORKS ARE RARE passage migrants from the Continent, but their true status is unclear due to escapes or deliberate releases from collections, both at home and abroad. In Norfolk, a wanderer from Thrigby Wildlife Park was reported during most of the NBA summer recording periods. Although seen in Broadland from 9th February 2007, it did not appear to leave the Park much during the NBA winter periods. In 2001, another free-flying bird from Great Witchingham Wildlife Park was also on the loose.

A few White Storks were recorded during the NBA summer periods that were almost certainly wild migrants. On 2nd April 2000, two flew west along the north Norfolk coast, continuing northwest over the Wash, only to be relocated the next day at Holkham Park, where they remained intermittently for five days. On 1st June 2005, a single White Stork also flew west along the north Norfolk coast before drifting south at Titchwell and was seen three days later at Blackborough End Tip, where it was watched gaining height before moving off southeast. In 2006, single White Storks were noted on five dates between 18th April and 21st May at various north Norfolk localities: these may well have involved an unknown number of continental visitors.

In all, three tetrads (two 10-km squares) provided NBA records in winter and five tetrads in summer. The only previous atlas record for the county was from TG50 in the *1981–84 Winter Atlas*.

Glossy Ibis
Plegadis falcinellus

GLOSSY IBIS IS A RARE vagrant to Norfolk from southern Europe. During the NBA years, one was found in the Breydon/Berney area on 3rd July 2004 where it remained intermittently until 1st April 2005. The same bird, or another, was subsequently seen at Hickling Broad on 11th and 14th June and at Berney Marshes on 27th June 2005. There are no previous atlas records for the county.

Black Kite
Milvus migrans

BLACK KITES ARE RARE spring and summer visitors from the Continent and during the NBA period overflying migrants were reported in June 2001 and April 2003 and from April to June in 2007.

During 28th November 2006 to 13th April 2007, a juvenile showing characteristics of the eastern race *lineatus*, known as Black-eared Kite, which had been found a few days earlier in Lincolnshire, was seen at scattered localities across Norfolk from Terrington Marsh in the west to Cley in the east, and briefly at Ranworth in Broadland. It particularly favoured the Dersingham/Snettisham area. There are no previous records of this race in Britain.

There had been no previous atlas records for the county.

White-tailed Eagle
Haliaeetus albicilla

WHITE-TAILED EAGLES are occasional winter visitors to Norfolk, probably mostly from Fenno-

DAVID TIPLING

White-tailed Eagle

Scandia. During the NBA winters, birds were seen in a remarkable 18 tetrads and in eight of the 62 Norfolk 10-km squares. Individuals were quite mobile within winters, however, and occupied different areas within the county in different winters. No birds were recorded in Norfolk by any of the previous atlas projects.

An immature that arrived in north Norfolk in late November 1999 remained in northwest Norfolk until mid March 2000. Amazingly, an adult (the first in the county since 1945) also appeared near Fring in early January 2000 and was seen flying with the immature over Barrow Common on 11th January. The adult was last reported flying out to sea at West Runton on 1st February. Another immature was present in northwest Norfolk in the winter of 2004/05 for three weeks before spending a few days at Welney.

Pallid Harrier
Circus macrourus

PALLID HARRIER has been extending its breeding range into northwest Europe in recent years and has become more frequent as a vagrant to Britain.

The first Norfolk record involved a juvenile female found at Cockthorpe on 24th December 2002, which remained in north and northwest Norfolk until 30th March 2003. On many nights, it roosted with other harriers at Warham Greens. This constituted the first known instance of overwintering in northern Europe. A different first-summer female was present at Blakeney Point on 16th–17th May 2003.

Also recorded (Table 3.1): Red-footed Falcon

Spotted Crake
Porzana porzana

AS A RESULT of its secretive habits and the possibilities of spring migrants calling while on passage, the scattered western European breeding distribution is poorly known. The British breeding population seems to fluctuate but was estimated to be 73 calling males in 1999 (*APEP06*). The Spotted Crake was not uncommon as a breeding bird in the Broads and Fens up to the middle of the 1800s, but the last confirmation of breeding in Norfolk was as long ago as 1908.

Spotted Crakes have been recorded almost annually in Norfolk since the early 1950s but about two-thirds of the records have been in late summer and autumn, when birds are on passage. Males were heard calling in five of the NBA summers, with four localities hosting the species in 2001 and 2002. The most favoured site has been Strumpshaw, where in 2001 two males were calling, one of which was present for most of June, and in 2002 up to three males were heard from early April until 1st July and a pair were heard duetting in mid April. Surlingham Marsh, Wheatfen, Ranworth Marsh, Hickling Broad and Welney also hosted calling males during the period.

The *1988–91 Atlas* found Spotted Crake to be present in summer in one Norfolk 10-km square. The *1981–84 Winter Atlas* recorded the species in two 10-km squares, but no winter birds were reported during the NBA period.

Corncrake
Crex crex

CORNCRAKES WERE ONCE common breeders in Norfolk but the three non-breeding summer records during the NBA years are typical of its recent status as an exceedingly rare migrant. Six 10-km squares in Norfolk were occupied by calling birds during the *1968–72 Atlas*, although breeding has not been proven in the county since 1965. In 2003, a reintroduction programme began releasing captive-bred birds in Cambridgeshire.

There were three records during the NBA summers, at Reepham on 1st May 2000, Great Bircham on 14th–20th May 2002 and at Breydon Water on 23rd June 2006. Although not unprecedented, one at Coldham Hall near Surlingham on 29th December 2004 was a highly unusual winter record.

Black-winged Stilt
Himantopus himantopus

THE LONG-TERM presence of a Black-winged Stilt at Titchwell, overlapping with the NBA period, was one of the most extraordinary events in Norfolk's recent ornithological history.

Black-winged Stilts in Europe have a scattered breeding distribution, mainly around the Mediterranean, and winter in West Africa. They are irregular spring overshoots to Britain, often in pairs, and have bred on several occasions, at least twice successfully. In 1987, a pair at Holme raised two young. Between then and May 1993, five more Black-winged Stilts were recorded in Norfolk, some of which may have been returning birds. On 21st August 1993, one was found with Oystercatchers at Snettisham; after three days it had moved to Thornham and Titchwell, which was to become its home for the next 12 years (Kimber 2005). This famous bird was given the name 'Sammy' and was probably seen by over a million people (Eele 2006). During his stay, Sammy was occasionally reported from Holme, Brancaster GM, Overy Staithe and Scolt Head, where his presence in April and June caused some alarm in the ternery. He became less adventurous in his last two years and was last seen sheltering behind some bushes on the saltmarsh on 21st May 2005.

Also during the NBA years, a pair was seen at Hockwold Washes and later at Fowl Mere, near Croxton, in May 2002, and in 2005 one flew southwest at Holme on 29th April and two were found at Welney six days later. No birds had been recorded in Norfolk by any of the previous atlas projects.

Also recorded (Table 3.1): Collared Pratincole, Killdeer, Kentish Plover

Dotterel
Charadrius morinellus

NORFOLK, ALTHOUGH not quite as flat as people might think, seems unusual habitat for this mostly montane plover. Small groups are annual, however, on spring passage. In autumn, occasional birds linger into November but winter records are very rare and there were none during the NBA period. The NBA database contains records of spring passage migrants in eight tetrads but this is an incomplete summary of the distribution during the period. No birds were recorded in Norfolk by any of the previous atlas projects.

Also recorded (Table 3.1): Pacific Golden Plover

Temminck's Stint
Calidris temminckii

TEMMINCK'S STINT IS a scarce but regular spring and autumn migrant through the county. No birds were recorded in Norfolk in any of the previous atlas projects. There are NBA records from 14 tetrads in spring but not all passage records from the county during the period have been added to the database.

White-rumped Sandpiper
Calidris fuscicollis

WHITE-RUMPED SANDPIPER is a rare autumn vagrant from North America, seen in Britain mostly between June and October. One that arrived at Cley on 9th October 2006 remained in the Cley/Salthouse area until 26th December.

Also recorded (Table 3.1): Pectoral Sandpiper

Curlew Sandpiper
Calidris ferruginea

CURLEW SANDPIPERS COMMUTING between the central Siberian Arctic and West Africa are scarce but regular spring and autumn migrants on the Norfolk coast. There are NBA summer records from 20 tetrads, with the earliest on 8th April 2007 at Cley.

Winter records in Britain are rare. There were two winter records in Norfolk during the NBA years, at Breydon on 7th December 2001 and at Titchwell on 1st–6th December 2004. No birds were recorded in Norfolk in any of the previous atlas projects.

Also recorded (Table 3.1): Stilt Sandpiper, Broad-billed Sandpiper, Dowitcher sp

Whimbrel
Numenius phaeopus

PARTIES OF WHIMBREL often migrate diurnally and may be seen widely across the county in spring and autumn. The database includes 310 birds recorded from 58 tetrads during the NBA summers but not every record from the *NBR* is included in this total. Summering in the county is unusual. Wintering is rare, with a single record in TF62 during the *1981–84 Winter Atlas* and one during the NBA period, at Morston on 26th January 2004.

Lesser Yellowlegs
Tringa flavipes

LESSER YELLOWLEGS IS a very rare vagrant from North America. During the NBA years, three were recorded during the winter months: singles were at Cantley BF from 8th November to 8th December 2002, at Stiffkey from 14th September 2004 to 24th April 2005, and at Thornham Harbour from 13th January to 10th February 2007. There are no previous atlas records for the county.

Wood Sandpiper
Tringa glareola

WOOD SANDPIPER IS a scarce but regular spring and autumn migrant through the county. In the April–June periods, they were recorded from at least 23 tetrads, although the data are incomplete. No birds were recorded in Norfolk by any of the previous atlas projects.

Also recorded (Table 3.1): Red-necked Phalarope

Grey Phalarope
Phalaropus fulicarius

GREY PHALAROPES ARE scarce passage migrants around the Norfolk coast, mainly in autumn. Winter records are not unusual. The species was reported in four of the NBA winters, and in six different tetrads. None lingered and most records referred to birds seen in flight close inshore, exceptions to this being one at Kelling WM on 5th December 2002, one feeding on a whale carcass at Terrington Marsh on 2nd February 2003 and one on the sea at Cley on 19th December 2005. There are no previous atlas records for the county.

Pomarine Skua
Stercorarius pomarinus

ALTHOUGH RELATIVELY SCARCE on passage, this skua is the commonest in Norfolk during the winter months. There are NBA records from ten tetrads (six 10-km squares) in winter and from one tetrad in summer, although these figures underestimate the true distribution at both seasons. There is just one previous atlas record for the county, from TG33 during the *1981–84 Winter Atlas*.

Arctic Skua
Stercorarius parasiticus

ARCTIC SKUAS ARE recorded less than annually in spring in Norfolk, and none were recorded for NBA in any of the summer periods. The species is rare in Britain in winter but provided NBA records in six Norfolk tetrads (four 10-km squares). The only previous atlas record was from one 10-km square in winter during 1981–84.

Also recorded (Table 3.1): Long-tailed Skua

Great Skua
Stercorarius skua

GREAT SKUAS ARE scarce in spring in Norfolk, and just one was recorded for NBA. The species is irregular in Britain in winter but there were NBA records in seven Norfolk tetrads (five 10-km squares). The only previous atlas records for the county were from three 10-km squares in the *1981–84 Winter Atlas*.

Also recorded (Table 3.1): Sabine's Gull

Kittiwake
Rissa tridactyla

KITTIWAKES OCCUR OFF Norfolk coasts for much of the year but are seen mainly on autumn and spring passage and are comparatively scarce in midsummer and midwinter. For much of the year, the birds concerned roam very widely within and beyond the North Sea and do not really represent a summering or wintering population within the county. There have, however, been isolated and unsuccessful breeding attempts at four localities on the north coast of Norfolk during 1946–94, and the possibility of nesting should be borne in mind for future surveys.

There are NBA records from two tetrads in summer and from 19 in winter. The *1981–84 Winter Atlas* recorded Kittiwakes from 12 of Norfolk's 10-km squares, in comparison to NBA's eight, but it is likely that both these atlases underestimated the full distribution. Previous breeding atlases show confirmed nesting in three Norfolk 10-km squares during 1968–72 and two in 1988–91, and one of possible nesting at Happisburgh during the *1980–85 NBBS*.

Also recorded (Table 3.1): Slender-billed Gull, Bonaparte's Gull

Ross's Gull
Rhodostethia rosea

ROSS'S GULL IS a very rare vagrant to Britain and an adult at Cley on 31st December 2005, which was still present on the following day, represented only the second county record, one having been found there in May 1984.

Also recorded (Table 3.1): Laughing Gull

Ring-billed Gull
Larus delawarensis

RING-BILLED GULL is a rare vagrant to Norfolk from North America, with seven records between 1991 and 1996. In 2005 there were four further records, two of which fell within the NBA recording periods. A bird in its second year was found at Cley on 28th May and a first-winter bird was at Breydon on 18th December.

Also recorded (Table 3.1): Caspian Tern, Whiskered Tern, White-winged Black Tern

Roseate Tern
Sterna dougallii

IN THE EASTERN Atlantic, the Roseate Tern nests only in scattered, rather mobile colonies in Britain, Ireland, France and the Azores, and spends the winter off West Africa. For at least the last 200 years, the number of British breeding pairs has fluctuated widely, with a marked decline during the 1800s, followed by substantial recovery in the 20th century due to better protection at the colonies. Through loss of breeding habitat and high mortality in the wintering areas, however, numbers fell once again during the 1970s and 1980s.

The species has always been rare as a breeding bird in Norfolk, where only Scolt Head comes close to providing its preferred location on small, offshore islands. Between the early 1920s and late 1940s up to three pairs nested almost annually at either Scolt Head or Blakeney Point, but no further breeding attempts were made until 1996–2000. A single atlas record during 1988–91 did not relate to breeding.

DAVID TIPLING

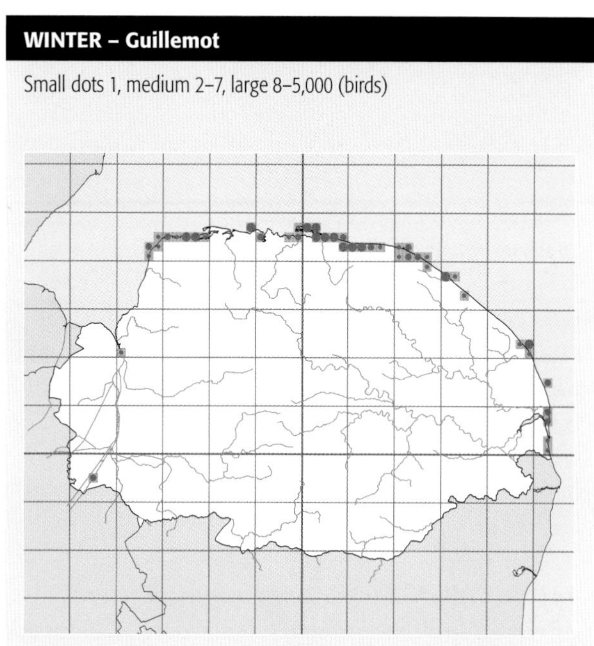

Roseate Terns were recorded annually during the NBA summers, and in five different tetrads. Only in 2000, however, was a breeding attempt made – for the fifth successive year in the county – but the single chick that hatched died in poor weather two days later. At a second site in the same year, a pair displayed but nesting did not occur.

Guillemot
Uria aalge

AUKS ARE OFTEN observed passing offshore from Norfolk, and sometimes feeding, but have no nesting habitat available to them in Norfolk or elsewhere in southeastern Britain. Wintering auks are irregular off Norfolk coasts and seem to be part of much wider populations wintering within and probably beyond the North Sea. Guillemots are generally the most abundant of the species observed.

A population estimate with a remarkably broad range of 50–30,000 applies to Guillemots in the NBA winters but fewer than 1,000 birds are seen in a normal winter. Quite exceptionally, around 20,000–30,000 birds were present in 2000/01, with 20,000 estimated in the Blakeney–Salthouse area alone on 4th January and 7,000 in the Horsey/Waxham area three days later. In December 2006, several thousand were once again recorded off the north Norfolk coast, with up to 2,000 off Blakeney Point/Cley and 1,000 off Burnham Overy Dunes.

The only inland records concerned up to four in the Welney/Denver area on 29th January 2005, but singles were on the River Ouse at King's Lynn on 16th January 2000 and in Brancaster Harbour on 20th February 2003.

In total, 14 Norfolk 10-km squares were recorded as occupied in winter, according to NBA, whereas 16 had been occupied during the *1981–84 Winter Atlas*. Only a few were noted off the coast during the NBA summer recording period, most, if not all, involving birds flying past. There were no previous breeding atlas records for the county.

Razorbill
Alca torda

THE NBA DATABASE contains winter records from 11 tetrads (seven 10-km squares). The only previous atlas records for the county were from 11 10-km squares in winter during the *1981–84 Winter Atlas*. The winter population during the NBA period was probably in the range 10–100 birds, although nearly 400 were present off Cley in December 2006. Small numbers were also reported from various sites around the coast during the NBA summer recording period but, as for Guillemot, most records were of birds flying past. There were no previous breeding atlas records for the county.

Black Guillemot
Cepphus grylle

THE NBA DATABASE contains winter records from four tetrads in three 10-km squares. The only previous atlas records for the county are from two 10-km squares in winter during the *1981–84 Winter Atlas*. Four or five individuals were involved in total, with all but one of the records being off the north coast between Hunstanton and Titchwell. One in Brancaster Harbour on 27th April 2005 was the only record during the NBA summer recording periods.

Little Auk
Alle alle

THE NBA DATABASE contains winter records from 21 tetrads in 11 10-km squares. The only previous atlas records for the county are also from 11 10-km squares in winter, during the *1981–84 Winter Atlas*. In late January 2003, during an exceptional winter movement, there were day-counts of up to 60 birds around the coast and three were found well inland at Watlington, Fakenham and Thurne. The winter population during the NBA period was probably in the range 0–100 birds, with fewer than five birds being the norm; the vast majority of records were of Little Auks in flight offshore. The only record during the NBA summer recording period concerned a partly oiled bird on the sea at Lessingham on 10th May 2002.

Puffin
Fratercula arctica

THE NBA DATABASE contains winter records from nine tetrads (eight 10-km squares). The only previous atlas records for the county are from six 10-km squares in winter during the *1981–84 Winter Atlas*. The winter population during the NBA period was probably in the range 0–3 birds, this species being most frequently observed in the county as a late autumn migrant. However, it was also reported during the summer recording period in six out of the eight NBA years, involving one to three birds, mainly in May.

Ring-necked Parakeet*
Psittacula krameri

RING-NECKED PARAKEET is an introduced species to Britain that was admitted to category C of the *British List* in 1984. Its population has expanded considerably since then but remains centred on the southeast counties of England. The most recent breeding record in Norfolk was in the King's Lynn area just prior to 1974. The only previous atlas records for the county were from the *1981–84 Winter Atlas*, when one 10-km square was occupied.

During the NBA years, the species was recorded in three of the winter periods, with one at Caister from summer 1999 until January 2000, a pair in a Burnham Market garden in February 2001 and one at King's Lynn in February 2002. It was also seen during two of the summer recording periods: one flew west at Holkham on 26th May and the same bird or another was present in northwest Norfolk from late June to September 2002 and one was at Hellesdon in June 2004.

Observers should always bear in mind the difficulty of eliminating other species of parakeets when birds are seen poorly or in flight. At least nine other species of parrot were specifically identified in Norfolk during the NBA period (Table 3.2).

Also recorded (Table 3.1): Alpine Swift, European Bee-eater, Hoopoe

Wryneck
Jynx torquilla

DURING THE NBA years, Wrynecks were recorded from 36 tetrads in the summer period, ten of which were inland. All records referred to passage migrants, and the number of records each spring varied from two to 13 (in 2003 and 2004). The earliest was on 13th April 2003 at Snettisham and the only June record concerned one at Runham on 14th June 2004. Wryneck is a former breeding bird in Norfolk but, despite occasional subsequent midsummer records, sometimes of two together, no breeding has been confirmed in the county since 1955. In the *1968–72 Atlas*, possible breeding was recorded in TL89 and probable breeding in TL99.

Red-backed Shrike
Lanius collurio

THE RED-BACKED SHRIKE has not bred in Norfolk since 1988 although small numbers of spring migrants continue to be recorded annually.

The species breeds throughout much of continental Europe except for the far north and much of the Iberian Peninsula. A long-term reduction in breeding numbers in Britain accelerated from about 1950, although 300 pairs were still present in 1952. Within 20 years, the British total had fallen to 80–90 pairs of which three-quarters were in East Anglia, but just over ten years later, in 1983, the last pair to nest in north Norfolk did so at Holme. The species last bred in the county at Santon Downham in 1988, although a male occupied the same general area for several weeks in each of the next two years. The causes of this catastrophic decline are uncertain but probably include scrub and hedge clearance, the decline of large insects, perhaps associated with the increased use of pesticides, and losses to egg collectors.

During the NBA period, 1–13 Red-backed Shrikes were recorded annually on spring migration. The vast majority were single birds at coastal sites, with Winterton (a former breeding site) being particularly favoured. Occasional birds were recorded at inland localities including Sculthorpe Moor, Hindringham, Costessey and Narborough. Most were present just briefly but occasional birds lingered for a few days, the longest-staying being a female at Blakeney Friary Hills on 1st–17th June 2007. Some of the males were heard singing and a male and female were present on Blakeney Point on 10th May 2004. In all, 20 tetrads were found to be occupied by migrants but with no indication of further breeding. An analysis over the last 20 years has revealed a trend for the birds to arrive in late May and June, considerably later than when the species bred in the county.

Previous atlas data for the county were recorded from 22 (35%) of the county's 10-km squares in the *1968–72 Atlas*, six tetrads, all in different 10-km squares in the *1980–85 NBBS* and from just one square during 1988–91.

Also recorded (Table 3.1): Lesser Grey Shrike, Woodchat Shrike

Penduline Tit
Remiz pendulinus

PENDULINE TIT IS a rare vagrant to Norfolk, with three records during the NBA period. A first-winter male was found at Berney Marshes on 5th December 1999. Males of unknown age were observed at Titchwell on 8th–9th April 2000 and at Weybourne on 1st April 2001, the latter bird being seen later at Salthouse before it flew off southwards. There were no previous atlas records for the county.

Also recorded (Table 3.1): Short-toed Lark, Red-rumped Swallow

DAVID TIPLING

Wryneck

Yellow-browed Warbler
Phylloscopus inornatus

YELLOW-BROWED WARBLER is a scarce autumn migrant from Siberia. Larger than usual numbers arrived in the autumn of 2002 including one at Stiffkey Meals on 11th October, which remained in that area until 25th March 2003. It was the first known case of a Yellow-browed Warbler overwintering in Norfolk. There were no previous atlas records for the county.

Hume's Warbler
Phylloscopus humei

HUME'S WARBLER is a rare vagrant from Siberia. Three were present during the NBA winter periods. One was at Great Yarmouth cemetery from 30th November to 4th December 2003 and in 2006 singles were at Holkham Park during 2nd–18th January and by Horsey Mere from 24th January to 6th February. There were no previous atlas records for the county.

Also recorded (Table 3.1): Iberian Chiffchaff

Dartford Warbler
Sylvia undata

DARTFORD WARBLERS have a small world range, bounded by Britain, Italy and Morocco. It is a largely resident species in Britain and numbers fluctuate with the severity of winter weather.

SUMMER – Dartford Warbler

Small dots 1 ('pair')
Shading – breeding proved or considered likely

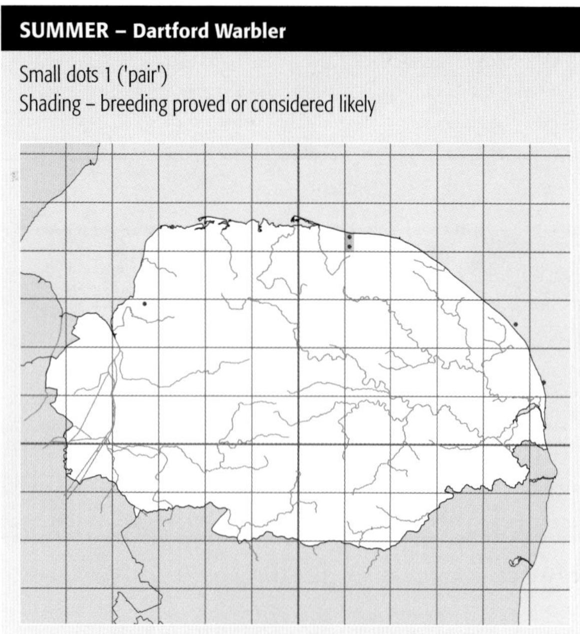

Only 11 pairs were thought to remain in Britain after the exceptionally harsh 1962/63 winter. There has since been a marked upturn in its status, corresponding with a remarkable increase and spread of the breeding population in southern England.

WINTER – Dartford Warbler

Small dots 1, medium 2 (birds)

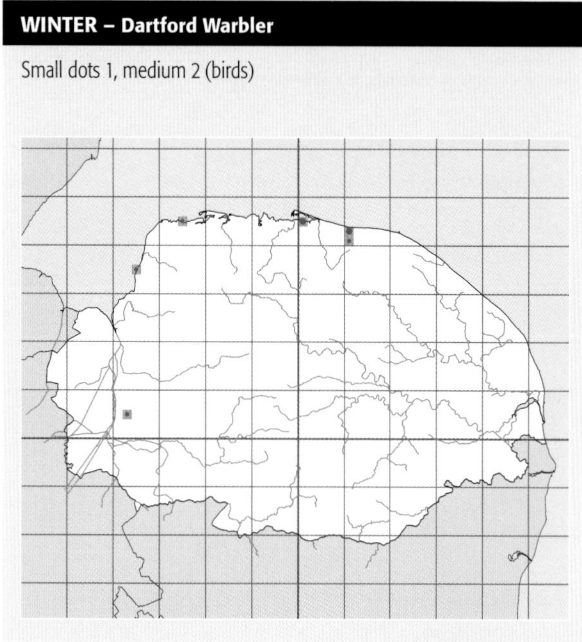

Up to 1990 there had been only seven records of Dartford Warblers in Norfolk, none having been reported in the county by the previous atlases. The first indication that the species might be added to the list of Norfolk breeding birds occurred in 1997, when a male sang at an inland site between March and July. It was not until 2005, however, that matters progressed: a singing male, present at a north Norfolk site from January to May, was joined by two females. In the same year, a male was reported to be holding territory in the Brecks, with a female at another Breckland site, but these records were not available to be mapped.

By 2006, over 100 breeding pairs were present on Suffolk coastal heathlands, and up to two birds were resident at a site in north Norfolk. Breeding in the county was finally proved for the first time in 2007, when two pairs each successfully raised two broods of three young on Kelling Heath (Wagstaff 2008).

During the NBA period, records were obtained from ten well-scattered tetrads, of which six were occupied in summer, and a partly overlapping group of six in winter, of which one was well inland. Two tetrads were occupied by birds thought to be breeding.

Also recorded (Table 3.1): Marmora's Warbler, Subalpine Warbler, Sardinian Warbler

Savi's Warbler
Locustella luscinioides

A SAVI'S WARBLER killed at Limpenhoe in May 1819 is the earliest-known British record. Small numbers bred in the Fens and Broadland up to around 1850, but later the species became extinct as a British breeding bird. Kent was recolonised in 1960 but fewer than 30 singing males have been reported across England in any year and recent decades have seen a decline.

Between 1967 and the mid 1990s, at least one singing male was present in Norfolk in almost every summer but appearances have become less frequent in recent years. Savi's Warblers were recorded in just five NBA years, peaking in 2001, with single singing males at Holme/Thornham and Hickling Broad, and two at Strumpshaw. Ranworth Ward Marsh, Brayden Marshes and Burnham Norton also hosted the species in other NBA years.

Records during the NBA summers came from six tetrads. There are previous atlas records in TG04 during 1968–72, in eight tetrads (four 10-km squares) during 1980–85, and in five 10-km squares during 1988–91.

Also recorded (Table 3.1): Booted Warbler, Icterine Warbler, Blyth's Reed Warbler

Marsh Warbler
Acrocephalus palustris

MARSH WARBLERS BREED commonly across much of central and eastern Europe and, although they have declined as a British breeding bird since about 1950, their range has expanded northwards in Fenno-Scandia and northwest Russia. The number of breeding pairs and singing males in Britain fluctuates annually, but generally in recent years fewer than 20 males have been recorded.

Although Marsh Warblers were first proved to breed in Norfolk as recently as 1999, singing males have been recorded in the county almost annually since the mid 1980s. None, however, was recorded in the county by the previous atlases.

In 1999, the year before NBA began, a pair bred in east Norfolk and three other singing males were present at the same site (Heath 2000). Although none returned to the breeding area the following summer, a female was present for two weeks in 2001 and a male that sang there in early June 2002 was briefly joined by a female, but there was no further evidence of breeding. During the NBA years, singing males were also reported from a further eight localities in north and central Norfolk, as well as at other sites in Broadland.

Rose-coloured Starling
Pastor roseus

ROSE-COLOURED STARLING is a rare vagrant from eastern Europe, with birds usually arriving in mid to late summer. Their appearance is very erratic and this is demonstrated by the arrival pattern during the NBA years, with nearly all reports during the NBA periods falling in the two years 2001 and 2002. An adult was at Frettenham on 11th–13th June 2001, while nine were reported in June 2002, including three together in a Sheringham garden on 14th. Winter records included a wandering juvenile in the Waxham/Horsey area from 1st September to 3rd December 2001 and one in Great Yarmouth on 14th–17th January 2002, which may well have been the same bird. Another was at Marham on 16th December 2003. There were no previous atlas records for the county.

Dipper
Cinclus cinclus

THE DIPPER IS a scarce winter visitor to Norfolk, mostly or entirely from mainland Europe. Birds apparently of the nominate race *cinclus*, colloquially known as Black-bellied Dipper, were recorded during three of the NBA winter recording periods and twice in April. A long-staying bird was present at Itteringham Mill from November 1999 to 1st March 2001, one was at Letheringsett from 18th February to 13th March 2004 and another was at Cockley Cley on 12th December 2005. In spring, singles were at Holkham Park Lake on 5th April 2000 and one was watched circling high before heading off east at Overstrand in the early morning of 19th April 2006.

There were previous atlas records from four of Norfolk's 10-km squares in winters during 1981–84.

Ring Ouzel
Turdus torquatus

ALTHOUGH NORFOLK HOLDS no suitable breeding habitat for this species, Ring Ouzels, presumably heading mainly for Scandinavia, were widely distributed as spring migrants across both inland and coastal Norfolk during the NBA period, often in small groups. At least 100 tetrads were visited.

Winter records are occasional in the county, but there were none during the NBA winters. The *1981–84 Winter Atlas* reported a single record from TG42.

SUMMER – Ring Ouzel

Small dots 1, medium 2, large 3–13 ('pairs')

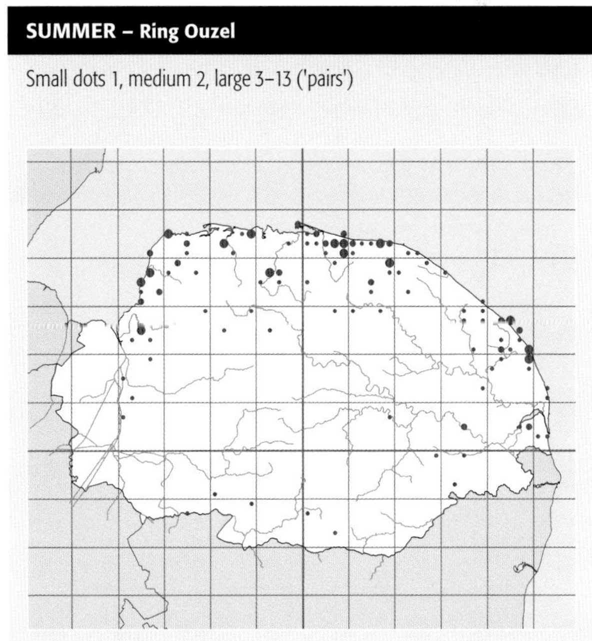

Also recorded (Table 3.1): Thrush Nightingale, Bluethroat

Desert Wheatear
Oenanthe deserti

DESERT WHEATEAR IS a rare vagrant to Britain, with most records relating to arrivals in late autumn or early winter. The only one to be recorded in Norfolk during the NBA period was on the beach at Holkham Bay from 27th November to 11th December 1999. None had been recorded by the previous atlas surveys.

Also recorded (Table 3.1): Red-breasted Flycatcher

Pied Flycatcher
Ficedula hypoleuca

TO NORFOLK BIRDWATCHERS, the Pied Flycatcher is best known as an autumn passage migrant but small numbers are recorded in spring and the species has nested in the county on two occasions.

The Pied Flycatcher has a wide European breeding range but within Britain is confined to the north and west. It winters in West Africa, south of the Sahara Desert. During the 19th century, sporadic breeding occurred in eastern England, particularly following large spring influxes of Scandinavian Pied Flycatchers. This was the scenario that preceded Norfolk's first breeding record in 1978, when a pair bred successfully in a pine tree at Felbrigg Park. In 1996, a female laid a clutch of four infertile eggs in a nest box at Holme; no male was ever seen, and the nest was subsequently deserted. Other males have also been recorded in song in midsummer, mainly at locations along the Cromer to Holt ridge, and have even been seen entering nest boxes.

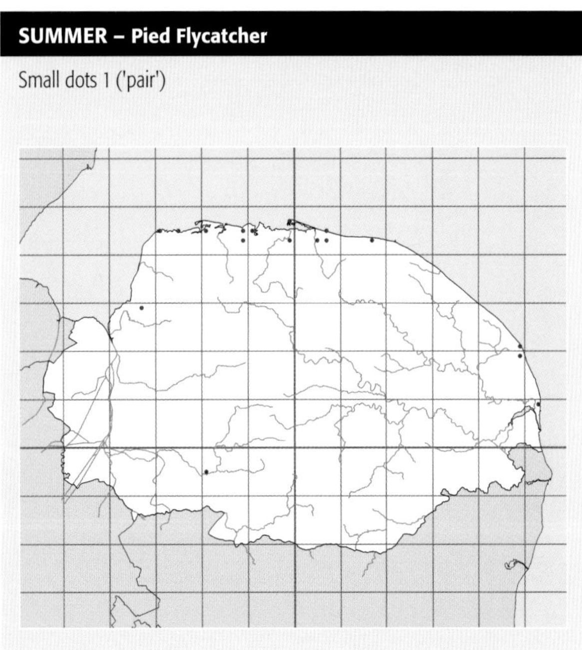

During the NBA summer periods, small numbers of Pied Flycatchers were recorded annually, mainly in late April and May, but also twice in June (at Blakeney Point and Scolt Head). Seventeen tetrads in ten 10-km squares are mapped. The majority of records related to coastal migrants, but a male was in song in the Stanford TA on 27th April 2000 and a male was displaying to a female throughout the morning at Dersingham Bog on 25th April 2006. A brown-plumaged male at Blakeney Point on 7th May 2006 was likely to have been from the eastern European part of the range (Stoddart 2007).

During 1980–85, breeding was recorded as 'possible' in four tetrads in three different 10-km squares. Two 10-km squares were recorded as occupied during the *1988–91 Atlas*, but none in 1968–72.

Also recorded (Table 3.1): Alpine Accentor, Citrine Wagtail

Richard's Pipit
Anthus richardi

RICHARD'S PIPIT IS best known as a scarce autumn migrant from western Siberia, but it also occurs more rarely in Norfolk in winter and spring. During the NBA years it was recorded in six of the springs, extreme dates being 3rd April and 7th May. All sightings referred to single birds, apart from two at Happisburgh in April 2000.

The sole winter record during the NBA period concerned one at Terrington Marsh on 21st February 2007 that was seen to fly over from Lincolnshire. The *1981–84 Winter Atlas* contains two records from TG14 and another from TG24.

Also recorded (Table 3.1): Tawny Pipit

Olive-backed Pipit
Anthus hodgsoni

ALTHOUGH A RARE autumn vagrant, Olive-backed Pipit had been unrecorded in Norfolk in winter. One at Lynford Arboretum during 1st–20th February 2002 was therefore most unexpected.

Also recorded (Table 3.1): Red-throated Pipit

Serin
Serinus serinus

THE SERIN HAS BEEN recorded annually in Norfolk since 1990, with the exception of 2005. Most Norfolk records have involved birds overshooting on spring passage. Some of the males have been heard in song and have even held territories. Most notable was a male with a very distinctive Wren-like song that was present in the Holkham/Wells area for many weeks during the spring and summer between 1984 and 1987.

In all the NBA years, except for 2005, up to three Serins were reported annually on spring passage at coastal sites, with records falling between 1st April and 31st May. The presence of two breeding pairs in the county in 2003 was exceptional. In that year, a pair of Serins arrived at Holkham Meals at the end of May and, although their first breeding attempt ended in failure, with the clutch probably predated by a Jay or grey squirrel, they reared two young from a second nest. Amazingly, another pair nested in an extensive garden on the outskirts of Norwich but there was no evidence of success (Bloomfield 2004).

Originally confined to the Mediterranean region, the species spread north into central Europe during the 19th century. It first bred in Britain in 1967, but no more than two pairs have subsequently bred in any one year and prior to the Norfolk records in 2003, no confirmed breeding had been reported in Britain since a pair nested in Kent in 1996. Breeding was at least likely in two tetrads in two 10-km squares in the *1980–85 NBBS* and in two 10-km squares in the *1988–91 Atlas*. There has been no progress, therefore, in the colonisation of southern Britain by Serins that was so eagerly anticipated fifty years ago!

Arctic Redpoll
Carduelis hornemanni

ARCTIC REDPOLL IS an irregular winter vagrant to Britain from Fenno-Scandia and northern Russia. The species was recorded in four of the NBA winters, on each occasion in the company of other species of redpoll. An adult male was at Swanton Novers on 8th January 2001, an adult male and two first-winters were at Titchwell from 8th December 2001 to 23rd February 2002, two were at Barton Turf on 28th January 2002 and singles were at Titchwell from 3rd December 2004 to 4th April 2005 and Little Thornage from 17th February to 12th March 2006. Birds were of the *exilipes* race in each case where racial determination was possible. There were no previous atlas records for the county.

DAVID TIPLING

Arctic Redpoll

Two-barred Crossbill
Loxia leucoptera

TWO-BARRED CROSSBILL is a rare vagrant and an adult female at Sandringham on 8th–15th December 2002 was the only record during the NBA recording periods. There were no previous atlas records for the county.

Also recorded (Table 3.1): Common Rosefinch, Rose-breasted Grosbeak

Pine Bunting
Emberiza leucocephalos

PINE BUNTING IS a rare vagrant to western Europe from Siberia. One at Choseley from 28th February to 11th March 2004 was only the second to be recorded in Norfolk. There were no previous atlas records for the county.

Also recorded (Table 3.1): Ortolan Bunting, Rustic Bunting

Little Bunting
Emberiza pusilla

LITTLE BUNTINGS NEST from northern Fenno-Scandia eastwards across Russia and winter mainly in India. It is generally an autumn vagrant in Norfolk, with occasional birds remaining in winter, as did one at Morston, which was present from 16th October 2005 to 17th February 2006. Only four have ever been recorded in Norfolk in spring, including a male in song at Blakeney Point on 1st June 2003. There had been no previous atlas records for the county.

All additional species recorded by NBA that are on the Norfolk List

Table 3.1 For species marked with an asterisk, some or all of the records may have been of individuals that were not truly wild. Dots or numbers indicate presence during each NBA season: numbers are the numbers of individuals recorded. The total numbers of tetrads with records are also given, where known; dots indicate unquantified records. Grand totals of occupied tetrads, where known, are drawn from the NBA database.

SPECIES *Scientific name*	99/00 W	2000 S	00/01 W	2001 S	01/02 W	2002 S	02/03 W	2003 S	03/04 W	2004 S	04/05 W	2005 S	05/06 W	2006 S	06/07 W	2007 S	W tetrads	S tetrads
Lesser White-fronted Goose* *Anser erythropus*	●		●	●	●		●		●		●	●	●	●	●	●	5	1
Snow Goose* *Anser caerulescens*	●			●	●	●	●	●	●	●		1			2		17	1
Red-breasted Goose* *Branta ruficollis*	1		2	●	1			●		●		●		●	●	2	13	1
Ruddy Shelduck* *Tadorna ferruginea*	●	●	●	●	●	●	●	●	●	●	●	●	●	●	●	●	12	18
American Wigeon *Anas americana*					1		2	1	1				1		1	1	6	3
Green-winged Teal *Anas carolinensis*	3	2		1		1	1	1	2	3	4		3		1	1	9	4
Blue-winged Teal *Anas discors*		1										1						2
Red-crested Pochard* *Netta rufina*	●	●	●	●	●	●	●	●	●	●	●	●	●	●	●	●	16	10
Ring-necked Duck *Aythya collaris*								1										1
Ferruginous Duck* *Aythya nyroca*		1		2	2	1	1	2	3	1							14	3
King Eider *Somateria spectabilis*											1						4	
Surf Scoter *Melanitta perspicillata*					1	1	1										9	1
Lady Amherst's Pheasant* *Chrysolophus amherstiae*									●		●						2	
White-billed Diver *Gavia adamsii*			1														1	
Black-browed Albatross *Thalassarche melanophris*							1										1	
Sooty Shearwater *Puffinus griseus*			1	3			4									2	●	●
Manx Shearwater *Puffinus puffinus*		●		●		●		●	2	●	2	●		●	1	●	●	●
Balearic Shearwater *Puffinus mauretanicus*								1							3		4	1
Leach's Storm-petrel *Oceanodroma leucorhoa*				2														2

Table 3.1 (continued)

SPECIES *Scientific name*	99/00 W	2000 S	00/01 W	2001 S	01/02 W	2002 S	02/03 W	2003 S	03/04 W	2004 S	04/05 W	2005 S	05/06 W	2006 S	06/07 W	2007 S	W tetrads	S tetrads
Gannet *Morus bassanus*	●	●	●	●	●	●	●	●	●	●	●	●	●	●	●	●	●	●
Little Bittern *Ixobrychus minutus*																1		1
Night-heron* *Nycticorax nycticorax*	●		●	●	●	●		●	●	●	●	●			●	●	●	●
Squacco Heron *Ardeola ralloides*					1												1	
Cattle Egret* *Bubulcus ibis*														1			1	1
Great White Egret *Ardea alba*					1	5	2									2	11	5
Purple Heron *Ardea purpurea*		1				2				2		2		2		2		6
Black Stork *Ciconia nigra*						1												1
White Stork* *Ciconia ciconia*		●		●	1	●		2		●		●		●	●	●	●	●
Glossy Ibis *Plegadis falcinellus*											1	1					2	2
Black Kite *Milvus migrans*				1				2							1	3	●	●
White-tailed Eagle *Haliaeetus albicilla*	2										1						18	
Pallid Harrier *Circus macrourus*							1	1									6	1
Red-footed Falcon *Falco vespertinus*		2				4		6		6		2				1		11
Spotted Crake *Porzana porzana*				4		4				1				1		1		●
Corncrake *Crex crex*		1				1			1					1			1	3
Black-winged Stilt *Himantopus himantopus*	●	●	●	●	●	●	●	●	●	●	●	●					1	4
Collared Pratincole *Glareola pratincola*												1						3
Killdeer *Charadrius vociferus*														1				1
Kentish Plover *Charadrius alexandrinus*		3		1		3		2		2		1		2		2	1	7
Dotterel *Charadrius morinellus*		17				2		2		15		3		16		7		8
Pacific Golden Plover *Pluvialis fulva*						1								1				2
Temminck's Stint *Calidris temminckii*		32		19		20		10		47		22		15		15		●
White-rumped Sandpiper *Calidris fuscicollis*								1							1		2	1

Table 3.1 (continued)

SPECIES *Scientific name*	99/00 W	2000 S	00/01 W	2001 S	01/02 W	2002 S	02/03 W	2003 S	03/04 W	2004 S	04/05 W	2005 S	05/06 W	2006 S	06/07 W	2007 S	W tetrads	S tetrads
Pectoral Sandpiper *Calidris melanotos*						1								2		3		●
Curlew Sandpiper *Calidris ferruginea*		●		●	1	●		●		●	1	●		●		●	2	20
Stilt Sandpiper *Calidris himantopus*												1						3
Broad-billed Sandpiper *Limicola falcinellus*										2						1		3
Dowitcher sp. *Limnodromus sp.*		1																1
Whimbrel *Numenius phaeopus*		●		●		●		●	1	●		●		●		●	1	58
Lesser Yellowlegs *Tringa flavipes*							1				1	1			1		3	1
Wood Sandpiper *Tringa glareola*		●		●		●		●		●		●		●		●		23
Red-necked Phalarope *Phalaropus lobatus*		1		1		3						2		3		2		7
Grey Phalarope *Phalaropus fulicarius*							2		2				1		4		6	
Pomarine Skua *Stercorarius pomarinus*	●	7	●		●		●	1	●	4	●		●	1	●	5	●	●
Arctic Skua *Stercorarius parasiticus*	●	●	●	●	●	●	●	●		●	●	●	●	●	●	●	6	●
Long-tailed Skua *Stercorarius longicaudus*				2												1		●
Great Skua *Stercorarius skua*	●	2	●	2	●	1	●	1	●	4	●	3	●	1	●	3	●	●
Sabine's Gull *Xema sabini*		1																1
Kittiwake *Rissa tridactyla*	●	●	●	●	●	●	●	●	●	●		●		●	●	●	●	●
Slender-billed Gull *Chroicocephalus genei*		2																1
Bonaparte's Gull *Chroicocephalus philadelphia*								1								1		1
Ross's Gull *Rhodostethia rosea*													1				3	
Laughing Gull *Larus atricilla*														1				2
Ring-billed Gull *Larus delawarensis*												1	1				1	1
Caspian Tern *Hydroprogne caspia*				1		3						1						3
Whiskered Tern *Chlidonias hybrida*						1						1						2
White-winged Black Tern *Chlidonias leucopterus*		1								2				1		2		●

Table 3.1 (continued)

SPECIES *Scientific name*	99/00 W	2000 S	00/01 W	2001 S	01/02 W	2002 S	02/03 W	2003 S	03/04 W	2004 S	04/05 W	2005 S	05/06 W	2006 S	06/07 W	2007 S	W tetrads	S tetrads
Roseate Tern *Sterna dougallii*		●		●		●		●		●		●		●		●		5
Guillemot *Uria aalge*	●	●	●	●	●	●	●	●	●	●	●	●	●	●	●	●	●	●
Razorbill *Alca torda*		●	●	●	●	●	●	●		●	●	●	●	●	●	●	●	●
Black Guillemot *Cepphus grylle*	1											1	2		2		4	1
Little Auk *Alle alle*	●		●		●		●				●		●		●		21	
Puffin *Fratercula arctica*	●	●	●	●	●	●	●	●	●	●	●	●	●	●	●	●	●	●
Ring-necked Parakeet* *Psittacula krameri*	1		2		1	2				1				1			●	●
Alpine Swift *Apus melba*				1		1		2		2				1		2		●
European Bee-eater *Merops apiaster*		5		3		2				3		3		7		2		●
Hoopoe *Upupa epops*		1		2		6		2		3		4		5		4		●
Wryneck *Jynx torquilla*		5		9		4		13		13		7		4		2		36
Red-backed Shrike *Lanius collurio*		5		2		1		4		9		2		5		13		20
Lesser Grey Shrike *Lanius minor*								1										1
Woodchat Shrike *Lanius senator*		2										3		1		3		●
Penduline Tit *Remiz pendulinus*	1	1		1													1	3
Short-toed Lark *Calandrella brachydactyla*		1		1				2		1		1				1		●
Red-rumped Swallow *Cecropis daurica*										3		1		2		2		●
Yellow-browed Warbler *Phylloscopus inornatus*							1		1								3	
Hume's Warbler *Phylloscopus humei*									1				2				4	
Iberian Chiffchaff *Phylloscopus ibericus*																1		1
Dartford Warbler *Sylvia undata*		1						1			1	3	1	1	6	6	6	6
Marmora's Warbler *Sylvia sarda*				1														1
Subalpine Warbler *Sylvia cantillans*				1		4				1								●
Sardinian Warbler *Sylvia melanocephala*				1				2										3

Table 3.1 (continued)

SPECIES *Scientific name*	99/00 W	2000 S	00/01 W	2001 S	01/02 W	2002 S	02/03 W	2003 S	03/04 W	2004 S	04/05 W	2005 S	05/06 W	2006 S	06/07 W	2007 S	W tetrads	S tetrads
Savi's Warbler *Locustella luscinioides*				4		1				2				1		1		6
Booted Warbler *Hippolais caligata*																1		1
Icterine Warbler *Hippolais icterina*				1		3				1						5		●
Blyth's Reed Warbler *Acrocephalus dumetorum*																1		1
Marsh Warbler *Acrocephalus palustris*		1		2		1		6		1		1				1		●
Rose-coloured Starling *Pastor roseus*				1	1	9			1								●	●
Dipper *Cinclus cinclus*	1	1							1				1	1			●	●
Ring Ouzel *Turdus torquatus*		●		●		●		●		●		●		●		●		100
Thrush Nightingale *Luscinia luscinia*								1		1								2
Bluethroat *Luscinia svecica*				2		2				1						2		●
Desert Wheatear *Oenanthe deserti*	1																1	
Red-breasted Flycatcher *Ficedula parva*								1		2						1		●
Pied Flycatcher *Ficedula hypoleuca*		●		●		●		●		●		●		●		●		17
Alpine Accentor *Prunella collaris*										1								1
Citrine Wagtail *Motacilla citreola*										1								1
Richard's Pipit *Anthus richardi*		5		2		1		1		1				1	1		1	●
Tawny Pipit *Anthus campestris*		4		1		1		4						1				●
Olive-backed Pipit *Anthus hodgsoni*					1												1	
Red-throated Pipit *Anthus cervinus*		4				1												●
Serin *Serinus serinus*		2		2		2		7		3				1		1		●
Arctic Redpoll *Carduelis hornemanni*			1		5						1	1	1				6	1
Two-barred Crossbill *Loxia leucoptera*							1										1	
Common Rosefinch *Carpodacus erythrinus*		2				1		1		2				1		3		●
Rose-breasted Grosbeak *Pheucticus ludovicianus*														1				1

Table 3.1 (continued)

SPECIES *Scientific name*	99/00 W	2000 S	00/01 W	2001 S	01/02 W	2002 S	02/03 W	2003 S	03/04 W	2004 S	04/05 W	2005 S	05/06 W	2006 S	06/07 W	2007 S	W tetrads	S tetrads
Pine Bunting *Emberiza leucocephalos*									1								1	
Ortolan Bunting *Emberiza hortulana*		1		1														2
Rustic Bunting *Emberiza rustica*														1				1
Little Bunting *Emberiza pusilla*								1					1				3	1

3.2 Escapes and non-established introductions

The primary aim of the NBA, as already stated, has been to establish a baseline during the first decade of the 21st century, against which future changes in the county avifauna can be measured. One of the changes already under way, and likely to continue strongly into the future, is the trend for non-native birds to become more successful at establishing themselves in the British climate. All too often, birdwatchers have dismissed non-native birds as irrelevant, especially if the species is not on the official *British List*. Looking back, it is easy to find cases where fundamental changes in the British status of an introduced bird have not been documented as well as they should have been: in Norfolk terms, these include the rise of Greylag and Barnacle Geese, and the introduction, ultimately unsuccessful, of Night-heron. Looking forward, we want to be in at the start of documenting the rise of the next non-native to establish itself, whichever species that may turn out to be.

To ensure that our baseline applied to every non-native species, it was important that observers reported all birds that were noted in the wild during fieldwork, whether they were thought to be genuinely wild, feral or escapes from captivity. It is not possible for us to know how successful the NBA recording has been in this regard. We suspect, however, that there were still observers during the NBA period who regarded certain birds as unworthy of notice: evidence for this, perhaps, is the lack of even a single record of Muscovy Duck or Indian Peafowl in the 2007 *NBR*. Additional records for many species were obtained from the *NBR*.

Table 3.2 cross-tabulates all the species and their occurrence in the 16 summer and winter NBA periods. Dots in the cells of the table indicate presence during each NBA season and an empty cell indicates that no record was found. The order of species and the scientific names that are used are those recommended for international use by Gill & Donsker (2010), on behalf of the International Ornithological Congress.

Many of the records are just brief occurrences of wildly exotic species, as single individuals that seem most unlikely ever to meet a mate and breed in the wild state. The main relevance of such birds to British ornithology appears to lie in providing identification pitfalls for the unwary observer! A much wider set of such species occurred during the years that NBA was running but not during any of the summer or winter periods: details of these are in the *NBR*.

At the opposite end of the scale, there are species that are already nesting in the wild in Britain and whose breeding population could already be on the increase. Black Swan, for example, may well be in the early stages of establishing a feral population: a brief text for this species, and maps for three other species widely recorded – Ross's Goose, Muscovy Duck and Indian Peafowl – conclude the chapter.

Black Swan
Cygnus atratus

THE BLACK SWAN is native to Australia. It is a category E species as defined by the BOU Records Committee but occurs widely in Britain as an introduction or escape, with breeding confirmed annually since 1996. A naturalised population exists in the Netherlands and establishment in Britain and France could soon follow.

Small numbers were recorded in each of the NBA years and a pair with a single juvenile was seen at Salhouse in 2007, possibly representing the first instance of successful breeding in Norfolk. Records were generally of single birds, although pairs were noted at several sites. Individuals are sometimes quite mobile around the county. The favoured localities during the NBA were in Broadland and at the northern coastal reserves. The highest counts were of seven at Breydon and six at Buckenham in 2000 and six at Welney in 2007.

The *1981–84 Winter Atlas* recorded birds in two of Norfolk's 10-km squares. Eight 10-km squares, none of them occupied during 1981–84, recorded birds during the NBA period. The only other previous atlas record was of breeding evidence from TG31 in 1988–91.

SUMMER – Black Swan

Small dots 1 ('pair')

Muscovy Duck
Cairina moschata

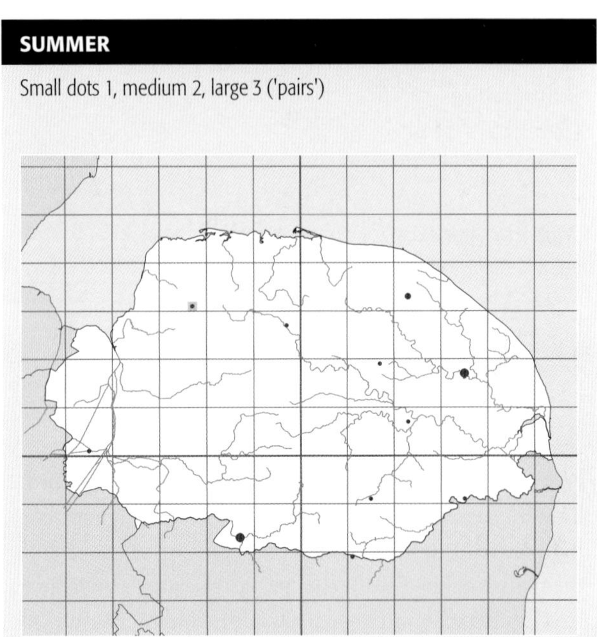

Ross's Goose
Chen rossii

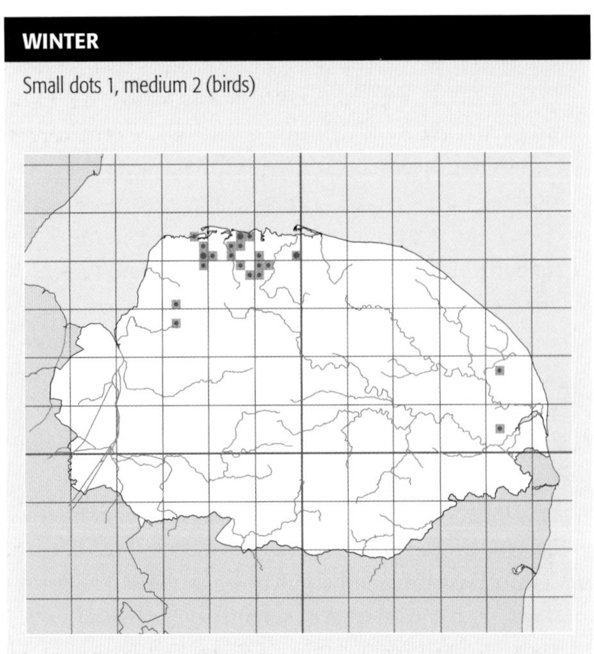

Indian Peafowl
Pavo cristatus

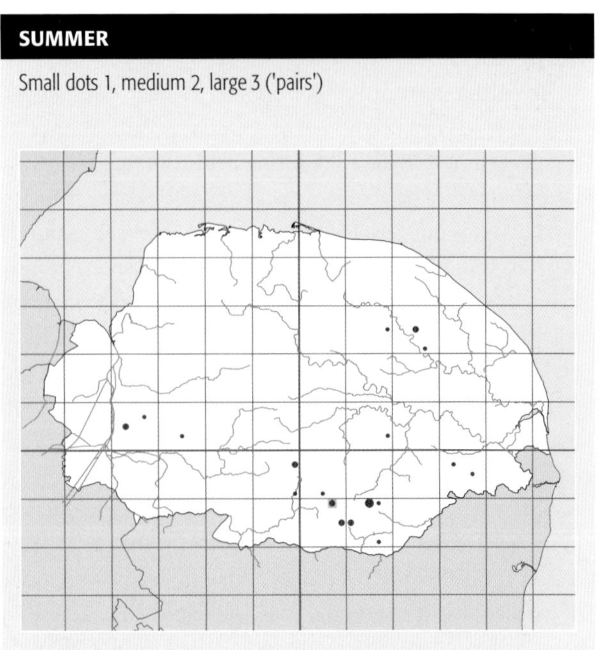

All escapes and non-established introductions recorded by NBA

Table 3.2 All escapes and non-established introduced bird species recorded by NBA. Species names and order are from Gill & Donsker (2010). Dots indicate presence during each NBA season.

SPECIES *Scientific name*	99/00 W	2000 S	00/01 W	2001 S	01/02 W	2002 S	02/03 W	2003 S	03/04 W	2004 S	04/05 W	2005 S	05/06 W	2006 S	06/07 W	2007 S
Helmeted Guineafowl *Numida meleagris*	●	●	●	●		●	●	●								
Reeves's Pheasant *Syrmaticus reevesii*	●	●		●	●	●		●		●		●		●		●
Indian Peafowl *Pavo cristatus*	●			●	●	●	●	●	●							
White-faced Whistling Duck *Dendrocygna viduata*			●	●	●	●	●	●				●				
Fulvous Whistling Duck *Dendrocygna bicolor*		●	●	●	●											
Swan Goose *Anser cygnoides*			●	●	●			●	●							
Bar-headed Goose *Anser indicus*	●	●	●	●	●	●	●	●	●	●	●	●	●	●		●
Ross's Goose *Chen rossii*			●	●	●	●	●	●	●	●	●	●		●	●	●
Emperor Goose *Chen canagica*			●	●	●		●					●			●	
Cackling Goose *Branta hutchinsii*	●	●														
Black Swan *Cygnus atratus*	●	●	●	●	●	●	●	●	●	●	●	●	●	●	●	●
Blue-winged Goose *Cyanochen cyanoptera*						●				●						●
South African Shelduck *Tadorna cana*					●	●		●					●		●	
Australian Shelduck *Tadorna tadornoides*						●				●						
Muscovy Duck *Cairina moschata*	●	●	●	●	●	●	●	●	●		●	●	●	●	●	
Wood Duck *Aix sponsa*		●			●	●					●			●		●
Ringed Teal *Callonetta leucophrys*				●												
Falcated Duck *Anas falcata*															●	●
Chiloé Wigeon *Anas sibilatrix*	●	●	●		●	●		●				●				
Cinnamon Teal *Anas cyanoptera*		●	●					●								

Table 3.2 (continued)

SPECIES *Scientific name*	99/00 W	2000 S	00/01 W	2001 S	01/02 W	2002 S	02/03 W	2003 S	03/04 W	2004 S	04/05 W	2005 S	05/06 W	2006 S	06/07 W	2007 S
Australasian Shoveler *Anas rhynchotis*		●														
Chestnut Teal *Anas castanea*														●		
White-cheeked Pintail *Anas bahamensis*			●						●				●	●	●	●
Yellow-billed Teal *Anas flavirostris*			●	●	●			●						●		
Yellow-billed Pintail *Anas georgica*					●											
Hottentot Teal *Anas hottentota*											●					
Marbled Duck *Marmaronetta angustirostris*		●														
Rosy-billed Pochard *Netta peposaca*						●		●			●	●	●			
Hooded Merganser *Lophodytes cucullatus*		●				●										
Lake Duck *Oxyura vittata*		●						●								
White-headed Duck *Oxyura leucocephala*						●										
African Sacred Ibis *Threskiornis aethiopicus*		●	●	●		●										
Great White Pelican *Pelecanus onocrotalus*					●											
Bald Eagle *Haliaeetus leucocephalus*	●															
Rüppell's Vulture *Gyps rueppellii*				●												
Harris's Hawk *Parabuteo unicinctus*	●									●		●	●	●	●	●
Red-tailed Hawk *Buteo jamaicensis*	●	●	●	●	●	●	●	●		●	●	●	●		●	●
Southern Crested Caracara *Caracara plancus*								●								
Lanner Falcon *Falco biarmicus*				●		●				●		●		●	●	●
Saker Falcon *Falco cherrug*	●		●		●	●		●				●				
Barbary Dove *Streptopelia 'risoria'*					●											
Laughing Dove *Spilopelia senegalensis*		●														
Cockatiel *Nymphicus hollandicus*		●	●	●				●		●			●			●
Eastern Rosella *Platycercus eximius*								●								

Table 3.2 (continued)

SPECIES *Scientific name*	99/00 W	2000 S	00/01 W	2001 S	01/02 W	2002 S	02/03 W	2003 S	03/04 W	2004 S	04/05 W	2005 S	05/06 W	2006 S	06/07 W	2007 S
Budgerigar *Melopsittacus undulatus*				●												
Superb Parrot *Polytelis swainsonii*																●
Rosy-faced Lovebird *Agapornis roseicollis*												●				
Red-and-green Macaw *Ara chloropterus*				●												
Blue-crowned Parakeet *Aratinga acuticaudata*					●	●										
Nanday Parakeet *Nandayus nenday*					●	●	●	●								
Yellow-headed Amazon *Amazona oratrix*			●													
Guinea Turaco *Tauraco persa*									●							
Eurasian Eagle-Owl *Bubo bubo*						●					●	●	●	●	●	
Indian Eagle-Owl *Bubo bengalensis*									●							
Lilac-breasted Roller *Coracias caudatus*				●												
Laughing Kookaburra *Dacelo novaeguineae*													●			
Northern Carmine Bee-eater *Merops nubicus*						●										
Australian Magpie *Gymnorhina tibicen*													●			
White-cheeked Starling *Spodiopsar cineraceus*		●														
White-shouldered Starling *Sturnia sinensis*						●										
Yellow-crowned Bishop *Euplectes afer*			●													
Java Sparrow *Lonchura oryzivora*								●								
Pin-tailed Whydah *Vidua macroura*							●									
Atlantic Canary *Serinus canaria*								●								●
Grey-headed Bullfinch *Pyrrhula erythaca*		●														
Chinese Grosbeak *Eophona migratoria*		●														
Japanese Grosbeak *Eophona personata*		●														
Meadow Bunting *Emberiza cioides*	●			●												

CHAPTER 4

The habitats of Norfolk
by P W Lambley

NORFOLK IS THE FIFTH LARGEST English county, behind North Yorkshire, Cumbria, Devon and Lincolnshire, and holds a correspondingly wide range of habitat types, each with a characteristic contribution to the county's avifauna. Some of these habitats are important nationally or internationally and might be unfamiliar, especially to readers outside the county. This chapter is a brief summary of Norfolk's regional topography and habitats, particularly as viewed from an ornithological standpoint.

Ours is a low-lying county: Beacon Hill, standing barely over a mile from the sea near West Runton, is the county's highest point at just 103 m asl. This is part of the Cromer to Holt ridge, which is made up of sands and gravels which were deposited during one of the ice advances of the last half-million years. The rest of the county is generally undulating, though incised by a number of river valleys including those of the Bure, Wensum, Yare and Waveney which flow in an easterly direction, reaching the sea at Great Yarmouth. The Nar, Wissey and Little Ouse flow westwards into Fenland and reach the Wash at King's Lynn via the Great Ouse. The east–west trend of these valleys provides flyways which are used by birds moving between the east coast and the Wash and the Fenland basin. Two rivers flow northwards – the Stiffkey and the Glaven. In the east, Broadland forms a distinct landscape area of slow-flowing rivers, grazing marshes, open waters and fens. In contrast, the rivers of the Fenland basin are almost entirely artificial; the landscape is mostly arable and divides into the fen peats and the silt fens, the latter lying closer to the sea. Centuries of exposure to drying winds have reduced the altitude to several metres below sea level in places.

Breckland, shared with Suffolk, is another distinct landscape, characterised by light sandy soils over chalk.

In the west, fringing the Wash and running south along the eastern edge of Fenland, is the greensand ridge, which is an area of acid sandy soils supporting heaths, mires and conifer plantations.

The county has a very extensive coastline which outlines the northern part of the bulge of East Anglia. The large embayment of the Wash is shared with Lincolnshire and has extensive sand and mud flats with some shingle. The only hard cliffs are at Hunstanton; these are composed of white and red chalk with a ginger-coloured sandstone (carstone) at the base. The north Norfolk coast is a barrier coast with sand dunes and shingle ridges developing parallel to the shore and saltmarshes forming behind them. Many of these saltmarshes have been claimed as farmland during the last 300–400 years. This coast is very exposed to the north and in fact there is no land between it and the North Pole. Further east there is a long line of soft clay cliffs which extend from Weybourne eastward to Happisburgh. They reach 65 m in places and are subject to substantial landslips. South of Happisburgh the coast is generally low lying and is backed by Broadland.

URBAN AREAS

Houses and gardens provide a habitat which can resemble scrub in structure and provides an important feature used by birds both in rural and urban areas. Gardens are becoming an increasingly important habitat for birds throughout the year. The lawns, shrubberies and mature trees provide feeding areas and nesting sites in towns, while gardens in rural areas are often oases in an otherwise arable desert. The provision of nestboxes and the popularity of feeding birds in gardens with nuts, seeds and kitchen scraps have undoubtedly helped to counterbalance the problems created by changes in agricultural practices in recent years. In particular, families such as the finches, thrushes and doves have greatly benefited from the presence of town and country gardens.

The traditional Norfolk pantiled roofs of the older cottages and houses provide nesting sites for House Sparrow, Starling and Swift. Derelict industrial sites, often dominated by buddleia *Buddleja*, were common in and around the major towns of Norwich, Great Yarmouth and King's Lynn until the late 20th century but are now disappearing rapidly.

WOODLAND

There is a surprising diversity of woodland in Norfolk. Around 8–10% of the county is wooded, a figure close to the average for England as a whole and higher than that for other counties in the East of England region (Smith & Gilbert 2001).

Ancient woodland (defined as in existence since 1600 without being replanted) occupies only a small area. However, Rackham (1986) states that, of the 64 types of ancient woodland so far recognised, 34 are known in Norfolk. The main areas of ancient woodland are in southeast Norfolk with a belt extending north through the middle of the county towards the north Norfolk coast. Most of this has been managed historically as coppice-with-standards, though this practice has now largely ceased except in some woodland nature reserves. In north Norfolk on the sands and gravels of the Cromer to Holt ridge there are stands of wood pasture where large pollards of oak *Quercus robur* and beech *Fagus sylvaticus* occur.

There are also woodlands which have appeared since the 1600s, through natural succession or planting. After 1900, traditional practices like the cutting of marsh hay and grazing began to die out and this has resulted in the growth of extensive areas of secondary alder *Alnus glutinosa* woodland in Broadland and birch *Betula*–oak on many heaths. Many smaller woods and copses throughout the county had been planted in the 18th and 19th centuries, often for game cover, or have grown up around old marl pits and other features that were difficult to cultivate. In recent years there has been another phase of planting; this time linked to various landscape initiatives and the availability of grants for projects linked to nature conservation. In Breckland, very extensive areas were planted with conifers in the 1920s and 1930s as a response to shortages of timber in the First World War. Thetford Forest, shared between Norfolk and Suffolk, is the largest manmade forest in lowland Britain. These forests are almost all coniferous and are felled on a rotational cycle.

JEFF BAKER/JEFF BAKER

Traditional Norfolk pantiled roofs offer valuable nesting sites for species such as House Sparrow, Starling and Swift. *East Harling.*

Large pollarded oaks are found mostly in north Norfolk. Such old trees offer opportunities for hole-nesting birds such as Tawny Owl and Nuthatch. *Bayfield Park*.

Young small-leaved lime coppice. *Swanton Novers Great Wood.*

Wood pasture

Woodlands with large pollards of oak occur mainly in north Norfolk, as for example the Bayfield Woods near Glandford, and a cluster within the boundaries of the old Stock Heath at Thursford. A few similar stands occur elsewhere in the county, as at Merton Park on the edge of Breckland. Such old pollards present many opportunities to hole-nesting birds such as Tawny Owl and Nuthatch. Small stands of pollarded beech woodland occur on the gravels of the Cromer to Holt ridge at Felbrigg and further east at Northrepps. These probably also represent remnants of wood pasture and may be the furthest north that stands of native beech reach in Britain, though it is also possible that they are early plantings. The ground flora of these woods is limited, with much bare ground but thickets of brambles *Rubus* in places.

Coppice-with-standards

Most of the ancient (pre-1600) mixed broad-leaved woods in Norfolk were historically managed as coppice-with-standards but, in many instances, coppicing has ceased and the woods have progressed to high forest or are in the process of doing so. Coppicing has been reactivated in many woods that are managed as nature reserves, for example, parts of Swanton Novers Great and Little Woods, Wayland Wood and Foxley Wood.

Most of the woods which have developed on the boulder clays are mixed broad-leaved woodland, including ash *Fraxinus excelsior*–oak–maple *Acer campestre* woods which prevail in the middle and southeast of the county. Within this overall grouping a number of other distinct types can be recognised, most notably lime *Tilia* and oak–hornbeam *Carpinus betulus* woods. Lime woods with small-leaved lime *Tilia cordata* are generally found on the better soils and include Hockering Wood, which is the third-largest such wood in England. These lime woods generally have few shrubs, as hazel *Corylus avellana* and other species do not flourish under the deep shade of lime. Hornbeam woods are a feature of southeast Norfolk and probably reach their northern natural limit just south of Norwich.

Far less common are woods of sessile oak *Quercus petraea*, which occur as overgrown coppiced stands at Edgefield Little Wood and within Swanton Novers Great Wood. Plateau alder woodland, which is a rare stand type nationally, occurs in some Norfolk woodland such as at Swanton Novers.

The complexity and diversity of woodland types in Norfolk is demonstrated in Swanton Novers Great and Little Woods, where contrasting soils occur in close proximity and support a range of woodland including oak–maple–hazel, lime, plateau and valley alder, sessile oak and several intermediate stand types (Sage 2006).

Secondary woodland

During the last century, many traditional practices such as grazing and marsh mowing ceased on commons, heaths and fens, allowing the development of secondary woodland. Oak–birch woodland is the successional community on heaths, with a ground or shrub flora generally dominated by bracken *Pteridium aquilinum* and bramble. As most of this has developed in the 20th century the trees are rarely of any great size. Around Felthorpe and on Marsham Heath there are extensive old planted stands of sweet chestnut *Castanea sativa*.

JEFF BAKER/JEFF BAKER

Alder carr along river valleys is particularly attractive to flocks of Siskin and Lesser Redpoll in late winter. *Little Ouse, Thetford.*

JEFF BAKER

Extensive areas of conifer can be found in Breckland. Typically, as seen here, areas are felled on a rotational basis producing several generations of plantations. *Thetford Forest.*

Carr woodland, dominated by alder and with nettle *Urtica dioica* in the herb layer, forms extensive stands in the floodplains of the Broadland rivers, where the marshes have been colonised following the decline in the cutting of marsh hay, reed and sedge. Sallow carr (dominated usually by grey willow *Salix cinerea*) occupies similar situations as the alder carr along the river valleys, around flooded gravel pits and within the Broadland fens. Elsewhere, smaller areas of alder occur throughout Norfolk's river valleys.

Plantations

There are extensive conifer plantations in Breckland and smaller ones elsewhere, especially on sandy and acid soils. Originally many were of Scots pine *Pinus sylvestris* but now Corsican pine *P. nigra*, Douglas fir *Pseudotsuga menziesii*, Norway spruce *Picea abies* and hybrid larches such as *Larix x marschlinsii* are grown more often. These and other conifers create extensive habitat for birds such as Goldcrest and Coal Tit and meet the more specialised needs of Crossbill, Siskin and Firecrest. In Thetford Forest the plantations are felled on a rotational cycle and, after felling, new clearings and young plantations, with or without rows of brash and tree stumps, are used by Woodlark and Nightjar.

Poplar *Populus* plantations are a feature of some of the river valleys, especially on the Fenland fringe where they have been the habitat for Norfolk's tiny and vulnerable population of Golden Oriole.

Scrub

Several scrub communities are widespread, usually dominated by hawthorn *Crataegus monogyna* or blackthorn *Prunus spinosa*. This habitat generally develops on unmanaged or under-managed commons or other grasslands, as at East Walton, Whitwell, Alderford, Salthouse Heath and Leziate. Blackthorn thicket is favoured by Nightingale and also holds Whitethroat and other warbler species. The non-native invasive *Rhododendron*, planted to ornament many Norfolk estates, forms impenetrable scrub or undergrowth in woodland and often spreads onto nearby heath, as for example at Westwick and Sandringham.

Bog myrtle *Myrica gale* forms dense stands on some of the greensand mires and in unmanaged parts of Broadland fens. On the fringes of the saltmarshes on the north Norfolk coast, shrubby seablite *Suaeda vera* forms a distinct kind of scrub, while on dunes at Holme and Hunstanton and on the cliffs at Overstrand there are extensive stands of sea buckthorn *Hippophae rhamnoides*: both these shrubs are well known to birdwatchers for sheltering migrant passerines in spring and especially in autumn.

HEATHLAND

Heathland in a Norfolk context is defined as vegetation dominated by heather *Calluna vulgaris*, bell heather *Erica cinerea*, cross-leaved heath *E. tetralix* or gorse *Ulex*, often with bracken. It has developed on the sandier parts of the greensand outcrop in west Norfolk and the glacial sands and gravels, especially in northeast Norfolk between Holt and Cromer.

The mixture of heather and gorse provides a colourful display of purple and yellow in late summer. It is this habitat which has recently been colonised by Dartford Warbler and also holds significant populations of some other species like Nightjar and Linnet. In winter it is hunted over by Hen Harrier, Rough-legged Buzzard and other raptors. On the greensand ridge and in Breckland, western gorse *Ulex gallii* is largely absent and a community of heather and sheep's fescue *Festuca ovina* generally prevails. On many heaths bracken spreads over significant areas, unless controlled.

Valley mires have developed where the topography is suitable within the boundaries of many of these heaths, as at Buxton Heath, Holt Lowes, Sheringham and Beeston Commons, Dersingham Bog and Roydon Common.

JEFF BAKER

Norfolk's heathland is typically made up of heathers, gorse and scattered pine and birch. *Kelling Heath.*

JEFF BAKER

Dry grasslands in Breckland offer ideal conditions for breeding birds, sometimes including Stone-curlew. *East Wretham Heath.*

GRASSLAND

Dry and unimproved grassland

Although chalk underlies about 60% of Norfolk there is very little typical chalk grassland, because the surface geology is mainly of glacial deposits of varying depth. Much of the chalk grassland outside Breckland is developed either on natural steep slopes, as at Ringstead Downs and Cockthorpe Common, or on manmade structures such as the Iron Age camp at Warham and a number of steep cuttings and embankments on disused railway lines, as at Walsingham and Narborough. Most such areas are too small, however, to make much impact on bird communities.

The largest areas of dry grassland occur in Breckland, where the underlying chalk is covered by sand. Freeze–thaw conditions in late glacial times produced a complex pattern of calcareous and acid soils, and their associated vegetation types, often in close proximity. However, the light soils and heavy grazing by sheep or rabbits mean that structurally the two types tend to look similar, with a short turf with fine-leaved grasses together with some low-growing herbs like thyme *Thymus*, and varying degrees of bare ground due to rabbit and mole activity. Where the soils are particularly light and sandy, a form of sand-dune vegetation develops, including species like sand sedge *Carex arenaria*. Breck grasslands are best developed at Weeting Heath, East Wretham Heath and more extensively within the Stanford Training Area. Wheatear and Stone-curlew traditionally breed on these grass heaths, especially where there are spreads of flint, but the former species is now almost extinct as a breeding bird in the county.

Old unimproved meadows outside Breckland and the chalk soils of north Norfolk are rare and tend to be confined to the heavier clays of south and mid Norfolk. Examples include those at Mattishall, Shelfanger (a Lammas meadow) and New Buckenham Common, and some of the better roadside verges and churchyards. Elsewhere a few scattered meadows survive, for example at The Brinks at Northwold. Acid grassland outside Breckland is rare, though that around Sculthorpe airfield is a semi-improved version.

Improved and semi-improved wet grassland

There are extensive areas of improved or semi-improved grazing marsh on the Wash at Snettisham and on the north Norfolk coast between Holme and Kelling. There are also very large areas of wet grassland in Broadland which extend up the valleys of the Ant, Bure, Yare and Wensum. These were traditionally grazed by cattle, and mostly still are. Of critical importance to the bird interest of these grazing marshes is the degree to which water levels are held in the networks of drainage ditches that drain these marshes. When managed so that high water levels in winter are lowered in spring, they can support large populations of wintering wildfowl such as Pink-footed Geese and Wigeon and then become suitable as breeding habitats for Lapwing, Redshank and other waders. Semi-improved and improved grassland is also a feature of most of the valleys of the Rivers Nar, Wissey and Little Ouse before they flow into the fenland basin. Unusually, in the middle reaches of the Nar and Wissey valleys there are examples of former water meadows with a complex series of drains and, although other waders now are largely gone from such habitats in the county, these can be still be suitable for breeding Lapwing.

OPEN WATERS

The main concentration of fresh open waters is in Broadland where there are about 50, varying in size from the expanse of Hickling Broad at about 140 ha to pools with a water surface of a quarter hectare or less. They are generally less than 4 m in depth (George 1992) and originated as medieval peat diggings. They are usually bordered by dense reed swamps as at Hickling and Horsey Mere or by willow scrub and alder carr as at Ranworth and Upton Broads.

JEFF BAKER

Grazing marshes on the north Norfolk coast are important areas for many species of wintering wildfowl. *The Serpentine, Cley-next-the-Sea.*

JEFF BAKER

Breckland meres often attract large numbers of wildfowl during cold winter months. *Ringmere, East Wretham.*

In addition there are many lakes created as part of 18th and 19th century landscaping schemes through the damming of streams, for example lakes in Gunton Park, at Blickling and at Stradsett. In the last 60 years there have also been many lakes created through gravel workings in the valleys, such as those along the River Wensum. Spreads of sand and gravel associated with the active workings provide habitats for nesting Little Ringed Plover and Oystercatcher, and even Common Tern. Vegetation tends to colonise quickly, however, once working ceases. Once disused, old pits have often been landscaped with birds and other wildlife in mind and become havens for breeding wildfowl.

In Breckland there are a number of naturally fluctuating meres, such as Ringmere and Langmere at East Wretham Heath, and Fowl Mere near Croxton, which are fed by groundwater, the levels reflecting rainfall months earlier. At times they are completely dry.

The rivers are generally slow flowing but are often stepped by the mills along their length with silted, deeper water immediately upstream and then faster-flowing stretches below. The latter are often frequented by Grey Wagtails and even on occasion by wintering Dippers.

MIRES AND SWAMPS

Although the county has a low rainfall, it has a wealth of wetlands which are probably unmatched by any other county in lowland Britain. This is a consequence of topography and geology, with chalk overlain by a series of both acid and calcareous drift deposits. They broadly group into floodplain wetlands, which are irrigated primarily by a river, and valley mires, maintained by springs and seepages which occupy slopes as well as the valley floor. The main floodplain wetlands are concentrated in Broadland. Valley mires are scattered through the rest of the county, but occur especially near the headwaters of the main rivers and on greensand. An unusual topographic variant of these mires are those developed in the ground ice depressions (pingos) in and around Breckland.

Broadland floodplain fens and swamps

Pure stands of common reed *Phragmites australis* are a feature of the edges of many of the Broads, and can be extensive. This is a favoured habitat of Reed Warbler, Marsh Harrier, Bearded Tit, Water Rail and Bittern. Reeds also fringe dykes in many places.

The herbaceous fens of Broadland form the largest expanse of species-rich fen in lowland Britain and have been described by Wheeler (1978). Particularly noteworthy are the common reed–milk parsley *Peucedanum palustre* communities, which are almost confined to the Broads. These cover 550 ha or 20% of the total fen area. The common reed–hemp agrimony *Eupatorium cannabinum* community is also widely distributed in Broadland. It is commonly found on freshwater ronds, the strips of land that lie between the river and flood embankment that are affected by winter flooding. In the Yare valley the sweet-grass *Glyceria maxima* swamp community is present although apparently it is less extensive than formerly. A community dominated by saw sedge *Cladium mariscus* is almost confined to the Ant and Thurne valleys. In the past these marshes were cut extensively for marsh products, such as reed for thatching, and small areas are still managed this way. Throughout these fens there are areas of open water – in dykes, remnant peat cuttings or duck decoys.

JEFF BAKER

Freshwater swamps dominated by extensive stands of common reed at Cley and Titchwell provides ideal habitat for Bearded Tit, Marsh Harrier and Reed Warbler. *Cley-next-the-Sea.*

Swamp communities outside Broadland

Freshwater swamps dominated by common reed are distributed in a band along the north Norfolk coast with large stands at Titchwell and Cley and smaller ones elsewhere, often linked by reed-fringed dykes. It is estimated that there are 142 ha in this area (Lambley 1997). Although much less extensive than those in the Broads they support Marsh Harriers and a few Bitterns. Smaller stands occur in the river valleys as at Guist Common, Boughton Fen and around Sculthorpe Moor, where there is also some saw sedge. They support the subset of wetland breeding birds which, unlike Bittern, do not require a large area of continuous swamp.

Valley mires

The valley mires in Norfolk are only matched in their number and interest by those on Anglesey and the Lleyn Peninsula in North Wales. They can be separated into acid, mixed and calcareous, reflecting the sources of water which feed them, though it is probably better to consider them as a broad continuum. They each generally have a range of vegetation types, from the wettest to the driest ground, often with areas of tall herb or swamp, mire and fen meadow, and on acid sites there is also a grading to wet heath. Frequently, willow carr has developed along the central stream.

The complex nature of the drift geology over the chalk means that water derived from several sources can feed a site. This gives rise to mixed mires which exhibit a range of lime-loving and lime-hating communities adjacent to one another and with some of the resultant communities not easy to classify. The communities include mire, fen meadow, and tall herbaceous fen including reed swamp.

Those on the greensand, notably at Roydon Common and Dersingham Bog, are set within areas of *Calluna* and *Erica* heath and are characterised

CHRIS KNIGHTS

Intertidal mud flats on the Wash support internationally important numbers of waders. *Snettisham.*

by a number of communities dominated by species of *Sphagnum* moss in the wettest areas. The bog asphodel *Narthecium ossifragrum–Sphagnum papillosum* community is well developed at these two sites with cranberry *Vaccinium oxycoccos*, round-leaved sundew *Drosera rotundifolia*, cotton-grass *Eriophorum angustifolium* and *Sphagnum fallax* also present. Lopham Fen, at the source of the River Waveney, together with the much smaller Redgrave Fen which lies in adjacent Suffolk, is the largest remaining river valley fen in England and provides an isolated breeding outpost for several wetland birds including Bearded Tit, Water Rail and Grasshopper Warbler.

Pingo systems are developed at a number of sites in or around Breckland, as at Thompson Common, East Walton Common and Adcock's Common. Tall herb fen, swamp fen, fen meadow and calcareous mire are developed in the pingos and there are often stands of saw sedge and common reed. These provide an ideal habitat for Sedge Warbler, Grasshopper Warbler and Water Rail. This is all set within a larger mosaic of unimproved grassland and scrub of various types.

COASTAL HABITATS

The inshore waters of the sea itself are a vital habitat for many bird species, such as sea duck, divers, grebes and auks in winter, and are the main feeding areas for the terns that breed along the north coast in summer.

Intertidal sand and mud

The Wash, which Norfolk shares with Lincolnshire, has very extensive areas of intertidal sand and mud that support internationally important flocks of waders. This is a crucial site for many species on the East Atlantic Flyway, which connects Arctic breeding grounds from central Canada to Siberia's Taimyr Peninsula with wintering sites in western and southern Africa. Adjoining intertidal flats on the northwest coast, eastward to Blakeney Harbour, extend 3–4 km seaward in places at low tide. These and Breydon Water provide additional intertidal feeding habitat for a wide range of wetland birds.

The intertidal zones are generally unvegetated except for seaweeds. Below low water, beds of eel grass *Zostera* occur in the harbour channels, though far less extensively than formerly. Post-glacial peat and the remains of submerged forest occur at Titchwell and provide a substrate for mussels *Mytilus edulis* and other shellfish, which in turn attract feeding waders such as Oystercatcher and Turnstone.

Saltmarsh

Norfolk has about 2,800 ha of saltmarsh, the sixth-largest total for this habitat for any county in Britain (Burd 1989). It occurs around the Wash, in northwest Norfolk and at Breydon Water on the east coast. Saltmarshes on the Wash, which are mostly on muddy substrates, were formerly grazed. This management is now being reinstated to lower the sward, largely for the benefit of birds. There are some pioneer communities mostly of rice-grass *Spartina* and annual seablite *Suaeda maritima*, though the lower saltmarsh is dominated by the saltmarsh grass *Puccinellia maritima*. For the most part these marshes are backed by sea-banks from reclamations, which continued into the 1960s.

The north Norfolk saltmarshes are generally developed on sandier substrates and were historically grazed, especially by sheep, though not in recent times. The lower zone of the saltmarsh is dominated in places by *Spartina*, as in Blakeney Harbour, but elsewhere by annuals such as samphire *Salicornia* and annual seablite with stands of sea aster *Aster tripolium*. Further up the shore the marshes are dominated by sea purslane *Atriplex portulacoides* or by communities of thrift *Armeria maritima* and sea lavender *Limonium vulgare*. This is followed by a number of communities of *Puccinellia maritima* with sea lavender–thrift and sea plantain *Plantago maritima*–thrift. In late summer these mid-zone marshes are a haze of purple with flowering sea lavender. In a few places, as at East Hills, small areas of upper saltmarsh are dominated by the rush *Juncus maritimus*.

In winter parties of Brent Geese graze on these marshes and the creek systems are used by Little Egrets and by waders such as Redshank, Curlew and Dunlin.

JEFF BAKER

Norfolk's saltmarshes provide important grazing habitat for wintering Brent Geese. *Blakeney.*

JEFF BAKER

Sand dune systems on Norfolk's coastline provide ideal habitat for nesting Sandwich, Common and Little Terns. *Wells-next-the-Sea.*

A feature of these marshes is the development of an often dense line of shrubby seablite at the spring high water mark, as at Blakeney Point, Burnham Norton and elsewhere. Freshwater springs emerge at the top of the saltmarsh between Brancaster and Thornham allowing the development there of tidal reedbeds.

Sand dunes

There are about 1,100 ha of dune system on the Norfolk coast, located mainly between Holme and Blakeney on the northwest coast and on the east coast from about Eccles-on-Sea to Great Yarmouth (Radley 1994). They range from slightly calcareous at Holme to very acid at Winterton, where there are extensive areas of dune heath. On the northwest coast they are fronted by extensive sand flats. In places these grade into saltmarsh, as at Holkham and Stiffkey.

The fore-dunes are sparsely vegetated with plants such as sea sandwort *Honkenya peploides*, sea rocket *Cakile maritima*, *Atriplex laciniata*, sea holly *Eryngium maritimum*, lyme-grass *Leymus arenarius* and sea couch *Elytrigia juncea*. In places this habitat can be quite wide, as at Winterton, Caister and around Brancaster. This is a favoured habitat for nesting Sandwich, Common and Little Terns, and also Ringed Plover and Oystercatcher. The higher but still mobile dunes are dominated by marram *Ammophila arenaria*.

The semi-fixed dunes are generally dominated by marram with red fescue *Festuca rubra*. This is well developed at the western end of the Holkham dune system. Dune grasslands are dominated by characteristic species such as lady's bedstraw *Galium verum*, red fescue and mouse-eared hawkweed *Pilosella officinarum*. More widespread are areas of short, dry lichen-dominated sand sedge dune, which are particularly characteristic of areas of sand over shingle, as at Blakeney Point. At Hunstanton and Holme, dunes support dense thickets of sea buckthorn, whilst areas of wild privet *Ligustrum vulgare* occur more generally. At Holkham a large proportion of the dunes were planted with trees in the 18th and 19th centuries and now support mature, naturally regenerating woodland of Corsican pine *Pinus nigra maritima* and holm oak *Quercus ilex*. This provides a beacon for land birds out at sea and opportunities for migrants such as warblers and thrushes to shelter and refuel.

Dune slacks are limited in extent in comparison with the dune systems in western Britain but, where they occur, support communities which require damp conditions such as creeping willow *Salix repens*–Yorkshire-fog *Holcus lanatus*. In places there are colourful displays of orchids, notably marsh helleborine *Epipactis palustris*, southern marsh orchid *Dactylorhiza praetermissa* and common spotted orchid *D. fuchsia*. The most extensive and the best known to birdwatchers is 'the Dell', near the Wells end of Holkham Pines.

At Winterton the extensive area of dune heath is the largest on the east coast of England. The community is characterised by heather with sand sedge and the grasses blue hair grass *Corynephorus canescens* and red fescue.

Shingle

Extensive shingle banks occur between Weybourne and Blakeney Point, with small but significant areas at Snettisham and at Scolt Head. The ridge between Kelling and Cley has, until recently, been bulldozed annually for many decades to maintain a high ridge for sea defence. Consequently the only vegetation has been annuals or biennials, with the flowers of yellow-horned poppy *Glaucium flavum* being particularly conspicuous. The landward side of the shingle ridge provides sheltered feeding sites for parties of wintering Snow Buntings and other passerines. Further west, towards Blakeney Point, the shingle is partially vegetated by species such as sea campion *Silene uniflora* and sea sandwort, whilst at the back of the ridge there are some extensive areas of shrubby seablite. On sheltered lateral spits a stable maritime grassland community develops, with buck's-horn plantain *Plantago coronopus*, thrift and red fescue. In very stable areas this develops into a lichen- *Cladonia*-dominated community with red fescue and scurvy grass *Cochleria* together with sea campion, thrift, smooth hawk's-beard *Crepis capillaris* and wall pepper *Sedum acre*. It

CHRIS KNIGHTS

Shingle ridge on the north Norfolk coast. *Cley-next-the-Sea.*

is to such habitats that vagrant birds from desert areas, such as Asian Desert Warbler and Trumpeter Finch, tend to be drawn.

A smaller area of shingle occurs at Snettisham and is favoured by a similar suite of passerines as the Cley–Kelling ridge.

Saline lagoons

A series of saline lagoons borders the landward side of the shingle ridge between Arnold's Marsh at Cley and Kelling Quags. They have a mixed sand, mud and shingle bottom and are mostly fringed by saltmarsh plants or in a few places by common reed. The aquatic vegetation is dominated by tasselweed *Ruppia*. The pools are used by waders such as Avocet, Redshank and Dunlin.

Similar pools were created by being incorporated into reclamations in the 18th and 19th centuries, including Broadwater at Holme, Salts Hole at Holkham and Abraham's Bosom at Wells. In addition, habitats which have many of the features of lagoons have been created at Titchwell and Cley Marshes as part of the management of these reserves.

Cliffs and rocky shore

Norfolk has about 29 km of coastal cliff (Lambley 1997). These are mostly composed of sands and clays, except at Hunstanton where there are hard rock cliffs of carstone overlain spectacularly with red and white chalk, the bedding planes providing secure ledges for nesting Fulmars. Between Weybourne and Happisburgh the cliffs are largely of soft sediments, particularly sands and clays. Where water drains from them, especially between West Runton and Mundesley, they are very unstable: frequent landslips create a mosaic of habitats from bare mud colonised by species such as coltsfoot *Tussilago farfara* through to stable grasslands with grasses such as red fescue and the colourful kidney vetch *Anthyllis vulneraria*. Flushes often have marsh horsetail *Equisetum palustre* and rushes, with small perched stands of common reed in places. Between Cromer and Overstrand there are dense stands of sycamore *Acer pseudoplatanus* and often impenetrable areas of sea buckthorn. The drier sections of cliff can be vertical but are still prone to erosion, especially by the wind. The periodic slipping provides faces for Sand Martins to nest. Pinnacles left by cliff falls and the extensive rough grassland on the slopes are used frequently by Kestrels.

CHRIS KNIGHTS

Hunstanton cliffs , composed of hard rock carstone overlain with red and white chalk, provide nesting ledges for Fulmars.

At West Runton the chalk is exposed on the foreshore and has large, peculiarly shaped flints known as paramoudras embedded in it that allow small rock pools to form. This is the only significant area of rocky intertidal shore between Flamborough Head and north Kent.

Islands

Norfolk has its very own seabird island at the Outer Trial Bank in the Wash, although this has been artificially created and is connected to the mainland over open mud at low tide. Initially colonised by terns, the site now holds the county's largest colonies of Herring and Lesser Black-backed Gulls. Scolt Head also becomes an island at high tide but is connected to the mainland by almost continuous saltmarsh.

The artificial reefs newly created off Sea Palling are effectively rocky islands, but have yet to develop any ornithological interest.

FARMLAND

Farmland occupies by far the greatest area of land in Norfolk. It is largely arable with pastures for livestock largely confined to Broadland, the north Norfolk coastal plain, parts of Breckland and along the courses of the major rivers.

The Norfolk landscape is broadly separated into late enclosure and old countryside. Late enclosure occupies the northwest of Norfolk and the Brecks and is characterised by large rectangular fields bounded by hawthorn hedges. In Breckland there are similarly large fields but in places lines of sheltering Scots pines were planted instead of hawthorn to mark field boundaries. The old countryside is retained mostly on the heavier clay soils of mid and south Norfolk. Its enclosure was more piecemeal and its hedges are generally much more mixed in composition. This was the area where there were significant losses of hedgerows during the 1950s to 1970s, though the process had begun before 1939.

The main crops grown now are winter wheat, winter barley (mostly for malting), maize, sugar beet and rape, with some potatoes, field beans and peas. In Breckland, carrots are grown on the light soils and in the Fens horticultural crops such as cabbage and leeks are also grown. The use of efficient insecticides and herbicides has meant that wheat, barley and in particular maize are largely free of insects and natural vegetation and therefore provide little food for birds. A significant change has been the loss of stubbles, which used commonly to remain through the winter prior to sowing in spring but now are typically ploughed and resown shortly after harvest. Since weedy stubbles provide valuable feeding opportunities during the winter months, their demise has had a major impact on farmland birds. Fields of sugar beet continue to provide a very significant habitat for wintering Pink-footed Geese, especially when the tops are left on the fields after lifting, but there could be a large decrease in the acreage of sugar beet grown in future because of the recent restructuring of the financial support.

In an attempt to counter the observed decline in many farmland birds there has been a marked

CHRIS KNIGHTS

Large Breckland fields are typically bounded by Scots pine to mark field boundaries. *Gooderstone.*

effort by government, through grant-aided schemes such as entry-level and higher-level Environmental Stewardship (ELS and HLS), to encourage farmers to provide bird-friendly features such as grass strips alongside hedgerows and strips of seed plants such as quinoa, millet, sunflower, fodder-radish and sweet clover. These options, which provide winter food and nesting cover for Grey Partridge, finches and other farmland birds, have had a strong uptake across the county but are highly vulnerable to future changes in government policy.

Beef cattle continue to graze the Broadland and the north Norfolk coastal grazing marshes but there has been a decline in stock numbers. This has had implications for many nature reserves, in particular where the management of the sward is important for breeding waders. The Breckland heaths are traditionally grazed by sheep, as at Weeting Heath and throughout the Stanford Training Area, where there is a hefted flock. A change in recent years is the loss of smallholders so that increasingly those who still have grazing animals have much higher stock numbers, which makes sensitive grazing for conservation more difficult.

Pigs are often kept outdoors, particularly on the lighter soils, and attract large feeding flocks of gulls, corvids, pigeons and finches. The largest gatherings of gulls, however, sometimes in tens of thousands, have been at sites around the county where chicken waste has been spread across the fields as a fertiliser. These large flocks have usually included a few rarities, such as Glaucous, Iceland and Caspian Gulls.

There has been a great loss of traditionally built barns and cattle sheds both to barn conversions and to dereliction, with a consequent loss of breeding sites for Barn Owls and Swallows in particular. Erection of Barn Owl nestboxes has been very popular, however, and successful in spreading the distribution to new areas of the county.

Commercial orchards occupy only a small area but particularly in the Fens provide an important habitat and food source for wintering thrushes.

The future of farming is particularly uncertain at present with changing policies on biofuels and subsidies and, whilst the price of cereals has risen rapidly, so have costs for fuels and fertiliser. As in the past, farmland birds will continue to reflect the changing farming scene.

Peter Lambley MBE graduated from Leicester University in Botany and worked for 15 years for Norfolk Museums Service before moving to the University of Papua New Guinea for four years. From 1989 to 2006 he worked in Norfolk as a Conservation Officer and lichen specialist for English Nature (now Natural England) and is an expert on Norfolk's diverse landscape.

CHAPTER 5

An overview of Norfolk's birds

by John H Marchant

THE THOROUGH AND EXTENSIVE MAPPING completed by volunteer birdwatchers for NBA during 1999–2007 provides a unique opportunity to review the distribution of the county's breeding and wintering birds at the turn of the millennium. Furthermore, because there have been previous bird atlas projects in the county, we are able to investigate the many changes in range that have occurred over recent decades. In addition, and for the first time, the population size of every regular breeding or wintering bird species in Norfolk has been estimated. The previous sections of the book have already discussed NBA's new distributional data and their implications at species level, and presented the population estimates. In this chapter, we provide a brief synthesis of these topics across species and assess the information that NBA can contribute to the conservation of birds in Norfolk.

The chapter has three main sections. The first describes the summer and winter avifaunas of Norfolk during the NBA period, using the new data we have just gathered. The second considers gains and losses in both summer and winter ranges, using information from previous atlas projects, including species that can be considered new to the county or to have gone extinct. In the closing section, we highlight some of the implications of the NBA for the future conservation of birds in the county, and the ways in which we hope conservationists and researchers will use the NBA database.

The UK Birds of Conservation Concern listings (*BoCC3*) provide a context for many of our comments and may need some introduction. The listings are designed to draw attention to those species whose trend or status is causing special concern: each native species is listed as green, amber or red, according to set criteria. The listings are reviewed every few years and *BoCC3* is an update of two earlier versions that were in place during the NBA period itself. Red listing most often results from a recent steep decrease in UK numbers or range – usually of more than 50% over a 25-year period. Birds may be amber listed through having more moderate declines over the same period – usually of 25–50% – or because their UK populations, irrespective of trend, are internationally important. Subspecies also have a conservation listing, which might differ from that of the parent species: for example, several breeding species are of greater concern at subspecies level because the British birds are of a race not found anywhere else.

The national population estimates we have used are from the latest report of the Avian Population Estimates Panel (*APEP06*) and refer to Great Britain, including the Isle of Man. The panel collates information and identifies the best available estimates – it does not produce estimates of its own. Although new studies have since revised or updated some of these figures, in general they relate well to the NBA period.

The limitations of our mapping data, of the comparisons with previous atlases and of the population estimates have been discussed already in introducing the main species texts. Caveats described at species level apply also to this overview. We limit our comments to simple descriptions of the data and present no complex statistics.

5.1 Norfolk's avifauna during 1999–2007

The NBA population estimates indicate that, during the NBA period, Norfolk was home to around 0.9 million (0.8–1.0 million) pairs of breeding birds, of 135 regularly breeding species. A further 23 or so species were regular in summer in Norfolk but did not nest in the county.

For the winter period, there were around 3.1 million (2.7–3.6 million) birds in the county, of 183 regular species. These figures include the local adults and young of resident species that survived until winter from the previous breeding season, and the winter visitors that arrive in Norfolk from as far away as arctic Canada and western Siberia.

At all seasons the regular bird species in Norfolk are joined unpredictably by scarce or rare visitors, which are not included in our totals. By the end of summer 2007, 422 bird species had accumulated on the Norfolk List, a prodigious figure for such a small area of the globe. Many additional species, some of which are listed in Table 3.2, have occurred in the county only as escapes or non-established introductions and are not part of the county list. These species are not considered further here.

Numbers of species per tetrad

The numbers of species found in each square are often plotted in bird atlases simply to show how well the atlas has covered every part of its area. Squares or regions might show up as under-covered on such a map and this can help the reader to distinguish the absence of a species from a shortage of survey effort. Where the atlas has been particularly thorough, however, or where effort has been similar across squares, the map could indicate the pattern of species richness across the atlas's area of coverage.

In Figures 5.1 and 5.2, we map the summer and winter distributions of the numbers of species found per tetrad by NBA observers. NBA coverage has not been uniform, with differing numbers of hours spent on set visits and a very patchy distribution of supplementary records, as discussed in the first chapter (Figures 1.3–1.6). Nevertheless, because NBA volunteers provided thorough coverage through set visits in very nearly every tetrad at each season, we feel these two maps do convey valuable information about the distribution of species richness across the county. For the summer map, only those species where breeding was considered to have been at least 'likely' have been included, because we feel that the richness of breeding species is of particular conservation interest.

The patterns of bird species richness across Norfolk in summer and winter are remarkably similar. Because neither map shows any obvious relationship to the patterns of survey coverage (Figures 1.3–1.6), there is no reason to think that differential effort has biased the picture. There are hotspots for breeding species in several, well-scattered areas of the county, including Breckland, the Broads and a band along much of the north coast (Figure 5.1). Norfolk's river valleys are also clearly relatively rich in breeding bird species and at least parts of all the major rivers can be traced. It is not the case, however, as some readers might have assumed, that the coastal zone stands out from the rest of the county: the coastal reserves hold many species that are rare or absent elsewhere, but often they lack species that prefer more sheltered habitats and that are widespread elsewhere.

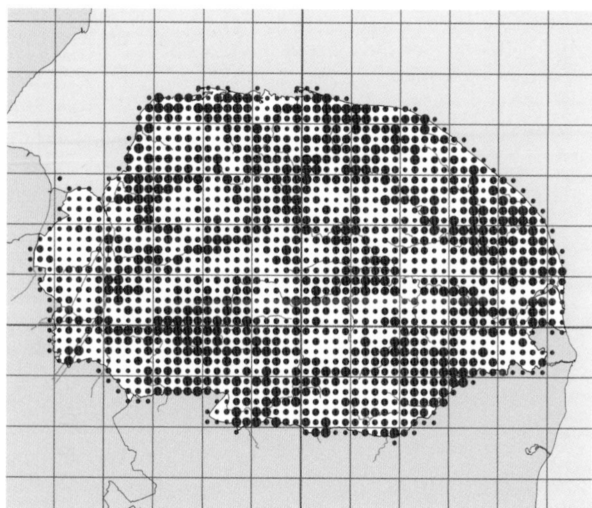

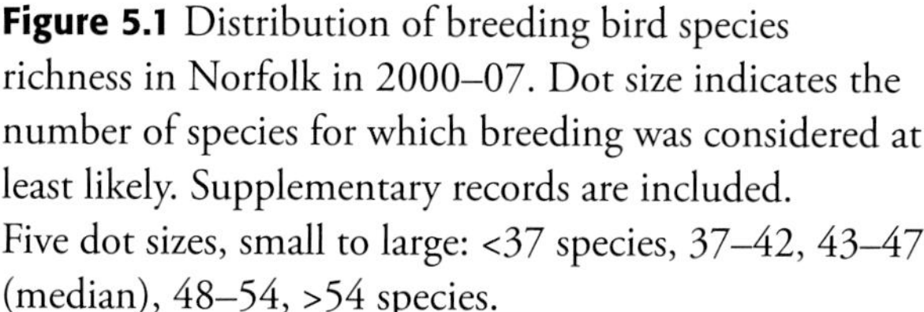

Figure 5.1 Distribution of breeding bird species richness in Norfolk in 2000–07. Dot size indicates the number of species for which breeding was considered at least likely. Supplementary records are included.
Five dot sizes, small to large: <37 species, 37–42, 43–47 (median), 48–54, >54 species.

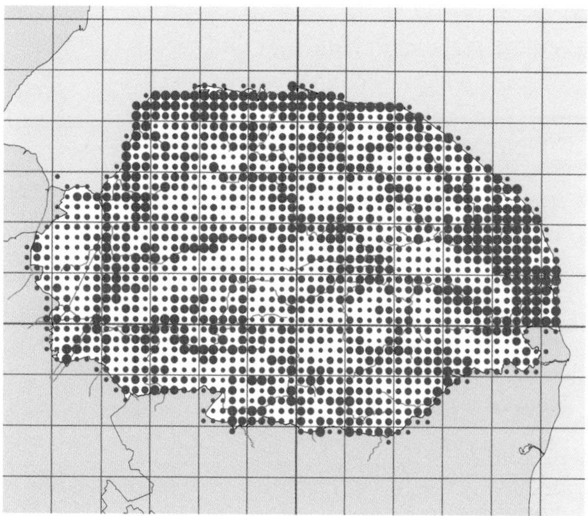

Figure 5.2 Distribution of wintering bird species richness in Norfolk in 1999–2007. Dot size indicates the number of species recorded, including supplementary records.
Five dot sizes, small to large: <40 species, 40–46, 47–51 (median), 52–60, >60 species.

On the winter map (Figure 5.2), the Broads are much more prominent than for breeding birds and Breckland less so. The coastal zone and the river valleys are more sharply defined than in summer, further emphasising the special importance of wetland habitats for bird species richness in winter.

Most abundant and widespread species

In Tables 5.1 and 5.2, we list the dozen species we consider to have been the most abundant breeding and wintering species in the county during the NBA period. These have been ranked according to the midpoints of their NBA population estimates. The number of occupied tetrads is also tabulated, as a measure of how widespread the species were at this scale.

There are no surprises among the breeding species (Table 5.1). These are all species likely to appear in the top 12 breeding birds in any English county. Comparing the list with that of the most abundant species breeding in Britain as a whole (*APEP06*), the only species that is missing from the Norfolk top 12 is Willow Warbler, which has been replaced in our list by Rook. BBS data for the county paint a very similar picture (*fide* A F Brown), allowing us to conclude that BBS can provide a very robust means of recording change in abundance at county scale.

Woodpigeon comes top of the NBA list: this species was sixth nationally but we estimate it to have been by far the most abundant breeding bird in Norfolk. It is notable that two of Norfolk's most abundant breeding birds – House Sparrow and Skylark – are red-listed, having shown major declines in their abundance in the UK during recent decades (*Birdtrends*). Although these species are still very common breeding birds in Norfolk, we cannot assume this will always be the case: their trends will continue to need careful monitoring.

Wren, and then Blackbird, Chaffinch and Woodpigeon, were found breeding in the highest numbers of tetrads across the county. Whitethroat, with an estimated 13,000–15,000 breeding pairs in Norfolk, was the only species not tabulated that was found breeding in more than 90% of tetrads (91%). House Sparrow was less widespread than most of the other abundant species, being absent from many forested and agricultural landscapes in the county and more concentrated into towns and villages. Rook, as a colonial bird nesting in rookeries sometimes of several hundred pairs, was in tenth position in terms of breeding population size but nested in only 29% of tetrads.

Table 5.1 The most abundant bird species breeding in Norfolk, 2000–07. Tetrads 'occupied' are those where breeding was proved or considered likely.

Species	ESTIMATED POPULATION (BREEDING PAIRS)	TETRADS OCCUPIED	*BoCC3* LISTING
Woodpigeon	100,000–120,000	1,405 (96%)	green
Wren	60,000–70,000	1,418 (97%)	green
Blue Tit	60,000–70,000	1,379 (95%)	green (amber at race level)
Chaffinch	50,000–70,000	1,407 (96%)	green (amber at race level)
Blackbird	45,000–55,000	1,408 (97%)	green
Robin	40,000–50,000	1,390 (95%)	green
Great Tit	40,000–50,000	1,357 (93%)	green (amber at race level)
House Sparrow	40,000–50,000	1,222 (84%)	red
Skylark	25,000–30,000	1,358 (93%)	red
Rook	25,000–30,000	423 (29%)	green
Pheasant	20,000–30,000	1,357 (93%)	unlisted
Dunnock	20,000–25,000	1,379 (95%)	amber

Table 5.2 The most abundant bird species in Norfolk in winter, 1999–2007.

Species	ESTIMATED POPULATION (INDIVIDUALS)	TETRADS OCCUPIED	*BoCC3* LISTING
Woodpigeon	300,000–350,000	1,419 (97%)	green
Starling	250,000–280,000	1,332 (91%)	red
Blue Tit	140,000–180,000	1,397 (96%)	green (amber at race level)
Wren	140,000–160,000	1,404 (96%)	green
Chaffinch	120,000–160,000	1,395 (96%)	green (amber at race level)
Blackbird	120,000–150,000	1,422 (98%)	green
Pink-footed Goose	100,000–150,000	168 (12%)	amber
Pheasant	100,000–150,000	1,384 (95%)	unlisted
Robin	100,000–150,000	1,390 (95%)	green
Great Tit	100,000–130,000	1,367 (94%)	green (amber at race level)
Rook	75,000–150,000	1,125 (77%)	green
House Sparrow	90,000–120,000	1,200 (82%)	red

The winter rankings (Table 5.2) contain ten of the same species that were most abundant as breeding birds, and in approximately the same order. Woodpigeon was by far the most abundant wintering species and accounted for more than 10% of the county's total bird population at that season. Skylark and Dunnock, which are in the top rankings for breeding birds, are replaced in the winter rankings by Starling and Pink-footed Goose.

Norfolk's winter population of Pink-footed Geese is of outstanding global conservation importance. This species winters almost exclusively in Britain, with much smaller numbers in neighbouring countries, especially the Netherlands, Denmark and Ireland. Within Britain, three of the top six roost sites for this species are on the Norfolk coast (Holkham Marshes, Scolt Head and Snettisham). Whereas the other most numerous species in Norfolk were also widespread, Pink-footed Geese were recorded in only 12% of the county's tetrads.

The red-listed Starling and House Sparrow remain, despite their declines in breeding population, among the most numerous winter birds in the county. With a county breeding population of only around 20,000 pairs, the Starlings in Norfolk in winter are overwhelmingly visitors from northern Europe.

DAVID TIPLING

'It is extraordinary that the most abundant birds in Norfolk at both seasons should include Pheasant, a native of Asia that occurs in Britain only because it has been released to be hunted.'

Most of the most abundant species occupied a few more tetrads in winter than in summer. Blackbird, followed by Woodpigeon and Wren, was the most widespread species at tetrad level in Norfolk during the NBA winter periods.

It is extraordinary that the most abundant birds in Norfolk at both seasons should include Pheasant, a native of Asia that occurs in Britain only because it has been released to be hunted. Since 1980–85, the numbers of Pheasants released by the shooting industry in Britain each year have approximately doubled and – since the national estimate is 35 million (PACEC 2006) – it is likely now that around a million poults are reared and released each autumn in Norfolk alone. A million dwarfs all population estimates for other birds in the county! By December, though, most released Pheasants will have succumbed to predation or illness, or hit cars, and our winter population estimate for Norfolk reflects this. The input of such an enormous non-native biomass every autumn must surely have a heavy negative impact on natural biodiversity, but the effects have not been properly quantified. The positive side of Pheasant rearing for bird conservation is that it encourages estate owners to retain small woodlands that they might otherwise convert to arable fields and to plant 'game cover' crops that often benefit seed-eating birds.

Species for which Norfolk holds nationally important numbers

With population sizes estimated now for all of Norfolk's birds, we are able for the first time to compare county figures with national ones and to assess for which species the Norfolk population might be of special national significance. The *APEP06* estimates for Great Britain do not all cover the same range of years and some date from before the start of the NBA period. There are gaps in the *APEP06* listings, especially for breeding birds that also winter, and the units of assessment may vary. Nevertheless, by standardising the units, and taking the midpoints of the ranges for Great Britain and Norfolk estimates, we have been able to assess the proportion that our Norfolk figure represents of the total population of the species across Great Britain. This is naturally a

Table 5.3 Norfolk breeding birds of national importance during 2000–07, according to population estimates for Great Britain (*APEP06*) and for Norfolk (NBA). Units are pairs (P) or breeding pairs (bp), except where stated.

Species	GB BREEDING POPULATION	NORFOLK BREEDING POPULATION	ESTIMATED % OF BRITISH BREEDING POPULATION IN NORFOLK	*BoCC3* LISTING
Egyptian Goose	(no estimate)	750–900 bp	>90%	unlisted
Crane	(4 P)	2–9 bp	>80%	amber
Montagu's Harrier	7 territorial females	2–6 nesting females	>50%	amber
Marsh Harrier	201 females	90–120 nesting females	>50%	amber
Stone-curlew	214–227 P	90–130 bp	>40%	amber (red at race level)
Avocet	877 P	300–500 bp	>40%	amber
Bearded Tit	504–559 P	200–250 bp	>40%	amber
Bittern	28 males	10–19 booming males	>40%	red
Cetti's Warbler	645 males	100–400 singing males	>33%	green
Sandwich Tern	10,536 P	3,000–4,500 bp	>33%	amber
Golden Pheasant	85–118 P	20–35 bp	>20%	unlisted
Red-crested Pochard	29 P	5–10 bp	>20%	unlisted
Little Tern	1,947 P	400–600 bp	>20%	amber
Firecrest	80–250 males	15–60 singing males	>20%	amber
Gadwall	770 P	150–200 bp	>20%	amber
Water Rail	450–900 P	100–200 bp	>20%	green
Quail	4–315 males	20–50 singing males	>20%	amber
Little Egret	(146–162 P)	0–130 bp	>10%	amber
Greylag Goose (re-established)	29,900 adults	2,000–3,500 bp	>10%	unlisted
Woodlark	1,426–1,552 P	180–300 bp	>10%	amber
Black Redstart	25–73 P	4–10 bp	>10%	amber
Barn Owl	3,000–5,000 P	400–600 bp	>10%	amber
Great Crested Grebe	8,000 adults	450–500 bp	>10%	green

very imprecise calculation, given the errors associated with both sets of figures. Rather than present the calculated proportion of the British population that is in Norfolk, therefore, we give an estimated minimum figure that reflects the lack of precision.

Table 5.3 shows the breeding species for which Norfolk appears to have the greatest national importance, ranked by the estimated proportion of the national population that breeds in the county. Species with an estimated proportion greater than 10% are listed: given Norfolk's land area, estimates in the region of 2.5% would be in proportion to Britain as a whole. Species breeding less than annually in Norfolk have been omitted. Egyptian Goose is included, although *APEP06* does not give a national breeding estimate.

The breeding species for which Norfolk is nationally important are mostly rare species with British breeding populations of fewer than a thousand pairs. Among the rare birds, Norfolk's Cranes, Avocets, Marsh and Montagu's Harriers and Stone-curlews stand out as of particular national significance. Sandwich and Little Terns have more-substantial British populations, of which Norfolk nevertheless holds a high proportion. With more than a third of British Sandwich Terns nesting in Norfolk, and more than 20% of Little Terns, it is clear that their successful nesting on the county's beaches is of vital importance to maintaining Britain's tern populations.

Other more numerous breeding birds for which Norfolk emerges as especially important include Barn Owl, Great Crested Grebe and Water Rail. There are also several introduced species in Table 5.3, most notably Egyptian and Greylag Goose. Although Britain has native populations, Greylags in Norfolk are derived almost entirely from ill-considered releases

Table 5.4 Norfolk wintering birds of national importance during 1999–2007, according to population estimates for Great Britain (*APEP06*) and for Norfolk (NBA). Units are individual birds.

Species	GB WINTER POPULATION	NORFOLK WINTER POPULATION	ESTIMATED % OF BRITISH WINTER POPULATION IN NORFOLK	*BoCC3* LISTING
Egyptian Goose	1,000	1,500–2,000	>90%	unlisted
Crane	(no estimate)	11–36	>90%	amber
Pink-footed Goose	241,000	100,000–150,000	>50%	amber
Water Pipit	<100	20–120	>50%	amber
Marsh Harrier	(no estimate)	80–120	>50%	amber
Bewick's Swan	8,070	3,000–5,000	>40%	amber
Ruff	700	275–375	>40%	red
Taiga Bean Goose	400	140–200	>40%	red
Bearded Tit	(no estimate)	500–600	>40%	amber
Whooper Swan	5,720	1,500–2,500	>33%	amber
Cetti's Warbler	(no estimate)	250–800	>33%	green
Golden Pheasant	(no estimate)	60–80	>20%	unlisted
Tundra Bean Goose	100	20–40	>20%	red
Bittern	50–150	20–40	>20%	amber
Shore Lark	<300	10–150	>20%	amber
Black-tailed Godwit	15,390	3,500–4,500	>20%	red
Greylag Goose (re-established)	29,900	6,000–8,000	>20%	amber
Knot	283,600	40,000–80,000	>20%	amber
White-fronted Goose (European)	5,790	900–1,400	>10%	green (red at race level)
Little Egret	800–900	50–250	>10%	amber
Lapland Bunting	200–500	25–100	>10%	amber
Golden Plover	250,000	35,000–50,000	>10%	amber
Spotted Redshank	136	15–25	>10%	amber
Little Grebe	7,770	1,000–1,200	>10%	amber
Shoveler	14,800	1,500–2,000	>10%	amber
Bar-tailed Godwit	61,590	6,000–8,000	>10%	amber
Common Scoter	50,000	5,000–6,000	>10%	red
Red-throated Diver	4,850	400–600	>10%	amber
Gadwall	17,100	1,500–2,000	>10%	amber
Snow Bunting	9,000–13,500	400–2,000	>10%	amber
Coot	173,000	15,000–20,000	>10%	green
Barn Owl	(no estimate)	1,000–1,500	>10%	amber

onto shooting estates that began here in 1933; having first been recorded nesting in 1960, their numbers now easily exceed those of all other breeding geese in the county and are increasing rapidly. Breeding by Gadwall in the county originated with the offspring of a pinioned pair. Ruddy Shelduck has not been included in the table because, although up to three introduced pairs have nested in the county, nesting is not yet annual; these are among very few instances of this species breeding in Britain.

For Little Egret, the *APEP06* Great Britain figure refers to 2002, the year in which breeding was first reported in Norfolk. Nevertheless, Norfolk held more than 10% of the national breeding total towards the end of the NBA period.

Table 5.4 tabulates the equivalent data for the winter period, again with all species listed where Norfolk holds more than 10% of the British population as recorded by *APEP06*. The data provided for winter populations by *APEP06* are less complete than those for the summer, so for some resident species the table includes inferences from the Great Britain breeding estimates.

In addition to various resident breeding species for which Norfolk is of national importance year round, the winter table includes many species of winter visitor for which Norfolk is a primary destination. Alongside Pink-footed Goose, for which we have already highlighted Norfolk's winter population as being of global significance, there are many other waterfowl of national importance in the county, including both subspecies of Bean Goose, European White-fronted Goose, Bewick's and Whooper Swans, Shoveler and Common Scoter. Several waders surpass the 10% threshold: these include Knot and other species that are common on the Wash, but also some farmland and marshland species such as Ruff, Golden Plover and Spotted Redshank.

Norfolk is also an important winter destination for several passerine winter visitors that are scarce or rare nationally. Water Pipits, leaving the high Alps in search of lowland water meadows, find much suitable habitat in Norfolk. From the Arctic and the mountains of Scandinavia, Shore Larks, Lapland Buntings and Snow Buntings are all more abundant on eastern than western coasts in Britain, with Norfolk again holding at least 10% of their British winter populations. Twite does not emerge from the present analysis but, until recent severe declines, Norfolk held an exceptionally important fraction of the South Pennine breeding population.

5.2 Changes in range since previous atlases

Each of our main species texts shows a table, and many a map, of changes in occupied squares detected by NBA in comparison with previous atlases. In this section, we draw information on breeding and winter range changes together, across species. For breeding birds, we concentrate on changes at tetrad level since the *1980–85 NBBS,* whereas in winter our comparison is with the *1981–84 Winter Atlas* and the unit is the 10-km square. We remind readers once again that the totals of occupied squares, and consequently their percentage changes, are wholly dependent on the size set for the squares. In general, range changes are very much faster at tetrad level but are more susceptible to changes in effort between the atlases. At the 10-km level, any changes found in square occupancy are likely to represent substantial changes in range and be of greater significance for the species concerned.

We discuss 'extinctions' of breeding and wintering species first, followed by the largest proportional losses and then the gains, including the species that have colonised Norfolk as breeding birds or are new as winter visitors.

Extinctions of breeding and wintering species in Norfolk since 1980–85

Wrynecks *Jynx torquilla* were widespread nesting birds in Norfolk less than a century ago. A decline that began with local losses quickly became more extensive and led within a few decades to extinction within Norfolk and then throughout Britain. Atlas projects such as ours can alert conservationists early to problems that are developing, and might give time for conservation measures to be developed and to take effect before extinction occurs at regional or national level.

Only one British bird, the Great Auk *Pinguinus impennis*, has become globally extinct during recent times. By 'extinction' in a Norfolk context, we mean a loss to the county. Such losses may be either temporary or permanent, and might be difficult to define where occurrences in the county tend to be sporadic. We can identify a number of species, however, where losses to the county are part of wider, national or international trends and are therefore likely to be long lasting and possibly permanent.

We report, with a considerable sense of loss, that the following three species, formerly established as breeding birds in Norfolk and recorded as such during atlas work in 1980–85, were not noted breeding during the NBA period.

Red-backed Shrike has already begun to fade gradually from folk memory as a regular nesting species in Britain, although isolated instances of breeding still occur. Breckland and the coastal heaths of East Anglia were the last traditional breeding localities to be deserted. The last proven breeding in Norfolk was near Santon Downham in 1988, at a site where birds continued to summer until 1990. The reasons for the species' national demise are not fully understood but declines of the large insects that form a substantial fraction of the diet of the smaller shrikes might have played a major part.

Wood Warbler formerly nested regularly in some of Norfolk's woodlands, such as the mixed deciduous woods along the Cromer to Holt ridge and around Norwich, but was never common or widespread. It began to decline in the mid 1950s. Surprisingly, the *1980–85 NBBS* recorded an increase in range from the *1968–72 Atlas*, with breeding confirmed in eight tetrads, each in a different 10-km square. Breeding was proved most recently in the county in 1995. Occasional songsters still hold territory in some years, but the species occurs now almost exclusively as a very scarce spring and early autumn migrant. The Wood Warbler's breeding range in Britain has become increasingly confined to its strongholds in western valleys.

Whinchat has also withdrawn rapidly from eastern England as a nesting species in recent decades and has met a speedy extinction in Norfolk. It was widespread as a breeding bird in fen, heath and some coastal habitats in Norfolk as recently as 1968–72, but fewer than ten pairs were breeding by 1980–85, these being largely confined to Breckland heaths, especially those in the Stanford TA. That remnant population has now disappeared too, with no breeding recorded anywhere in Norfolk since 1992. Whinchat is now just a scarce passage migrant through Norfolk, occurring irregularly throughout the county in spring and in autumn. Within Britain, the species has abandoned all but a few lowland sites and retreated to moorland fringes in the upland regions of the north and west.

A further 15 species were placed in the possible, probable or proven nesting categories in Norfolk tetrads in 1980–85 but produced no records of likely or confirmed breeding during 2000–07: these were Eider, Lady Amherst's Pheasant, Hen Harrier, Merlin, Kentish Plover, Ruff, Common Sandpiper, Green Sandpiper, Turnstone, Kittiwake, Fieldfare, Redwing, Savi's Warbler, Pied Flycatcher and Parrot Crossbill. Of these, however, breeding within Norfolk has only ever been proved for nine species – Lady Amherst's Pheasant (most recently in 1973), Hen Harrier (1861), Kentish Plover (1983), Ruff (1977), Common Sandpiper (1980), Kittiwake (1974), Savi's Warbler (most recent year not identifiable), Pied Flycatcher (1996) and Parrot Crossbill (1985). These species have never been more than rare or sporadic as breeding birds in Norfolk, and it is unclear whether there has been any real change in their breeding status since 1980–85.

No regular winter visitors to the county have been lost since the *1981–84 Winter Atlas*. That survey did record several unexpected winter rarities that were not found during the NBA period, however. These were Parrot Crossbill, Spotted Crake and Yellow Wagtail each in two 10-km squares and Sand Martin, Reed Warbler and Ring Ouzel in one square each. Only the loss of Parrot Crossbill is noteworthy, since this species was briefly a year-round resident in the county.

Losses of breeding range

Substantial losses of breeding range are naturally of major conservation significance. Some of the species concerned might be the next to be lost from Norfolk's nesting avifauna. In many cases, losses are not confined to Norfolk and have already raised national or international concern.

In terms of net loss of occupied tetrads, range losses have been most severe for Turtle Dove, which has lost 457 previously occupied Norfolk tetrads, and for Cuckoo. In the two decades leading up to NBA, the proportion of tetrads in the county occupied by Turtle Doves has fallen from 80% to less than half. The national trends for this species have indicated a withdrawal from the northern and western fringes of its previous range and a concentration into eastern England, and East Anglia in particular. It is alarming, since East Anglia is within the core of the Turtle Dove's distribution, that its occupation of Norfolk tetrads has fallen so steeply over this recent period.

Decline of the Cuckoo across the UK has resulted in a rapid stepwise move from green listing at the turn of the millennium to red listing by 2009. Losses have been severe in England since the mid 1980s (*Birdtrends*). At the Norfolk scale, the net loss of 431 tetrads means that there were large areas of the county over which the distinctive and familiar call of the Cuckoo could no longer be heard. In the main, it is farmland sites for the species that have been lost, whereas Norfolk's wetlands and both coastal and inland grasslands mostly retain at least some of their Cuckoos – for the present.

Numerical loss of breeding tetrads is a powerful way to assess range contractions but might overlook

Table 5.5 Species with the greatest proportional losses of breeding tetrads in Norfolk between 1980–85 and 2000–07.

Species	1980–85	2000–07	NET LOSS OF TETRADS	% LOSS OF TETRADS	*BoCC3* LISTING
Wheatear	66 (5%)	2 (<1%)	64	-97%	amber
Short-eared Owl	33 (2%)	2 (<1%)	31	-94%	amber
Hawfinch	27 (2%)	2 (<1%)	25	-93%	red
Lesser Redpoll	441 (30%)	41 (3%)	400	-91%	red
Golden Oriole	21 (1%)	2 (<1%)	19	-90%	red
Wigeon	17 (1%)	3 (<1%)	14	-82%	amber
Common Snipe	322 (22%)	62 (4%)	260	-81%	amber
Black-tailed Godwit	5 (<1%)	1 (<1%)	4	-80%	red
Lesser Spotted Woodpecker	265 (18%)	59 (4%)	206	-78%	red
Teal	101 (7%)	25 (2%)	76	-75%	amber
Black Redstart	18 (1%)	5 (<1%)	13	-72%	amber
Willow Tit	224 (15%)	67 (5%)	157	-70%	red
Long-eared Owl	76 (5%)	23 (2%)	53	-70%	green
Tree Sparrow	522 (36%)	173 (12%)	349	-67%	red
Sand Martin	221 (15%)	83 (6%)	138	-62%	amber
Garganey	21 (1%)	10 (<1%)	11	-52%	amber
Shoveler	107 (7%)	51 (3%)	56	-52%	amber
Golden Pheasant	48 (3%)	23 (2%)	25	-52%	unlisted
Curlew	71 (5%)	37 (3%)	34	-48%	amber
Redstart	41 (3%)	23 (2%)	18	-44%	amber
Redshank	167 (11%)	97 (7%)	70	-42%	amber
Common Crossbill	49 (3%)	29 (2%)	20	-41%	green
Cuckoo	1,081 (74%)	650 (45%)	431	-40%	red
Turtle Dove	1,161 (80%)	704 (48%)	457	-39%	red
Ringed Plover	95 (7%)	62 (4%)	33	-35%	amber
Montagu's Harrier	6 (<1%)	4 (<1%)	2	-33%	amber
Nightingale	212 (15%)	142 (10%)	70	-33%	amber
Spotted Flycatcher	683 (47%)	467 (32%)	216	-32%	red
Corn Bunting	117 (8%)	80 (5%)	37	-32%	red
Yellow Wagtail	272 (19%)	187 (13%)	85	-31%	red

scarcer species, for which the loss of fewer tetrads might nonetheless be significant. For this reason, we have tabulated those species with the greatest proportional losses of breeding tetrads since 1980–85 (Table 5.5). The species shown are those occurring in at least five tetrads in 1980–85 and where a loss of more than 30% of breeding tetrads was recorded. Seven colonial species – Grey Heron, Sandwich Tern, Little Tern, Fulmar, Common Tern, Black-headed Gull and Common Gull – also fit these criteria but have been omitted because their apparent range decreases could be artefacts of the differences in application of criteria for 'possible' and 'likely' breeding between the two tetrad atlases.

The species near the top of Table 5.5 because of a high proportional decrease in tetrad occupation, and with only a handful of tetrads still occupied during 2000–07, are likely to be those closest to following Red-backed Shrike, Whinchat and Wood Warbler into breeding extinction in the county. The species of greatest concern in this context are Wheatear, Short-eared Owl, Hawfinch, Golden Oriole, Wigeon and Black-tailed Godwit. Wheatear has a very similar history of national range loss to Whinchat; it retained a tiny toehold as a nesting bird in 2000–07, in Stanford TA, but its

Table 5.6 Greatest range losses for bird species in Norfolk in winter: totals and percentages of 10-km squares occupied in winter atlases.

Species	1981–84	1999–2007	NET LOSS OF 10-KM SQUARES	% LOSS OF 10-KM SQUARES	*BoCC3* LISTING
Tree Sparrow	60 (97%)	44 (71%)	16	-27%	red
White-fronted Goose	26 (42%)	20 (32%)	6	-23%	green (red at race level)
Hen Harrier	46 (74%)	36 (58%)	10	-22%	red
Rock Pipit	17 (27%)	14 (23%)	3	-18%	green
Short-eared Owl	36 (58%)	30 (48%)	6	-17%	amber
Hooded Crow	20 (32%)	17 (27%)	3	-15%	green
Lesser Spotted Woodpecker	47 (76%)	40 (65%)	7	-15%	red
Great Grey Shrike	14 (23%)	12 (19%)	2	-14%	unlisted
Willow Tit	52 (84%)	45 (73%)	7	-13%	red
Bearded Tit	17 (27%)	15 (24%)	2	-12%	amber
Bewick's Swan	28 (45%)	25 (40%)	3	-11%	amber
Ringed Plover	19 (31%)	17 (27%)	2	-11%	amber

loss from Norfolk as a nesting species appears to be imminent. Wheatear was formerly a common and widespread nesting bird in the county, and Hawfinch too was once quite widespread; the other species have always been rare. For opportunistic species, such as Short-eared Owl and Wigeon, it is especially likely that isolated instances of breeding might recur.

Lesser Redpoll, Lesser Spotted Woodpecker, Snipe, Willow Tit and Long-eared Owl remained as likely breeders in only a few dozen Norfolk tetrads during 2000–07, after losses of at least 70% of occupied tetrads since the 1980s. Although they still occupied over a hundred tetrads during the NBA period, there have been very substantial range contractions at tetrad scale for Tree Sparrow, Nightingale, Spotted Flycatcher and Yellow Wagtail, as well as for Cuckoo and Turtle Dove. Clearly, these are all species whose status in the county must be monitored with extra care over the coming years. Some of these, too, might be heading for countywide extinction.

Most species listed in Table 5.5 for range contraction within Norfolk are already red- or amber-listed birds of UK conservation concern, mostly because of a strong national population decline. Long-eared Owl is always a difficult bird to survey but appears to have undergone a substantial range contraction in Norfolk, despite its green-listed status in the UK as a whole. Crossbill is also on the green list but is a species with large unpredictable population fluctuations: its range contraction since 1980–85 might be only temporary, therefore.

Losses of winter range

NBA is the first tetrad atlas ever of Norfolk's winter birds. Range change can therefore be assessed only at the 10-km scale, in comparison to the *1981–84 Winter Atlas*. The comparisons are based on the 62 10-km squares that belong clearly to Norfolk, rather than to a neighbouring county. At the 10-km scale, only the most severe range decreases are detectable.

The biggest losses in winter range since 1981–84 are listed in Table 5.6. As with the losses of breeding range (Table 5.5), they are reported only for species present initially in at least five squares. Because of the far lower sensitivity to change at the 10-km scale, however, we include all losses greater than 10% in the winter table.

Some species otherwise qualifying for Table 5.6 have been omitted. House Martin has never wintered in Norfolk but migrants occur sporadically in November and even in December. Its wider occurrence in the *1981–84 Winter Atlas* than in NBA was almost certainly due solely to the inclusion of late November records in the first atlas. NBA recorded Razorbill, Kittiwake, Guillemot and Fulmar in fewer squares but it is unclear whether any real change in winter range has occurred in these species: NBA was inefficient in recording seabirds, relative to the *1981–84 Winter Atlas*, probably because its instructions for set visits specifically excluded birds seen only in flight.

Table 5.7 New breeding species in Norfolk in 2000–07, not recorded during the *1980–85 NBBS.*

Species	POPULATION ESTIMATE 2000–07	TETRADS OCCUPIED	*BoCC3* LISTING
Barnacle Goose	5–20 bp	11	amber
Cormorant	75–120 bp	4	green (amber at race level)
Ruddy Shelduck	0–3 bp	3	unlisted
Little Egret	0–130 bp	3	amber
Mediterranean Gull	3–14 bp	3	amber
Dartford Warbler	0–2 bp	2	amber
Goosander	0–1 bp	2	green
Red-crested Pochard	5–10 bp	1	unlisted
Night-heron	0–8 bp	1	unlisted
Little Gull	0–1 bp	1	amber
White-fronted Goose	0–1 bp	1	green (red at race level)
Bean Goose	0–1 bp	1	amber
Spoonbill	0–1 bp	1	amber
Spotted Crake	0–4 singing males	1	amber

The most severe and shocking winter range losses detected by NBA are those for Tree Sparrow and Hen Harrier. Tree Sparrow has undergone massive population decline across England since the 1960s, amounting to 97% in the 40 years to 2007 (*Birdtrends*). In Norfolk, they disappeared completely from 16 10-km squares just within the two decades leading up to NBA: range loss in east Norfolk was almost complete. While this has been the most extensive loss of winter range that NBA has recorded, the species retained a toehold in more than two thirds of 10-km squares and the most recent signs are that the population nationally has begun to recover.

Winter range loss for Hen Harrier in Norfolk has amounted to ten 10-km squares, nearly all in inland parts of the county, especially Fenland and the Brecks. Norfolk's wintering Hen Harriers breed mainly in northern Britain, where overall there has been an increase in numbers since 1998 (*Birdtrends*). It is unclear whether the section of the population that winters in Norfolk has failed to increase, or whether the loss of winter range here is due to disturbance at roosts or to other factors operating within the county. Short-eared Owls, too, were not only more numerous but also much more widespread in Norfolk in the 1980s than during the NBA period.

Lesser Spotted Woodpecker and Willow Tit are mainly resident birds in the county and their range decreases in Norfolk, like that of Tree Sparrow, have been the result of severe and sustained declines in breeding population that have been noted across Britain (*Birdtrends*).

Breeding species gained since 1980–85

Although scarcely a replacement for species becoming rare or already lost to the county, many species have increased their ranges within Norfolk and some have colonised the county from outside. Some of these changes might result from successful conservation efforts and others from more natural causes, perhaps linked in some cases to climate change.

There are 14 species that nested in Norfolk during 2000–07, or were recorded by NBA as likely to have done so, but were not noted even as possible nesting species in any Norfolk tetrad during 1980–85: these are listed in Table 5.7. Of these species, breeding was not proven for either Spoonbill or Spotted Crake within the NBA period.

The most numerous of the new colonists by 2007 was Little Egret, despite its first records of nesting in Norfolk being as recent as 2002 and its colonisation of Britain having begun only in 1996. Its arrival has been sudden and dramatic! Cormorant had reached a similar number of pairs by 2007. It had returned to Norfolk as a nesting bird in 1988 after an absence of 71 years, and then was absent again during 1993–97.

As many as six species proven to breed for the first time in Norfolk since the *1980–85 NBBS* are species that are not native breeding birds in Britain, but have

Table 5.8 Species recorded as wintering species in at least three 10-km squares in Norfolk during 1999–2007 but not at all during 1981–84.

Species	POPULATION ESTIMATE 1999–2007 (INDIVIDUALS)	OCCUPIED 10-KM SQUARES	*BoCC3* LISTING
Little Egret	50–250	32 (52%)	amber
Yellow-legged Gull	30–50	26 (42%)	amber
Common Redpoll	1–65	22 (35%)	green
Caspian Gull	10–15	17 (27%)	unlisted
White-tailed Eagle	0–1	8 (13%)	red
Ruddy Shelduck	5–20	7 (11%)	unlisted
Great White Egret	0–2	7 (11%)	unlisted
Dartford Warbler	0–5	5 (8%)	amber
American Wigeon	0–1	5 (8%)	unlisted

been deliberately or accidentally introduced. Of these, Barnacle Goose is by far the most numerous, although it is unclear how many of Norfolk's feral Barnacles breed in Suffolk, or even on the Continent, rather than within the county. Breeding was first noted in Norfolk in 1995 and during the NBA period was proven or thought likely in 11 tetrads. Red-crested Pochards were known to have nested ferally only at Pensthorpe, where a colony has been allowed to flourish. These and other introduced wildfowl in the county might all eventually follow the pattern set by Egyptian, Canada and Greylag Geese – a long period of low breeding numbers, confined to areas near the release points, followed by exponential increase and range expansion.

The place of Ruddy Shelduck on the Norfolk List, it should be stressed, rests solely on a single possible vagrant from the Asian and African breeding range that was found dead at Snettisham in 1892 (*BoN*). The birds now being seen with increasing regularity in the county, as breeders and as non-breeding visitors, are probably all part of the non-native population, originally from avicultural sources, which is now established and spreading in western Europe. Those nesting in Norfolk have been the first to do so in Britain.

The sources of feral Night-herons and Bean Geese in Norfolk (Great Witchingham Wildlife Park and the Otter Trust at Earsham, respectively) have both now closed. The introductions of these two species have almost certainly failed, although a few feral Bean Geese remain at large.

Aside from Cormorant and Little Egret, the only other native species firmly established as a new colonist is Mediterranean Gull. Breeding by Dartford Warblers has continued since the NBA period, but these birds may be vulnerable to severe winter weather. Nesting by Goosanders remains sporadic.

Wintering species gained since 1981–84

NBA observers found a number of species in the winter months that had not been recorded at all in Norfolk's 62 10-km squares during the *1981–84 Winter Atlas*. The most regular of these are listed in Table 5.8, which includes only those species recorded in at least five 10-km squares during the NBA period. In addition, King Eider, Surf Scoter and Hume's Warbler were each observed in four Norfolk 10-km squares during the winters 1999/2000–2006/07 and Black Kite, Pallid Harrier, Lesser Yellowlegs, Arctic Redpoll and Little Bunting each in three squares; these are all rare species in Britain and none has a UK conservation priority listing.

Little Egret, a breeding colonist, was the most abundant and widespread of these new wintering species. By 2006/07, wintering Little Egrets had been found in more than half of all Norfolk's 10-km squares. Great White Egret is also becoming much more regular in Britain at all seasons but has not yet begun to nest; absent from Norfolk during the *1981–84 Winter Atlas*, it was found in seven 10-km squares during the NBA winters, with up to two birds in winters 2001/02 and 2002/03 (Table 3.1).

The *1981–84 Winter Atlas* did not distinguish Common and Lesser Redpolls, since at that time Lesser Redpoll was not regarded as a separate species. The status of Common Redpoll probably

Table 5.9 Species with the greatest proportional gains of breeding tetrads in Norfolk between 1980–85 and 2000–07.

Species	1980–85	2000–07	NET GAIN OF TETRADS	% GAIN OF TETRADS	*BoCC3* LISTING
Buzzard	1 (<1%)	113 (8%)	112	11,200%	green
Woodlark	10 (<1%)	111 (8%)	101	1,010%	amber
Hobby	7 (<1%)	50 (3%)	43	614%	green
Ruddy Duck	3 (<1%)	21 (1%)	18	600%	unlisted
Avocet	6 (<1%)	41 (3%)	35	583%	amber
Sparrowhawk	128 (9%)	562 (39%)	434	339%	green
Lesser Black-backed Gull	4 (<1%)	13 (<1%)	9	225%	amber
Egyptian Goose	88 (6%)	276 (19%)	188	214%	unlisted
Cetti's Warbler	37 (3%)	109 (7%)	72	195%	green
Greylag Goose	109 (7%)	305 (21%)	196	180%	amber
Green Woodpecker	326 (22%)	835 (57%)	509	156%	amber
Jackdaw	525 (36%)	1,153 (79%)	628	120%	green
Carrion Crow	525 (36%)	1,153 (79%)	628	120%	green
Blackcap	640 (44%)	1,286 (88%)	646	101%	green
Firecrest	7 (<1%)	14 (1%)	7	100%	amber
Stonechat	19 (1%)	37 (3%)	18	95%	green
Great Spotted Woodpecker	538 (37%)	1,027 (70%)	489	91%	green (amber at race level)
Oystercatcher	218 (37%)	411 (28%)	193	89%	amber
Marsh Harrier	46 (3%)	85 (6%)	39	85%	amber
Collared Dove	672 (46%)	1,224 (84%)	552	82%	green
Siskin	27 (2%)	49 (3%)	22	81%	green
Magpie	618 (42%)	1,101 (75%)	483	78%	green
Lesser Whitethroat	302 (21%)	524 (36%)	222	74%	green
Whitethroat	775 (53%)	1,333 (91%)	558	72%	amber
Grey Wagtail	57 (4%)	97 (7%)	40	70%	amber
Feral Pigeon	228 (16%)	386 (26%)	158	69%	green
Barn Owl	340 (23%)	568 (39%)	228	67%	amber
Goshawk	3(<1%)	5 (<1%)	2	67%	green

has not changed greatly during the last two decades and its appearance in Table 5.8 is therefore purely an artefact of changing taxonomy. Similarly, Yellow-legged and Caspian Gulls were both regarded as part of the Herring Gull complex during the *1981–84 Winter Atlas*, and not recorded separately, but are now treated as species in their own right. They would both have been either rare or absent in winters 1981/82–1983/84, however: they have since increased greatly in numbers and range within Britain, in line with their expanding breeding populations in mainland Europe. Yellow-legged Gulls now frequently accompany winter flocks of Lesser Black-backs in the county.

Of the remaining species in Table 5.8, only Ruddy Shelduck occurred in every NBA winter (see Table 3.1). This species has now become a breeding resident within Norfolk, as well as an irregular visitor from the Continent.

Gains in breeding range

Substantial gains of breeding tetrads have been recorded for many species between the 1980–85 *NBBS* and the NBA. The species with at least a two-thirds gain, and that were found in at least five tetrads during the NBA summers, are listed in Table 5.9, in order of their proportional gain in breeding tetrads. This table excludes the new colonists (Table 5.7). Improved

DAVID TIPLING

'Blackcap heads the list of expanding species in terms of net gain of tetrads.'

coverage for NBA might have contributed to the gains in some cases but, in nearly every species listed (Lesser Whitethroat perhaps being an exception), we are confident that a real range expansion has occurred. Many of the species that have increased their range within Norfolk are also expanding or increasing on an English or British scale. Where the species concerned are native, this is clearly excellent news for the county's biodiversity! There are also substantial range gains for several non-native species, which may in contrast be detrimental.

At the top of the list of proportional range gains soars the Buzzard, which occupied only one tetrad in 1980–85 but has since spread to all parts of the county. This colonisation has been part of a phenomenal eastward expansion of the British range to encompass the eastern half of England, which had been almost unoccupied by Buzzards in 1968–72. Several other raptor species have markedly expanded their ranges within the county, including Hobby, Sparrowhawk and Marsh Harrier. Goshawk, whose breeding populations in Britain stem from unplanned reintroductions, has also spread but remains surprisingly rare in the county.

Blackcap heads the list of expanding species in terms of net gain of tetrads. The *1980–85 NBBS* map shows large areas of Norfolk, especially in the far west and the southeast, from which Blackcaps were unrecorded, whereas two decades later it was recorded from twice as many tetrads and was found commonly in all parts of the county. Two other *Sylvia* warblers, Whitethroat and Lesser Whitethroat, also showed big gains in range. To some extent, this must reflect climate change, benefiting these three migrant species on their breeding and wintering grounds – but there are many other migrant birds showing opposite trends. In the UK as a whole, Lesser Whitethroats are fluctuating, without a clear long-term trend, and numbers during the NBA period were relatively low (*Birdtrends*).

Corvids, particularly Carrion Crow and Jackdaw, also scored very highly in terms of the numbers of tetrads gained. Magpies remained absent from parts of northwest Norfolk, however, presumably excluded by game interests. Green and Great Spotted Woodpeckers, formerly concentrated into the best-wooded parts of the county, are now almost ubiquitous and widely familiar as garden birds.

Several quite rare or restricted breeding species within the county remained so but showed large proportional increases in breeding range, as measured at tetrad level. Chief among these was Woodlark, which increased its number of breeding tetrads by a factor of ten, aided by extensive felling and replanting in Thetford Forest and by removal of encroaching conifers on northwestern heaths. Breeding Avocets, Cetti's Warblers and Firecrests also fared well.

Among non-natives, Ruddy Duck increased the most, proportionately. Since the close of the NBA period, however, this problem species has been much reduced nationally by an eradication programme, which now appears to be approaching a successful conclusion. Egyptian Goose more than trebled its range between the two atlas periods, and the increase for Greylag Goose was even greater than Egyptian's in terms of numbers of tetrads. Surprisingly, in view of its rapid growth in numbers on the UK scale (*Birdtrends*), Canada Goose gained only 30 tetrads (15%) between the two atlases.

Gains in winter range

The species with at least a doubling in the number of occupied 10-km squares since the *1981–84 Winter*

Table 5.10 Biggest range gains for bird species in Norfolk in winter: totals and percentages of 10-km squares occupied in winter atlases. Species with a proportional gain of 100% or more are listed.

Species	1981–84	1999–2007	NET GAIN OF 10-KM SQUARES	% GAIN OF 10-KM SQUARES	*BoCC3* LISTING
Mandarin Duck	1 (2%)	21 (34%)	20	2,000%	unlisted
Red-crested Pochard	1 (2%)	14 (23%)	13	1,300%	unlisted
Woodlark	2 (3%)	20 (32%)	18	900%	amber
Ferruginous Duck	1 (2%)	10 (16%)	9	900%	unlisted
Goshawk	6 (2%)	43 (69%)	37	617%	green
Ruddy Duck	3 (10%)	21 (34%)	18	600%	unlisted
Peregrine	7 (11%)	48 (77%)	41	586%	green (amber at race level)
Pomarine Skua	1 (2%)	6 (10%)	5	500%	green
Mediterranean Gull	6 (10%)	34 (55%)	28	467%	amber
Red Kite	3 (5%)	17 (27%)	14	467%	amber
Buzzard	10 (16%)	56 (90%)	46	460%	green
Snow Goose	2 (3%)	11 (18%)	9	450%	unlisted
Waxwing	10 (16%)	52 (84%)	42	420%	green
Firecrest	5 (16%)	25 (40%)	20	400%	amber
Marsh Harrier	8 (13%)	30 (48%)	22	275%	amber
Stonechat	11 (18%)	37 (60%)	26	236%	green
Chiffchaff	14 (23%)	46 (74%)	32	229%	green
Cetti's Warbler	7 (11%)	21 (34%)	14	200%	green
Iceland Gull	5 (8%)	15 (24%)	10	200%	amber
Red-breasted Goose	2 (3%)	6 (10%)	4	200%	unlisted
Long-eared Owl	8 (2%)	22 (35%)	14	175%	green
Common Sandpiper	3 (5%)	8 (13%)	5	167%	amber
Avocet	4 (6%)	10 (16%)	6	150%	amber
Grey Wagtail	24 (39%)	57 (92%)	33	138%	amber
Little Stint	3 (5%)	7 (11%)	4	133%	green
Blackcap	17 (27%)	39 (63%)	22	129%	green
Black Redstart	7 (11%)	16 (26%)	9	129%	amber
Smew	13 (21%)	29 (47%)	16	123%	amber
Water Pipit	6 (10%)	13 (21%)	7	117%	amber
Oystercatcher	20 (32%)	42 (68%)	22	110%	amber
Merlin	23 (37%)	48 (77%)	25	109%	amber
Barnacle Goose	17 (27%)	35 (56%)	18	106%	amber
Pink-footed Goose	19 (31%)	38 (61%)	19	100%	amber

Atlas, and found in at least five 10-km squares during the NBA winters, are listed in Table 5.10, in order of their proportional gain in 10-km squares. This table excludes the new wintering species (Table 5.8).

In contrast to the short list of major winter range losses in Norfolk since the *1981–84 Winter Atlas* (Table 5.6), there has been a much larger number of species showing strong winter range increases. As highlighted for the breeding atlas comparisons, however, differences in coverage might have contributed to this pattern. The influences of the longer period of winters for NBA and the increased effectiveness of its cover cannot be quantified, but might have exaggerated some of the apparent gains.

The most striking feature of Table 5.10 is the prominence of non-native species among those with the greatest proportional increases in winter range. Among the top six birds in the table are Mandarin and Ruddy

Duck, which are both wholly non-native species in Britain, and Red-crested Pochard and Ferruginous Duck, for which large but unknown proportions of records will have been of escapes or of birds of introduced stock. Barnacle Goose made a substantial net gain of winter 10-km squares, also largely (but probably not exclusively) because of growth in its introduced populations.

Diurnal birds of prey feature strongly in the winter table, as they did in the breeding period (Table 5.9), with Buzzard, Peregrine and Goshawk among the top four species in terms of numbers of winter squares gained. Merlin, Marsh Harrier and Red Kite were also much more widespread in winter than during 1981–84. Buzzard, Goshawk and Marsh Harrier have also made strong gains as breeding birds (Table 5.9) and, since many individuals spend all year in the county, it is clear that the summer and winter gains for these species are linked. The spread of Marsh Harriers in winter contrasts markedly with range loss for Hen Harriers (Table 5.6).

Overall population increase is likely to have been the major driving force behind the spread of species such as Pink-footed Goose, Mediterranean Gull and Cetti's Warbler as wintering birds in the county. The spread of Pink-footed Goose as a wintering bird in Norfolk confirms the county's position as of primary significance for this species on the global scale.

Waxwing was recorded from 42 more 10-km squares than during the *1981–84 Winter Atlas* and ranks second only to Buzzard in the number of winter squares gained. It would be misleading, however, to describe this as a range expansion. Waxwing is an irruptive species and is very irregular in its occurrence in Norfolk, being rare in most winters, or even absent, but numerous and widespread in occasional 'Waxwing winters'. The eight-year NBA period, as against the three years for the *1981–84 Winter Atlas*, was always more likely to include at least one good winter for the species and, remarkably, there were four 'Waxwing winters' during NBA fieldwork.

Winters in Norfolk during the NBA period were relatively mild, and the climate globally is gradually becoming warmer. Climate change might well be driving the expansion of some of Norfolk's wintering species that have southerly winter distributions or that are partial migrants (with some but not all individuals leaving Britain for the winter). The relatively mild winters of the NBA period, compared to the early 1980s, probably lay behind the much wider wintering distributions in the county of partial migrants such as Grey Wagtail, Chiffchaff, Stonechat, Blackcap, Firecrest and Woodlark. They probably also enhanced winter survival and aided expansion of some resident birds, such as Little Egret, Dartford Warbler and Cetti's Warbler.

5.3 Implications of NBA results for bird conservation

A strong conclusion from the atlas comparisons within the NBA database is that the county's breeding and winter birds are generally faring rather well. Since the 1980s, there have been more new species and range expansions (Tables 5.7–5.10) than losses and range contractions (Tables 5.5–5.6). The change maps in the species texts show far more green for gains than black for losses, although more thorough coverage for NBA will have contributed to this pattern. To some extent, these positive changes are the fruit of conservation efforts during the two decades since the *1980–85 NBBS* was conducted.

There are negatives, too, however. Some previously widespread birds have become extinct as Norfolk breeders since the 1980s. Many others are in retreat across the county and threats remain to many important sites and habitats. The continued presence of several species as nesting birds, including Bitterns, Stone-curlews, terns, Montagu's Harriers and Woodlarks, is almost certainly dependent on the maintenance or enhancement of existing conservation effort. Many non-native species are increasing their ranges across Norfolk and this cannot be good for natural biodiversity; indeed, it might be an indication of developing problems that will increasingly require expensive remedial management.

The work of NBA volunteers in compiling this atlas has helped to provide focus to some of the major current issues for bird conservation in Norfolk. These issues mostly concern vulnerable and declining species, rather than the many positive changes that NBA has also found.

Bird conservation issues identified by NBA

The following bullet points condense some of the most important issues for conservation at county level that emerge from NBA. The example species, drawn from the subsets tabulated in this chapter, are listed only once each and are often not the only species that are relevant within each group. The main species texts provide further details for these birds.

Norfolk holds a relatively high proportion of the British population for a broad range of breeding and wintering bird species (Tables 5.3 & 5.4). These are generally species that thrive in Norfolk, because of the habitats available to them and perhaps the climate. Nevertheless, the conservation effort that is being expended within the county contributes disproportionately strongly to the welfare of the British population as a whole.The Norfolk contribution is especially significant where the species are amber- or red-listed birds of UK conservation concern. We also draw attention here, however, to some green-listed species, such as Water Rail and Cetti's Warbler, for which Norfolk is nationally important.

- Rare and apparently conservation-dependent species: **Crane, Montagu's Harrier**
- Scarce species largely dependent on extensive reedbeds: **Marsh Harrier, Bearded Tit, Bittern, Cetti's Warbler, Water Rail**
- Vulnerable species nesting on farmland: **Stone-curlew, Quail, Barn Owl**
- Vulnerable species nesting in heathland or in woodland: **Woodlark, Firecrest**
- Terns nesting on Norfolk beaches: **Sandwich Tern, Little Tern**
- Wintering geese and swans from the Arctic: **Pink-footed Goose, Bewick's** and **Whooper Swans,** Taiga and Tundra **Bean Geese,** European **White-fronted Goose**
- Winter waders: **Ruff, Black-tailed** and **Bar-tailed Godwits, Knot, Golden Plover, Spotted Redshank**
- Winter-visiting passerines: **Water Pipit, Shore Lark, Lapland Bunting, Snow Bunting** (and Twite)
- Birds wintering offshore: **Common Scoter, Red-throated Diver**

Species whose distributions NBA shows to be contracting across the county (Tables 5.5 & 5.6) raise further, potentially more urgent alerts. Some species may be heading for extinction, with little that conservationists can do to alter their situation. In other cases, a timely and well-directed intervention might help the species to halt its loss of range and even to begin to regain lost ground.

- Species apparently in greatest danger of imminent extinction as breeding species in Norfolk: **Wheatear, Short-eared Owl, Hawfinch**
- Breeding waders of wet meadows: **Snipe, Black-tailed Godwit, Curlew, Redshank**
- Rarer breeding ducks: **Wigeon, Teal, Garganey, Shoveler**
- Woodland birds in steep national decline: **Lesser Redpoll, Lesser Spotted Woodpecker, Willow Tit, Redstart, Nightingale, Spotted Flycatcher**
- Farmland birds in steep national decline: **Tree Sparrow, Turtle Dove, Corn Bunting, Yellow Wagtail**
- Other breeding birds contracting their Norfolk ranges: **Black Redstart, Long-eared Owl, Sand Martin, Cuckoo, Ringed Plover**
- Winter raptors contracting their Norfolk ranges: **Hen Harrier**

Finally, non-native species and introduced populations of native species are almost all spreading as breeding and wintering birds within Norfolk. Further increases may add to the problems, including agricultural damage, bank erosion, fouling of amenity parkland and competitive exclusion of native wildfowl, that are already being caused by non-native geese.

- Potentially invasive introductions: **Egyptian Goose, Greylag Goose**, also **Barnacle Goose** and all other non-native species from Tables 5.7 & 5.10

This NBA-based approach to identifying bird conservation issues within Norfolk will, we hope, provide conservationists and policy-makers with extra perspective on how best to maintain and enhance Norfolk's biodiversity. By presenting an NBA viewpoint, we aim to encourage conservation practitioners and others with an influence in this field to make use of the county's atlas data to benefit avian biodiversity.

Contribution of tetrad atlases to bird conservation in Norfolk

Much bird conservation effort in Norfolk is directed towards the protection and management of particular sites. These include the county's famous nature reserves, run by bodies such as RSPB, Natural England, NWT, SWT and WWT, but also a wide range of other sites, owned by private individuals or by statutory bodies, that are managed primarily for wildlife or with nature conservation as a high priority. Many of these have formal recognition, for example as SSSIs or SPAs. Habitat creation and maintenance at such sites provides protection, not just for birds, but for a range of whole ecosystems whose existence would otherwise be under threat, especially from commercial interests.

Rare breeding birds sometimes choose to breed in unexpected and unpredictable places. Marsh and Montagu's Harriers, for example, frequently nest in fields of growing crops, as do Stone-curlews. A flexible approach to site protection, in addition to a network of nature reserves and managed sites, is needed to extend security to species like these. There are already efficient systems in place, involving volunteer birdwatchers as well as conservation professionals, that gather the necessary information and mobilise the available resources as required. At the limited scales of conserving the rarer species and the most important sites, therefore, it is unlikely that NBA results have a significant role to play.

Birds of conservation concern include many common and widespread species, however, as well as rarities with restricted ranges. The *BoCC3* red list holds many familiar birds that are in need of conservation action because of their strong population decline across Britain: if not halted, and preferably reversed, these declines will lead eventually to extinction. Plotting the NBA distributions of red-listed birds across the county (Figures 5.3 & 5.4) makes the point very clearly that birds of conservation concern breed and winter throughout the county. Bird conservation, therefore, is far from being restricted to Norfolk's reserves and other listed sites, despite the high profile of many of these and the rare species that occur there – rather, it is an issue that is local to every part of the county.

Where NBA can make its greatest contribution to the conservation of Norfolk's birds is by providing data for birds of conservation concern that, rather than being concentrated into protected sites, are widely distributed across the countryside. Without an up-to-date atlas, this information would be at best patchy or outdated.

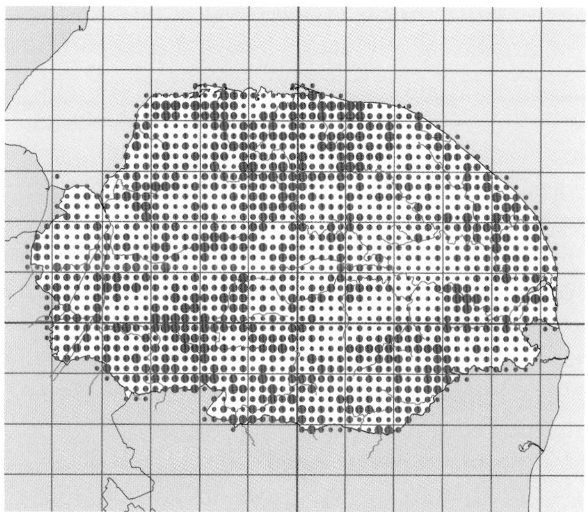

Figure 5.3 Distribution of red-listed breeding bird species in Norfolk in 2000–07. Dot size indicates the number of red-listed species (*BoCC3*) for which breeding was considered at least likely. Five dot sizes, small to large: 1–6 species, 7–8, 9 (median), 10–11, 12–17 species.

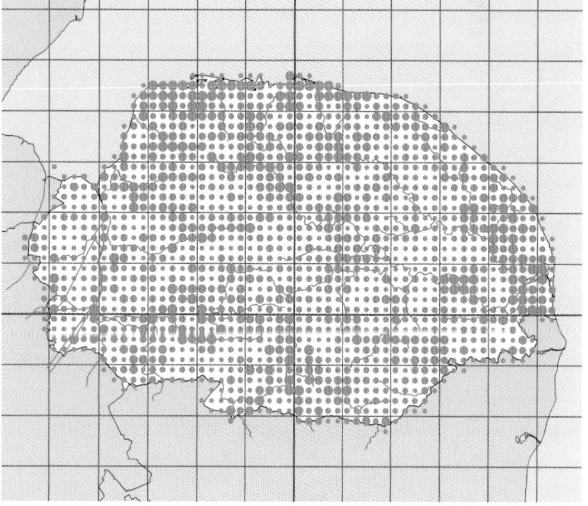

Figure 5.4 Distribution of red-listed wintering bird species (*BoCC3*) in Norfolk in 1999–07. Dot size indicates the number of species recorded in each tetrad. Five dot sizes, small to large: 1–7 species, 8–9, 10 (median), 11–12, 13–19 species.

For species that are dispersed widely across the countryside, conservationists have limited opportunity to influence habitat management on a broad-enough scale to yield measurable results. Offering advice and financial incentives to farmers for wildlife-friendly management, however, for example through environmental stewardship schemes, has proved to be a valuable and effective way of improving habitat quality for farmland birds on the necessary county-wide scale. In considering where conservation resources should be deployed to best advantage, it is clearly helpful to know the distribution of the birds that might benefit.

We have already presented such data at species level in the main species texts in this book. Further information, for example the finer detail of counts by species and tetrad, is available in the database itself. Mapping and data analysis can be useful not only for species but also for groups of species, to provide a simpler and more accessible summary of multi-layered data. Useful groups of species are those that share habitat types, to determine geographical areas where conservation action affecting particular habitats could be most effective, or biological characteristics that might indicate the kind of action that could be appropriate.

As examples, we have chosen some habitat-based species groupings that are presently of relevance to conservation practice. They are drawn from the Bird Conservation Targeting Project (BCTP), a collaboration of a wide range of organisations with responsibility for conservation management in the UK. The aim of BCTP is to provide information to landowners on where birds of conservation interest are present and to relevant agencies to help determine where it would be most effective to apply broad-scale conservation measures, such as environmental stewardship. The project has its own lists of scarce and declining farmland and woodland bird species and assemblages of species, for which maps are available on the project's web pages (*www.rspb.org.uk/ourwork/conservation/projects/targeting*).

Here, we present the NBA maps for the BCTP arable, wet grassland and woodland assemblages. These maps are hugely more detailed and up to date than those previously available through BCTP. The map for the arable assemblage (Figure 5.5) shows those regions that still hold some of the most threatened birds of arable farmland. The areas with the highest numbers of these species are those in greatest need of conservation measures, such as stewardship, designed to boost their existing populations. These areas include the higher parts of Fenland in southwest Norfolk, a band inland from the northwest coast, and farmland by the lower sections of Broadland rivers. Most tetrads in the county hold more than one of the relevant arable species, however.

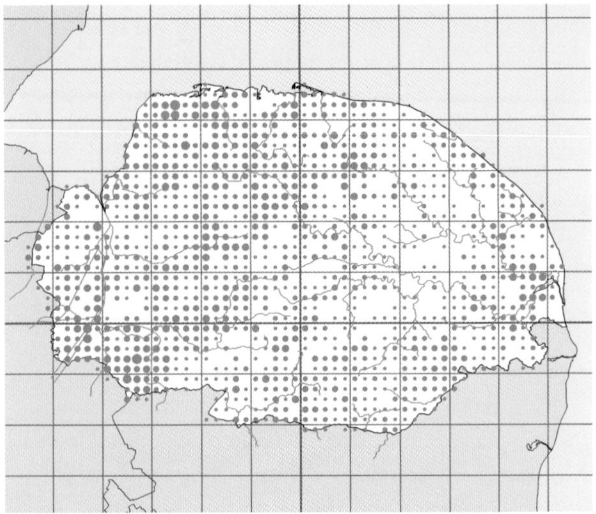

Figure 5.5 Distribution of 'arable assemblage' breeding species in Norfolk in 2000–07. Dot size, scaled 1–6, indicates the number of species in the assemblage for which breeding was considered at least likely. Species are Grey Partridge, Lapwing, Turtle Dove, Tree Sparrow, Yellow Wagtail and Corn Bunting.

The wet grassland assemblage (Figure 5.6) includes two of the same species (Lapwing and Yellow Wagtail) but shows a much more concentrated distribution of important areas – on the Ouse Washes and the lower valley of the Little Ouse, along the marshes of the north coast and the lower parts of the Broadland rivers. Large areas of mid Norfolk and lower Fenland currently hold none at all of these species.

NBA shows that rarer woodland species (Figure 5.7) are found mainly in Thetford Forest and its surroundings, near the Sandringham woodlands, and along the Cromer to Holt ridge, with some smaller concentrations elsewhere. The pre-eminence of Breckland for rare woodland birds, and Thetford Forest in particular, is very clear.

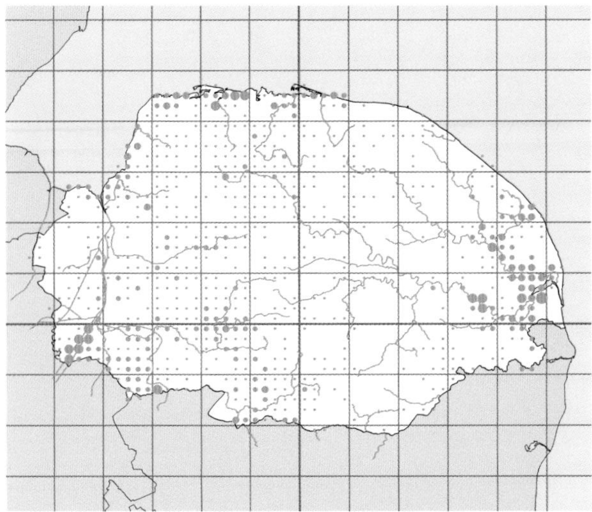

Figure 5.6 Distribution of 'wet grassland assemblage' breeding species in Norfolk in 2000–07. Dot size, scaled 1–5, indicates the number of species in the assemblage for which breeding was considered at least likely. Species are Lapwing and Yellow Wagtail (both also in the arable assemblage), Snipe, Curlew and Redshank.

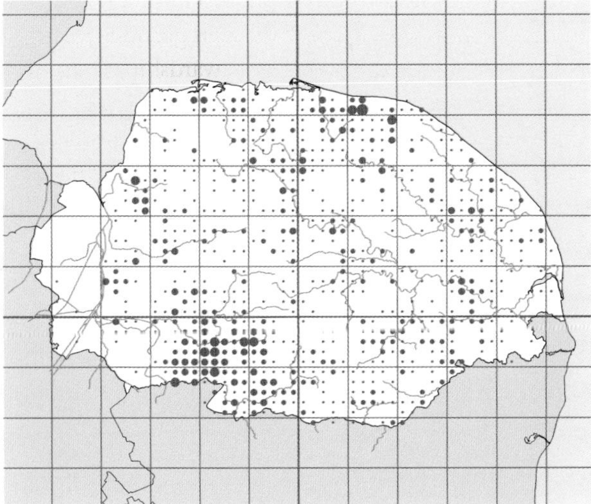

Figure 5.7 Distribution of 'woodland assemblage' breeding species in Norfolk in 2000–07. Dot size, scaled 1–6, indicates the number of species in the assemblage for which breeding was considered at least likely. Species are Lesser Spotted Woodpecker, Marsh Tit, Spotted Flycatcher, Redstart, Tree Pipit and Hawfinch.

Not surprisingly, none of these species was found in any Fenland squares.

The NBA database potentially provides a very wide range of qualitative and quantitative species or cross-species summaries, far beyond those we have been able to present in this book. Many external data sets exist that might be available for analysis alongside NBA bird data, covering for example the distributions of climatic variables, soil types, habitats, and plants and animals that birds use for food or shelter. Naturally, the limitations of the data must be respected. Nevertheless, NBA presents many opportunities for pure research and for applied studies, directed for example towards conservation.

A new tetrad atlas of birds for Norfolk would ideally be started by about 2020. This next atlas, whenever it takes place, would be able to compare results for all tetrads with previous breeding atlases in 1980–85 and 1999–2007 and for some tetrads with data from the current *Atlas 2007–11*, for both summer and winter. Until the next full set of tetrad data supersedes them, we proffer the NBA book and database as research tools – and hope they will be used to good effect, to the benefit of Norfolk's breeding and wintering birds.

Acknowledgements

THE NBA PROJECT HAS BEEN possible only through the support of very many people. We are very grateful to everyone who has helped. Although we cannot name everyone, we would like to take this opportunity to thank the people listed below for their contribution to the project. At the same time, we apologise to anyone we have inadvertently omitted or misrepresented.

Planning and organisation

An Atlas Working Group oversaw the considerable amount of work that was necessary to set up the NBA project and guide it through the fieldwork period. Aside from the authors, with Moss Taylor as project co-ordinator, the following served on the Atlas Working Group for all or part of the fieldwork period: Len Bentley, Alan Collins, Fred Cooke, Graham Coxall, Phil Heath, Bill Landells, Steve Piotrowski, Mike Reed, Andy Wilson and Martin Woodcock. Particular thanks must go to Andy Wilson, who wrote the fieldworker instructions, designed the recording forms and edited the first two annual newsletters, and to Mike Reed, who created the database into which all the records were input.

During the twelve months before fieldwork started in December 1999, pilot work had been undertaken to establish the most appropriate recording methods and to test the proposed recording forms and instructions. The following observers took part in the pilot fieldwork: Nick Acheson, Len Bentley, Andrew Bloomfield, Peter Cawley, Alan Collins, Graham Coxall, Jay Davidson, Simon Gillings, Trevor Girling, Andrew Goodall, Su Gough, J Harris, Phil Heath, David Hennessy, Gavin Horsley, George Jackson, Pat Jackson, Philip Jackson, Andy Kane, David Lester, Moss Taylor, the late Ray Waters, Andy Wilson, Cath Wilson and Peter Wilson.

Observers for set visits

Without doubt, the greatest debt of gratitude must go to the volunteers who between them spent many thousands of hours undertaking fieldwork for the Norfolk Bird Atlas and who visited virtually every corner of Norfolk. Over 400 observers submitted records, of whom 312 contributed set visits. To this band of dedicated enthusiasts, we are extremely grateful. Besides Norfolk, observers were resident in Suffolk (ten), Cambridgeshire (ten), Lincolnshire (two), Bedfordshire (two), West Midlands (two), Yorkshire and Inverness-shire. The following observers carried out or assisted with set visits:

Peter Allard, Alison & Chris Allen, Jenny Allsop, Jed Andrews, Dave Appleton, Graham Appleton, James Appleton, D A Arend, Norman Arlott, Simon Aspinall, David Austen, Keith Bailey, John Balaam, Vanda Balfour, Linda Ballard, Dawn Balmer, Paul Banham, David & Jos Banthorpe, Sophie Barker, Terry Barker, Colin Bartholomew, Gillian Beckett, P A Beckett, David Bednall, P Benson, R A Benson, Len Bentley, Stewart Betts, J Bevan, Mike Birtwell, J Bishop, Mike Blair, Bryan Bland, Andrew Bloomfield, Rosina Booth, Irene Boston, Bob Bradley, Steven Bramham-Jones, Ann Brewster, Tom Bridge, Grahame & Catherine Brind, Gilbert Brooking, Christine Brown, Sue Bryan, David Bryant, Michael & Ann Bugden, Alec & Mrs R M Bull, Tim Burke, Niall Burton, Richard Burton, Mrs M Butler, John Buxton, Patricia Callis, Richard Caney, David & Christine Cannon, Peter Cawley, Peter & Stella Chance, Mark Chipperfield, Ann & Geoff Cleall, Peter Clement, Jon Clifton, Bob Cobbold, Mark Cocker, Adrian Cohen, Brian Cole, John Cole, Hugh Colledge, Alan Collins, Peter Colston, Fred Cooke, Jason Cork, Tim Cowan, Maurice Cowley, Graham Coxall, Anne & Peter Crawley, Graeme Cresswell, Mike & Megan Crewe, J Cricket, Kath Daly, Trevor Davies, Tim Dean, John Dicks, Ian & Gill Doble, Peter Dolton, Bill Drayton, Christopher Dunn, Tony Eadson, Graham Easy, John Eaton, David & Betty Ellis, Noel Elms, Nick Elsey, Kell Eradus, Jenny Evans, Andrew Excell, Francis Farrow, Peter Feakes, Roger Fickling, G Figg, John Filowiat, Graham Firmage, Mick Fiszer, Gordon Follows, David Fosh, Colin Freeman, Anthony Frost, David Fuller, Rob Fuller, John Furse, Mrs J E Gaffney, Steve Gantlett, Adrian Gardiner, Bob & Karin Garner, Dave Garner, Graeme Garner, Nick Gatward, Judy & John Geeson, Nick Gibbons, Jenny Gill, Roy Goldsmith, Andrew Goodall, Peter & Jean Gooden, Rob Gordon, Su Gough, Andrew Green, Katharine Greenland, Jeremy Greenwood, Ray Gribble, Andrew

Grieve, Bridget Griffin, Allan Hale, Paul Halford, Laurie Hall, Liz Hammler, Phil Hammond, John Hampshire, Kevin Hand, Michael Hannet, Mike Harcup, Ron Harold, Alan Harris, Jeremy Hastings, John & Ann Haysom, J Hayward, Phil Heath, Ian Henderson, David Hennessy, Keith & Ann Herber, Russ Heselden, Graeme Hewson, Ian & Edna Hines, John Hobbs, Ron Hoblyn, Howard Hobson, Steve Holloway, Paul Holness, Charles Holt, Peter & Anne Horsefield, Margaret Hosking, Stephen Howell, Chris Hudson, Colin Hudson, Alec Humphrey, Alwyn Jackson, Dave Jackson, Philip Jackson, Paul Jeffery, Ian Johnson, Stuart Johnson, Chris Jones, Geoff & Ann Jones, R E & J M Jones, Andy Kane, John Kemp, T Kett, Will Kirby, Colin Kirtland, Peter Kitchener, Tony Knight, Mark & Rosemary Knights, Bill Landells, Rowena & Reg Langston, Chris Lansdell, R Lawrence, Neil Lawton, Paul Lee, Dave Leech, David P Lester, the late Stewart Linsell, Phil Littler, Pat Lorber, Michael Lovatt, John Lovett, Graeme Lyons, Dot Machin, Jim & Doreen Mackman, Anne Mansfield, Monica & Owen Marks, Antony Marter, Andrew Martin, Chris Mason, Vince Matthews, James McCallum, Mrs U V Mead, Mr & Mrs J S Mighell, Pete Milford, Paul Monsey, Peter & Sue Morrison, Dorian Moss, Ashley Murphy, Ben Murphy, Andy Musgrove, Eddy Myers, David & Eileen Neale, Tony Nelson, Paul Newport, Jane Nightingale, Brian Nixon, Mary Norden, Mark Nowers, Bob Osborne, D L Ovenden, Nick & Frankie Owens, Nigel Packer, Phil Parker, James Parry, Tony Peach, Sid Perry, Dave Phillips, S Pinder, Steve Piotrowski, Bernard Pleasance, Richard & Julie Porter, Ian Prentice, Fraser Purvis, Michael Rae, Malcolm Rains, Mike Raven, David Reeve, Chris Regan, Ivan Rich, Nigel Rich, David & Mrs R M Richmond, I Robinson, Rob Robinson, Eric Rogers, Michael Rooney, Mr Rowe & Mrs Marian Rowe, Adam Rowlands, Jonathan Russ, Ashley Saunders, Mick Saunt, John Savidge, Charles Sayer, Jim Scott, Trevor & Linda Scott, Rod Scott-Smith, J Searle, John Sharpe, Graham Sherwin, Rosemary Shrive, Ian Simper, Gavin Siriwardena, Roger Skeen, R Smith, Steve Smith, John Spooner, Jennifer Standish, Michael Steggles, Darrell Stevens, Tim Strudwick, Mike Sweeney, C R Taylor, Laurie Taylor, Pam Taylor, Mike Thame, Paul & Val Thompson, John Threadgold, Mike Toms, Derek & Jan Toomer, Nick Torry, John Townshend, Roger Townsin, Pam Tregunna, John Trimble, A M Tubb, Michael Turner, Roger Turner, Rosemary Votier, Clive & Alison Wakes-Miller, Graham Walford, John Warham, Rachel Warren, the late Ray Waters, C H Watson, Nicola Watson, Dave Weaver, Mr & Mrs David Webb, Chris Wheeler, David & Christine White, John Whitelegg, Ric & Jane Wickham, Dan Williams, Andy Wilson, Cath Wilson, Mike Wilson, Peter Wilson, David Wood, Gary Wright and Stewart Wright.

The following deserve special mention for, in addition to the two authors (who were the most prolific contributors of data), completing fifty or more set visits: Bill Landells (212), Fred Cooke (169), Steve Piotrowski (150), Ann & Geoff Cleall & P Benson (84), Phil Heath (84), Andrew Grieve & John Buxton (82), Peter Allard (78), John Filowiat (76), Mike Birtwell (72), Tony Nelson, Hugh Colledge & Mike Thame (71), David Bryant (70), Kevin Hand (68), Chris Regan (66), Laurie Hall (58), Peter Feakes & J Cricket (58), David Lester (56), Gordon Follows (56), Michael & Ann Bugden (56), Len Bentley (55), Mike Blair (54), Graeme Hewson (52), Linda Ballard (52) and Mr & Mrs J S Mighell (50).

Other contributions of data

The BTO generously provided data gathered during various single species surveys, including the Heronries Census, Firecrest surveys 2002–07, Nightjar Survey 2004 and Woodlark Survey 2006. We are grateful to Greg Conway for help in data extraction for various surveys. Through Peter Lack, BTO also provided electronic versions of data from the *1968–72 Atlas, 1981–84 Winter Atlas* and *1988–91 Atlas*.

The Norfolk & Norwich Naturalists' Society and Geoffrey Kelly granted access to the master cards of tetrad data collected for the *1980–85 NBBS*.

We acknowledge the help and information provided by Tim Cowan and the RSPB (Stone-curlew) and John Middleton and the North West Norfolk Ringing Group (Barn Owl). Finally, Giles and Judy Dunmore were most helpful in providing county records before publication in the *NBR*, and they and Andy Stoddart helped answer various queries.

Funding and other support

We are most grateful to the following organisations and individuals who helped to fund the project: Birdline East Anglia, Rosina Booth, British Ornithologists' Union, BTO, the late Lord Buxton, Cley Bird Club, Grange Farm, Great Yarmouth Bird Club, Mike & Jean Holliday, David Love, Norfolk Wildlife Trust, and the RSPB.

The Norfolk & Norwich Naturalists' Society was NBA's major financial sponsor. Through the generosity of the Sarnia Trust, they paid for printing the recording forms, instructions and newsletters, and financed the input of records from the *1980–85 NBBS* into the NBA database. We would like to express our deep gratitude to David Richmond, the Society's Treasurer, for persuading his Council of the long-term value of the NBA project.

The fieldwork for this type of project is only possible with the goodwill of landowners, and we are grateful to every landowner who granted access to NBA fieldworkers. Sometimes, both parties benefited from the information that was gathered. A letter of introduction, distributed to all fieldworkers as a means of verifying to landowners the nature of the survey work being undertaken, undoubtedly improved the thoroughness of NBA coverage. This letter carried the logos of various local and national organisations, indicating their support, and we were extremely grateful to BTO, Broads Authority, Country Landowners' Association, Farming and Wildlife Advisory Group, Norfolk Bird Club, Norfolk Ornithologists' Association and Norfolk Wildlife Trust for allowing us to use their logos in this way.

Artwork and photography

Martin Woodcock coordinated the preparation of new pen-and-ink illustrations for the NBA project. He was able to persuade many of his fellow Norfolk-based artists to contribute the superb selection of vignettes. We would like to thank Martin and the following other artists whose artwork appears in this book:
Richard Allen, Norman Arlott, Jeff Baker, Andy Benson, Bryan Bland, Gil Brooking, Alan Burtenshaw, Steve Cale, Simon Gillings, Robert Gillmor, Alan Harris, Russ Heselden, Richard Johnson, Richard Millington, Nick Owens, Andy Stoddart, Thelma Sykes, John Wagstaff, Ian Wallace, Peter Wilson, and Gary Wright.

We are also very grateful to artists who were recruited to prepare specific artwork that, in the end, lost out to text, maps or photographs and did not find space in this book.

David Tipling made available his extensive photographic library and the majority of photographs appearing in this book are from this source. For this, we offer our sincere thanks. Chris Knights provided many photographs too and we thank him too for his contribution. A special mention is due also to Jim Almond who helped to fill in some of the gaps of rare or scarcer species. We are most grateful to the other photographers whose work appears in the book:
Jeff Baker, Chris Cook, Ian Cook, Dean Eades, Edmund Fellowes, Mike Gould, Trevor Gunby, Dave Mansell, Abbie Marland, Andrew Moon, Steve Ray, Gary Thoburn, and Damian Waters.

Contributions to book production

We are most grateful to the BTO Director, Andy Clements, and to Peter Lambley for their original contributions to the text.

Fred Cooke, Martin Woodcock, Bill Landells, Dawn Balmer, Pete Wilson, Andy Brown and Andy Clements commented on draft text. We are especially grateful to Fred Cooke for drafting sections of the first chapter, and for his enthusiastic encouragement at all stages of the project.

Conversion of the NBA database to meaningful maps was a major task. We are extremely grateful to Andy Musgrove for the complex programming he undertook for Access and GIS applications to test map styles and automate the output of the final maps. Some of the most difficult programming was to produce contour maps of density that took into account observer effort, for which we have not found space in this book. Graham Austin and Greg Conway provided further help with the database and maps.

We are most grateful to BTO Books for bringing this book to publication. This involved a number of BTO staff in a professional capacity. In particular, we would like to express our thanks to Jeff Baker, who spent very many hours in his role as production manager and to Mike Toms, Sam Rider and Sandra Sparkes as proof-readers. Design was by Chris O'Connor of O'Connor Design Consultants.

References

Most references are given in the text in standard author/date format but a few publications, because they are quoted so frequently, are given in almost all contexts in a shortened form.

Shortened references (in alphanumeric order)

1968–72 Atlas Sharrock, J.T.R. (ed) (1976) *The Atlas of Breeding Birds in Britain and Ireland*. T. & A.D. Poyser, Berkhamsted.

1980–85 NBBS Kelly, G.I. (1986) *The Norfolk Bird Atlas*. Occasional Publication 1. Norfolk & Norwich Naturalists' Society, Hunstanton.

1981–84 Winter Atlas Lack, P. (ed) (1986) *The Atlas of Wintering Birds in Britain and Ireland*. T. & A.D. Poyser, Calton.

1988–91 Atlas Gibbons, D.W., Reid, J.B. & Chapman, R.A. (eds) (1993) *The New Atlas of Breeding Birds in Britain and Ireland: 1988–1991*. T. & A.D. Poyser, London.

APEP06 Baker, H., Stroud, D.A., Aebischer, N.J., Cranswick, P.A., Gregory, R.D., McSorley, C.A., Noble, D.G. & Rehfisch, M.M. (2006) Population estimates of birds in Great Britain and the United Kingdom. *British Birds* 99, 25–44. (*www.britishbirds.co.uk/wp-content/uploads/2010/10/APEP21.pdf*)

Atlas 2007–11 *www.bto.org/birdatlas*

BirdGuides *www.birdguides.com*

BirdTrack *www.bto.org/birdtrack*

Birdtrends Baillie, S.R., Marchant, J.H., Leech, D.I., Joys, A.C., Noble, D.G., Barimore, C., Downie, I.S., Grantham, M.J., Risely, K. & Robinson, R.A. (2010) *Breeding Birds in the Wider Countryside: their conservation status 2009*. Research Report 541. BTO, Thetford. (*www.bto.org/birdtrends*)

BoCC3 Eaton, M.A., Brown, A.F., Noble, D.G., Musgrove, A.J., Hearn, R.D., Aebischer, N.J., Gibbons, D.W., Evans, A. & Gregory, R.D. (2009) Birds of Conservation Concern 3: the population status of birds in the United Kingdom, Channel Islands and Isle of Man. *British Birds* 102, 296–341. (*www.britishbirds.co.uk/wp-content/uploads/2010/10/Birds-of-Conservation-Concern3.pdf*)

BoN Taylor, M., Seago, M., Allard, P. & Dorling, D. (1999) *The Birds of Norfolk*. Pica Press, Sussex.

British List British Ornithologists' Union (2010) (*http://thebritishlist.blogspot.com*)

BWP1 Cramp, S. & Simmons, K.E.L. (eds) (1977) *The birds of the Western Palearctic. Volume I. Ostrich to Ducks*. Oxford University Press, Oxford.

BWP2 Cramp, S. & Simmons, K.E.L. (eds) (1980) *The birds of the Western Palearctic. Volume II. Hawks to Bustards*. Oxford University Press, Oxford.

BWP3 Cramp, S. & Simmons, K.E.L. (eds) (1983) *The birds of the Western Palearctic. Volume III. Waders to Gulls*. Oxford University Press, Oxford.

BWP4 Cramp, S. (ed) (1985) *The birds of the Western Palearctic. Volume IV. Terns to Woodpeckers*. Oxford University Press, Oxford.

BWP5 Cramp, S. (ed) (1988) *The birds of the Western Palearctic. Volume V. Tyrant Flycatchers to Thrushes*. Oxford University Press, Oxford.

BWP6 Cramp, S. (ed) (1992) *The birds of the Western Palearctic. Volume VI. Warblers*. Oxford University Press, Oxford.

BWP7 Cramp, S. & Perrins, C.M. (eds) (1993) *The birds of the Western Palearctic. Volume VII. Flycatchers to Shrikes*. Oxford University Press, Oxford.

BWP8 Cramp, S. & Perrins, C.M. (eds) (1994) *The birds of the Western Palearctic. Volume VIII. Crows to Finches*. Oxford University Press, Oxford.

BWP9 Cramp, S. & Perrins, C.M. (eds) (1994) *The birds of the Western Palearctic. Volume IX. Buntings and New World Warblers*. Oxford University Press, Oxford.

Migration Atlas Wernham, C.V., Toms, M.P., Marchant, J.H., Clark, J.A., Siriwardena, G.M. & Baillie, S.R. (eds) (2002) *The Migration Atlas: movements of the birds of Britain and Ireland*. T. & A.D. Poyser, London.

NBR Norfolk Bird & Mammal Reports. Published annually by the Norfolk & Norwich Naturalists' Society.

Riviere Riviere, B.B. (1930) *A History of the Birds of Norfolk.* H.F. & G. Witherby, London.

Stevenson Stevenson, H. (1866–90) *The Birds of Norfolk.* Three volumes. John Van Voorst and Gurney & Jackson, London.

The Birdwatchers' Code RSPB on behalf of BTO and others (widely available online, *eg www.bto.org/sites/default/files/u10/downloads/taking-part/health/bwc.pdf*)

Author/date references

Allard, P. (2000a) Black-tailed Godwits at Breydon Water. *Norfolk Bird Club Bulletin* 39, 10–11.

Allard, P. (2000b) More Avocets and Black-tails at Breydon. *Norfolk Bird Club Bulletin* 42, 13–14.

Allard, P. (2003) Studies of Mediterranean Gulls at Great Yarmouth in winter 2002/2003. *Norfolk Bird Club Bulletin* 51, 18–21.

Allard, P. (2007) Population explosion of nesting gulls in Great Yarmouth. *Norfolk Bird & Mammal Report* 2006, 325–328.

Atkinson, P.W. (1996) The origins, moult, movements and changes in number of Bar-tailed Godwits *Limosa lapponica* on the Wash, England. *Bird Study* 43, 60–72.

Ballance, D.K. & Smith, A.J. (2008) Recording areas of Great Britain. *British Birds* 101, 1–17.

Balmer, D. (2008) Goosander breeding on River Little Ouse at Thetford. *Norfolk Bird & Mammal Report* 2007, 174.

Balmer, D.E., Browne, S.J. & Rehfisch, M.M. (1996) A year in the life of Golden Pheasants *Chrysolophus pictus*. In *The introduction and naturalisation of birds* (eds Holmes, J.S. & Simons, J.R.), pp 87–93. The Stationery Office, London. (*www.jncc.gov.uk/pdf/pub96_naturalisationbirds_pt11.pdf*)

Bloomfield, A. (2003a) Are Norfolk's Pinkfeet facing an uncertain future, both at home and abroad? *Norfolk Bird Club Bulletin* 49, 5–7.

Bloomfield, A. (2003b) More roof-nesting Oystercatchers. *Norfolk Bird Club Bulletin* 52, 30–31.

Bloomfield, A. (2004) The Serin – its history in Norfolk and the first county breeding records. *Norfolk Bird & Mammal Report* 2003, 287–291.

Bloomfield, A. & McCallum, J. (1999) The Stock Dove and its status in North Norfolk. *Norfolk Bird Club Bulletin* 33, 5–6.

BOURC (2010) British Ornithologists' Union Records Committee: 38th report (October 2009). *Ibis* 152, 199–204.

Brown, A. & Grice, P. (2005) *Birds in England.* T. & A.D. Poyser, London.

Browne, S.J. (2004) Some aspects of Chaffinch *Fringilla coelebs* biology, based on an analysis of individuals ringed during 1991 to 2003 in Norfolk, England. *Ringing & Migration* 22, 75–82.

Burd, F. (1989) *The saltmarsh survey of Great Britain: an inventory of British saltmarshes.* Research and Survey in Nature Conservation 17. Nature Conservancy Council, Peterborough.

Cadbury, C.J. (2005) Bearded Tit and other reed-swamp passerine populations in the Hickling Broad complex 1980–2004. *Norfolk Bird & Mammal Report* 2004, 273–281.

Carson, C.A., Cornford, G.A. & Thomas, G.J. (1977) Little Gulls nesting on the Ouse Washes. *British Birds* 70, 331–332.

Cocker, M. (2004) Sample census and observations of breeding Rooks in south-east Norfolk. *Norfolk Bird & Mammal Report* 2003, 274–277.

Cocker, M. (2007) The Rook/Jackdaw roost at Buckenham Carrs. *Norfolk Bird & Mammal Report* 2006, 318–324.

Dagley, J.R. (1994) Golden Orioles in East Anglia and their conservation. *British Birds* 87, 205–219.

Dolton, C.S. & Brooke, M. de L. (1999) Changes in the biomass of birds breeding in Great Britain, 1968–88. *Bird Study* 46, 274–278.

Donald, P.F. & Evans, A.D. (1994) Habitat selection by Corn Buntings *Miliaria calandra* in winter. *Bird Study* 41, 199–210.

Dorling, D. (2001) Barnacle Geese at Hethersett. *Norfolk Bird Club Bulletin* 44, 8–10.

Dye, K.R. (2003) Roof nesting Oystercatchers at Great Yarmouth, Norfolk. *Norfolk Bird Club Bulletin* 51, 21–23.

Dye, K. (2007) First recorded roof-nesting by Common Terns in Norfolk. *Norfolk Bird & Mammal Report* 2006, 329–330.

Dye, K., Fiszer, M. & Allard, P. (2009) *Birds New to Norfolk*. Wren Publishing, Sheringham.

Eele, P. (2006) 'Sammy' – the most watched bird in Britain? *Norfolk Bird & Mammal Report* 2005, 302.

Eele, P. (2008) Breeding Little Gulls at RSPB Titchwell Marsh Nature Reserve – summer 2007. *Norfolk Bird & Mammal Report* 2007, 173.

Elms, N. (2005) Honey Buzzard breeding sites in Norfolk. *Norfolk Bird Club Bulletin* 57, 28–29.

George, M. (1992) *The land use, conservation and ecology of Broadland.* Packard Publishing, Chichester.

Gill, F. & Donsker, D. (eds) (2010) *IOC World Bird Names* (version 2.5). (*www.worldbirdnames.org*)

Green, A. (2007) *Breeding bird survey of Redgrave and Lopham Fen 2007.* SPEC Environmental Consultants, Bungay.

Hampshire, J. (2003) Winter food for Reed Buntings. *Norfolk Bird Club Bulletin* 51, 25–26.

Hampshire, J. (2005) Should the increasing numbers of Carrion Crows in parts of Norfolk concern us? *Norfolk Bird Club Bulletin* 57, 15–17.

Hampshire, J. (2006) Stubb Mill harrier roost – an update. *Cley Bird Club Newsletter* 75, 14–15.

Harold, R. & Bloomfield, A. (2005) The Little Egret in Norfolk. *Norfolk Bird & Mammal Report* 2004, 262–272.

Heath, P. (2000) Marsh Warblers breeding in Norfolk – a new county breeding species. *Norfolk Bird Club Bulletin* 42, 9–11.

Hill, D. (1988) Population dynamics of the Avocet *Recurvirostra avosetta* breeding in Britain. *Journal of Animal Ecology* 57, 638–669.

Hoblyn, R. (2006) Breckland 2005 – a good year for forest birds. *Norfolk Bird Club Bulletin* 60, 24–26.

Hoblyn, R., Secker, J. & Landells, B. (2004) A mixed bag from the Thetford Forest. *Norfolk Bird Club Bulletin* 54, 27–29.

Holloway, S. (1996) *The Historical Atlas of Breeding Birds in Britain and Ireland: 1875–1900.* T. & A.D. Poyser, London.

Kelly, G.I. (1986) *The Norfolk Bird Atlas.* Occasional Publication 1. Norfolk & Norwich Naturalists' Society, Hunstanton.

Kemp, J. (1981) Breeding Long-eared Owls in West Norfolk. *Norfolk Bird & Mammal Report* 1980, 262–264.

Kemp, J. (1982) West Norfolk Long-eared Owl Survey. *Norfolk Bird & Mammal Report* 1981, 90–91.

Kemp, J. (2004) The Whooper Swan in Norfolk. *Norfolk Bird & Mammal Report* 2003, 281–282.

Kimber, R. (2005) Goodbye Sammy. *Norfolk Bird Club Bulletin* 59, 6–8.

Lambley, P.W. (1997) *North Norfolk.* Natural Area Profile 47. English Nature, Peterborough. (*www.english-nature.org.uk/science/natural/profiles/naProfile47.pdf*)

Lawton, N. (1999) Shorelarks in Norfolk – past and present. *Norfolk Bird Club Bulletin* 32, 4–8.

Mason, C.F. (1998) Habitats of the song thrush *Turdus philomelos* in a largely arable landscape. *Journal of Zoology* 244, 89–93.

Mason, C.F. (2003) Some correlates of density in an urban Blackbird *Turdus merula* population. *Bird Study* 50, 185–188.

Mason, C.F. & Macdonald, S.M. (1999a) Habitat use by Lapwings and Golden Plovers in a largely arable landscape. *Bird Study* 46, 89–99.

Mason, C.F. & Macdonald, S.M. (1999b) Estuarine feeding by Lapwings *Vanellus vanellus* and Golden Plovers *Pluvialis apricaria. Wildfowl* 50, 205–207.

Mason, C.F. & Macdonald, S.M. (2000) Corn Bunting *Miliaria calandra* populations, landscape and land-use in an arable district of eastern England. *Bird Conservation International* 10, 169–186.

Mason, C.F. & Macdonald, S.M. (2004) Distribution of foraging rooks, *Corvus frugilegus,* and rookeries in a landscape in eastern England dominated by winter cereals. *Folia Zoologica* 53, 179–188. (*www.ivb.cz/folia/53/2/179–188.pdf*)

McCallum, J. (2001) *Wild goose winter: observations of geese in north Norfolk*. Silver Brant Publications, Wells-next-the-Sea.

Morrison, P. (2006) The changing status of Firecrest in Norfolk. *Norfolk Bird & Mammal Report* 2005, 279–283.

PACEC (2006) *The Economic and Environmental Impact of Sporting Shooting*. Public and Corporate Economic Consultants, Cambridge. (*www.shootingfacts.co.uk*)

Paston, S. (2001) The House Sparrow in Norwich during autumn/winter 2000 – a population study. *Norfolk Bird & Mammal Report* 2000, 289–293.

Piotrowski, S.H. (2003) *The Birds of Suffolk*. Christopher Helm, London.

Rackham, O. (1986) The ancient woods of Norfolk. *Transactions of the Norfolk & Norwich Naturalists' Society* 27, 166 –177.

Radley, G.P. (1994) *Sand Dune Vegetation Survey of GB: a national inventory. Part 1: England.* Joint Nature Conservation Committee, Peterborough.

Richardson, R.A., Seago, M.J. & Church, A. (1957) Collared Doves in Norfolk: a bird new to the British List. *British Birds* 50, 239–246.

Sage, B. (2002) *The Ecology of the Egyptian Goose at Holkham Park, Norfolk*. Occasional Publication 8. Norfolk & Norwich Naturalists' Society.

Sage, B. (2006) Swanton Novers NNR and its Coleoptera. *Transactions of the Norfolk & Norwich Naturalists' Society* 39, 10–57.

Seago, M.J. (1967) *Birds of Norfolk*. Jarrold, Norwich.

Seago, M.J. (1999) 1998 Great Crested Grebe survey. *Norfolk Bird Club Bulletin* 33, 12–13.

Smith, S. & Gilbert, J. (2001) *The National Inventory of Woodland and Trees – England*. Forestry Commission, Edinburgh. (*www.forestry.gov.uk/pdf/niengland.pdf/$FILE/niengland.pdf*)

SOVON (1987) *Atlas van de Nederlandse Vogels*. SOVON, Arnhem.

Stoddart, A. (2007) An interesting Pied Flycatcher. *Norfolk Bird & Mammal Report* 2006, 334–335.

Taylor, M. (1997) The origins of Rock Pipits in Norfolk. *Norfolk Bird & Mammal Report* 1995, 606–607.

Wagstaff, J. (2008) Dartford Warbler – the first county breeding records. *Norfolk Bird & Mammal Report* 2007, 175–177.

Wheeler, B. (1978) The wetland communities of the River Ant valley, Norfolk. *Transactions of the Norfolk & Norwich Naturalists' Society* 24, 153–187.

Williamson, J. (2000) Hobbies – masters of the hunt. *Norfolk Bird Club Bulletin* 41, 4–5.

Williamson, J.R. (2003a) The Marsh Harrier in Norfolk – a review of its historical and current status. *Norfolk Bird & Mammal Report* 2002, 276–282.

Williamson, J. (2003b) Grey Wagtails in the Wensum Valley. *Norfolk Bird Club Bulletin* 51, 6–8.

Williamson, J. (2004) More breeding Grey Wagtails. *Norfolk Bird Club Bulletin* 53, 13–15.

Williamson, J. (2005) Breeding Honey Buzzards – some personal observations. *Norfolk Bird Club Bulletin* 58, 29–31.

Williamson, J. (2006) Have House Sparrows changed their nesting habits? *Norfolk Bird Club Bulletin* 60, 29–30.

Wilson, A. (2000) The 1999 Nightingale Survey. *Norfolk Bird & Mammal Report* 1999, 286–289.

Wilson, A.M., Henderson, A.C.B. & Fuller, R.J. (2002) Status of the Common Nightingale *Luscinia megarhynchos* in England at the end of the 20th century with particular reference to climate change. *Bird Study* 49, 193–204.

Wilson, P.M. (2001) Gulls at Saddlebow in 2000. *Norfolk Bird Club Bulletin* 44, 12–19.

Wilson, P. & Balmer, D. (2002) Yellow-legged Gulls in Norfolk: 1961–2001. *Norfolk Bird & Mammal Report* 2001, 273–280.

Gazetteer

THE FOLLOWING LIST of Norfolk locations is intended as an aid to readers who wish to locate on the map places that are mentioned in the text. It is not a complete gazetteer for the county. The Ordnance Survey 10-km reference (*eg* TF72) is followed by a tetrad letter from the 'DINTY' system (A for the tetrad in the southwest corner of a 10-km square, and Z for the tetrad in the northeast; see Figure 1.1.).

There are two important caveats that users of this gazetteer must bear in mind. First, many of the listed place names cover parts of more than one tetrad: thus, even a small locality might lie across up to four tetrads. Observers should therefore always check against the Ordnance Survey maps or a trusted web site before assigning a tetrad reference to an individual record.

Second, many Norfolk place names crop up more than once in the county. Confusingly, for example, the 'Eccles' referred to in *NBR* is almost always Eccles on Sea – not Eccles itself, which is next to Snetterton circuit. Billingford near Swanton Morley, in the Wensum valley, is matched by another Billingford of similar size by the River Waveney near Scole. Whereas Roydon Common, a site well known to birdwatchers, is near King's Lynn, Roydon Fen, a Wildlife Trust reserve with important local populations of reedbed birds, is near Diss. These are far from being the only examples!

A

Abbey Farm, Flitcham....TF72I
Abel Heath, Blickling....TG12T
Abraham's Bosom....TF94C
Acle....TG41A
Adcock's Common....TF71I
Admiralty Point, Terrington....TF52T
Aldeby....TM49L
Aldeby Tip....TM49R
Alder Carrs, Gillingham....TM49G
Alderfen Broad....TG31P
Alderford....TG11J
Anmer....TF72P
Antingham....TG23L
Arnold's Marsh, Cley....TG04S
Ashill....TF80X
Attleborough....TM09M
Attlebridge....TG11I
Aylmerton....TG13Z
Aylsham....TG12Y

B

Babingley....TF62T
Baconsthorpe....TG13I
Bacton....TG33L
Bacton Gas Terminal....TG33H
Bagmore Pit....TF89R
Bagthorpe Wood....TF83B
Banham....TM08U
Barnham Broom Fen....TG00T
Barnham Broom GC....TG00Z
Barnhamcross Common....TL88Q
Barrow Common....TF74W
Barton Broad....TG32Q
Barton Turf....TG32K
Bawburgh Pits....TG10U
Bawsey CP....TF61U
Bayfield Lake & Woods....TG04K
Beachamwell....TF70M
Beacon Hill, West Runton....TG14V
Bedingham Green....TM29W
Beeston....TF91C
Beeston Common & Bump....TG14R
Beeston Regis....TG14R
Beetley....TF91U
Belaugh....TG21Z
Belton....TG40W
Bergh Apton....TG30A
Berney Marshes....TG40S
Billingford (near Scole)....TM17U
Billingford (near Swanton Morley)....TG01E
Billockby....TG41G
Binham....TF93Z
Bintree Mill....TF92X
Bircham Newton....TF73R

Bittering GP TF91I
Blackborough End TF61X
Blackfleet Broad TG42K
Blakeney TG04G
Blakeney Freshes TG04H
Blakeney Harbour TF94Y
Blakeney Point TF94Y
Blakeney Quay TG04H
Blickling Hall TG12U
Bodham Wood TG14A
Bodney TL89J
Booton TG12B
Boughton Fen TF70A
Bowthorpe TG10U
Bowthorpe Marsh TG10Z
Boyland Common TM08X
Boyland Grove TM08X
Bradenham TF90J
Bradfield Hall Farm TG23R
Bramble Hill, Horsey TG42R
Brancaster TF74S
Brancaster Harbour TF74X
Brancaster Marshes TF74S
Brancaster Staithe coastal TF74X
Brancaster Staithe inland TF74W
Brandon Creek TL69A
Brayden Marshes TG42L
Bressingham Common TM08Q
Bressingham Fen TM08Q
Brettenham Heath TL98C
Breydon Lumps TG50E
Breydon Water TG40Y
Bridgham Heath TL98I
Brigg Street TG20J
Briggate Mill TG32D
Briningham TG02H
Brinton TG03H
Brisley TF92K
Briston TG03R
Broadwater, Holme TF74C
Brograve Farm TG42M
Brooke TM29Z
Broome Common TM39K
Broome Pits TM39K
Brundall TG30J
Buckenham Marshes TG30M
Buckenham Tofts TL89H
Bulls' Run, Stanford TA TL89R
Bunwell TM19G
Burgh Castle TG40S
Burgh Castle Marshes TG40X
Burgh Common TG41L
Burgh St Peter TM49R
Burnham Deepdale TF84C
Burnham Market TF84G
Burnham Norton TF84G
Burnham Norton Marsh TF84H
Burnham Overy Marshes TF84M
Burnham Overy Mill TF84G
Burnham Overy Staithe TF84M
Burnham Thorpe TF84K
Burntfen Broad TG31J
Buxton TG22G
Buxton Heath TG12U
Bylaugh SF TG01J

C

Caister GC TG51F
Caister on Sea TG51G
Caistor St Edmunds TG20H
California TG51C
Calthorpe Broad TG42C
Calthorpe Street TG42C
Cantley BF TG30W
Cantley Marsh TG30R
Carbrooke TF90L
Cart Gap TG32Z
Castle Acre TF81C
Castle Rising TF62S
Catfield Common TG42A
Catfield Fen TG32Q
Catton Park TG21F
Cawston Heath TG12R
Chedgrave TM39U
Choseley Barns TF74L
Choseley Farm TF74K
Church Fen, Brundall TG30J
Church Marsh TG30D
Claxton Corner TG30G
Claxton Marshes TG30M
Clenchwarton TF52V
Cley TG04L
Cley Marshes TG04M
Clippesby TG41H
Cockley Cley TF70X
Cockley Cley Lake TF70W

Honingham TG11A
Hopton TG50F
Hopton Point, Stanford TA TL89T
Horning Hall Marshes TG31T
Horning, Horning Ferry TG31N
Horsey Corner TG42R
Horsey Gap TG42S
Horsey Mere TG42L
Horsford TG11Y
Horstead Mill TG21U
Houghton Park TF72Y
Houghton St Giles TF93H
Houghton Woods TF72U
Hoveton Great Broad TG31D
Hoveton Hall TG32A
Hoveton Little Broad TG31I
How Hill TG31U
Hunstanton TF64Q
Hunstanton GC TF64W
Hunworth TG03S

I

Ickburgh TL89C
Illington TL89P
Incleborough Hill TG14W
Ingham TG32X
Irstead TG32Q
Irstead Street TG31U
Itteringham Mill TG13K

K

Kelling Quags & WM TG04W
Kelling Triangle TG04V
Ken Hill GM & Wood TF63S
Kenninghall TM08I
Kettlestone TF92U
King's Lynn BF TF61D
King's Lynn Docks TF62A
King's Lynn GC TF62L
Kirstead Green TM29Y

L

Lady Anne's Drive, Holkham TF84X
Lamas TG22L
Lamb's Marsh, Irstead Street TG31U
Langford TL89I
Langham TG04C
Langley Green TG30L
Langley Marshes TG30R
Langmere (Diss) TM18V
Langmere, East Wretham TL98E
Larling TL98Z
Lenwade TG11E
Lessingham TG32Z
Letheringsett TG03U
Leziate TF61Z
Limpenhoe Marshes TG30W
Litcham Common TF81Y
Little Barningham TG13G
Little Cressingham TF80Q
Little Massingham TF72X
Little Plumstead TG31B
Little Reedham Marsh TG31U
Little Snoring Airfield TF93R
Little Thornage TG03U
Loddon TM39U
Long Hills, Blakeney Point TG04D
Long Stratton TM19W
Lopham Fen TM07P
Lound TM59E
Lower Stow Bedon TL99S
Ludham, Ludham Airfield TG31Z
Ludham Bridge TG31T
Lynford Arboretum TL89H
Lynford GP TL89C
Lyng TG01T
Lyng Easthaugh GP TF91Y
Lynn Point TF62B

M

Marham Fen TF71F
Marlingford TG10J
Marsham TG12W
Marsham Heath TG12R
Martham Broad TG42K
Martham Ferry TG41P
Martham South Broad TG42K
Massingham Heath TF72Q
Matlaske TG13M
Mattishall TG01K
Mautby Hall & Decoy TG41V
Melton Constable TG03L
Merton TL99E
Merton Park TL99D
Methwold TF79H
Middleton GP TF61X

Glossary of abbreviations used in the text

APEP — Avian Population Estimates Panel
BBS — Breeding Bird Survey
BCTP — Bird Conservation Targeting Project
BF — Beet Factory
BO — Bird Observatory
BoCC — Birds of Conservation Concern
BOU — British Ornithologists' Union
BTO — British Trust for Ornithology
BWI — BirdWatch Ireland
CBC — Common Birds Census
CP — Country Park or Coastal Park
FM — Fresh Marshes
GC — Golf Course
GIS — Geographical Information System
GM — Grazing Marshes
GP — Gravel Pit
GWCT — Game & Wildlife Conservation Trust
JNCC — Joint Nature Conservation Committee
NarVOS — Nar Valley Ornithological Society
NBA — Norfolk Bird Atlas 1999–2007
NBBS — Norfolk Breeding Bird Survey 1980–85
NBR — Norfolk Bird Report
NNR — National Nature Reserve
NWT — Norfolk Wildlife Trust
OS — Ordnance Survey
OTB — Outer Trial Bank
RBBP — Rare Breeding Birds Panel
RC — Relief Channel
RSPB — Royal Society for the Protection of Birds
SF — Sewage Farm
SOC — Scottish Ornithologists' Club
SPA — Special Protection Area
SSSI — Site of Special Scientific Interest
SWT — Suffolk Wildlife Trust
TA — Training Area
TTV — Timed Tetrad Visit
UEA — University of East Anglia
WBBS — Waterways Breeding Bird Survey
WBS — Waterways Bird Survey
WeBS — Wetland Bird Survey
WM — Water Meadows
WWT — Wildfowl & Wetlands Trust

Index of species names

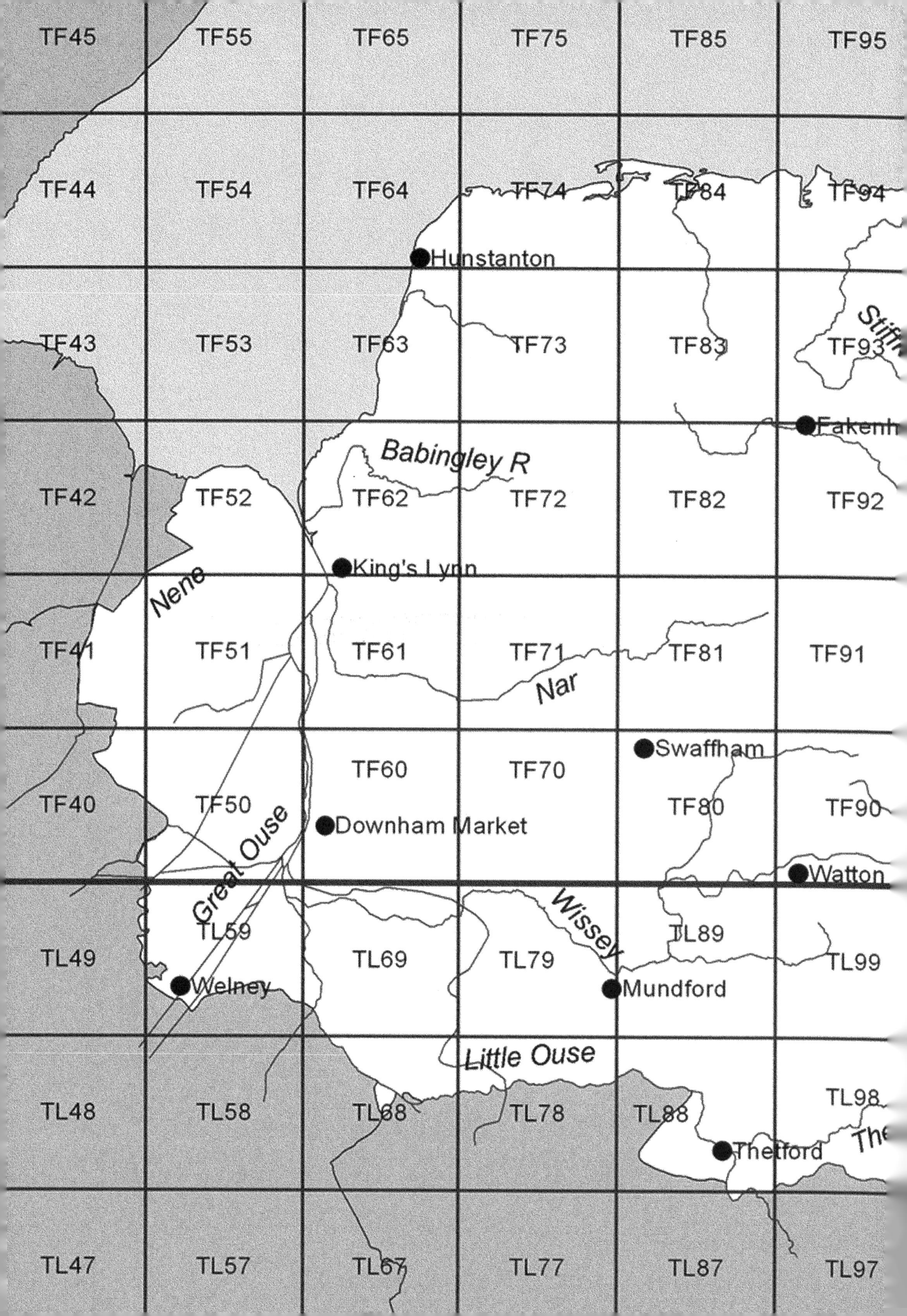

TF45 TF55 TF65 TF75 TF85 TF95

TF44 TF54 TF64 TF74 TF84 TF94

Hunstanton

TF43 TF53 TF63 TF73 TF83 TF93

Stiff

Fakenh

Babingley R

TF42 TF52 TF62 TF72 TF82 TF92

King's Lynn

Nene

TF41 TF51 TF61 TF71 TF81 TF91

Nar

Swaffham

TF60 TF70

TF40 TF50 TF80 TF90

Great Ouse

Downham Market

Watton

Wissey

TL59 TL89

TL49 TL69 TL79 TL99

Welney

Mundford

Little Ouse

TL48 TL58 TL68 TL78 TL88 TL98

Thetford

The

TL47 TL57 TL67 TL77 TL87 TL97